Contemporary Mathematics

Third Custom Edition for College of Lake County

Taken from:

Excursions in Modern Mathematics, Eighth Edition
by Peter Tannenbaum

Mathematical Ideas, Thirteenth Edition
by Charles D. Miller, Vern E. Heeren, John Hornsby, and Christopher Heeren

D1307546

Cover Art: Courtesy of Friedrich Saurer/Photo Researchers, Inc.

Taken from:

Excursions in Modern Mathematics, Eighth Edition
by Peter Tannenbaum
Copyright © 2010, 2007, 2004, 2001, 1998, 1995, 1992 by Pearson Education, Inc.
Published by Prentice Hall
Upper Saddle River, New Jersey 07458

Mathematical Ideas, Thirteenth Edition
by Charles D. Miller, Vern E. Heeren, John Hornsby, and Christopher Heeren
Copyright © 2012, 2008, 2004 by Pearson Education, Inc.
Published by Addison Wesley
Boston, Massachusetts 02116

This special edition published in cooperation with Pearson Learning Solutions.

All trademarks, service marks, registered trademarks, and registered service marks are the property of their respective owners and are used herein for identification purposes only.

Pearson Learning Solutions, 330 Hudson Street, New York, New York 10013
A Pearson Education Company
www.pearsoned.com

Printed in the United States of America

2 3 4 5 6 7 8 9 10 V092 19 18 17 16 15

000200010272007081

CC

ISBN 10: 1-323-29466-X
ISBN 13: 978-1-323-29466-6

Contents

PART 2 Management Science

Preface

This book started more than 20 years ago as a set of lecture notes for a new, experimental "math appreciation" course (these types of courses are described, sometimes a bit derisively, as "math for poets"). Over time, the lecture notes grew into a book and the "poets" turned out to be social scientists, political scientists, economists, psychologists, environmentalists, and many other "ists." Over time, and with the input of many users, the contents have been expanded and improved, but the underlying philosophy of the book has remained the same since those handwritten lecture notes were handed out to my first group of students.

Excursions in Modern Mathematics is a travelogue into that vast and alien frontier that many people perceive mathematics to be. My goal is to show the open-minded reader that mathematics is a lively, interesting, useful, and surprisingly rich human activity.

The "excursions" in *Excursions* represent a collection of topics chosen to meet the following simple criteria.

> 66 To most outsiders, modern mathematics is unknown territory. Its borders are protected by dense thickets of technical terms; its landscapes are a mass of indecipherable equations and incomprehensible concepts. Few realize that the world of modern mathematics is rich with vivid images and provocative ideas. 99
>
> – Ivars Peterson,
> The Mathematical Tourist

- **Applicability.** There is no need to worry here about that great existential question of college mathematics: What is this stuff good for? The connection between the mathematics presented in these excursions and down-to-earth, concrete real-life problems is transparent and immediate.*

- **Accessibility.** As a general rule, the excursions in this book do not presume a background beyond standard high school mathematics—by and large, intermediate algebra and a little Euclidean geometry are appropriate and sufficient prerequisites. (In the few instances in which more advanced concepts are unavoidable, an effort has been made to provide enough background to make the material self-contained.) A word of caution—this does not mean that the excursions in this book are easy! In mathematics, as in many other walks of life, simple and basic is not synonymous with easy and superficial.

- **Modernity.** Unlike much of traditional mathematics, which is often hundreds of years old, most of the mathematics in this book has been discovered within the last 100 years, and in some cases within the last couple of decades. Modern mathematical discoveries do not have to be the exclusive province of professional mathematicians.

- **Aesthetics.** The notion that there is such a thing as beauty in mathematics is surprising to most casual observers. There is an important aesthetic component in mathematics, and just as in art and music (which mathematics very much resembles), it often surfaces in the simplest ideas. A fundamental objective of this book is to develop an appreciation of the aesthetic elements of mathematics.

Outline

The excursions are organized into five independent parts, each touching on a different area where mathematics and the real world interface.

- **Part 1 Social Choice.** This part deals with mathematical applications to politics, social science, and government. How are *elections* decided? (Chapter 1); How

*Just days before this edition went to press, the American mathematician Lloyd S. Shapley—whose method for computing power is discussed in Chapter 2—was awarded the 2012 Nobel Prize in Economics.

can the *power* of individuals, groups, or voting blocs be measured? (Chapter 2); How can assets commonly owned be *divided* in a *fair* and equitable manner? (Chapter 3); How are seats *apportioned* in a legislative body? (Chapter 4).

- **Part 2 Management Science.** This part deals with questions of efficiency—how to manage some valuable resource (time, money, raw materials) so that utility is maximized. Examples of the types of applications discussed in this part are: How do we *cover* a network with the least amount of backtracking? (Chapter 5); How do we find the least expensive route that *visits* a specified set of locations? (Chapter 6); How do we create efficient networks that *connect* people or things? (Chapter 7); How do we schedule a project so that it is completed as early as possible? (Chapter 8).

- **Part 3 Growth.** In this part we discuss, in very broad terms, the mathematics of growth and decay, profit and loss. In Chapter 9 we cover mathematical models of *population growth*, mostly biological and human populations but also populations of inanimate "things" like garbage, pollution, etc. Since money plays such an important role in our lives, it deserves a chapter of its own. In Chapter 10 we discuss the basics of *financial mathematics* with particular emphasis on how to make money grow.

- **Part 4 Shape and Form.** In this part we cover a few connections between mathematics and the shape and form of objects—natural or man-made. What is *symmetry*? What *types* of symmetries exist in nature and art? (Chapter 11); What kind of geometry lies hidden behind the *kinkiness* of the many irregular shapes we find in nature? (Chapter 12); What is the connection between the *Fibonacci numbers* and the *golden ratio* (two abstract mathematical constructs) and the *spiral* forms that we regularly find in nature? (Chapter 13).

- **Part 5 Statistics.** In one way or another, statistics affects all our lives. Government policy, insurance rates, our health, our diet, and our political lives are all governed by statistical information. This part deals with how the statistical information that affects our lives is collected, organized, and interpreted. What are the purposes and strategies of *data collection*? (Chapter 14); How is data *organized, presented,* and *summarized*? (Chapter 15); How do we use mathematics to measure *uncertainty* and *risk*? (Chapter 16); How do we use mathematics to model, analyze, and make predictions about *real-life, bell-shaped* data sets? (Chapter 17).

New in This Edition

- **Hello Chapter 17.** For its first seven editions, this book consisted of 16 chapters organized in four parts, four chapters in each part. Nice symmetry, not much flexibility. This edition is the first break with the four-by-four model: 17 chapters organized into five parts (4, 4, 2, 3, 4 chapters, respectively). What in the seventh edition was a mini-excursion in Population Growth has been upgraded to full chapter status (Chapter 9) in this edition. Combined with the chapter on Financial Mathematics (Chapter 10), these two form a new Part 3.

- **Really Real Examples.** This edition has over 300 examples, many of them new. Among the new examples is a renewed focus on *real-life events and real-life data* (as opposed to examples involving a real-life application but illustrated with an imaginary situation and made-up data—something that is often unavoidable since real-world data can be messy, noisy, and big). Approximately 25% of the examples in this book are now really real (application, story, data—the works). The examples cover a wide swath of life—popular culture, sports, politics, government, society, the environment, health, and finance.

- **Exercises.** This edition has over 1250 exercises, and about 20% are new. There are approximately 1000 Walking exercises, and they are now organized into sections that match the sections in the chapter. This should greatly facilitate the scheduling of assignments. Running exercises will challenge students' ability and are revised in this edition to make them less rigorous, yet still challenging.

- **Glossary of Key Concepts.** The end of each chapter now includes a glossary with a short definition or explanation of the key concepts in the chapter providing ease of study and review.

- **Goodbye Mini-Excursions, etc.** In spite of the addition of a new chapter, this edition is shorter than previous editions. This miracle was accomplished by pruning some chapters and moving discretionary material such as biographical profiles, references, and some of the mini-excursions to MyMathLab®.

- **MyMathLab** for the Eighth Edition offers new features that make the online assessment more closely tied to the text's approach.

  - **Applets,** designed by the author, help students visualize the more difficult concepts. These can be assigned as media assignments in MyMathLab. Applet references appear as margin notes in the text directing students to the MyMathLab course.

  - **New assignable MathXL® exercises** relate to the applets, so students explore the concepts and develop their understanding using these applets and then answer related MathXL questions.

  - **A Ready-To-Go** MyMathLab Course is available, which offers the same robust experience as a standard course but makes course set-up even easier.

In addition to the changes listed above, most chapters have undergone a significant revision for this edition. The following is a chapter-by-chapter list of major changes:

- **Chapter 1.** Arrow's fairness criteria are now discussed together in one section at the end of the chapter. This reorganization allows for more flexibility in teaching this chapter. Instructors who want to cover the fairness criteria and Arrow's Impossibility Theorem in more detail can now do so; instructors who prefer to skip this part of the material can seamlessly do so as well. Many new examples of voting situations from popular culture, sports, and politics have been added.

- **Chapter 2.** There is a new section that covers the enumeration of subsets and permutations. This puts all the mathematics used in the chapter in one place.

- **Chapter 3.** A subsection on Auctions, Reverse Auctions, and Negative Bidding has been added to Section 3.5 The Method of Sealed Bids.

- **Chapter 4.** A new section on the Huntington-Hill method (Section 4.5) has been added. Adams's and Webster's methods have been combined into one section (Section 4.4). The quota rule and the apportionment paradoxes are now organized into a single section at the end of the chapter (Section 4.6).

- **Chapter 5.** Euler's theorems and Fleury's algorithm are now combined into a single section (Section 5.3), and a more detailed discussion of the topic of semi-eulerization of graphs has been added (Section 5.4).

- **Chapter 6.** This chapter has undergone a significant reorganization. There are fewer sections and the algorithms (brute-force, nearest-neighbor/repetitive nearest-neighbor, and cheapest-link) are now covered in separate sections.

- **Chapter 7.** The topic of Maximum Spanning Trees has been added. By popular demand, the material on shortest networks is gone. The chapter has been greatly streamlined.

- **Chapter 8.** Critical paths and the critical-path algorithm are now combined into a single section (Section 8.5). The old section on scheduling with independent tasks has been deleted.

- **Chapter 9.** This is a new chapter. Much of the material is taken from Mini-Excursion 3 in the seventh edition, but with a much greater emphasis on sequences in general and population sequences in particular.

- **Chapter 10.** This chapter has been completely rewritten. The emphasis of this chapter now is on the real-life applications of money management. Savings, investment, and consumer debt are the primary topics discussed.

- **Chapter 13.** This was Chapter 9 in previous editions. There is a bigger focus now on the mathematical properties of Fibonacci numbers and the golden ratio.

- **Chapter 14.** This chapter (old Chapter 13) has been reorganized into three major themes (enumeration, measurement, and cause-effect). Each of these themes corresponds to a section of the chapter. Many real-life examples have been added.

- **Chapter 15.** This chapter is a minor reorganization of the material in the old Chapter 14 with many new really real examples added.

- **Chapter 16.** This chapter now includes two new sections—one introduces expected values (Section 16.4), the other applies the concept of expected value to the measurement of risk (Section 16.5). Some of the material comes from the old Mini-Excursion 4, but several new examples have been added. This chapter is quite a bit longer than the old Chapter 15 it replaces.

- **Chapter 17.** This chapter (previously Chapter 16) has been streamlined into four sections. There is now much more emphasis on modeling real-world approximately normally distributed data with the properties of normal distributions. Several really real examples have been added.

A Final Word to the Reader

66 It's not what you look at that matters, it's what you see. 99

– Henry David Thoreau

My goal in writing this book is to shine a small light on all that mathematics can be when looked at in the right way—useful, interesting, subtle, beautiful, and accessible. I hope that you will see something of that in this book.

Peter Tannenbaum

Supplementary Materials

Student Supplement

Student Resource Guide
Dale R. Buske, St. Cloud State University
ISBN 13: 978-0-321-83721-9; ISBN 10: 0-321-83721-5

- In addition to the worked-out solutions to odd-numbered exercises from the text, this guide contains "selected hints" that point the reader in one of many directions leading to a solution and keys to student success, including lists of skills that will help prepare for the chapter exams.

Instructor Supplements

Instructor's Edition
ISBN 13: 978-0-321-83720-2; ISBN 10: 0-321-83720-7

- Includes answers to all Walking and Jogging exercises in a separate section in the back of the book.

The following supplements are ONLINE ONLY and are available for download in the Pearson Higher Education catalogs or inside your MyMathLab course:

Instructor's Guide and Solutions Manual
Dale R. Buske, St. Cloud State University

- Contains solutions to all the exercises in the text as well as a variety of resources for in-classroom use.

Instructor's Testing Manual
Joseph P. Kudrle, University of Vermont

- Contains four alternate tests per chapter. Two have multiple-choice exercises, and two have free-response exercises.

Insider's Guide

- Includes resources designed to help faculty with course preparation and helpful teaching tips.
- Includes learning outcomes, skill objectives, ideas for the classroom, worksheets, and project ideas from current users of the text.

PowerPoint® Lecture Slides

- Fully editable classroom presentations cover important topics and example from the text.

TestGen®

TestGen® (*www.pearsoned.com/testgen*) enables instructors to build, edit, print, and administer tests using a computerized bank of questions developed to cover all the objectives of the text. TestGen is algorithmically based, allowing instructors to create multiple but equivalent versions of the same question or test with the click of a button. Instructors can also modify test bank questions or add new questions. The software and testbank are available for download from Pearson Education's online catalog.

Online Resources

MyMathLab®

Online Course (access code required)

MyMathLab delivers **proven results** in helping individual students succeed.

- MyMathLab has a consistently positive impact on the quality of learning in higher education math instruction. MyMathLab can be successfully implemented in any environment—lab-based, hybrid, fully online, traditional—and demonstrates the quantifiable difference that integrated usage has on student retention, subsequent success, and overall achievement.
- MyMathLab's comprehensive online gradebook automatically tracks your students' results on tests, quizzes, homework, and in the study plan. You can use the gradebook to quickly intervene if your students have trouble, or to provide positive feedback on a job well done. The data within MyMathLab is easily exported to a variety of spreadsheet programs, such as Microsoft Excel. You can determine which points of data you want to export and then analyze the results to determine success.

MyMathLab provides **engaging experiences** that personalize, stimulate, and measure learning for each student.

- **Exercises:** The homework and practice exercises in MyMathLab are correlated to the exercises in the textbook, and they regenerate algorithmically to give students unlimited opportunity for practice and mastery. The software offers immediate, helpful feedback when students enter incorrect answers.
- **Multimedia Learning Aids:** Exercises include guided solutions, sample problems, animations, videos, and eText clips for extra help at the point of use.
- **Expert Tutoring:** Although many students describe the whole of MyMathLab as "like having your own personal tutor," students using MyMathLab do have access to live tutoring from Pearson, from qualified math and statistics instructors who provide tutoring sessions for students via MyMathLab.

And, MyMathLab comes from a **trusted partner** with educational expertise and an eye on the future.

- Knowing that you are using a Pearson product means knowing that you are using quality content. That means that our eTexts are accurate and our assessment tools work. Whether you are just getting started with MyMathLab or have a question along the way, we're here to help you learn about our technologies and how to incorporate them into your course.

New in the MyMathLab course

- A new type of problem making the Applets assignable, helping to assess understanding of the concepts and the applications of the applet.
- Applets integrated into the multimedia textbook.
- An Image Resource Library contains art from the text for instructors to edit provided PowerPoints, create their own presentations, or handouts.

To learn more about how MyMathLab combines proven learning applications with powerful assessment, visit **www.mymathlab.com** or contact your Pearson representative.

MyMathLab® | **Ready-to-Go Course (access code required)**

These new Ready-to-Go courses provide students with all the same great MyMathLab features but make it easier for instructors to get started. Each course includes pre-assigned homeworks and quizzes to make creating your course even simpler. Ask your Pearson representative about the details for this particular course or to see a copy of this course.

MathXL® | **Online Course (access code required)**

MathXL® is the homework and assessment engine that runs MyMathLab. (MyMathLab is MathXL plus a learning management system.)

With MathXL, instructors can:

- Create, edit, and assign online homework and tests using algorithmically generated exercises correlated at the objective level to the textbook.
- Create and assign their own online exercises and import TestGen tests for added flexibility.
- Maintain records of all student work tracked in MathXL's online gradebook.

With MathXL, students can:

- Take chapter tests in MathXL and receive personalized study plans and/or personalized homework assignments based on their test results.
- Use the study plan and/or the homework to link directly to tutorial exercises for the objectives they need to study.

- Access supplemental animations and video clips directly from selected exercises.

MathXL is available to qualified adopters. For more information, visit our website at www.mathxl.com, or contact your Pearson representative.

Acknowledgments

This edition benefited from the contributions and opinions of a large number of people. Special thanks to Dale Buske and Katie Tannenbaum, who read early drafts of the manuscript and provided many useful comments and suggestions, and to Dale Buske, Deidre Smith, Karla Karstens, and Margaret Morrow for their valuable contributions to the new and updated exercise sets.

The following is a list of reviewers for the last two editions (asterisks indicate reviewers of this eighth edition).

Lowell Abrams, *George Washington University*
*Diane Allen, *Idaho State University*
Erol Barbut, *Washington State University*
*Gregory Budzban, *Southern Illinois University*
*Lynn Clark, *Westfield State University*
*Irene C. Corriette, *Cameron University*
*Robert V. DeLiberato, *Saint Joseph's University*
Lauren Fern, *University of Montana*
Karla Karstens, *University of Vermont*
*Lynne H. Kendall, *Regis University*
Randa Lee Kress, *Idaho State University*
*Diana Lee, *Highline Community College*
Margaret A. Michener, *University of Nebraska at Kearney*
Mika Munakata, *Montclair State University*
Kenneth Pothoven, *University of South Florida*
Salvatore Sciandra Jr., *Niagara County Community College*
Deirdre Smith, *University of Arizona*
*Paul K. Swets, *Angelo State University*
W. D. Wallis, *Southern Illinois University*
*Cathleen M. Zucco-Teveloff, *Rowan University*

Many people contributed to previous editions of this book. Special thanks to Robert Arnold, Dale Buske (again), and to the following reviewers: Teri Anderson, Guanghwa Andy Chang, Carmen Artino, Donald Beaton, Terry L. Cleveland, Leslie Cobar, Crista Lynn Coles, Kimberly A. Conti, Ronald Czochor, Nancy Eaton, Lily Eidswick, Kathryn E. Fink, Stephen I. Gendler, Marc Goldstein, Josephine Guglielmi, Abdi Hajikandi, William S. Hamilton, Cynthia Harris, Harold Jacobs, Peter D. Johnson, Stephen Kenton, Tom Kiley, Katalin Kolossa, Jean Krichbaum, Thomas Lada, Kim L. Luna, Mike Martin, Thomas O'Bryan, Daniel E. Otero, Philip J. Owens, Matthew Pickard, Lana Rhoads, David E. Rush, Shelley Russell, Kathleen C. Salter, Theresa M. Sandifer, Paul Schembari, Marguerite V. Smith, William W. Smith, Hilary Spriggs, David Stacy, Zoran Sunik, John Watson, and Sarah N. Ziesler.

Last, but not least, the *real movers and shakers* that made this new edition possible and deserve special recognition: mover and shaker in-chief (and Senior Acquisitions Editor) Marnie Greenhut, Executive Marketing Manager Roxanne McCarley, Senior Project Manager Patty Bergin, Senior Content Editor Elizabeth Bernardi, Assistant Editor Elle Driska, Marketing Assistant Caitlin Crain, Media Producer Aimee Thorne, and Project Manager at Cenveo Publisher Services, Sherry Berg.

PART 2

Management Science

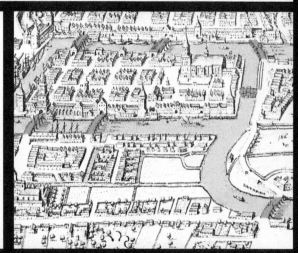

5 The Mathematics of Getting Around

Euler Paths and Circuits

United Parcel Service (UPS) is the largest package delivery company in the world. On a typical day UPS delivers roughly 15 million packages to over 6 million customers worldwide; on a busy day much more than that (the week before Christmas 2011, UPS delivered more than 120 million packages). Such remarkable feats of logistics require tremendous resources, superb organization, and (surprise!) a good dose of mathematics. In this chapter we will discuss some of the mathematical ideas that make this possible.

On a normal day a UPS driver delivers somewhere between 200 and 500 packages. In rural areas where there may be considerable distances between delivery points, the number is closer to 200; in highly populated urban areas where the delivery points are close to each other the number is closer to 500. But in both cases one of the keys to success in delivering all the packages is the efficiency of the delivery route. Efficient routing means, among other things, keeping *deadheading* (the term used to describe driving over the same section of road more than once) at a minimum, and this is where the mathematics comes in: How do you design a route that minimizes the total amount of "wasted" travel?

Problems like those faced by a UPS driver (or a FedEx driver, or a mail carrier for that matter) trying to minimize the total length of his or her route are known as *street-routing problems*, and they have applications to other types of situations such as routing garbage trucks, security patrols, tourist buses, and even late-night pizza deliveries.

Section 5.1 introduces the concept of a *street-routing problem* and shows examples in several different settings and applications. Keep in mind that many of the examples in this section are scaled down in size and scope to keep things simple—in real life the same application will occur on a much larger scale. Regardless of the scale, the mathematical theory behind street-routing problems is one and the same, and we owe much of this theory to the genius of one man—the Swiss mathematician Leonhard Euler. Euler's role was so significant that in this chapter we will see his last name (pronounced "oiler," by the way) used both as a noun (*Euler circuit*, *Euler path*) and as a verb (*eulerizing*, *semi-eulerizing*). Section 5.2 introduces *graphs*—the key mathematical tool that allows us to tackle street-routing problems— and some of the concepts and terminology associated with graphs. Section 5.3 gives the mathematical infrastructure needed to solve street-routing problems, consisting of three key facts (*Euler's Circuit Theorem*, *Euler's Path Theorem*, and the *Sum of Degrees Theorem*) and an algorithm known as *Fleury's Algorithm*. In Section 5.4 we will learn how to combine all the preceding ideas to develop the strategies needed to solve street-routing problems in general.

Leonhard Euler (1707–1783)

5.1   Street-Routing Problems

We will start this section with a brief discussion of routing problems. What is a **routing problem**? To put it in the most general way, routing problems are concerned with finding ways to route the delivery of *goods* and/or *services* to an assortment of *destinations*. The goods or services in question could be packages, mail, newspapers, pizzas, garbage collection, bus service, and so on. The delivery destinations could be homes, warehouses, distribution centers, terminals, and the like.

There are two basic questions that we are typically interested in when dealing with a routing problem. The first is called the *existence* question. The existence question is simple: Is an actual route possible? For most routing problems, the existence question is easy to answer, and the answer takes the form of a simple yes or no. When the answer to the existence question is yes, then a second question—the *optimization question*—comes into play. Of all the possible routes, which one is the *optimal route*? (*Optimal* here means "the best" when measured against some predetermined variable such as *cost*, *distance*, or *time*.) In most management science problems, the optimization question is where the action is.

In this chapter we will learn how to answer both the existence and optimization questions for a special class of routing problems known as **street-routing problems**. The common thread in all street-routing problems is what we might call, for lack of a better term, the *pass-through requirement*—the requirement that the route must pass at least once through some specified set of connections. In other words, in a street-routing problem the pass-through requirement means that each street (or bridge, or lane, or highway) within a defined area (be it a town, an area of town, or a subdivision) must be covered by the route. We will refer to these types of routes as *exhaustive routes*. The most common services that typically require exhaustive routing are mail delivery, police patrols, garbage collection, street sweeping, and snow removal. More exotic examples can be census taking, precinct walking, electric meter reading, routing parades, tour buses, and so on.

To clarify some of the ideas we will introduce several examples of street-routing problems (just the problems for now—their solutions will come later in the chapter).

EXAMPLE 5.1   THE SECURITY GUARD PROBLEM

After a rash of burglaries, a private security guard is hired to patrol the streets of the Sunnyside neighborhood shown in Fig. 5-1. The security guard's assignment is to make an exhaustive patrol, on foot, through the entire neighborhood. Obviously, he doesn't want to walk any more than what is necessary. His starting point is the corner of Elm and J streets across from the school (*S* in Fig. 5-1)—that's where he usually parks his car. (This is relevant because at the end of his patrol he needs to come back to *S* to pick up his car.) Being a practical person, the security guard would like the answers to the following questions:

1. Is it possible to start and end at *S*, cover every block of the neighborhood, and pass through each block *just once*?

2. If some of the blocks will have to be covered more than once, what is an *optimal* route that covers the entire neighborhood? ("Optimal" here means "with the minimal amount of walking.")

3. Can a better route (i.e., less walking) be found by choosing a different starting and ending point? We will answer all of these questions in Section 5.4.

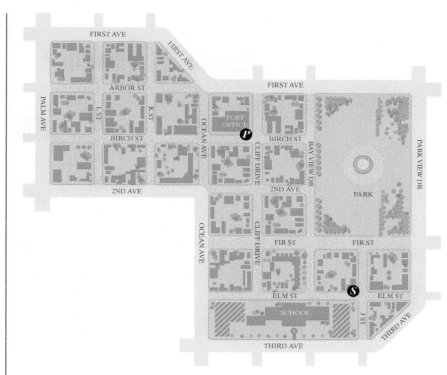

FIGURE 5-1   The Sunnyside neighborhood.

EXAMPLE 5.2   THE MAIL CARRIER PROBLEM

A mail carrier has to deliver mail in the same Sunnyside neighborhood (Fig. 5-1). The difference between the mail carrier's route and the security guard's route is that the mail carrier must make *two* passes through blocks with buildings on both sides of the street and only one pass through blocks with buildings on only one side of the street (and where there are no buildings on either side of the street, the mail carrier does not have to walk at all). In addition, the mail carrier has no choice as to her starting and ending points—she has to start and end her route at the local post office (*P* in Fig. 5-1). Much like the security guard, the mail carrier wants to find the optimal route that would allow her to cover the neighborhood with the least amount of walking. (Put yourself in her shoes and you would do the same—good weather or bad, she walks this route 300 days a year!)

EXAMPLE 5.3   THE UPS DRIVER PROBLEM

Now we consider the case of a UPS driver who must deliver packages around the Sunnyside neighborhood. The red crosses in Fig. 5-2 indicate the locations (homes or businesses) where packages are to be delivered (it's the week before Christmas so there is an unusually large number of packages to be delivered).

   Unlike the mail carrier (required to pass through every block of the neighborhood where there are homes or businesses), the UPS driver has to pass only through those blocks where there are red crosses, and only once through such blocks (if the delivery is on the opposite side of the street he just crosses the street on foot). In addition, because of other deliveries, the UPS driver must enter the neighborhood through the street indicated by the "in" arrow and exit the neighborhood through the street indicated by the "out" arrow. Once again, we want to determine (and we will in Section 5.4) the most *efficient* route that will allow the UPS driver to deliver all those packages. The requirements for the route are (a) enter and exit the neighborhood where indicated in Fig. 5.2 and (b) pass through every block where there

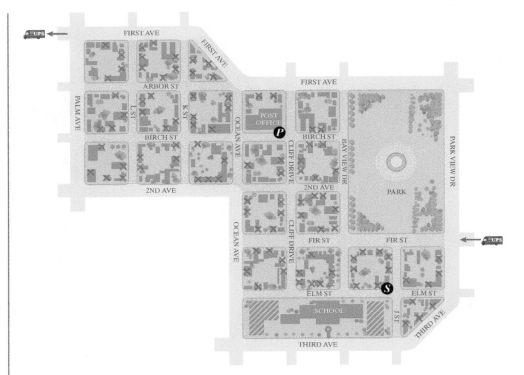

FIGURE 5-2 UPS delivery locations marked with a red cross.

are delivery locations marked with red crosses. [Note: In general, UPS drivers are mostly concerned with the total time it takes to complete their package deliveries rather than the total distance traveled, and often go out of their way to avoid left-turn signals or streets with a lot of traffic. This makes the routing problem more complicated; therefore, to keep things simple we will assume that in this example driving time is proportional to distance traveled (this happens, for example, when there is little or no traffic or when traffic moves evenly throughout the neighborhood). Under this assumption the most efficient route is still the shortest route.]

Our next example is primarily of historical interest. Euler was introduced to the Königsberg bridges puzzle in the early 1700s as a recreational puzzle that might potentially be solved using mathematical ideas, but nobody was clear as to what kind of mathematics was needed. Euler's great contribution was in developing a new mathematical theory (now known as *graph theory*) that could be used to solve the bridges puzzle as well as much more practical and complex problems. We will be introduced to Euler's ideas in the next three sections.

EXAMPLE 5.4 | THE KÖNIGSBERG BRIDGES PUZZLE

This story starts in the 1700s in the medieval town of Königsberg, in Eastern Europe. A map of the city at that time is shown in Fig. 5-3, with the river Pregel running through town, the two islands on the river, and the north and south banks all connected by the seven bridges shown in red. (*Note*: Present-day Königsberg has a different layout, as two of the bridges no longer exist.) A little game played by the locals at the time was to try to take a walk around town fully crossing every bridge once and only once (i.e., no bridge could be skipped and no bridge could be crossed twice). Nobody was able to do this successfully and a widely held belief in the town was that such a walk was indeed impossible. What was asked of Euler was to rigorously prove this. He did this, and much more. We will soon learn how he did it.

KONINGSBERGA

FIGURE 5-3 Map of the medieval town of Königsberg (Prussia) in the 1700s.

If we think of the bridges as playing a role analogous to that of the streets in the Sunnyside neighborhood, the Königsberg bridges puzzle becomes another street-routing problem. The negative answer to the puzzle means that no route that satisfies the restrictions of the problem (pass through each bridge once and only once) exists.

Our next example is an expanded and modernized version of the Königsberg bridges problem.

EXAMPLE 5.5 THE BRIDGES OF MADISON COUNTY

Madison County is a quaint old place, famous for its beautiful bridges. The Madison River runs through the county, and there are four islands (A, B, C, and D) and 11 bridges joining the islands to both banks of the river (R and L) and one another (Fig. 5-4). A famous photographer is hired to take pictures of each of the 11 bridges for a national magazine. The photographer needs to drive across each bridge once for the photo shoot. The problem is that there is a $25 toll (the locals call it a "maintenance tax") every time an out-of-town visitor drives across a bridge, and the photographer wants to minimize the total cost of the trip. The street-routing problem here is to find a route that passes through each bridge at least once and recrosses as few bridges as possible. Moreover, the photographer can start the route on either bank of the river and, likewise, end it on either bank of the river.

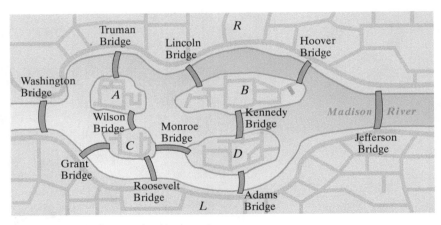

FIGURE 5-4   Bridges on the Madison River.

5.2   An Introduction to Graphs

■ A note of warning: The graphs we will be discussing here have no relation to the graphs of functions you may have studied in algebra or calculus.

The key tool we will use to tackle the street-routing problems introduced in Section 5.1 is the notion of a **graph**. The most common way to describe a *graph* is by means of a picture. The basic elements of such a picture are a set of "dots" called the **vertices** of the graph and a collection of "lines" called the **edges** of the graph. (Unfortunately, this terminology is not universal. In some applications the word "nodes" is used for the vertices and the word "links" is used for the edges. We will stick to vertices and edges as much as possible.) On the surface, that's all there is to it—edges connecting vertices. Below the surface there is a surprisingly rich theory. Let's look at a few examples first.

EXAMPLE 5.6   BASIC GRAPH CONCEPTS

Figure 5-5 shows several examples of graphs. We will discuss each separately.

■ Figure 5-5(a) shows a graph with six vertices labeled *A, B, C, D, E,* and *F* (it is customary to use capital letters to label the vertices of a graph). For convenience we refer to the set of vertices of a graph as the **vertex set**. In this graph, the vertex set is $\{A, B, C, D, E, F\}$. The graph has 11 edges (described by listing, in any order, the two vertices that are connected by the edge): *AB, AD, BC,* etc.

□ When two vertices are connected by an edge we say that they are **adjacent vertices**. Thus, *A* and *B* are adjacent vertices, but *A* and *E* are not adjacent. The edge connecting *B* with itself is written as *BB* and is called a **loop**. Vertices *C* and *D* are connected twice (i.e., by two separate edges), so when we list the edges we include *CD* twice. Similarly, vertices *E* and *F* are connected by three edges, so we list *EF* three times. We refer to edges that appear more than once as **multiple edges**.

□ The complete list of edges of the graph, the **edge list**, is *AB, AD, BB, BC, BE, CD, CD, DE, EF, EF, EF.*

□ The number of edges that meet at each vertex is called the **degree** of the vertex and is denoted by $\deg(X)$. In this graph we have $\deg(A) = 2$, $\deg(B) = 5$ (please note that the loop contributes 2 to the degree of the vertex), $\deg(C) = 3$, $\deg(D) = 4$, $\deg(E) = 5$, and $\deg(F) = 3$. It will be important in the next section to distinguish between vertices depending on whether their degree is an odd or an even number. We will refer to vertices like *B, C, E,* and *F* with an odd degree as **odd vertices** and to vertices with an even degree like *A* and *D* as **even vertices**.

■ Figure 5-5(b) is very similar to Fig. 5-5(a)—the only difference is the way the edge *BE* is drawn. In Fig. 5-5(a) edges *AD* and *BE* cross each other, but the

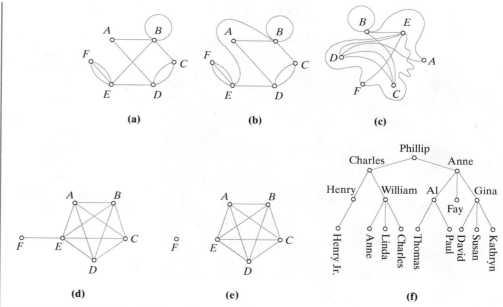

FIGURE 5-5 (a), (b), and (c) are all pictures of the same graph; (d) is a simple, connected graph; (e) is a simple, disconnected graph; and (f) is a graph labeled with names instead of letters.

crossing point is not a vertex of the graph—it's just an irrelevant crossing point. Fig. 5-5(b) gets around the crossing by drawing the edge in a more convoluted way, but the way we draw an edge is itself irrelevant. The key point here is that as graphs, Figs. 5-5(a) and 5-5(b) are the same. Both have exactly the same vertices and exactly the same edge list.

- Figure 5-5(c) take the idea one step further—it is in fact, another rendering of the graph shown in Figs. 5-5(a) and (b). The vertices have been moved around and put in different positions, and the edges are funky—no other way to describe it. Despite all the funkiness, this graph conveys exactly the same information that the graph in Fig. 5-5(a) does. You can check it out— same set of vertices and same edge list. The moral here is that while graphs are indeed pictures connecting "dots" with "lines," it is not the specific picture that matters but the story that the picture tells: which dots are connected to each other and which aren't. We can move the vertices around, and we can draw the edges any funky way we want (straight line, curved line, wavy line, etc.)—none of that matters. The only thing that matters is the set of vertices and the list of edges.

- Figure 5-5(d) shows a graph with six vertices. Vertices *A, B, C, D,* and *E* form what is known as a **clique**—each vertex is connected to each of the other four. Vertex *F*, on the other hand, is connected to only one other vertex. This graph has no loops or multiple edges. Graphs without loops or multiple edges are called **simple graphs**. There are many applications of graphs where loops and multiple edges cannot occur, and we have to deal only with simple graphs. (In Examples 5.7 and 5.8 we will see two applications where only simple graphs occur.)

- Figure 5-5(e) shows a graph very similar to the one in Fig. 5-5(d). The only difference between the two is the absence of the edge *EF*. In this graph there are no edges connecting *F* to any other vertex. For obvious reasons, *F* is called an **isolated** vertex. This graph is made up of two separate and disconnected "pieces"—the clique formed by the vertices *A, B, C, D,* and *E* and the isolated vertex *F*. Because the graph is not made of a single "piece," we say that the graph is **disconnected**, and the separate pieces that make up the graph are called the *components* of the graph.

- Figure 5-5(f) shows a connected simple graph. The vertices of this graph are names (there is no rule about what the labels of a vertex can be). Can you guess what this graph might possibly represent?

| **EXAMPLE 5.7** | AIRLINE ROUTE MAPS |

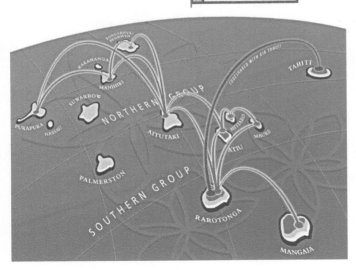

Figure 5-6 shows the route map for a very small airline called Air Rarotonga. Air Rarotonga serves just 10 islands in the South Pacific, and the route map shows the direct flights that are available between the various islands. In essence, the route map is a graph whose vertices are the islands. An edge connects two islands if there is a direct flight between them. No direct flight, no edge. The picture makes a slight attempt to respect geographical facts (the bigger islands are drawn larger but certainly not to scale, and they sit in the ocean more or less as shown), but the point of an airline route map is to show if there is a direct flight from point X to point Y, and, in that regard, accurate geography is not all that important.

FIGURE 5-6   Air Rarotonga route map.

| **EXAMPLE 5.8** | THE FACEBOOK SOCIAL GRAPH |

Do you know who your friends' friends are? In the off-line world—where friendships are tight and relationships are personal—you probably have some idea. In the Facebook world—where "friendships" are cheap—you probably have a fairly limited picture of the complex web of friendships that connect your own set of Facebook friends.

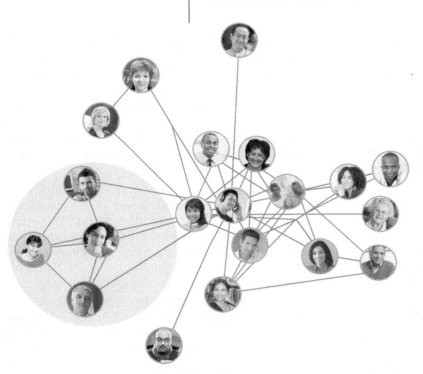

But worry no more. Thanks to the Facebook Social Graph (FSG), you can have a complete picture of how your Facebook friends are connected. The FSG is a Facebook app available for free to anyone on Facebook. [To create your own FSG (and you are strongly encouraged to do it now, not just for the curiosity factor but because it will help you navigate this example) go to your Facebook account, click on "Apps and Games," find "Social Graph" (you may have to do a search for it) and click "Allow."]

The vertices of the FSG are all your Facebook friends. You are not included because it is understood that you are a friend of everyone on the graph. An edge connecting two of your friends means that they are friends. Fig. 5-7 shows the FSG of a real person (who will remain nameless), but the FSG is at its most useful when used in a dynamic way. When you run the mouse over a particular friend X, the app will highlight all the connections between X and your other

FIGURE 5-7   The social graph: The friendship connections among your friends.

friends. Some X's are "hubs" connected to many people (if you are married it is very likely that your spouse is a hub, since you typically share most of your friends); other X's might be isolated vertices (the guy sitting next to you on the airplane with whom you exchanged pleasantries and ended up being a Facebook friend). The FSG also high-lights "clusters" of friendships. These clusters represent groups of individuals who are all friends with each other (your high school buddies perhaps, or coworkers, or family).

The main point of Examples 5.7 and 5.8 is to highlight how powerful (and useful) the concept of a graph can be. Granted, the Air Rarotonga route map is small (just right to illustrate the point), but if you think big you can imagine a United Airlines route map instead, with hundreds of destinations and thousands of flights connecting them. The fundamental idea is still the same—graphs convey visually a tremendous amount of information that would be hard to convey in any other form. Can you imagine describing the complex web of relationships in your Facebook Social Graph or in a United Airlines route map any other way? Airline route maps and friendship graphs are always simple graphs, without loops (airlines don't routinely schedule flights that go around in circles, and by definition, friendship is a connection between two different persons) or multiple edges (either there are direct flights connecting X and Y or there aren't, and X and Y are either friends or they aren't).

EXAMPLE 5.9   PATHS AND CIRCUITS

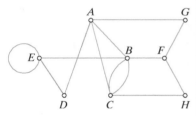

FIGURE 5-8   Graph for Example 5.9.

We say that two edges are **adjacent edges** when they share a common vertex. In Fig. 5-8 for example, AB is adjacent to AC and AD (they share vertex A), as well as to BC, BF, and BE (they share vertex B). A sequence of *distinct* edges each adjacent to the next is called a **path**, and the number of edges in the path is called the **length** of the path. For example in Fig. 5-8, the edges AB, BF, and FG form a path of length 3. A good way to think of a path is as a real-world path—a way to "hike" along the edges of the graph, traveling along the first edge, then the next, and so on. To shorten the notation, we describe the path by just listing the vertices in sequence separated by commas. For example A, B, F, G describes the path formed by the edges AB, BF, and FG.

Here are a few more examples of paths in Fig. 5-8:

- A, B is a path of length 1. Any edge can be thought of as a path of length 1—not very interesting, but it allows us to apply the concept of a path even to single edges.

- A, B, C, A, D, E is a path of length 5 starting at A and ending at E. The path goes through vertex A a second time, but that's OK. It is permissible for a path to revisit some of the vertices. On the other hand, A, C, B, A, C does not meet the definition of a path because the edges of the path cannot be revisited and here AC is traveled twice. So, in a path it's OK to revisit some of the vertices but not OK to revisit any edges.

- A, B, C, A, D, E, E, B is a path of length 7. Notice that this "trip" is possible because of the loop at E.

- A, B, C, A, D, E, B, C is also a legal path of length 7. Here we can use the edge BC twice because there are in fact two distinct edges connecting B and C.

When a trip along the edges of the graph closes back on itself (i.e., starts and ends with the same vertex) we specifically call it a **circuit** rather than a path. Thus, we will restrict the term *path* to open-ended trips and the word *circuit* to closed trips.

Here are a few examples of circuits in Fig. 5-8:

- A, D, E, B, A is a circuit of length 4. Even though it appears like the circuit designates A as the starting (and ending) vertex, a circuit is independent of where we designate the start. In other words, the same circuit can be written as D, E, B, A, D or E, B, A, D, E, etc. They are all the same circuit, but we have to choose one (arbitrary) vertex to start the list.

- B, C, B is a circuit of length 2. This is possible because of the double edge BC. On the other hand, B, A, B is not a circuit because the edge AB is being traveled twice. (Just as in a path, the edges of a circuit have to be distinct.)

- E, E is a circuit of length 1. A loop is the only way to have a circuit of length 1.

In Example 5.9 we saw several examples of paths (and circuits) that are part of the graph in Fig. 5-8, but the important idea we will discuss next in this: Can the path (or circuit) be the entire graph, not just a part of it? In other words, we want to consider the possibility of a path (or a circuit) that *exhausts* all the edges of the graph.

An **Euler path** (named after Leonhard Euler) is a path that covers *all* the edges of the graph. Likewise, an **Euler circuit** is a circuit that covers all the edges of the graph. In other words, we have an Euler path (or circuit) when the entire graph can be written as a path (or circuit).

EXAMPLE 5.10 EULER PATHS AND EULER CIRCUITS

Figures 5-9, 5-10, and 5-11 illustrate the three possibilities that can occur:

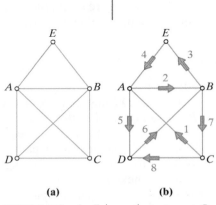

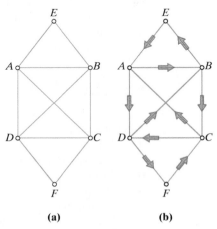

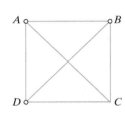

FIGURE 5-9 An Euler path starting at *C* and ending at *D*.

FIGURE 5-10   An Euler circuit.

FIGURE 5-11   No Euler path or circuit.

- The graph in Fig. 5-9(a) has an Euler path—in fact, it has several. One of the possible Euler paths is shown in Fig. 5-9(b). The path starts at C and ends at D—just follow the arrows and you will be able to "trace" the edges of the graph without retracing any (just like in elementary school).

- The graph in Fig. 5-10(a) has many possible Euler circuits. One of them is shown in Fig. 5-10(b). Just follow the arrows. Unlike the Euler path in Fig. 5-9(b), the arrows are not numbered. You can start this circuit at any vertex of the graph, follow the arrows, and you will return to the starting vertex having covered all the edges once.

- The graph in Fig. 5-11 has neither an Euler path nor an Euler circuit. That's the way it goes sometimes—some graphs just don't have it!

We introduced the idea of a *connected* or *disconnected* graph in Example 5.6. Formally, we say that a graph is **connected** if you can get from any vertex to any other vertex along some path of the graph. Informally, this says that you can get from any point to any other point by "hiking" along the edges of the graph. Even more informally, it means that the graph is made of one "piece." A graph that is not connected is called **disconnected** and consists of at least two (maybe more) separate "pieces" we call the **components** of the graph.

EXAMPLE 5.11   BRIDGES

Figure 5-12 shows three different graphs. The graph in Fig. 5-12(a) is connected; the graph in Fig. 5-12(b) is disconnected and has two components; the graph in Fig. 5-12(c) is disconnected and has three components (the isolated vertex *G* is a component—that's as small a component as you can get!).

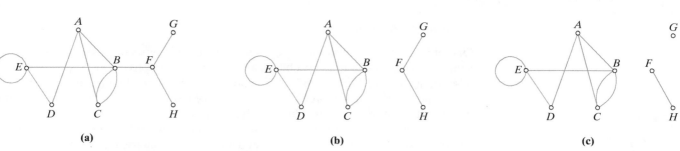

FIGURE 5-12   (a) A connected graph, (b) two components, and (c) three components.

Notice that the only difference between the *disconnected* graph in Fig. 5-12(b) and the *connected* graph in Fig. 5-12(a) is the edge BF. Think of *BF* as a "bridge" that connects the two components of the graph in Fig. 5-12(b). Not surprisingly, we call such an edge a *bridge*. A **bridge** in a connected graph is an edge that keeps the graph connected—if the bridge were not there, the graph would be disconnected. The graph in Fig. 5-12(a) has three bridges: *BF*, *FG*, and *FH*.

For the reader's convenience, Table 5-1 shows a summary of the basic graph concepts we have seen so far.

Vertices
- **adjacent:** any two vertices connected by an edge
- **vertex set:** the set of vertices in a graph
- **degree:** number of edges meeting at the vertex
- **odd (even):** degree is an odd (even) number
- **isolated:** no edges connecting the vertex (i.e., degree is 0)

Edges
- **adjacent:** two edges that share a vertex
- **loop:** an edge that connects a vertex with itself
- **multiple edges:** more than one edge connecting the same two vertices
- **edge list:** a list of all the edges in a graph
- **bridge:** an edge in a connected graph without which the graph would be disconnected

Paths and circuits
- **path:** a sequence of edges each adjacent to the next, with no edge included more than once, and starting and ending at different vertices
- **circuit:** same as a path, but starting and ending at the same vertex
- **Euler path:** a path that covers all the edges of the graph
- **Euler circuit:** a circuit that covers all the edges of the graph
- **length:** number of edges in a path or a circuit

Graphs
- **simple:** a graph with no loops or multiple edges
- **connected:** there is a path going from any vertex to any other vertex
- **disconnected:** not connected; consisting of two or more components
- **clique:** a set of completely interconnected vertices in the graph (every vertex is connected to every other vertex by an edge)

TABLE 5-1   Glossary of basic graph concepts

Graphs as Models

One of Euler's most important insights was that certain types of problems can be conveniently rephrased as graph problems and that, in fact, graphs are just the right tool for describing many real-life situations. The notion of using a mathematical concept to describe and solve a real-life problem is one of the oldest and grandest traditions in mathematics. It is called *modeling*. Unwittingly, we have all done simple forms of modeling before, all the way back to elementary school. Every time we turn a word problem into an arithmetic calculation, an algebraic equation, or a geometric picture, we are modeling. We can now add to our repertoire one more tool for modeling: graph models.

In the next set of examples we are going to illustrate how we can use graphs to *model* some of the street-routing problems introduced in Section 5.1.

EXAMPLE 5.12   MODELING THE BRIDGES OF KÖNIGSBERG PUZZLE

The Königsberg bridges puzzle introduced in Example 5.4 asked whether it was possible to take a stroll through the old city of Königsberg and cross each of the seven bridges once and only once. Figure 5-13 shows the evolution of a graph model that we can use to answer this question. Figure 5-13(a) shows the original map of the city in the 1700s. Figure 5-13(b) is a "leaner" version of the map, with lots of obviously irrelevant details removed. A little further reflection should convince us that many details in Fig. 5-13(b) are still irrelevant to the question. The shape and size of the islands, the width of the river, the lengths of the bridges—none of these things really matter. So, then, what does matter? Surprisingly little. *The only thing that truly matters to the solution of this problem is the relationship between land masses (islands and banks) and bridges.* Which land masses are connected to each other and by how many bridges? This information is captured by the red edges in Fig. 5-13(c). Thus, when we strip the map of all its superfluous information, we end up with the graph model shown in Fig. 5-13(d). The four vertices of the graph represent each of the four land masses; the edges represent the seven bridges. In this graph an *Euler circuit* would represent a stroll around the town that crosses each bridge once and ends back at the starting point; an *Euler path* would represent a stroll that crosses each bridge once but does not return to the starting point.

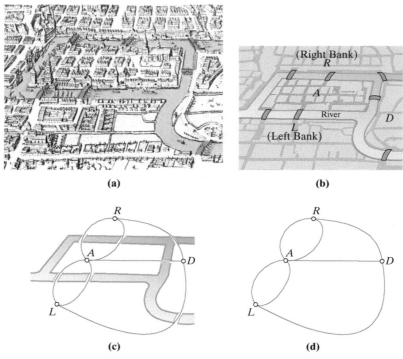

FIGURE 5-13   (a) Königsberg map, (b) a leaner version, (c) an even leaner version, and (d) the graph model.

As big moments go this one may not seem like much, but Euler's idea to turn a puzzle about walking across bridges in a quaint medieval city into an abstract question about graphs was a "eureka" moment in the history of mathematics.

EXAMPLE 5.13   MODELING THE SECURITY GUARD PROBLEM

In Example 5.1 we were introduced to the problem of the security guard who needs to walk the streets of the Sunnyside neighborhood [Fig. 5-14(a)]. The graph in Fig. 5-14(b)—where each edge represents a block of the neighborhood and each vertex an intersection—is a graph model of this problem. The questions raised in Example 5.1 can now be formulated in the language of graphs.

1. Does the graph in Fig. 5-14(b) have an Euler circuit that starts and ends at S?
2. What is the fewest number of edges that have to be added to the graph so that there is an Euler circuit?

We will learn how to answer such questions in the next couple of sections.

EXAMPLE 5.14   MODELING THE MAIL CARRIER PROBLEM

Unlike the security guard, the mail carrier in Example 5.2 must make two passes through every block that has homes on both sides of the street (she has to physically place the mail in the mailboxes), must make one pass through blocks that have homes on only one side of the street, and does not have to walk along blocks where there are no houses. In this situation an appropriate graph model requires two edges on the blocks that have homes on both sides of the street, one edge for the blocks that have homes on only one side of the street, and no edges for blocks having no homes on either side of the street. The graph that models this situation is shown in Fig. 5-14(c).

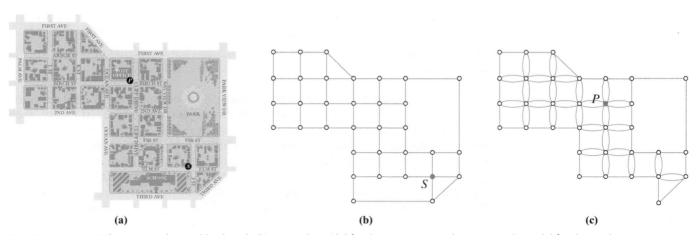

| (a) | (b) | (c) |

FIGURE 5-14   (a) The Sunnyside neighborhood. (b) A graph model for the security guard. (c) A graph model for the mail carrier.

EXAMPLE 5.15   MODELING THE UPS DRIVER PROBLEM

In Example 5.3 we discussed the UPS driver street-routing problem. The circumstances for the UPS driver are slightly different than those of the mail carrier. First, the UPS driver has to cover only those blocks where he has packages to deliver, shown by the red crosses in Fig. 5-15(a). Second, because of other deliveries outside the neighborhood, his route requires that he enter and exit the neighborhood at opposite ends, as shown in Fig. 5-15(a). Third, the driver can deliver packages on both sides of the street in a single pass. Taking all of these factors into account, we use the graph in Fig. 5-15(b) as a model for the UPS driver problem, with the required starting and ending points of the route shown in red.

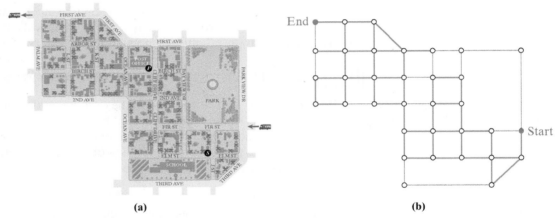

(a)

(b)

FIGURE 5-15   A graph model for the UPS driver.

5.3 | Euler's Theorems and Fleury's Algorithm

In this section we are going to develop the basic theory that will allow us to determine if a graph has an Euler circuit, an Euler path, or neither. This is important because, as we saw in the previous section, what are Euler circuit or Euler path questions in theory are real-life street-routing questions in practice. The three theorems we are going to see next (all due to Euler) are surprisingly simple and yet tremendously useful.

■ EULER'S CIRCUIT THEOREM

- If a graph is *connected* and *every vertex is even*, then it has an Euler circuit (at least one, usually more).

- If a graph has *any odd vertices*, then it does not have an Euler circuit.

If we want to know if a graph has an Euler circuit or not, here is how we can use Euler's circuit theorem. First we make sure the graph is connected. (If it isn't, then no matter what else, an Euler circuit is impossible.) If the graph is connected, then we start checking the degrees of the vertices, one by one. As soon as we hit an odd vertex, we know that an Euler circuit is out of the question. If there are no odd vertices, then we know that the answer is yes—the graph does have an Euler circuit! (The theorem doesn't tell us how to find it—that will come soon.) Figure 5-16 illustrates the three possible scenarios. The graph in Fig. 5-16(a) cannot have an Euler circuit for the simple reason that it is disconnected. The graph in Fig. 5-16(b) is connected, but we can quickly spot odd vertices (*C* is one of them; there are others). This graph has no Euler circuits either. But the graph in Fig. 5-16(c) is connected and all the vertices are even. This graph does have Euler circuits.

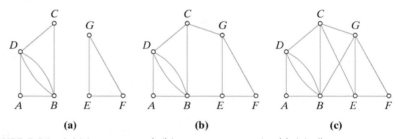

(a)   **(b)**   **(c)**

FIGURE 5-16   (a) Not connected; (b) some vertices are odd; (c) all vertices are even.

The basic idea behind Euler's circuit theorem is that as we travel along an Euler circuit, every time we go through a vertex we use up two different edges at that vertex—one to come in and one to go out. We can keep doing this as long as the vertices are even. A single odd vertex means that at some point we are going to come into it and not be able to get out. An analogous theorem will work with Euler paths, but now we do need odd vertices for the starting and ending points of the path. All the other vertices have to be even. Thus, we have the following theorem.

■ EULER'S PATH THEOREM

- If a graph is *connected* and has *exactly two odd vertices*, then it has an Euler path (at least one, usually more). Any such path must start at one of the odd vertices and end at the other one.

- If a graph has *more than two* odd vertices, then it cannot have an Euler path.

◼ EXAMPLE 5.16 THE BRIDGES OF KÖNIGSBERG PUZZLE SOLVED

Back to the Königsberg bridges problem. In Example 5.12 we saw that the layout of the bridges in the old city can be modeled by the graph in Fig. 5-17(a). This graph has four odd vertices; thus, neither an Euler circuit nor an Euler path can exist. We now have an unequivocal answer to the puzzle: *There is no possible way anyone can walk across all the bridges without having to recross some of them!* How many bridges will need to be recrossed? It depends. If we want to start and end in the same place, we must recross at least two of the bridges. One of the many possible routes is shown in Fig. 5-17(b). In this route the bridge connecting L and D is crossed twice, and so is one of the two bridges connecting A and R. If we are allowed to start and end in different places, we can do it by recrossing just one of the bridges. One possible route starting at A, crossing bridge LD twice, and ending at R is shown in Fig. 5-17(c).

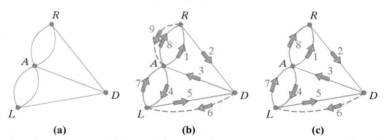

FIGURE 5-17 (a) The original graph with four odd vertices; (b) a walk recrossing bridges DL and RA; (c) a walk recrossing bridge DL only.

Euler's circuit theorem deals with graphs with zero odd vertices, whereas Euler's path theorem deals with graphs with two or more odd vertices. The only scenario not covered by the two theorems is that of graphs with just *one* odd vertex. Euler's third theorem rules out this possibility—a graph cannot have just one odd vertex. In fact, Euler's third theorem says much more.

■ EULER'S SUM OF DEGREES THEOREM

- The sum of the degrees of all the vertices of a graph equals twice the number of edges (and, therefore, is an even number).
- A graph always has an even number of *odd* vertices.

Euler's sum of degrees theorem is based on the following basic observation: Take any edge—let's call it XY. The edge contributes once to the degree of vertex X and once to the degree of vertex Y, so, in all, that edge makes a total contribution of 2 to the sum of the degrees. Thus, when the degrees of all the vertices of a graph are added, the total is twice the number of edges. Since the total sum is an even number, it is impossible to have just one odd vertex, or three odd vertices, or five odd vertices, and so on. To put it in a slightly different way, *the odd vertices of a graph always come in twos.*

Table 5-2 is a summary of Euler's three theorems. It shows the relationship between the number of odd vertices in a connected graph G and the existence of Euler paths or Euler circuits. (The assumption that G is connected is essential—a disconnected graph cannot have Euler paths or circuits regardless of what else is going on.)

Number of odd vertices	Conclusion
0	G has Euler circuit
2	G has Euler path
4, 6, 8, . . .	G has neither
1, 3, 5, . . .	This is impossible!

■ **TABLE 5-2**   Euler's theorems (summary)

Euler's theorems help us answer the following existence question: Does the graph have an Euler circuit, an Euler path, or neither? But when the graph has an Euler circuit or path, how do we find it? For small graphs, simple trial-and-error usually works fine, but real-life applications sometimes involve graphs with hundreds, or even thousands, of vertices. In these cases a trial-and-error approach is out of the question, and what is needed is a systematic strategy that tells us how to create an Euler circuit or path. In other words, we need an *algorithm*.

Fleury's Algorithm

There are many types of problems that can be solved by simply following a set of procedural rules—very specific rules like *when you get to this point, do this, . . . after you finish this, do that*, and so on. Given a specific problem X, an **algorithm** for solving X is a set of *procedural rules* that, when followed, always lead to some sort of "solution" to X. X need not be a mathematics problem—algorithms are used, sometimes unwittingly, in all walks of life: directions to find someone's house, the instructions for assembling a new bike, and a recipe for baking an apple pie are all examples of real-life algorithms. A useful analogy is to think of the problem as a *dish* we want to prepare and the algorithm as a *recipe* for preparing that dish.

In many cases, there are several different algorithms for solving the same problem (there is more than one way to bake an apple pie); in other cases, the problem does not lend itself to an algorithmic solution. In mathematics, algorithms are either *formula* driven (you just apply the formula or formulas to the appropriate inputs) or *directive* driven (you must follow a specific set of directives). In this part of the book (Chapters 5 through 8) we will discuss many important algorithms of the latter type.

Algorithms may be complicated but are rarely difficult. (There is a world of difference between complicated and difficult—accounting is complicated, calculus is difficult!) You don't have to be a brilliant and creative thinker to implement most algorithms—you just have to learn how to follow instructions carefully and methodically. For most of the algorithms we will discuss in this and the next three chapters, the key to success is simple: practice, practice, and more practice!

We will now turn our attention to an algorithm that finds an *Euler circuit* or an *Euler path* in a connected graph. Technically speaking, these are two separate algorithms, but in essence they are identical, so they can be described as one. (The algorithm we will give here is attributed to a Frenchman by the name of M. Fleury, who is alleged to have published a description of the algorithm in 1885. Other than his connection to this algorithm, little else is known about Monsieur Fleury.)

The idea behind Fleury's algorithm can be paraphrased by that old piece of folk wisdom: *Don't burn your bridges behind you.* In graph theory the word *bridge* has a very specific meaning—it is the only edge connecting two separate sections (call

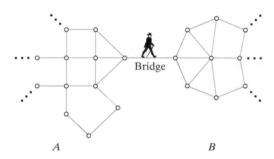

FIGURE 5-18 The bridge separates the two sections. Once you cross from A to B, the only way to get back to A is by recrossing the bridge.

them *A* and *B*) of a graph, as illustrated in Fig. 5-18. This means that if you are in *A*, you can only get to *B* by crossing the bridge. If you do that and then want to get back to *A*, you will need to recross that same bridge. It follows that if you don't want to recross bridges, you better finish your business at *A* before you move on to *B*.

Thus, Fleury's algorithm is based on a simple principle: To find an Euler circuit or an Euler path, *bridges are the last edges you want to cross*. Only do it if you have no choice! Simple enough, but there is a rub: The graph whose bridges we are supposed to avoid is not necessarily the original graph of the problem. Instead, it is that part of the original graph that has yet to be traveled. The point is this: Once we travel along an edge, we are done with it! We will never cross it again, so from that point on, as far as we are concerned, it is as if that edge never existed. Our only concern is how we are going to get around in the *yet-to-be-traveled* part of the graph. Thus, when we talk about bridges that we want to leave as a last resort, we are really referring to *bridges of the to-be-traveled part of the graph*.

■ FLEURY'S ALGORITHM FOR FINDING AN EULER CIRCUIT (PATH)

- **Preliminaries.** Make sure that the graph is connected and either (1) has no odd vertices (circuit) or (2) has just two odd vertices (path).

- **Start.** Choose a starting vertex. [In case (1) this can be any vertex; in case (2) it must be one of the two *odd* vertices.]

- **Intermediate steps.** At each step, if you have a choice, *don't choose a bridge of the yet-to-be-traveled part* of the graph. However, if you have only one choice, take it.

- **End.** When you can't travel any more, the circuit (path) is complete. [In case (1) you will be back at the starting vertex; in case (2) you will end at the other odd vertex.]

■ For a completely different algorithm, known as **Hierholzer's algorithm**, see Exercise 75.

■ MyMathLab®
The applet *Euler Paths and Euler Circuits* in the Applets section of MyMathLab allows you to practice Fleury's algorithm using this approach.*

The only complicated aspect of Fleury's algorithm is the bookkeeping. With each new step, the untraveled part of the graph changes and there may be new bridges formed. Thus, in implementing Fleury's algorithm it is critical to separate the *past* (the part of the graph that has already been traveled) from the *future* (the part of the graph that still needs to be traveled). While there are many different ways to accomplish this (you are certainly encouraged to come up with one of your own), a fairly reliable way goes like this: Start with *two* copies of the graph. Copy 1 is to keep track of the "future"; copy 2 is to keep track of the "past." Every time you travel along an edge, *erase* the edge from copy 1, but mark it (say in red) and label it with the appropriate number on copy 2. As you move forward, copy 1 gets smaller and copy 2 gets redder. At the end, copy 1 has disappeared; copy 2 shows the actual Euler circuit or path.

It's time to look at a couple of examples.

EXAMPLE 5.17 IMPLEMENTING FLEURY'S ALGORITHM

The graph in Fig. 5-19(a) is a very simple graph—it would be easier to find an Euler circuit just by trial-and-error than by using Fleury's algorithm. Nonetheless, we will do it using Fleury's algorithm. The real purpose of the example is to see the algorithm at work. Each step of the algorithm is explained in Figs. 5-19(b) through (h).

---

*MyMathLab code required.

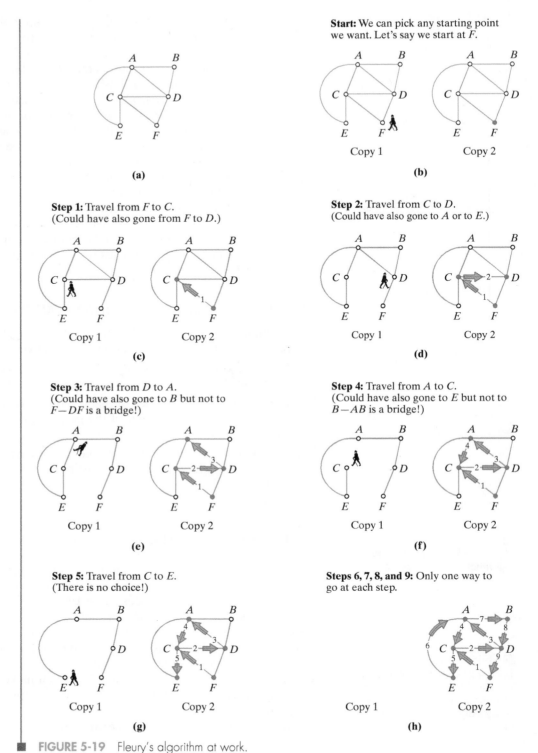

Start: We can pick any starting point we want. Let's say we start at *F*.

Step 1: Travel from *F* to *C*. (Could have also gone from *F* to *D*.)

Step 2: Travel from *C* to *D*. (Could have also gone to *A* or to *E*.)

Step 3: Travel from *D* to *A*. (Could have also gone to *B* but not to *F* — *DF* is a bridge!)

Step 4: Travel from *A* to *C*. (Could have also gone to *E* but not to *B* — *AB* is a bridge!)

Step 5: Travel from *C* to *E*. (There is no choice!)

Steps 6, 7, 8, and 9: Only one way to go at each step.

FIGURE 5-19 Fleury's algorithm at work.

EXAMPLE 5.18 FLEURY'S ALGORITHM FOR EULER PATHS

We will apply Fleury's algorithm to the graph in Figure 5-20. Since it would be a little impractical to show each step of the algorithm with a separate picture as we did in Example 5.17, you are going to have to do some of the work. Start by making two copies of the graph. (If you haven't already done so, get some paper, a pencil, and an eraser.)

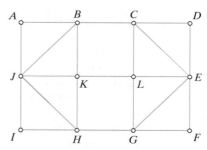

FIGURE 5-20

- **Start.** This graph has two odd vertices, *E* and *J*. We can pick either one as the starting vertex. Let's start at *J*.
- **Step 1.** From *J* we have five choices, all of which are OK. We'll randomly pick *K*. (Erase *JK* on copy 1, and mark and label *JK* with a 1 on copy 2.)
- **Step 2.** From *K* we have three choices (*B*, *L*, or *H*). Any of these choices is OK. Say we choose *B*. (Now erase *KB* from copy 1 and mark and label *KB* with a 2 on copy 2.)
- **Step 3.** From *B* we have three choices (*A*, *C*, or *J*). Any of these choices is OK. Say we choose *C*. (Now erase *BC* from copy 1 and mark and label *BC* with a 3 on copy 2.)
- **Step 4.** From *C* we have three choices (*D*, *E*, or *L*). Any of these choices is OK. Say we choose *L*. (EML—that's shorthand for erase, mark, and label.)
- **Step 5.** From *L* we have three choices (*E*, *G*, or *K*). Any of these choices is OK. Say we choose *K*. (EML.)
- **Step 6.** From *K* we have only one choice—to *H*. Without further ado, we choose *H*. (EML.)
- **Step 7.** From *H* we have three choices (*G*, *I*, or *J*). But for the first time, one of the choices is a bad choice. We should not choose *G*, as *HG* is a bridge of the yet-to-be-traveled part of the graph (Fig. 5-21). Either of the other two choices is OK. Say we choose *J*. (EML.)

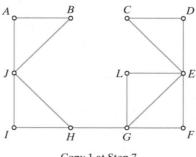

Copy 1 at Step 7

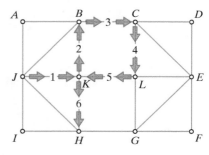

Copy 2 at Step 7

FIGURE 5-21

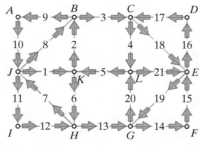

FIGURE 5-22

- **Step 8.** From *J* we have three choices (*A*, *B*, or *I*), but we should not choose *I*, as *JI* has just become a bridge. Either of the other two choices is OK. Say we choose *B*. (EML)
- **Steps 9 through 13.** Each time we have only one choice. From *B* we have to go to *A*, then to *J*, *I*, *H*, and *G*.
- **Steps 14 through 21.** Not to belabor the point, let's just cut to the chase. The rest of the path is given by *G*, *F*, *E*, *D*, *C*, *E*, *G*, *L*, *E*. There are many possible endings, and you should find a different one by yourself.

The completed Euler path (one of hundreds of possible ones) is shown in Fig. 5-22.

5.4 Eulerizing and Semi-Eulerizing Graphs

In this section we will finally answer some of the street-routing problems introduced in Section 5.1. The common thread in all these problems is to find routes that (1) cover all the edges of the graph that models the original problem and (2) recross the fewest number of edges. The first requirement typically comes with the problem; the second requirement comes from the desire to be as efficient as possible. In many applications, each edge represents a unit of cost. The more edges along the route, the higher the cost of the route. In a street-routing problem the first pass along an edge is a requirement of the job. Any additional pass along that edge represents a wasted expense (these extra passes are often described as *deadhead* travel). Thus, an optimal route is one with the fewest number of deadhead edges. (This is only true under the assumption that each edge equals one unit of cost.)

We are now going to see how the theory developed in the preceding sections will help us design optimal street routes for graphs with many (more than two) odd vertices. The key idea is that we can turn odd vertices into even vertices by adding "duplicate" edges in strategic places.

Eulerizations

EXAMPLE 5.19   COVERING A 3-BY-3 STREET GRID

The graph in Fig. 5-23(a) models a 3-block-by-3-block street grid. The graph has 24 edges, each representing a block of the street grid. How can we find an optimal route that covers all the blocks of the street grid and ends back at the starting point?

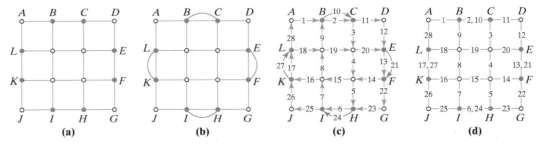

FIGURE 5-23   (a) The original graph model (odd vertices shown in red); (b) an optimal eularization; (c) an Euler circuit; (d) an optimal route on the street grid.

Our first step is to identify the odd vertices in the graph model. This graph has eight odd vertices (B, C, E, F, H, I, K, and L), shown in red. When we add a duplicate copy of edges BC, EF, HI, and KL, we get the graph in Fig. 5-23(b). This is called an **eulerization** of the original graph—in this **eulerized** version the vertices are all even, so we know this graph has an Euler circuit. Moreover, with eight odd vertices we need to add *at least* four duplicate edges, so this is the best we can do.

Figure 5-23(c) shows one of the many possible Euler circuits, with the edges numbered in the order they are traveled. The Euler circuit described in Fig. 5-23(c) represents a route that covers every block of the 3-by-3 street grid and ends back at the starting point, using only four deadhead blocks [Fig. 5-23(d)]. The total length of this route is 28 blocks (24 blocks in the grid plus 4 deadhead blocks), and this route is optimal—no matter how clever you are or how hard you try, if you want to travel along each block of the grid and start and end at the same point, you will have to pass through a minimum of 28 blocks! (There are many other ways to do it using just 28 blocks, but none with fewer than 28.)

EXAMPLE 5.20   COVERING A 4-BY-4 STREET GRID

The graph in Fig. 5-24(a) models a 4-block-by-4-block street grid consisting of 40 blocks. The 12 odd vertices in the graph are shown in red. We want to find a route that covers each of the 40 blocks of the street grid, ends back at the starting point, and has the fewest number of deadhead blocks. To do this, we first eulerize the graph by adding the fewest possible number of edges. Figure 5-24(b) shows how *not to do it!* This graph violates the cardinal rule of eulerization—you can only duplicate edges that are part of the original graph. Edges *DF* and *NL* are new edges, not duplicates, so Fig. 5-24(b) is out! Figure 5-24(c) shows a legal eulerization, but it is not optimal, as it is obvious that we could have accomplished the same thing by adding fewer duplicate edges. Figure 5-24(d) shows an *optimal eulerization* of the original graph—one of several possible. Once we have an optimal eulerization, we have the blueprint for the optimal route on the street grid. Regardless of the specific details, we now know that the route will travel along 48 blocks—the 40 original blocks in the grid plus 8 deadhead blocks. A route can be found by using Fleury's algorithm on the graph shown in Fig. 5-24(a). We leave the details to the reader. (By the way, in a grid such as this one, a route can be easily found using common sense and trial and error.)

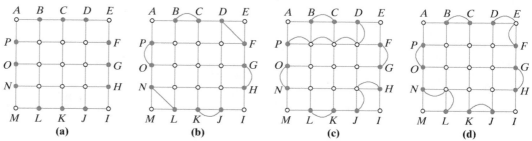

FIGURE 5-24   (a) The original graph model (odd vertices shown in red). (b) Bad move — *DF* and *NL* were not edges of the original graph! (c) An eulerization, but not an optimal one! (d) One of the many possible optimal eulerizations.

EXAMPLE 5.21   THE SECURITY GUARD PROBLEM SOLVED

We are now ready to solve the security guard street-routing problem introduced in Example 5.1 and subsequently modeled in Example 5.13. Let's recap the story: The security guard is required to walk each block of the Sunnyside neighborhood at least once and he wants to deadhead as few blocks as possible. He usually parks his car at *S* (there is a donut shop on that corner) and needs to end his route back at the car. Figure 5-25 shows the evolution of a solution: Fig. 5-25(a) shows the original neighborhood that the security guard must cover; Fig. 5-25(b) shows the graph model of the problem (with the 18 odd vertices of the graph highlighted in red); Fig. 5-25(c) shows an eulerization of the graph in (b), with the 9 duplicate edges shown in red. This is the fewest number of edges required to eulerize the graph in Fig. 5-25(b), so the eulerization is optimal. The eulerized graph in Fig. 5-25(c) has all even vertices, and an Euler circuit can be found. Since a circuit can be started at any vertex we will start the circuit at *S*. Figure 5-25(d) shows one of the many possible optimal routes for the security guard (just follow the numbers). Note that using a different starting vertex will not make the route shorter, so the security guard can continue parking in front of the donut shop—it will not hurt!

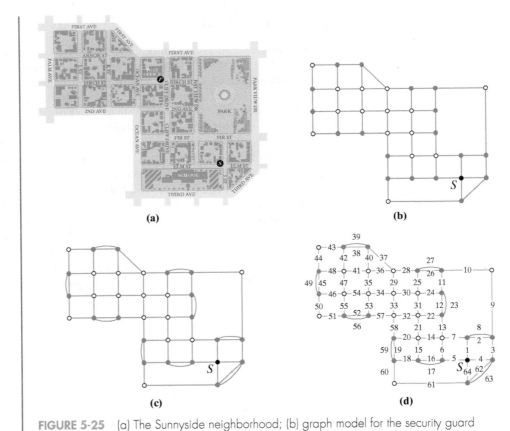

FIGURE 5-25 (a) The Sunnyside neighborhood; (b) graph model for the security guard problem; (c) an optimal eulerization of (b); (d) an optimal route for the security guard.

EXAMPLE 5.22 THE MAIL CARRIER PROBLEM SOLVED

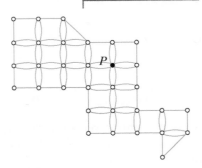

FIGURE 5-26 Graph model for the mail carrier.

The solution to the mail carrier problem follows essentially the same story line as the one for the security guard. Let's recap this story: The mail carrier needs to start and end her route at the post office (P), cover both sides of the street when there are buildings on both sides, and cover just one side on blocks where there are buildings on only one side, with no need to cover any streets where there are no buildings (like the back side of the park and the school). Fig. 5-26 shows the graph model for the mail carrier (see Example 5.14). The interesting thing about this graph is that every vertex is already even (there are some vertices of degree 2 in the corners, there are a couple of vertices of degree 6, and there are lots of vertices of degrees 4 and 8). This means that the graph does not have to be eulerized, as it has Euler circuits in its present form. An optimal route for the mail carrier can be found by finding an Euler circuit of the graph that starts and ends at P. We know how to do that and leave it as an exercise for the reader to find such a route. There are hundreds of possible routes that will work. (*Note:* Although Fleury's algorithm is a sure bet, in a case like this trial and error is almost guaranteed to work best.)

Semi-Eulerizations

In cases where a street route is not required to end back where it started (either because we can choose to start and end in different places or because the starting and ending points are required to be different) we are looking for Euler paths, rather than Euler circuits. In these cases we are looking for a graph that has two odd vertices and the rest even. We need the two odd vertices to give us a starting and ending point for our route. The process of adding additional edges to a graph so that all the vertices except two are even is called a **semi-eulerization**, and we say that the graph has been *semi-eulerized*.

EXAMPLE 5.23   THE BRIDGES OF MADISON COUNTY SOLVED

In Example 5.5 we introduced the problem of routing a photographer across all the bridges in Madison County, shown in Fig. 5-27(a). To recap the story: The photographer needs to cross each of the 11 bridges at least once (for her photo shoot). Each crossing of a bridge costs $25, and the photographer is on a tight budget, so she wants to cover all the bridges once but recross as few bridges as possible. The other relevant fact is that the photographer can start her trip at either bank of the river and end the trip at either bank of the river. Figure 5-27(b) is a graph model of the Madison bridges layout. A la Euler, we let the vertices represent the land masses and the edges represent the bridges. The graph has four odd vertices (R, L, B, and D). The photographer can start the shoot at either bank and end at either bank—say she chooses to start the route at R and end it at L. Figure 5-27(c) shows a semi-eulerization of the graph in (b), with R and L left as odd vertices, and the edge BD (i.e., the Kennedy bridge) recrossed so that now B and D are even vertices. The numbers in Fig. 5-27(c) show one possible optimal route for the photographer, with a total of 12 bridge crossings and a total cost of $300.

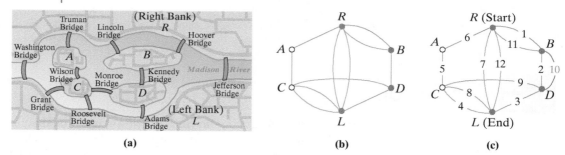

FIGURE 5-27   (a) The original layout; (b) graph model; (c) semi-eulerization of (b) and an optimal route.

EXAMPLE 5.24   THE UPS DRIVER PROBLEM DECONSTRUCTED

In Example 5.3 we introduced the street-routing problem facing a UPS driver who has to make package deliveries around the Sunnyside neighborhood during the Christmas season. Figure 5-28(a) shows all the locations (marked with red crosses) where the driver must deliver packages. Figure 5-28(b) shows the graph model of the problem (see Example 5.15), with the odd vertices highlighted in red. Two of those odd vertices happen to be the designated starting and ending points of his route. We solve this problem by finding an optimal semi-eulerization of the graph with the starting and ending points left alone. One optimal semi-eulerization is shown in Fig. 5-28(c). It has 10 additional edges shown in red. These represent the deadhead blocks the driver will have to cover a second time. The last step is to find an Euler path in Fig. 5-28(c) with the designated starting and ending points—that would give us an optimal route. This can be done using Fleury's algorithm (or trial and error), and we leave this final detail as an exercise for the UPS driver.

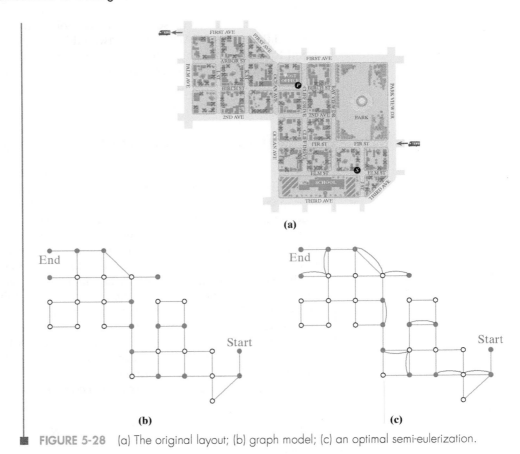

FIGURE 5-28   (a) The original layout; (b) graph model; (c) an optimal semi-eulerization.

Conclusion

In this chapter we got our first introduction to two fundamental ideas. First, we learned about a simple but powerful concept for describing relationships within a set of objects—the concept of a *graph*. This idea can be traced back to Euler, some 270 years ago. Since then, the study of graphs has grown into one of the most important and useful branches of modern mathematics.

The second important idea of this chapter is the concept of a *graph model*. Every time we take a real-life problem and turn it into a mathematical problem, we are, in effect, modeling. Unwittingly, we have all done some form of mathematical modeling at one time or another—first using arithmetic and later using equations and functions to describe real-life situations. In this chapter we learned about a new type of modeling called graph modeling, in which we use graphs and the mathematical theory of graphs to solve certain types of routing problems.

By necessity, the routing problems that we solved in this chapter were fairly simplistic—crossing a few bridges, patrolling a small neighborhood, routing a UPS driver. We should not be deceived by the simplicity of these examples—larger-scale variations on these themes have significant practical importance. In many big cities, where the efficient routing of municipal services (police patrols, garbage collection, etc.) is a major issue, the very theory that we developed in this chapter is being used on a large scale, the only difference being that many of the more tedious details are mechanized and carried out by a computer. (In New York City, for example, garbage collection, curb sweeping, snow removal, and other municipal services have been scheduled and organized using graph models since the 1970s, and the improved efficiency has yielded savings estimated in the tens of millions of dollars a year.)

KEY CONCEPTS

5.1 Street-Routing Problems

- **routing problems:** problems concerned with routing the delivery of goods or services to a set of destinations, **140**

- **street-routing problems:** problems where a specified set of connections (roads, bridges, edges) must be traveled at least once, **140**

5.2 An Introduction to Graphs

- **vertex set:** the set of vertices of a graph, **144**

- **edge list:** a list of all the edges of a graph, **144**

- **adjacent vertices:** two vertices connected by an edge, **144**

- **loop:** an edge that connects a vertex with itself, **144**

- **multiple edges:** two or more edges connecting the same two vertices, **144**

- **degree:** number of edges meeting at the vertex, **144**

- **odd (even) vertex:** a vertex of odd (even) degree, **145**

- **clique:** a set of vertices with the property that any two are adjacent, **145**

- **simple graph:** a graph with no loops or multiple edges, **145**

- **isolated vertex:** a vertex of degree 0, **145**

- **adjacent edges:** two edges with a shared vertex, **147**

- **path:** a sequence of edges each adjacent to the next, with no edge included more than once, and starting and ending at different vertices, **147**

- **circuit:** same as a path but starting and ending at the same vertex, **147**

- **length:** number of edges in a path or a circuit, **147**

- **Euler path:** a path that travels along each edge of a graph once and only once, **148**

- **Euler circuit:** a circuit that travels along each edge of a graph once and only once, **148**

- **connected graph:** a graph such that there is a path going from any vertex to any other vertex, **148**

- **disconnected graph:** a graph that is not connected; it has two or more connected components, **148**

- **components:** the connected "pieces" that make up a graph, **148**

- **bridge:** an edge in a connected graph without which the graph would be disconnected, **149**

5.3 Euler's Theorems and Fleury's Algorithm

- **Euler's Circuit Theorem:** a connected graph has an Euler circuit if and only if all vertices are even, **152**

- **Euler's Path Theorem:** a connected graph has an Euler path if and only it has two odd vertices, **153**

- **Euler's Sum of Degrees Theorem:** the sum of the degrees of all the vertices equals twice the number of edges, **153**

- **algorithm:** a set of procedural rules that when followed produces the answer to some problem, **154**

■ **Fleury's algorithm:** an algorithm for finding Euler circuits or Euler paths in a graph; it builds the Euler circuit (path) edge by edge—choosing a bridge of the yet-to-be traveled part of the graph only when there is no other choice, **154**

5.4 Eulerizing and Semi-Eulerizing Graphs

■ **eulerization:** the process of duplicating edges in a graph to make it have all even vertices, **158**

■ **semi-eulerization:** the process of duplicating edges in a graph to make it have all but two even vertices, **161**

EXERCISES

WALKING

5.1 Street-Routing Problems

No exercises for this section.

5.2 An Introduction to Graphs

1. For the graph shown in Fig. 5-29,

   (a) give the vertex set.

   (b) give the edge list.

   (c) give the degree of each vertex.

   (d) draw a version of the graph without crossing points.

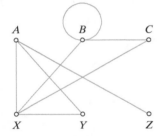

FIGURE 5-29

2. For the graph shown in Fig. 5-30,

   (a) give the vertex set.

   (b) give the edge list.

   (c) give the degree of each vertex.

   (d) draw a version of the graph without crossing points.

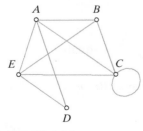

FIGURE 5-30

3. For the graph shown in Fig. 5-31,

   (a) give the vertex set.

   (b) give the edge list.

   (c) give the degree of each vertex.

   (d) give the number of components of the graph.

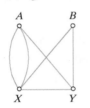

FIGURE 5-31

4. For the graph shown in Fig. 5-32,

   (a) give the vertex set.

   (b) give the edge list.

   (c) give the degree of each vertex.

   (d) give the number of components of the graph.

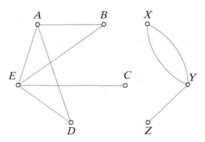

FIGURE 5-32

5. Consider the graph with vertex set $\{K, R, S, T, W\}$ and edge list *RS, RT, TT, TS, SW, WW, WS*. Draw two different pictures of the graph.

24. The Kangaroo Lodge of Madison County has 10 members ($A, B, C, D, E, F, G, H, I$, and J). The club has five working committees: the Rules Committee (A, C, D, E, I, and J), the Public Relations Committee (B, C, D, H, I, and J), the Guest Speaker Committee (A, D, E, F, and H), the New Year's Eve Party Committee (D, F, G, H, and I), and the Fund Raising Committee (B, D, F, H, and J).

(a) Suppose we are interested in knowing which pairs of members are on the same committee. Draw a graph that models this problem. (*Hint:* Let the vertices of the graph represent the members.)

(b) Suppose we are interested in knowing which committees have members in common. Draw a graph that models this problem. (*Hint:* Let the vertices of the graph represent the committees.)

25. Table 5-3 summarizes the Facebook friendships between a group of eight individuals [an *F* indicates that the individuals (row and column) are Facebook friends]. Draw a graph that models the set of friendships in the group. (Use the first letter of the name to label the vertices.)

	Fred	Pat	Mac	Ben	Tom	Hale	Zac	Cher
Fred		F			F	F		
Pat	F				F	F		F
Mac				F			F	
Ben			F				F	
Tom	F	F				F		
Hale	F	F			F			F
Zac			F	F				
Cher		F				F		

■ **TABLE 5-3**

26. The Dean of Students' office wants to know how the seven general education courses selected by incoming freshmen are clustered. For each pair of general education courses, if 30 or more incoming freshmen register for both courses, the courses are defined as being "significantly linked." Table 5-4 shows all the significant links between general education courses (indicated by a 1). Draw a graph that models the significant links between the general education courses. (Use the first letter of each course to label the vertices of the graph.)

	Math	Chemistry	Biology	English	Physics	History	Art
Math		1	1	1	1		
Chemistry	1		1				
Biology	1	1		1		1	
English	1		1		1	1	1
Physics	1			1		1	1
History			1	1	1		1
Art				1	1	1	

■ **TABLE 5-4**

27. Figure 5-40 shows the downtown area of the small village of Kenton. The village wants to have a Fourth of July parade that passes through all the blocks of the downtown area, except for the 14 blocks highlighted in yellow, which the police department considers unsafe for the parade route. Draw a graph that models this street-routing problem.

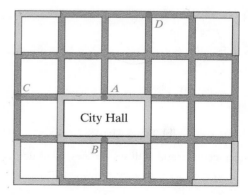

FIGURE 5-40

28. Figure 5-40 shows the downtown area of the small village of Kenton. At regular intervals at night, a police officer must patrol every downtown block at least once, and each of the six blocks along City Hall at least twice. Draw a graph that models this street-routing problem.

5.3 Euler's Theorems and Fleury's Algorithm

In Exercises 29 through 34 choose from one of the following answers and provide a short explanation for your answer.

(A) the graph has an Euler circuit.

(B) the graph has an Euler path.

(C) the graph has neither an Euler circuit nor an Euler path.

(D) the graph may or may not have an Euler circuit.

(E) the graph may or may not have an Euler path. You do not have to show an actual path or circuit.

29. (a) Fig. 5-41(a) **(b)** Fig. 5-41(b)

   (c) A graph with six vertices, all of degree 2

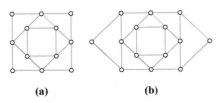

(a)   **(b)**

FIGURE 5-41

30. (a) Fig. 5-42(a) **(b)** Fig. 5-42(b)

   (c) A graph with eight vertices: six vertices of degree 2 and two vertices of degree 3

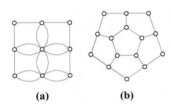

(a)   **(b)**

FIGURE 5-42

31. (a) Fig. 5-43(a) **(b)** Fig. 5-43(b)

   (c) A disconnected graph with six vertices, all of degree 2

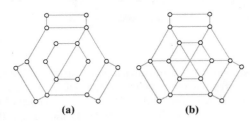

(a)   **(b)**

FIGURE 5-43

32. (a) Fig. 5-44(a) **(b)** Fig. 5-44(b)

   (c) A disconnected graph with eight vertices: six vertices of degree 2 and two vertices of degree 3

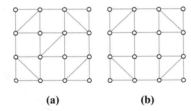

(a)   **(b)**

FIGURE S-44

33. (a) Fig. 5-45(a) **(b)** Fig. 5-45(b)

   (c) A graph with six vertices, all of degree 1. [*Hint*: Try Exercise 9(c) first.]

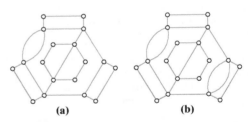

(a)   **(b)**

FIGURE 5-45

34. (a) Fig. 5-46(a) **(b)** Fig. 5-46(b)

   (c) A graph with eight vertices, all of degree 1.

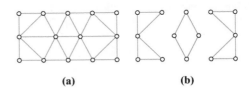

(a)   **(b)**

FIGURE 5-46

35. Find an Euler circuit for the graph in Fig. 5-47. Show your answer by labeling the edges 1, 2, 3, and so on in the order in which they are traveled.

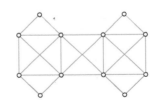

FIGURE 5-47

36. Find an Euler circuit for the graph in Fig. 5-48. Show your answer by labeling the edges 1, 2, 3, and so on in the order in which they can be traveled.

FIGURE 5-48

37. Find an Euler path for the graph in Fig. 5-49. Show your answer by labeling the edges 1, 2, 3, and so on in the order in which they are traveled.

FIGURE 5-49

38. Find an Euler path for the graph in Fig. 5-50. Show your answer by labeling the edges 1, 2, 3, and so on in the order in which they are traveled.

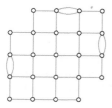

FIGURE 5-50

39. Find an Euler circuit for the graph in Fig. 5-51. Use *B* as the starting and ending point of the circuit. Show your answer by labeling the edges 1, 2, 3, and so on in the order in which they are traveled.

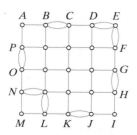

FIGURE 5-51

40. Find an Euler circuit for the graph in Fig. 5-52. Use *S* as the starting and ending point of the circuit. Show your answer by labeling the edges 1, 2, 3, and so on in the order in which they are traveled.

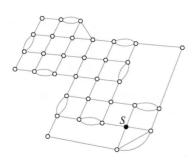

FIGURE 5-52

41. Suppose you are using Fleury's algorithm to find an Euler circuit for a graph and you are in the middle of the process. The graph in Fig. 5-53 shows both the already traveled part of the graph (the red edges) and the yet-to-be traveled part of the graph (the blue edges).

(a) Suppose you are standing at *P*. What edge(s) could you choose next?

(b) Suppose you are standing at *B*. What edge should you *not* choose next?

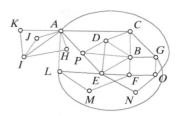

FIGURE 5-53

42. Suppose you are using Fleury's algorithm to find an Euler circuit for a graph and you are in the middle of the process. The graph in Fig. 5-53 shows both the already traveled part of the graph (the red edges) and the yet-to-be traveled part of the graph (the blue edges).

(a) Suppose you are standing at *C*. What edge(s) could you choose next?

(b) Suppose you are standing at *A*. What edge should you *not* choose next?

5.4 Eulerizing and Semi-Eulerizating Graphs

43. Find an optimal eulerization for the graph in Fig. 5-54.

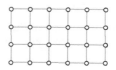

FIGURE 5-54

44. Find an optimal eulerization for the graph in Fig. 5-55.

FIGURE 5-55

45. Find an optimal eulerization for the graph in Fig. 5-56.

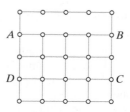

FIGURE 5-56

46. Find an optimal eulerization for the graph in Fig. 5-57.

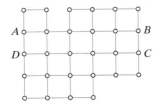

FIGURE 5-57

47. Find an optimal semi-eulerization for the graph in Fig. 5-56. You are free to choose the starting and ending vertices.

48. Find an optimal semi-eulerization for the graph in Fig. 5-57. You are free to choose the starting and ending vertices.

49. Find an optimal semi-eulerization of the graph in Figure 5-56 when A and D are required to be the starting and ending points of the route.

50. Find an optimal semi-eulerization of the graph in Figure 5-57 when A and B are required to be the starting and ending points of the route.

51. Find an optimal semi-eulerization of the graph in Figure 5-56 when B and C are required to be the starting and ending points of the route.

52. Find an optimal semi-eulerization of the graph in Fig. 5-57 when A and D are required to be the starting and ending points of the route.

53. A security guard must patrol on foot the streets of the Green Hills subdivision shown in Fig. 5-39. The security guard wants to start and end his walk at the corner labeled A, and he needs to cover each block of the subdivision at least once. Find an optimal route for the security guard. Describe the route by labeling the edges 1, 2, 3, and so on in the order in which they are traveled. (*Hint:* You should do Exercise 21 first.)

54. A mail carrier must deliver mail on foot along the streets of the Green Hills subdivision shown in Fig. 5-39. His route must start and end at the Post Office, labeled P in the figure. The mail carrier must walk along each block twice if there are houses on both sides of the street and once along blocks where there are houses on only one side of the street. Find an optimal route for the mail carrier. Describe the route by labeling the edges 1, 2, 3, and so on in the order in which they are traveled. (*Hint:* You should do Exercise 22 first.)

55. This exercise refers to the Fourth of July parade problem introduced in Exercise 27. Find an optimal route for the parade that starts at A and ends at B (see Fig. 5-40). Describe the route by labeling the edges 1, 2, 3, . . . etc. in the order they are traveled. [*Hint:* Start with the graph model for the parade route (see Exercise 27); then find an optimal semi-eulerization of the graph that leaves A and B odd; then find an Euler path in this new graph.]

56. This exercise refers to the Fourth of July parade problem introduced in Exercise 27. Find an optimal route for the parade that starts at C and ends at D (see Fig. 5-40). Describe the route by labeling the edges 1, 2, 3, . . . etc. in the order they are traveled. [*Hint:* Start with the graph model for the parade route (see Exercise 27); then find an optimal semi-eulerization of the graph that leaves C and D odd; then find an Euler path in this new graph.]

JOGGING

57. Assume you want to trace the diagram of a basketball court shown in Fig. 5-58 without retracing any lines. How many times would you have to lift your pencil to do it? Explain.

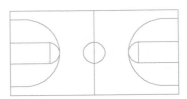

FIGURE 5-58

58. **(a)** Explain why in every graph the sum of the degrees of all the vertices equals twice the number of edges.

(b) Explain why every graph must have an even number of odd vertices.

59. If G is a connected graph with no bridges, how many vertices of degree 1 can G have? Explain your answer.

60. **Regular graphs.** A graph is called *regular* if every vertex has the same degree. Let G be a connected regular graph with N vertices.

(a) Explain why if N is odd, then G must have an Euler circuit.

(b) When N is even, then G may or may not have an Euler circuit. Give examples of both situations.

61. **Complete bipartite graphs.** A complete bipartite graph is a graph having the property that the vertices of the graph can be divided into two groups A and B and each vertex in A is adjacent to each vertex in B, as shown in Fig. 5-59. Two vertices in A are never adjacent, and neither are two vertices in B. Let m and n denote the number of vertices in A and B, respectively, and assume $m \leq n$.

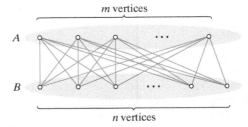

FIGURE 5-59

(a) Describe all the possible values of m and n for which the complete bipartite graph has an Euler circuit. (*Hint:* There are infinitely many values of m and n.)

(b) Describe all the possible values of m and n for which the complete bipartite graph has an Euler path.

62. Consider the following game. You are given N vertices and are required to build a graph by adding edges connecting these vertices. Each time you add an edge you must pay $1. You can stop when the graph is connected.

(a) Describe the strategy that will cost you the least amount of money.

(b) What is the minimum amount of money needed to build the graph? (Give your answer in terms of N.)

63. Consider the following game. You are given N vertices and allowed to build a graph by adding edges connecting these vertices. For each edge you can add, you make $1. You are not allowed to add loops or multiple edges, and you must stop before the graph is connected (i.e., the graph you end up with must be disconnected).

(a) Describe the strategy that will give you the greatest amount of money.

(b) What is the maximum amount of money you can make building the graph? (Give your answer in terms of N.)

64. Figure 5-60 shows a map of the downtown area of the picturesque hamlet of Kingsburg. You have been hired by the Kingsburg Chamber of Commerce to organize the annual downtown parade. Part of your job is to plan the route for the parade. An *optimal* parade route is one that keeps the bridge crossings to a minimum and yet crosses each of the seven bridges in the downtown area at least once.

(a) Find an optimal parade route if the parade is supposed to start in North Kingsburg but can end anywhere.

(b) Find an optimal parade route if the parade is supposed to start in North Kingsburg and end in South Kingsburg.

(c) Find an optimal parade route if the parade is supposed to start in North Kingsburg and end on island B.

(d) Find an optimal parade route if the parade is supposed to start in North Kingsburg and end on island A.

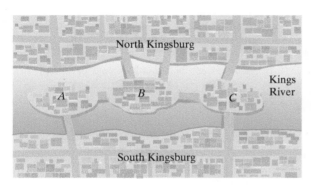

FIGURE 5-60

65. A policeman has to patrol on foot the streets of the subdivision shown in Fig. 5-61. The policeman needs to start his route at the police station, located at X, and end the route at the local coffee shop, located at Y. He needs to cover each block of the subdivision at least once, but he wants to make his route as efficient as possible and duplicate the fewest possible number of blocks.

(a) How many blocks will he have to duplicate in an optimal trip through the subdivision?

(b) Describe an optimal trip through the subdivision. Label the edges 1, 2, 3, and so on in the order the policeman would travel them.

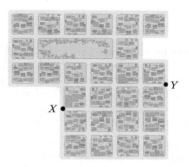

FIGURE 5-61

Exercises 66 through 68 refer to Example 5.23. In this example, the problem is to find an optimal route (i.e., a route with the fewest bridge crossings) for a photographer who needs to cross each of the 11 bridges of Madison County for a photo shoot. The layout of the 11 bridges is shown in Fig. 5-62. You may find it helpful to review Example 5.23 before trying these two exercises.

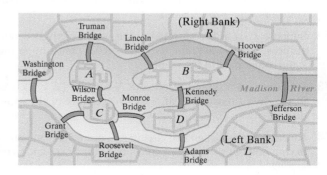

FIGURE 5-62

66. Describe an optimal route for the photographer if the route must start at B and end at L.

67. Describe an optimal route for the photographer if the route must start and end in D and the first bridge crossed must be the Adams Bridge.

68. Describe an optimal route for the photographer if the route must start and end in the same place, the first bridge crossed must be the Adams bridge, and the last bridge crossed must be the Grant Bridge.

69. This exercise comes to you courtesy of Euler himself. Here is the question in Euler's own words, accompanied by the diagram shown in Fig. 5-63.

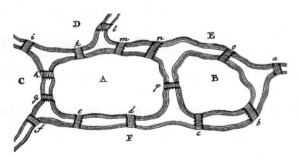

FIGURE 5-63

Let us take an example of two islands with four rivers forming the surrounding water. There are fifteen bridges marked a, b, c, d, etc., across the water around the islands and the adjoining rivers. The question is whether a journey can be arranged that will pass over all the bridges but not over any of them more than once.

What is the answer to Euler's question? If the "journey" is possible, describe it. If it isn't, explain why not.

RUNNING

70. Suppose G is a connected graph with N vertices, all of even degree. Let k denote the number of bridges in G. Find the value(s) of k. Explain your answer.

71. Suppose G is a connected graph with $N - 2$ even vertices and two odd vertices. Let k denote the number of bridges in G. Find all the possible values of k. Explain your answer.

72. Suppose G is a disconnected graph with exactly two odd vertices. Explain why the two odd vertices must be in the same component of the graph.

73. Suppose G is a simple graph with N vertices $(N \geq 2)$. Explain why G must have at least two vertices of the same degree.

74. Kissing circuits. When two circuits in a graph have no edges in common but share a common vertex v, they are said to be *kissing at v*.

(a) For the graph shown in Fig. 5-64, find a circuit kissing the circuit A, D, C, A (there is only one), and find two different circuits kissing the circuit A, B, D, A.

(b) Suppose G is a connected graph and every vertex in G is even. Explain why the following statement is true: *If a circuit in G has no kissing circuits, then that circuit must be an Euler circuit.*

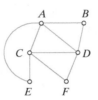

FIGURE 5-64

75. Hierholzer's algorithm. *Hierholzer's algorithm* is another algorithm for finding an Euler circuit in a graph. The basic idea behind Hierholzer's algorithm is to start with an arbitrary circuit and then enlarge it by patching to it a *kissing circuit*, continuing this way and making larger and larger circuits until the circuit cannot be enlarged any farther. (For the definition of kissing circuits, see Exercise 74.) More formally, Hierholzer's algorithm is as follows:

Step 1. Start with an arbitrary circuit C_0.

Step 2. Find a kissing circuit to C_0. If there are no kissing circuits to C_0, then you are finished—C_0 is itself an Euler circuit of the graph [see Exercise 74(b)]. If there is a kissing circuit to C_0, let's call it K_0, and let V denote the vertex at which the two circuits kiss. Go to Step 3.

Step 3. Let C_1 denote the circuit obtained by "patching" K_0 to C_0 at vertex V (i.e., start at V, travel along C_0 back to V, and then travel along K_0 back again to V). Now find a kissing circuit to C_1. (If there are no kissing circuits to C_1, then you are finished—C_1 is your Euler circuit.) If there is a kissing circuit to C_1, let's call it K_1, and let W denote the vertex at which the two circuits kiss. Go to Step 4.

Steps 4, 5, and so on. Continue this way until there are no more kissing circuits available.

(a) Use Hierholzer's algorithm to find an Euler circuit for the graph shown in Fig. 5-65 (this is the graph model for the mail carrier in Example 5.14).

(b) Describe a modification of Hierholzer's algorithm that allows you to find an Euler path in a connected graph having exactly two vertices of odd degree. (*Hint*: A path can also have a kissing circuit.)

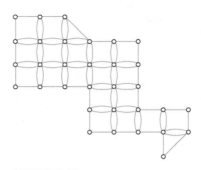

FIGURE 5-65

PROJECTS AND PAPERS

1 Original Sources

Whenever possible, it is instructive to read about a great discovery from the original source. Euler's landmark paper in graph theory with his solution to the Königsberg bridge problem was published in 1736. Luckily, the paper was written in a very readable style and the full English translation can be found in the following article: "The Bridges of Konigsberg," by Leonhard Euler (translated by James Newman), *Scientific American*, vol. 89 (1953), pp. 66–70.

Write a summary/analysis of Euler's original paper. Include (1) a description of how Euler originally tackled the Königsberg bridge problem, (2) a discussion of Euler's general conclusions, and (3) a discussion of Euler's approach toward finding an Euler circuit/path.

2 Computer Representation of Graphs

In many real-life routing problems, we have to deal with very large graphs—a graph could have thousands of vertices and tens of thousands of edges. In these cases algorithms such as Fleury's algorithm (as well as others we will study in later chapters) are done by computer. Unlike humans, computers are not very good at interpreting pictures, so the first step in using computers to perform computations with graphs is to describe the graph in a way the computer can understand it. The two most common ways to do so are by means of matrices.

In this project you are asked to write a short research paper describing the use of matrices to represent graphs. Explain (1) what is a **matrix**, (2) what is the **adjacency matrix** of a graph, and (3) what is the **incidence matrix** of a graph. Illustrate some of the graph concepts from this chapter (degrees of vertices, multiple edges, loops, etc.) in matrix terms. Include plenty of examples. You can find definitions and information on adjacency and incidence matrices of graphs in many graph theory books.

3 The Chinese Postman Problem

A *weighted graph* is a graph in which the edges are assigned positive numbers called weights. The weights represent distances, times, or costs. Finding optimal routes that cover *all* the edges of a *weighted graph* is a problem known as the *Chinese postman problem*. (Chinese postman problems are a generalization of *Euler circuit* problems and, as a general rule, are much harder to solve, but most of the concepts developed in this chapter still apply.)

In this project you are asked to prepare a presentation on the Chinese postman problem for your class.

Some suggestions: (1) Give several examples to illustrate Chinese postman problems and how they differ from corresponding Euler circuit problems. (2) Describe some possible real-life applications of Chinese postman problems. (3) Discuss how to solve a Chinese postman problem in the simplest cases when the weighted graph has no odd vertices or has only two odd vertices (these cases can be solved using techniques learned in this chapter). (4) Give a rough outline of how one might attempt to solve a Chinese postman problem for a graph with four odd vertices.

6 The Mathematics of Touring

Traveling Salesman Problems

The Mars Science Laboratory *Curiosity* is a six-wheeled rover that looks like a dune buggy on steroids and cost NASA $2.5 billion to build and launch. *Curiosity*, loaded with fancy cameras and all kinds of scientific instruments, left Cape Canaveral, Florida, on November 26, 2011 and landed on the Gale crater region of Mars on August 6, 2012. *Curiosity*'s mission is to explore an area around the Gale crater where planetary scientists believe there is a good chance of finding chemical and biological markers that might be evidence of past or present life. To put it simply, *Curiosity* is on the hunt for tiny Martians, dead or alive.

*C*uriosity is built not for speed (it can cover only 600 to 700 feet per day) but rather for endurance and the ability to move over and around obstacles that might appear in its path. In other words, *Curiosity* is a rugged *traveler*, moving slowly but steadily through various locations on the rough and uncharted territory that is the surface of Mars. The less time *Curiosity* has to spend moving around, the more time it has to conduct its experiments, so one of the key aspects of *Curiosity*'s mission is to optimize its travels. This is where the mathematics comes in.

The general problem of optimizing the route of a *traveler* that must visit a specified set of *locations* is known as the *traveling salesman problem* (TSP). This name is misleading, and the typical *traveling salesman problem* has nothing to do with a traveling salesperson—the name applies to many important real-life problems, including the routing of a $2.5- billion roving laboratory on the surface of Mars.

This chapter starts with a general description of what constitutes a TSP, followed by several real-life examples of TSPs (Section 6.1). In Section 6.2 we introduce and discuss the key mathematical concepts that are used to model a TSP (*Hamilton circuits, Hamilton paths*, and *complete graphs*). In Sections 6.3, 6.4, and 6.5, we introduce four different algorithms for solving TSPs: the *brute-force, nearest-neighbor, repetitive nearest-neighbor*, and *cheapest-link* algorithms, and use these algorithms to "solve" the TSPs introduced in Section 6.1. In these sections we also discuss the pros and cons of the various algorithms and introduce the concepts of *inefficient* and *approximate* algorithms.

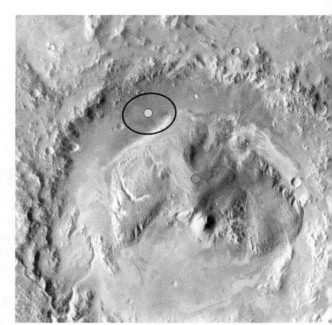

Flyby view of the Gale Crater, Mars. The interior of the black oval region is the intended playground for *Curiosity*'s exploits.

6.1 What Is a Traveling Salesman Problem?

The term *traveling salesman problem* (TSP) is catchy but a bit misleading, since most of the time the problems that fall under this heading have nothing to do with salespeople living out of a suitcase. The expression "traveling salesman" has traditionally been used as a convenient metaphor for many different real-life problems that share a common mathematical structure.

The three elements common to all TSPs (from now on we simply refer to any traveling salesman problem as a TSP) are the following:

- A traveler. The traveler could be a person (or a group), an object (a bus, a truck, an unmanned rover, etc.); it could even be a bee.
- A set of sites. These are the places or locations the traveler must visit. We will use N to denote the number of sites.
- A set of costs. These are positive numbers associated with the expense of traveling from a site to another site. Here the "cost" variable is not restricted to just *monetary* cost—it can also represent *distance* traveled or *time* spent on travel.

A *solution* to a TSP is a "trip" that starts and ends at a site and visits all the other sites once (but only once). We call such a trip a **tour**. An *optimal solution* (**optimal tour**) is a tour of minimal *total cost*. (Notice that we used *a tour* rather than *the tour*—in general a TSP has more than one optimal solution.)

Let's now look at some examples that should help clarify the types of problems we call TSPs. We will not solve any of these TSPs in this section, but we will discuss solutions in later sections.

EXAMPLE 6.1 A REAL TRAVELING SALESMAN'S TSP

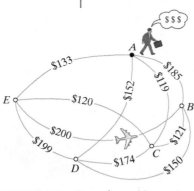

FIGURE 6-1 Cost of travel between cities.

Willy "the Traveler" is a traveling salesman who spends a lot of time on the road calling on customers. He is planning his next business trip, where he will visit customers in five cities we will call A, B, C, D, and E for short ($N = 5$). Since A is Willy's hometown, he needs to start and end his trip at A.

The graph in Fig. 6-1 shows the *cost* (in dollars) of a one-way ticket between any pair of cities (for simplicity we are assuming the cost of a one-way ticket is the same regardless of the direction of travel—something that is not always true in the crazy world of modern airline ticket prices). Like most people, Willy hates to waste money, so among the many possible ways he can organize the sales tour Willy wants to find the *cheapest* (i.e., an *optimal tour*). We will see the solution to Willy's TSP in Section 6.3, but if you want to give it a try on your own now, please feel free to do so.

EXAMPLE 6.2 THE INTERPLANETARY MISSION TSP

It is the year 2050. An unmanned mission to explore the outer planetary moons in our solar system is about to be launched from Earth. The mission is scheduled to visit Callisto, Ganymede, Io, Mimas, and Titan (the first three are moons of Jupiter; the last two of Saturn), collect rock samples at each, and then return to Earth with the loot. The graph in Fig. 6-2 shows the time (in years) required for exploration and travel between any two moons, as well as between Earth and any moon.

This is a long mission, and one of the obvious goals of the mission is to complete it in the least time. In this TSP, the *traveler* is the expedition spaceship, the *sites* are the moons plus the starting and ending site Earth ($N = 6$), and the *cost variable* is time. As in Example 6.1, the goal is to find an optimal tour. We will solve the interplanetary moons TSP in Sections 6.3, 6.4, and 6.5.

- Bees do it. In 2010, scientists at the University of London studying the travel patterns of foraging bumblebees as they search for their food source (flower nectar) made a surprising discovery: The bees fly from flower to flower not in the order in which they originally discover the flowers but in the order that gives the shortest overall route. In other words, the bees are routing their foraging trips by solving a TSP. Scientists still don't understand what methods bumblebees use to solve such complex mathematical problems, but the answer is clearly not by doing numerical calculations—the brain of a bee is the size of a grain of sand. Understanding the shortcuts that allow a humble bumblebee to solve a TSP is important, as it may be possible to program the same shortcuts in modern computer algorithms used to solve large-scale TSPs.

6.2 Hamilton Paths and Circuits

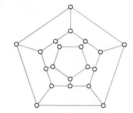

FIGURE 6-5   Hamilton's Icosian game.

In 1857, the Irish mathematician Sir William Rowan Hamilton invented a board game the purpose of which was to find a trip along the edges of the graph shown in Fig. 6-5 that visited each of the vertices once and only once, returning at the end to the starting vertex. (You may want to try your hand at it—the solution is shown on page 205.) Hamilton tried to market the game to make a little money, but he ended up just selling the rights to a London dealer for 25 pounds.

The only reason the story of Hamilton's Icosian game is of any interest to us is that it illustrates an important concept in this chapter—that of traveling along the edges of a connected graph with the purpose of visiting each and every one of the *vertices* once (but only once). This leads to the following two definitions:

- Hamilton path. A *Hamilton path* in a connected graph is a path that visits all the vertices of the graph once and only once.
- Hamilton circuit. A *Hamilton circuit* in a connected graph is a circuit that visits all the vertices of the graph once and only once.

In spite of the similarities in the definitions, Hamilton paths and circuits are very different from Euler paths and circuits and the two should not be confused. With Hamilton the name of the game is to visit all the *vertices* of the graph once; with Euler the name of the game is to pass through all the *edges* of the graph once.

EXAMPLE 6.5 GRAPHS WITHOUT HAMILTON CIRCUITS

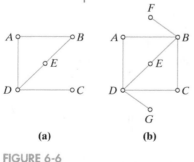

FIGURE 6-6

Figure 6.6 shows two graphs. The graph in Fig. 6.6(a) has no Hamilton circuits because once you visit *C* you are stuck there. On the other hand, the graph has several Hamilton paths. One of them is *C*, *D*, *E*, *B*, *A*; another one is *C*, *D*, *A*, *B*, *E*. We can *reverse* those two paths and get two more: *A*, *B*, *E*, *D*, *C* and *E*, *B*, *A*, *D*, *C*. Clearly, the Hamilton path has to start or end at *C*, so the four Hamilton paths listed above are the only ones possible. Note that the graph has two odd vertices, so from Euler's theorem for paths (page 153) we know that it has Euler paths as well.

The graph in Fig. 6.6(b) has no Hamilton circuits because once you visit *F* (or *G*) you are stuck there. Nor does the graph have Hamilton paths: The path has to start at either *F* or *G* and end at the other one, and there is no way to visit the other five vertices without going through some vertices more than once. Note that this graph also has two odd vertices, so we know that it has an Euler path.

EXAMPLE 6.6 LISTING HAMILTON CIRCUITS AND PATHS

The graph in Fig. 6.7(a) has no Euler circuits or paths (it has four odd vertices) but has lots of Hamilton circuits. We are going to try to list them all. To organize ourselves we will list the Hamilton circuits using A as the starting and ending point of the circuit. We'll start by going clockwise around the outside square and taking the "detour" to visit E at different times in the trip. This gives the following four Hamilton circuits: (1) A, B, C, D, E, A; (2) A, B, C, E, D, A; (3) A, B, E, C, D, A; and (4) A, E, B, C, D, A. [Figure 6-7(b) illustrates circuit (1) A, B, C, D, E, A]. We can also go around the outside square counterclockwise and get four more Hamilton circuits: (5) A, D, C, B, E, A; (6) A, D, C, E, B, A; (7) A, D, E, C, B, A; and (8) A, E, D, C, B, A. Notice that these last four are reversals of the first four.

What about Hamilton circuits that start at a different vertex—say for example B? Fortunately, we won't have to worry about finding more Hamilton circuits by changing the starting vertex. Any Hamilton circuit that starts and ends at B can be reinterpreted as a Hamilton circuit that starts and ends at A (or any other vertex, for that matter). For example, the circuit B, C, D, E, A, B is just the circuit A, B, C, D, E, A written in a different way [Fig. 6-7(b)]. In other words, a Hamilton circuit is defined by the ordering of the vertices and is independent of which vertex is used as the starting and ending point. This helps a great deal—*once we are sure that we listed all the Hamilton circuits that start and end at A, we know that we have listed all of them!* We will use this observation repeatedly in the next section.

In general, a graph has many more Hamilton paths than circuits. For one thing, each Hamilton circuit can be "broken" into a Hamilton path by deleting one of the edges of the circuit. For example, we can take the Hamilton circuit A, B, C, D, E, A shown in Fig. 6-7(b) and delete EA. This gives the Hamilton path A, B, C, D, E shown in Fig. 6-7(c). We can delete any other edge as well. If we delete CD from the Hamilton circuit A, B, C, D, E, A, we get the Hamilton path D, E, A, B, C [you can see this best if you look again at Fig. 6-7(b) and pretend the edge CD is gone]. You can do this with any of the eight Hamilton circuits of the graph—delete one of its edges and create a Hamilton path. This generates lots of Hamilton paths, so we will not list them all. On top of that, a graph can have Hamilton paths that are not "broken" Hamilton circuits. Figure 6-7(d) shows the Hamilton path A, B, E, D, C. This is not a path we would get from a Hamilton circuit—if it were we would be able to close it into a circuit, but to get from C back to A we would have to go through E once again. There are eight different Hamilton paths that do not come from Hamilton circuits, and we leave it to the reader to find the other seven (Exercise 9).

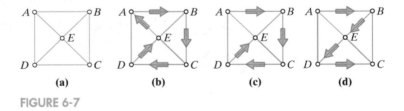

(a)   (b)   (c)   (d)

FIGURE 6-7

The following is a recap of the key points we should take away from Examples 6.5 and 6.6:

- Some graphs have neither Hamilton paths nor Hamilton circuits [see Fig. 6-6 (b)].
- Some graphs have Hamilton paths but no Hamilton circuits [see Fig. 6-6(a)].
- Any graph that has Hamilton circuits will automatically have Hamilton paths because you can always "break" a Hamilton circuit into a Hamilton path by deleting one of the edges of the circuit [see Figs. 6-7(b) and (c)].
- A graph can have Hamilton paths that do not come from a "broken" Hamilton circuit [see Fig. 6-7(d)].

- A Hamilton circuit or path can be reversed (i.e., traveled in the opposite direction). This gives a different Hamilton circuit or path. (Reversing the Hamilton circuit A, B, C, D, E, A gives the Hamilton circuit A, E, D, C, B, A.)
- The same Hamilton circuit can be written in many different ways by changing the chosen starting vertex. [A, B, C, D, E, A and B, C, D, E, A, B are two different descriptions of the Hamilton circuit in Fig. 6-7(b).]

Complete Graphs

A simple graph (i.e., no loops or multiple edges) in which the vertices are completely interconnected (every vertex is connected to every other vertex) is called a **complete graph**. Complete graphs are denoted by the symbol K_N, where N is the number of vertices. Figure 6-8 shows the complete graphs for $N = 3, 4, 5,$ and 6.

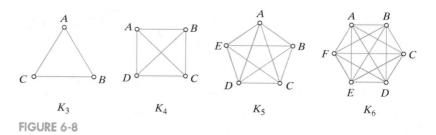

K_3 K_4 K_5 K_6

FIGURE 6-8

Listed below are four key properties of K_N:

1. The *degree* of every vertex in K_N is $N - 1$.
2. The number of *edges* in K_N is $\frac{N(N-1)}{2}$.
3. The number of *Hamilton paths* in K_N is $N! = 1 \times 2 \times 3 \times \cdots \times N$.
4. The number of *Hamilton circuits* in K_N is $(N - 1)! = 1 \times 2 \times 3 \times \cdots \times (N - 1)$.

Property (1) follows from the definition of K_N: since every vertex is adjacent to each of the other $N - 1$ vertices, the degree of each vertex is $N - 1$. Property (2) follows from property (1) and Euler's sum of degrees theorem (page 153): Since each vertex has degree $N - 1$, the sum of all the degrees is $N(N - 1)$ and the number of edges is $\frac{N(N-1)}{2}$. Properties (3) and (4) require a little more detailed explanation, so we will start by exploring in some detail the Hamilton circuits and paths in K_4 and K_5.

EXAMPLE 6.7 | HAMILTON CIRCUITS AND PATHS IN K_4

The six Hamilton circuits in K_4 are shown in Fig. 6-9. Listed using A as the starting and ending vertex they are: (a) A, B, C, D, A; (b) A, D, B, C, A; (c) A, B, D, C, A; and their respective reversals (d) A, D, C, B, A; (e) A, C, B, D, A; (f) A, C, D, B, A.

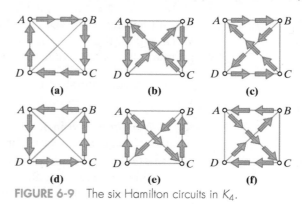

(a)   (b)   (c)

(d)   (e)   (f)

FIGURE 6-9   The six Hamilton circuits in K_4.

How do we know that Fig. 6-9 shows all possible Hamilton circuits? In a complete graph you can go from any vertex to any other vertex. Starting at A one can go to either B, C, or D; from there to either of the other two, from there to the only one left, and finally come back to A. This gives us $3 \times 2 \times 1 = 6$ different possibilities.

Each of the six Hamilton circuits can be broken into four different Hamilton paths (by deleting one of the edges). For example, the circuit in Fig. 6-9(a) gives us the following four Hamilton paths: (1) A, B, C, D; (2) B, C, D, A; (3) C, D, A, B; and (4) D, A, B, C. All in all, we get $6 \times 4 = 24$ Hamilton paths. Since the graph is complete, any Hamilton path can be closed into a Hamilton circuit (just join the starting and ending vertices of the path). It follows that there are no other possible Hamilton paths—just the 24 obtained from Hamilton circuits.

EXAMPLE 6.8 HAMILTON CIRCUITS AND PATHS IN K_5

The $4! = 1 \times 2 \times 3 \times 4 = 24$ Hamilton circuits in K_5 are shown in Table 6-1, written using A as the starting and ending vertex. Circuits (13) through (24) are the reversals of circuits (1) through (12), respectively. Any Hamilton circuit that starts and ends with A will have the other four "inside" vertices (B, C, D, and E) listed in between in some order. There are $4 \times 3 \times 2 \times 1 = 24$ ways to list the letters B, C, D, and E in order: 4 choices for the first letter, 3 choices for the second letter, 2 choices for the third letter, and a single choice for the last letter. This explains why Table 6-1 is a complete list of all the possible Hamilton circuits in K_5.

There are $24 \times 5 = 120$ Hamilton paths in K_5. For obvious reasons, we are not going to list them, but by now we should know how to generate them: Take any of the 24 Hamilton circuits and break it up by deleting one of its five edges. Figure 6-10 shows three of the 120 possible Hamilton paths: Fig. 6-10(a) is obtained by deleting edge DA from circuit (2) on Table 6-1, and Fig. 6-10(b) is obtained by deleting edge BC from circuit (11). We leave it as an exercise for the reader to figure out how the Hamilton path in Fig. 6-10(c) comes about.

(1) A, B, C, D, E, A	(13) A, E, D, C, B, A
(2) A, B, C, E, D, A	(14) A, D, E, C, B, A
(3) A, B, D, C, E, A	(15) A, E, C, D, B, A
(4) A, B, D, E, C, A	(16) A, C, E, D, B, A
(5) A, B, E, C, D, A	(17) A, D, C, E, B, A
(6) A, B, E, D, C, A	(18) A, C, D, E, B, A
(7) A, C, B, D, E, A	(19) A, E, D, B, C, A
(8) A, C, B, E, D, A	(20) A, D, E, B, C, A
(9) A, C, D, B, E, A	(21) A, E, B, D, C, A
(10) A, C, E, B, D, A	(22) A, D, B, E, C, A
(11) A, D, B, C, E, A	(23) A, E, C, B, D, A
(12) A, D, C, B, E, A	(24) A, E, B, C, D, A

■ **TABLE 6-1** The 24 Hamilton circuits in K_5

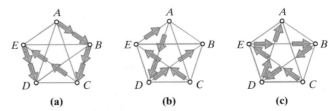

(a)   (b)   (c)

FIGURE 6-10 Three of the 120 possible Hamilton paths in K_5.

Another way to count the number of Hamilton paths in K_5 is to think in terms of *permutations*. (We first introduced permutations and their connection to factorials in Section 2.4. For a quick review of these concepts the reader is encouraged to revisit that section.) Each Hamilton path in K_5 is a permutation of the letters A, B, C, D, and E. It follows that the number of Hamilton paths equals the number of permutations of the five letters. This number is $5! = 120$.

When we generalize the preceding observations to a complete graph with N vertices we get the following improved version of properties (3) and (4):

3. A *Hamilton path* in K_N is equivalent to a *permutation of the N vertices*, and, therefore, the number of Hamilton paths is $N!$

4. A *Hamilton circuit* in K_N is equivalent to a permutation of the $N - 1$ "inside" vertices (i.e., all vertices except the starting/ending vertex), and, therefore, the number of Hamilton circuits is $(N - 1)!$

Table 6-2 shows the number of Hamilton circuits in K_N for $N = 3$ through 12. The numbers get big fast: K_{10} has 362,800 Hamilton circuits; K_{11} has over 3.6 million; K_{12} has close to 40 million. To understand the implications of how fast these numbers grow, imagine that you want to make a list of all the Hamilton circuits in K_N (like we did in Table 6-1 for K_5). Suppose you work really fast and can write down a Hamilton circuit each second and that you are superhuman and can do this 24 hours a day, 7 days a week. It would then take you over four days to write down all the Hamilton circuits in K_{10}, over a month to write down all the Hamilton circuits in K_{11}, and well over a year to write down all the Hamilton circuits in K_{12}.

A computer, of course, can do the job a lot faster than even the fastest human. Let's say, for the sake of argument, that you have unlimited access to SUPERHERO, the fastest computer on the planet and that SUPERHERO can generate one *quadrillion* (i.e., a million billion) Hamilton circuits per second. SUPERHERO could crank out the Hamilton circuits of K_{12} in a matter of nanoseconds. Problem solved! Not so fast. Let's up the ante a little and try to use SUPERHERO to generate the Hamilton circuits for K_{25}. Surprise! It would take SUPERHERO 20 years to do it! Table 6-3 shows how long it would take for even the world's fastest supercomputer to generate the Hamilton circuits in K_N for values of N ranging from 21 to 30. The numbers are beyond comprehension, and the implications will become clear in the next section.

N	Hamilton circuits
3	2
4	6
5	24
6	120
7	720
8	5040
9	40,320
10	362,880
11	3,628,800
12	39,916,800

■ TABLE 6-2

N	SUPERHERO computation time
21	40 minutes
22	14 hours
23	13 days
24	10 months
25	20 years
26	500 years
27	13,000 years
28	350,000 years
29	9.7 million years
30	280 million years

■ TABLE 6-3

6.3 The Brute-Force Algorithm

We start this section with the TSP introduced in Example 6.1.

EXAMPLE 6.9 THE REAL TRAVELING SALESMAN'S TSP SOLVED

In Example 6.1 we left Willy the traveling salesman hanging. What Willy would like from us, most of all, is to help him find the optimal (in this case *cheapest*) tour of the five cities in his sales territory. The cost of travel between any two cities is shown in Fig. 6.11 (this is exactly the same figure as Fig. 6-1). Notice that the underlying graph in Fig. 6-11 is just a fancy version of K_5 (five vertices each adjacent to the other four) with numbers associated with each of the 10 edges. In this TSP the numbers represent the cost of travel (in either direction) along that edge.

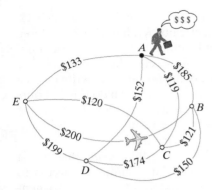

FIGURE 6-11

Table 6-4 lists the 24 possible tours that Willy could potentially take. The first and third columns of Table 6-4 gives the 24 different Hamilton circuits in K_5. This part is an exact copy of Table 6-1. Notice once again that the list is organized so that each tour in the third column is the reversed version of the corresponding tour in the first column. Listing the tours this way saves a lot of work because the cost of a tour is the same regardless of the direction of travel: Once we know the cost of a tour we know the cost of its reversal. (Please note that this is true only because we made the assumption that the cost of travel between two cities is the same regardless of the direction of travel. When the costs vary with the direction of travel then the shortcut won't work.) The middle column shows the total cost of each tour and the calculation that leads to it (for each tour just add the costs of the edges that make the tour).

Tour	Total cost	Tour
(1) A, B, C, D, E, A	185 + 121 + 174 + 199 + 133 = 812	(13) A, E, D, C, B, A
(2) A, B, C, E, D, A	185 + 121 + 120 + 199 + 152 = 777	(14) A, D, E, C, B, A
(3) A, B, D, C, E, A	185 + 150 + 174 + 120 + 133 = 762	(15) A, E, C, D, B, A
(4) A, B, D, E, C, A	185 + 150 + 199 + 120 + 119 = 773	(16) A, C, E, D, B, A
(5) A, B, E, C, D, A	185 + 200 + 120 + 174 + 152 = 831	(17) A, D, C, E, B, A
(6) A, B, E, D, C, A	185 + 200 + 199 + 174 + 119 = 877	(18) A, C, D, E, B, A
(7) A, C, B, D, E, A	119 + 121 + 150 + 199 + 133 = 722	(19) A, E, D, B, C, A
(8) A, C, B, E, D, A	119 + 121 + 200 + 199 + 152 = 791	(20) A, D, E, B, C, A
(9) A, C, D, B, E, A	119 + 174 + 150 + 200 + 133 = 776	(21) A, E, B, D, C, A
(10) A, C, E, B, D, A	119 + 120 + 200 + 150 + 152 = 741	(22) A, D, B, E, C, A
(11) A, D, B, C, E, A	152 + 150 + 121 + 120 + 133 = 676	(23) A, E, C, B, D, A
(12) A, D, C, B, E, A	152 + 174 + 121 + 200 + 133 = 780	(24) A, E, B, C, D, A

■ **TABLE 6-4**   The 24 possible tours in Example 6-9 and their costs, with the optimal tour(s), highlighted

Once we have the complete list of tours and their respective costs, we just choose the optimal tour(s). In this case, the optimal tours are (11) and its reversal (23). The cost is $676. Figure 6-12 shows both optimal tours.

A final note on Willy's sales trip: Was doing all this work worth it? In this case, yes. If Willy just chose the order of the cities at random, the worst-case scenario would be tour (6) or (18), costing $877. With just a little effort we found an optimal tour costing $676—a potential savings of $201.

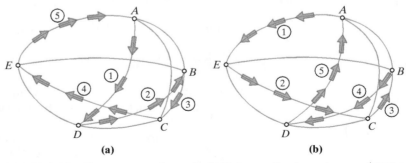

(a)   (b)

FIGURE 6-12   The two optimal tours for Willy's trip. (Total travel cost = $676.)

Before moving on to other TSP examples, let's connect a few dots. Our general assumption for a TSP is that there is a way to get from any location to any other location. If we think of the locations as the vertices of a graph, this means that every TSP has an underlying graph that is a complete graph K_N. In addition to the underlying graph, there are costs associated with each edge. A graph that has numbers associated with its edges is called a **weighted graph**, and the numbers are called **weights**. A tour in a TSP translates to a Hamilton circuit in the underlying graph, and an optimal tour translates into a Hamilton circuit of least total weight.

In short, the TSP is the concrete, real-life problem and its reformulation in terms of Hamilton circuits in a complete weighted graph is the mathematical model that represents the problem. In this model, *locations are vertices, costs are weights, tours are Hamilton circuits,* and *optimal tours are Hamilton circuits of least total weight.*

We can describe now the approach we used in Example 6.9 to solve Willy's TSP in a somewhat more formal language: We made a list of all possible Hamilton circuits (first and third columns of Table 6-4), calculated the total weight of each (middle column of Table 6-4), and picked the circuits with least total weight. This strategy is formally known as the **brute-force algorithm**.

THE BRUTE-FORCE ALGORITHM

- **Step 1.** Make a list of all the Hamilton circuits of the underlying graph K_N.
- **Step 2.** Calculate the total weight of each Hamilton circuit.
- **Step 3.** Choose a Hamilton circuit with least total weight.

> **"In theory, there is no difference between theory and practice. In practice, there is."**
>
> – *Yogi Berra*

The brute-force algorithm is based on a simple idea—when you have a finite number of options, try them all and you will always be able to determine which one is the best. In theory, we should be able to use the brute-force algorithm to solve any TSP. In practice, we can solve only small TSPs this way. It's easy to say "make a list of all the Hamilton circuits . . ."— doing it is something else. Just take a look again at Table 6-3. It would take the world's fastest supercomputer 20 years to do it with K_{25}; 280 millions years to do it with K_{30}. And keep in mind that in real-world applications a TSP with $N = 30$ locations is considered small. In some cases, a TSP might involve 50 or even 100 locations.

The brute-force algorithm is a classic example of what is formally known as an **inefficient algorithm**—an algorithm for which the computational effort needed to carry out the steps of the algorithm grows disproportionately with the size of the problem. The trouble with inefficient algorithms is that they can only be used to solve small problems and, therefore, have limited practical use. Even the world's fastest computer would be of little use when trying to solve a TSP with $N = 25$ locations using the brute-force algorithm.

Before we conclude this section we tackle one more example of how we might use the brute-force algorithm to solve a TSP.

EXAMPLE 6.10   THE INTERPLANETARY MISSION TSP SOLVED

We are revisiting the TSP introduced in Example 6-2. In this TSP the goal is to find the *fastest* tour for an interplanetary mission to five of the outer moons in our solar system. Moreover, the tour has to start and end at our home planet, Earth. This makes it a TSP with $N = 6$ vertices. Figure 6-13(a) shows the mission time (in years) for travel between any two moons and between Earth and any moon.

To use the brute-force algorithm we would start with a list of all the possible Hamilton circuits using Earth as the starting and ending vertex. The problem is that this list has $5! = 120$ different Hamilton circuits. That's more work than we care to do, so a full list is out of the question. Imagine now that we get a hint: The first stop in an optimal tour is Callisto. How much help is that? A lot. It means that the optimal tour must be a Hamilton circuit of the form $E, C, *, *, *, *, E$. The *'s

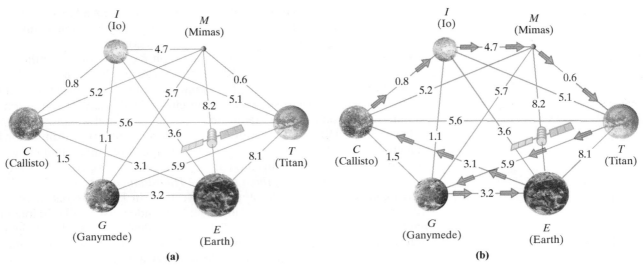

FIGURE 6-13   (a) Graph model for the interplanetary mission TSP. (b) An optimal tour.

are the letters G, I, M, and T in some order. Since there are only 4! = 24 possible permutations of these four letters, the brute-force algorithm becomes much more manageable: We make a list of the 24 Hamilton circuits of the form $E, C, *, *, *, *, E$, find their weights, and pick one (there are several) of least total weight. One of the optimal tours is shown in Fig. 6-13(b). The total length of this tour is 18.3 years. We leave it to the reader to verify the details.

6.4 The Nearest-Neighbor and Repetitive Nearest-Neighbor Algorithms

In this section we introduce a new method for solving TSPs called the *nearest-neighbor algorithm* (NNA). We will illustrate the basic idea of the nearest-neighbor algorithm using the interplanetary mission TSP once again. We found an optimal tour for this TSP in Example 6.10, so the point now is to see how the NNA does it.

EXAMPLE 6.11   THE INTERPLANETARY MISSION TSP AND THE NEAREST-NEIGHBOR ALGORITHM

Look at the graph in Fig. 6-13(a) once again and imagine planning the mission. Starting from Earth we could choose any of the moons for our first stop. Of all the choices, Callisto makes the most sense because in terms of travel time it is Earth's "nearest neighbor": Among the edges connecting E to the other vertices, EC is the one with the smallest weight. (Technically speaking we should call C the "smallest weight" neighbor, but that sounds a bit strange, so we use *nearest neighbor* as a generic term for the vertex connected by the edge of least weight.)

So we made it to Callisto. Where to next? Following the same logic, we choose to go to Callisto's nearest neighbor Io. From Io we go to Ganymede (the nearest neighbor we have not yet been to), from Ganymede to Mimas, from Mimas to Titan (the last moon left), and finally from Titan the mission comes back to Earth. This tour, called the *nearest-neighbor tour*, is shown in Fig. 6-14. The total length of this tour is 19.4 years, and that's a bit of bad news. In Example 6.10 we found an optimal tour with total length 18.3 years—this tour is more than a year longer.

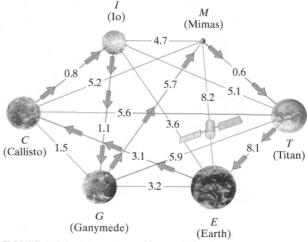

FIGURE 6-14   Nearest-neighbor tour for the interplanetary mission TSP.

Example 6.11 illustrates a common situation when trying to find solutions to TSPs. We can come up with very simple and fast methods for finding "good" tours, but these methods cut corners and don't necessarily produce the "best" (optimal) tour.

Formally, we will use the term **approximate algorithm** to describe any algorithm for solving TSPs that produces a tour, but not necessarily an optimal tour. The *nearest-neighbor* algorithm is an example of an *approximate* algorithm. We will discuss a different approximate algorithm called the *cheapest-link* algorithm in Section 6.5, and in Chapter 8 we will see approximate algorithms for solving a different type of problem (not a TSP).

Obviously, approximate algorithms are important and useful. The question is why? Why do we bother with methods that give *approximate* solutions when our objective is to find an *optimal* solution? The answer is that we are making a tradeoff between the solution and the amount of effort it takes to find it. Like in many walks of life, the choice is between perfection and expediency. If it takes 20 years to find the optimal tour in a TSP with $N = 25$ locations but we can find a *suboptimal* tour (i.e., a tour that is close to optimal) in a matter of minutes, shouldn't we consider the second a better option? Approximate algorithms are the mathematical version of the commonly used strategy of cutting corners for the sake of expediency.

To illustrate the usefulness of the nearest-neighbor algorithm we will now tackle a TSP with $N = 10$ cities.

EXAMPLE 6.12 THE CONCERT TOUR TSP AND THE NNA

In Example 6.4 we were introduced to the indie rock band Luna Park, just about to embark on a 10-city concert tour. Figure 6-15(a) shows the distances (in miles) between any two cities. Because the band members all live at A, the tour needs to start and end at A. The goal is to find the optimal (shortest distance) tour.

This is a TSP with $N = 10$ locations. Notice that we don't see a complete weighted graph, but the mileage chart provides exactly the same information as the graph would (and it does it in a much cleaner way). The only way we know for finding an optimal tour is the brute-force algorithm, and to use brute force would mean making a list of $9! = 362,880$ possible Hamilton circuits. Obviously, we are not about to do that, at least not without help. But, we now know of a quick-and-dirty shortcut — the nearest-neighbor algorithm. Let's try it and see what we get.

To implement the nearest-neighbor algorithm from a chart we use the following strategy: Start with the row labeled A, and look for the smallest number in that row. That number (119) identifies A's nearest neighbor, in this case C. We now go to row C and look for C's nearest neighbor. [Before we do that, it helps to cross out

	A	B	C	D	E	F	G	H	J	K
A	*	185	119	152	133	321	297	277	412	381
B	185	*	121	150	200	404	458	492	379	427
C	119	121	*	174	120	332	439	348	245	443
D	152	150	174	*	199	495	480	500	454	489
E	133	200	120	199	*	315	463	204	396	487
F	321	404	332	495	315	*	356	211	369	222
G	297	458	439	480	463	356	*	471	241	235
H	277	492	348	500	204	211	471	*	283	478
J	412	379	245	454	396	369	241	283	*	304
K	381	427	443	489	487	222	235	478	304	*

(a)

	A	B	C	D	E	F	G	H	J	K
A	*	185	119	152	133	321	297	277	412	381
B	185	*	121	150	200	404	458	492	379	427
C	119	121	*	174	120	332	439	348	245	443
D	152	150	174	*	199	495	480	500	454	489
E	133	200	120	199	*	315	463	204	396	487
F	321	404	332	495	315	*	356	211	369	222
G	297	458	439	480	463	356	*	471	241	235
H	277	492	348	500	204	211	471	*	283	478
J	412	379	245	454	396	369	241	283	*	304
K	381	427	443	489	487	222	235	478	304	*

(b)

FIGURE 6-15   (a) Mileage chart for the concert tour TSP. (b) The chart after the first four steps of the NNA (A, C, E, D, . . .).

the column for C (this helps make sure we don't go back to C in the middle of the tour). For similar reasons we also crossed out the A-column.] The smallest number available in row C is 120, and it identifies C's nearest-neighbor E. We now cross out the E-column and go to row E, looking for a nearest-neighbor. The smallest number available in row E is 199, and it identifies E's nearest-neighbor D. We cross out the D-column and continue [Fig. 6-15(b) shows the mileage chart at this point]: From D to its nearest-available neighbor B (150), from B to J (379), from J to G (241), from G to K (235), from K to F (222), from F to the only city left H (211), and finally end the tour by returning to A (277). This is the nearest-neighbor tour: A, C, E, D, B, J, G, K, F, H, A, and it has a total length of 2153 miles.

Example 6.12 clearly illustrates the tradeoff between perfection and expediency. We found a concert tour for the band, and it took only a few minutes, and we did it without the aid of a computer. That's the good news. But how good is the solution we found? More specifically, how much longer is the nearest-neighbor tour found in Example 6.12 than the optimal tour? To answer this question, we would need to know how long the optimal tour is. With the aid of a computer, special software, and a fair amount of effort, I was able to find the answer: The optimal concert tour has a total length of 1914 miles. This information allows us to look back and judge the "goodness" of the solution we found in Example 6.12. We do this by introducing the concept of *relative error*.

■ **Relative error of a tour.** Let C denote the total cost of a given tour and Opt denote the total cost of the optimal tour. The *relative error ε* of the tour is given by $\varepsilon = \frac{C - Opt}{Opt}$.

The best way to think of the relative error is as a *percent* (i.e., the amount of error expressed as a percent of the optimal solution).

We are now ready to pass judgment on the nearest-neighbor tour we found in Example 6.12: The relative error of the tour is $\varepsilon = \frac{2153 - 1914}{1914} \approx 0.1249 = 12.49\%$. Is a relative error of 12.49% good or bad? The answer very much depends on the circumstances: When cost is a critical variable—say, for example, the timing of an interplanetary mission—an error of 12.49% is high. When cost is less critical—say, for example, the distance covered by a rock band traveling around in a fancy motor coach—an error of 12.49% might be OK.

The Repetitive Nearest-Neighbor Algorithm

One of the interesting features of the nearest-neighbor algorithm is that the tour it produces depends on the choice of starting vertex. For the same TSP, a change in the choice of starting vertex can produce a different nearest-neighbor tour. (Note that this does not imply that the tours are always different—we might change

- Step 3. Once again, we scan the graph looking for the next cheapest link and find *IG* (1.1). We highlight it in red.

- Step 4. The next cheapest link in the graph is *CG* (1.5). We pick up our red pen and are about to highlight the link when we suddenly realize that this is not a good move. A red *CG* means that we would be forming a red circuit *C, I, G, C*. But tours (Hamilton circuits) can't contain partial circuits, so any edge that forms a partial circuit must be ruled out. (For convenience, we call this the *partial-circuit rule*.) So, even though *CG* is the next available cheapest link, we can't choose it because of the partial-circuit rule. We indicate this fact by ✕-ing out *CG* (the ✕ is like a little marker saying "do not travel along this link"). So, we try again. After *CG*, the next cheapest link is *CE* (3.1). No problem here, so we select it and highlight it in red.

- Step 5. The next cheapest link in the graph is *EG* (3.2). If we were to highlight *GE* in red we would be forming the partial red circuit *E, G, I, C, E*. Because of the partial-circuit rule, we must ✕-out *EG*. We scan the graph again and find that the next cheapest link is *IE*. If we were to highlight *IE* in red we would have the following problem: *three* red edges (*IE, IG,* and *IC*) meeting at one vertex. This is not possible in a tour, since it would require visiting that vertex more than once. (For convenience, we call this the *three-edge rule*.) So we ✕-out *IE* as well. [If you are doodling along with this narration, your picture at this point should look something like Fig. 6-16(b).] The next four cheapest links in order are *IM* (4.7), *IT* (5.1), *CM* (5.2), and *CT* (5.6). They all have to be ruled out because of the three-edge rule. This leads us to *GM* (5.7). This edge works, so we select it and highlight it in red.

- Step 6. Since $N = 6$ this should be the last step. The last step is a little easier than the others—there should be only one way to close the circuit. Looking at the graph we see that *E* and *T* are the two loose ends that need to be connected. We do that by adding the link *ET*. Now we are done.

This is the end of the busywork. We found a Hamilton circuit in the graph and from it we get two different tours, depending on the direction we choose to travel. Going clockwise gives the *cheapest-link tour E, C, I, G, M, T, E* with a total length of 19.4 years. Going counterclockwise gives us the reverse tour.

Notice that for the interplanetary mission TSP, the cheapest-link tour we just found is exactly the same as the nearest-neighbor tour we found in Example 6.11. This is a coincidence, and we should not read too much into it. In general, the cheapest-link tour is different from the nearest-neighbor tour, and there is no superiority of one over the other—sometimes the cheapest-link tour is better, sometimes it's the other way around.

A formal description of the cheapest-link algorithm is given below.

◾THE CHEAPEST-LINK ALGORITHM

- **Step 1.** Pick the *cheapest link* available. (If there is more than one, randomly pick one among the cheapest links.) Highlight the link in red (or any other color).
- **Step 2.** Pick the next cheapest link available and highlight it.
- **Steps 3, 4, . . ., N − 1.** Continue picking and highlighting the cheapest available link that (a) does not violate the *partial-circuit* rule (i.e., does not close a partial circuit) or (b) does not violate the *three-edge* rule (i.e., does not create three edges meeting at the same vertex).
- **Step N.** Connect the two vertices that close the red circuit. Once we have the Hamilton circuit, we can add a direction of travel (clockwise or counterclockwise). Either one gives us a **cheapest-link tour**.

Our next example illustrates how to implement the cheapest-link algorithm when we have to work from a chart rather than a graph. The main difficulty in this situation is that it is not easy to spot violations of the *partial-circuit* and *three-edge* rules when looking at a chart. A simple way around this difficulty is to create an auxiliary picture of the tour as it is being built, one edge at a time.

EXAMPLE 6.15 THE *CURIOSITY* TSP AND THE CLA

We are finally going to take a look at the *Curiosity* TSP introduced in the chapter opener and described in Example 6.3. The seven locations (G_1 through G_7) that the Mars rover *Curiosity* must visit and the distances (in meters) between pairs of locations are given in Fig. 6-17(a). We will use the cheapest-link algorithm working directly out of the distance chart. All we will need is an additional auxiliary graph that will help us visualize the links as we move through the steps of the algorithm. Figure 6-17(b) shows the auxiliary graph when we start—a blank slate of seven vertices G_1 through G_7 and no edges.

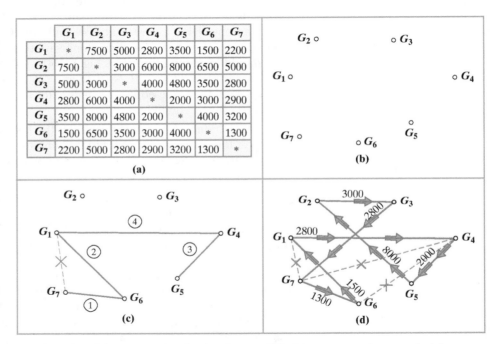

	G_1	G_2	G_3	G_4	G_5	G_6	G_7
G_1	*	7500	5000	2800	3500	1500	2200
G_2	7500	*	3000	6000	8000	6500	5000
G_3	5000	3000	*	4000	4800	3500	2800
G_4	2800	6000	4000	*	2000	3000	2900
G_5	3500	8000	4800	2000	*	4000	3200
G_6	1500	6500	3500	3000	4000	*	1300
G_7	2200	5000	2800	2900	3200	1300	*

(a)

(b)

(c)

(d)

FIGURE 6-17 (a) Distance chart for the *Curiosity* TSP, (b) starting auxiliary graph, (c) auxiliary graph at Step 4, and (d) cheapest-link tour (21,400 m).

- **Step 1.** We scan the distance chart looking for the smallest possible number. (*Note*: In a distance chart the half below the diagonal is the mirror image of the half above the diagonal, so we have to scan only one of the two halves.) The smallest number is 1300, and it belongs to the edge G_6G_7. This is the cheapest link, and we select it. We indicate this by connecting G_6 and G_7 in the auxiliary graph.

- **Step 2.** We scan the distance chart again looking for the next smallest number. The number is 1500, and it belongs to the edge G_1G_6. We select this edge and indicate that we are doing so by connecting G_1 and G_6 in the auxiliary graph.

- **Step 3.** The next smallest number in the chart is 2000, and it belongs to the edge G_4G_5. We select this edge and connect G_4 to G_5 in the auxiliary graph.

- **Step 4.** The next smallest number in the chart is 2200, and it belongs to the edge G_1G_7. When we go to the auxiliary graph we see that we can't select this edge because it would create the circuit G_1, G_7, G_6, G_1—a violation of the partial-circuit rule. We X-out G_1G_7 and scan the chart again, looking for the next smallest number after 2200. Here there is a tie with two entries equal to 2800: G_1G_4 and G_3G_7. We choose randomly one of these, say G_1G_4. This one is OK, and we select it by adding that edge to the auxiliary graph. At this point the auxiliary graph looks like Fig. 6-17(c).

- **Step 5.** We now try G_3G_7, the other edge with a cost of 2800. It works, so we add the edge G_3G_7 to the auxiliary graph.

- **Step 6.** The next smallest number in the chart is 2900, and it belongs to the edge G_4G_7. When we look at the auxiliary graph, we can see that this edge won't work because it would create a violation of the three-edge rule, both at G_4 and at G_7. So, we X-out the edge and look for the next smallest number. There are two entries tied at 3000: G_4G_6 and G_2G_3. Say we try G_4G_6 first. This choice violates both the three-edge and partial-circuit rules, so we X-it out. The second edge with weight 3000 is G_2G_3, and this one works. We select it, and add the edge to the auxiliary graph.

- **Step 7.** This is the last step, so we can go directly to the auxiliary graph. We see that the only way to close the Hamilton circuit is to add the edge G_2G_5.

We now have a Hamilton circuit. A *cheapest-link tour* is shown in Fig. 6-17(d): G_1, G_4, G_5, G_2, G_3, G_7, G_6, G_1. The total length is 21,400 m. (Traveling in the opposite direction gives the other cheapest-link tour).

How good is the cheapest-link tour we found in Example 6.15? At this point we have nothing to compare it with, so we just don't know. We will be able to answer the question in our next (and last) example.

EXAMPLE 6.16 THE *CURIOSITY* TSP AND THE NNA

We know only one way to find the optimal tour for the *Curiosity* TSP—use the brute-force algorithm, but this would require us to create a list with 6! = 720 Hamilton circuits. That's a lot of circuits to check out by hand.

A less ambitious approach is to try the nearest-neighbor algorithm and hope we get a good approximate tour. We leave the details as an exercise for the reader, but here it is: the *nearest-neighbor tour* (starting at G_1) is G_1, G_6, G_7, G_3, G_2, G_4, G_5, G_1 [Fig. 6-18(b)]. The total length of this tour is 20,100 m. This is a respectable improvement over the cheapest-link tour found in Example 6.15.

	G_1	G_2	G_3	G_4	G_5	G_6	G_7
G_1	*	7500	5000	2800	3500	1500	2200
G_2	7500	*	3000	6000	8000	6500	5000
G_3	5000	3000	*	4000	4800	3500	2800
G_4	2800	6000	4000	*	2000	3000	2900
G_5	3500	8000	4800	2000	*	4000	3200
G_6	1500	6500	3500	3000	4000	*	1300
G_7	2200	5000	2800	2900	3200	1300	*

(a)

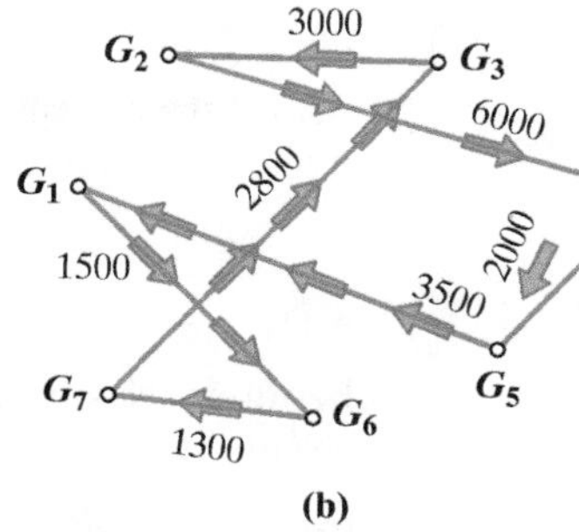

(b)

FIGURE 6-18   (a) Distance chart for the *Curiosity* TSP; (b) nearest-neighbor tour (20,100 m).

Out of curiosity, we decided to find, once and for all, an *optimal tour* for *Curiosity*. Using a computer and the brute-force algorithm we checked all 720 Hamilton circuits and came up with a surprise: There are several optimal tours, and one of them happens to be the nearest-neighbor tour shown in Fig. 6-18(b). In other words, in the case of the *Curiosity* TSP the nearest-neighbor algorithm (in a sense the most basic of all TSP algorithms) produced an optimal solution—a nice (and lucky) turn of events. Too bad we can't count on this happening on a consistent basis. Well, maybe next chapter.

Conclusion

TSP is the acronym for *traveling salesman problem*. TSPs are some of the most important and perplexing problems in modern mathematics. Important because there is a wide range of real-life applications that can be modeled by TSPs, and perplexing because nobody knows a general algorithm for finding optimal solutions to TSPs that works no matter how large the number of vertices is. It's likely that an *optimal and efficient general algorithm for solving TSPs is a mathematical impossibility* along the lines of Arrow's Impossibility Theorem in Chapter 1, but unlike Arrow, nobody has been able to prove this as a mathematical fact. Great fame and fortune await the first person that can do this.

Alternatively, there are many good *approximate algorithms* that can produce *suboptimal* (i.e., approximate) solutions to TSPs even when the number of vertices is very large. These algorithms represent a departure from the traditional notion that a math problem can have only one answer or that an answer is either right or wrong. In this chapter we discussed several *approximate algorithms* for solving TSPs and learned an important lesson: some math problems can have a perfect solution or an approximate solution. When the perfect solution is beyond the human ability to compute it, a good approximate solution that is easy to compute is not such a bad thing. Regardless of how we choose to tackle *traveling salesman problems*, the acronym TSP should not stand for *Totally Stumped and Perplexed*.

KEY CONCEPTS

6.1 What Is a Traveling Salesman Problem?

- **tour:** a trip that starts and ends at a site and visits all the other sites exactly once, **176**
- **optimal tour:** a tour of minimal total cost, **176**
- **TSP:** an acronym for *traveling salesman problem*, **176**

6.2 Hamilton Paths and Circuits

- **Hamilton circuit:** a circuit that visits all the vertices of a connected graph once and only once, **179**
- **Hamilton path:** a path that visits all the vertices of a connected graph once and only once, **179**
- **complete graph (K_N):** a graph with no loops or multiple edges such that any two distinct vertices are connected by an edge, **181**

6.3 The Brute-Force Algorithm

- **brute-force algorithm:** an algorithm that checks the cost of every possible Hamilton circuit and chooses the optimal one, **185**
- **inefficient algorithm:** an algorithm for which the computational effort needed to carry out the steps of the algorithm grows disproportionately with the size of the problem, **185**

6.4 The Nearest-Neighbor and Repetitive Nearest-Neighbor Algorithms

- **approximate algorithm:** an algorithm that produces a solution, but not necessarily an optimal solution, **187**
- **nearest-neighbor algorithm:** starts at a designated vertex and at each step it visits the nearest neighbor (among the vertices not yet visited) until the tour is completed, **186, 189**

■ **relative error:** for a tour with cost C, the ratio, $\frac{C - Opt}{Opt}$ (usually expressed in the form of a percentage), where Opt is the cost of an optimal tour, **188**

■ **repetitive nearest-neighbor algorithm:** finds the nearest-neighbor tour for each possible starting vertex and chooses the one of least cost among them, **188, 190**

■ **nearest-neighbor tour:** the tour obtained using the nearest-neighbor algorithm, **189**

■ **repetitive nearest-neighbor tour:** a tour obtained using the nearest-neighbor algorithm, **190**

6.5 The Cheapest-Link Algorithm

■ **partial-circuit rule:** a Hamilton circuit (tour) cannot contain any partial circuits, **191**

■ **three-edge rule:** a Hamilton circuit (tour) cannot have three edges coming out of a vertex, **191**

■ **cheapest-link algorithm:** at each step chooses the cheapest link available that does not violate the partial-circuit rule or the three-edge rule, **191**

■ **cheapest-link tour:** a tour obtained using the cheapest-link algorithm, **191**

 # EXERCISES

WALKING

6.1 What Is a Traveling Salesman Problem?

No exercises for this section.

6.2 Hamilton Paths and Circuits

1. For the graph shown in Fig. 6-19,

    (a) find three different Hamilton circuits.

    (b) find a Hamilton path that starts at A and ends at B.

    (c) find a Hamilton path that starts at D and ends at F.

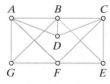

FIGURE 6-19

2. For the graph shown in Fig. 6-20,

    (a) find three different Hamilton circuits.

    (b) find a Hamilton path that starts at A and ends at B.

    (c) find a Hamilton path that starts at F and ends at I.

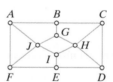

FIGURE 6-20

3. Find all possible Hamilton circuits in the graph in Fig. 6-21. Write your answers using A as the starting/ending vertex.

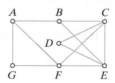

FIGURE 6-21

4. Find all possible Hamilton circuits in the graph in Fig. 6-22. Write your answers using A as the starting/ending vertex.

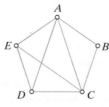

FIGURE 6-22

5. For the graph shown in Fig. 6-23,

   (a) find a Hamilton path that starts at A and ends at E.

   (b) find a Hamilton circuit that starts at A and ends with the edge EA.

   (c) find a Hamilton path that starts at A and ends at C.

   (d) find a Hamilton path that starts at F and ends at G.

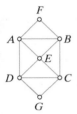

FIGURE 6-23

6. For the graph shown in Fig. 6-24,

   (a) find a Hamilton path that starts at A and ends at E.

   (b) find a Hamilton circuit that starts at A and ends with the edge EA.

   (c) find a Hamilton path that starts at A and ends at G.

   (d) find a Hamilton path that starts at F and ends at G.

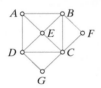

FIGURE 6-24

7. Suppose $D, G, E, A, H, C, B, F, D$ is a Hamilton circuit in a graph.

   (a) Find the number of vertices in the graph.

   (b) Write the Hamilton circuit using A as the starting/ending vertex.

   (c) Find two different Hamilton paths in the graph that start at A.

8. Suppose G, B, D, C, A, F, E, G is a Hamilton circuit in a graph.

   (a) Find the number of vertices in the graph.

   (b) Write the Hamilton circuit using F as the starting/ending vertex.

   (c) Find two different Hamilton paths in the graph that start at F.

9. Consider the graph in Fig. 6-25.

   (a) Find the five Hamilton paths that can be obtained by "breaking" the Hamilton circuit B,A,D,E,C,B (i.e., by deleting just one edge from the circuit).

   (b) Find the eight Hamilton paths that do not come from "broken" Hamilton circuits (i.e., cannot be closed into a Hamilton circuit). (*Hint:* See Example 6.6).

FIGURE 6-25

10. Consider the graph in Fig. 6-26.

   (a) Find all the Hamilton circuits in the graph, using B as the starting/ending vertex. (*Hint:* There are five Hamilton circuits and another five that are reversals of the first five.)

   (b) Find the four Hamilton paths that start at B and do not come from "broken" Hamilton circuits (i.e., cannot be closed into a Hamilton circuit).

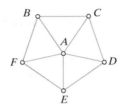

FIGURE 6-26

11. Consider the graph in Fig. 6-27.

   (a) Find all the Hamilton circuits in the graph, using A as the starting/ending vertex. You don't have to list both a circuit and its reversal—you can just list one from each pair.

   (b) Find all the Hamilton paths that do not come from "broken" Hamilton circuits (i.e., cannot be closed into a Hamilton circuit). You don't have to list both a path and its reversal—you can just list one from each pair.

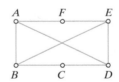

FIGURE 6-27

12. Consider the graph in Fig. 6-28.

   (a) Find all the Hamilton circuits in the graph, using A as the starting/ending vertex. You don't have to list both a circuit and its reversal—you can just list one from each pair.

   (b) Find all the Hamilton paths that do not come from "broken" Hamilton circuits (i.e., cannot be closed into a Hamilton circuit). You don't have to list both a path and its reversal—you can just list one from each pair. (*Hint:* Such paths must either start or end at C. You can just list all the paths that start at C— the ones that end at C are their reversals.)

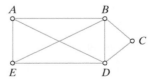

FIGURE 6-28

13. For the graph shown in Fig. 6-29,

    (a) find a Hamilton path that starts at *A* and ends at *F*.

    (b) find a Hamilton path that starts at *K* and ends at *E*.

    (c) explain why the graph has no Hamilton path that starts at *C*.

    (d) explain why the graph has no Hamilton circuits.

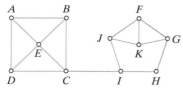

FIGURE 6-29

14. For the graph shown in Fig. 6-30,

    (a) find a Hamilton path that starts at *B*.

    (b) find a Hamilton path that starts at *E*.

    (c) explain why the graph has no Hamilton path that starts at *A* or at *C*.

    (d) explain why the graph has no Hamilton circuit.

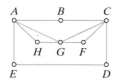

FIGURE 6-30

15. Explain why the graph shown in Fig. 6-31 has neither Hamilton circuits nor Hamilton paths.

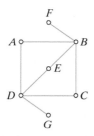

FIGURE 6-31

16. Explain why the graph shown in Fig. 6-32 has no Hamilton circuit but does have a Hamilton path.

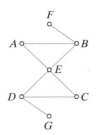

FIGURE 6-32

17. For the weighted graph shown in Fig. 6-33,

    (a) find the weight of edge *BD*.

    (b) find a Hamilton circuit that starts with edge *BD*, and give its weight.

    (c) find a Hamilton circuit that ends with edge *DB*, and give its weight.

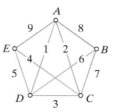

FIGURE 6-33

18. For the weighted graph shown in Fig. 6-34,

    (a) find the weight of edge *AD*.

    (b) find a Hamilton circuit that starts with edge *AD*, and give its weight.

    (c) find a Hamilton circuit that ends with edge *DA*, and give its weight.

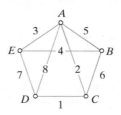

FIGURE 6-34

19. For the weighted graph shown in Fig. 6-35,

    (a) find a Hamilton path that starts at *A* and ends at *C*, and give its weight.

    (b) find a second Hamilton path that starts at *A* and ends at *C*, and give its weight.

    (c) find the optimal (least weight) Hamilton path that starts at *A* and ends at *C*, and give its weight.

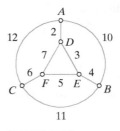

FIGURE 6-35

20. For the weighted graph shown in Fig. 6-36,

    (a) find a Hamilton path that starts at B and ends at D, and give its weight.

    (b) find a second Hamilton path that starts at B and ends at D, and give its weight.

    (c) find the optimal (least weight) Hamilton path that starts at B and ends at D, and give its weight.

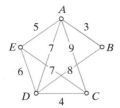

FIGURE 6-36

21. Suppose you have a supercomputer that can generate one *billion* Hamilton circuits per second.

    (a) Estimate (in years) how long it would take the supercomputer to generate all the Hamilton circuits in K_{21}.

    (b) Estimate (in years) how long it would take the supercomputer to generate all the Hamilton circuits in K_{22}.

22. Suppose you have a supercomputer that can generate one *trillion* Hamilton circuits per second.

    (a) Estimate (in years) how long it would take the supercomputer to generate all the Hamilton circuits in K_{26}.

    (b) Estimate (in years) how long it would take the supercomputer to generate all the Hamilton circuits in K_{27}.

23. (a) How many edges are there in K_{20}?

    (b) How many edges are there in K_{21}?

    (c) If the number of edges in K_{50} is x and the number of edges in K_{51} is y, what is the value of $y - x$?

24. (a) How many edges are there in K_{200}?

    (b) How many edges are there in K_{201}?

    (c) If the number of edges in K_{500} is x and the number of edges in K_{501} is y, what is the value of $y - x$?

25. In each case, find the value of N.

    (a) K_N has 120 distinct Hamilton circuits.

    (b) K_N has 45 edges.

    (c) K_N has 20,100 edges.

26. In each case, find the value of N.

    (a) K_N has 720 distinct Hamilton circuits.

    (b) K_N has 66 edges.

    (c) K_N has 80,200 edges.

6.3 The Brute-Force Algorithm

27. Find an optimal tour for the TSP given in Fig. 6-37, and give its cost.

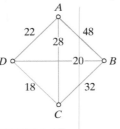

FIGURE 6-37

28. Find an optimal tour for the TSP given in Fig. 6-38, and give its cost.

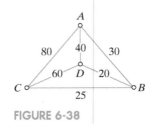

FIGURE 6-38

29. A truck must deliver furniture to stores located in five different cities $A, B, C, D,$ and E. The truck must start and end its route at A. The time (in hours) for travel between the cities is given in Fig. 6-39. Find an optimal tour for this TSP and give its cost in hours. (*Hint*: The edge AD is part of an optimal tour.)

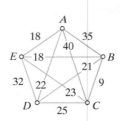

FIGURE 6-39

30. A social worker starts from her home A, must visit clients at $B, C, D,$ and E (in any order), and return home to A at the end of the day. The graph in Fig. 6-40 shows the distance (in miles) between the five locations. Find an optimal tour for this TSP, and give its cost in miles. (*Hint*: The edge AC is part of an optimal tour.)

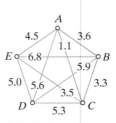

FIGURE 6-40

31. You are planning to visit four cities A, B, C, and D. Table 6-6 shows the time (in hours) that it takes to travel by car between any two cities. Find an optimal tour for this TSP that starts and ends at B.

	A	B	C	D
A	*	12	6	14
B	12	*	17	15
C	6	17	*	11
D	14	15	11	*

■ TABLE 6-6

32. An unmanned rover must be routed to visit four sites labeled A, B, C, and D on the surface of the moon. Table 6-7 shows the distance (in kilometers) between any two sites. Assuming the rover landed at C, find an optimal tour.

	A	B	C	D
A	0	4	18	16
B	4	0	17	13
C	18	17	0	7
D	16	13	7	0

■ TABLE 6-7

33. Consider a TSP with nine vertices labeled A through I.

   (a) How many tours are of the form $A, G, \ldots, A$? (*Hint*: The remaining seven letters can be rearranged in any sequence.)

   (b) How many tours are of the form $B, \ldots, E, B$?

   (c) How many tours are of the form $A, D, \ldots, F, A$?

34. Consider a TSP with 11 vertices labeled A through K.

   (a) How many tours are of the form $A, B, \ldots, A$? (*Hint*: The remaining nine letters can be rearranged in any sequence.)

   (b) How many tours are of the form $C, \ldots, K, C$?

   (c) How many tours are of the form $D, B, \ldots, K, D$?

6.4 The Nearest-Neighbor and Repetitive Nearest-Neighbor Algorithms

35. For the weighted graph shown in Fig. 6-41, (i) find the indicated tour, and (ii) give its cost. (*Note*: This is the TSP introduced in Example 6.1.)

   (a) The nearest-neighbor tour with starting vertex B

   (b) The nearest-neighbor tour with starting vertex C

   (c) The nearest-neighbor tour with starting vertex D

   (d) The nearest-neighbor tour with starting vertex E

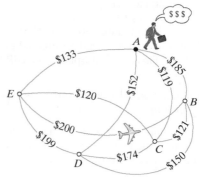

FIGURE 6-41

36. A delivery service must deliver packages at Buckman (B), Chatfield (C), Dayton (D), and Evansville (E) and then return to Arlington (A), the home base. Figure 6-42 shows a graph of the estimated travel times (in minutes) between the cities.

   (a) Find the nearest-neighbor tour with starting vertex A. Give the total travel time of this tour.

   (b) Find the nearest-neighbor tour with starting vertex D. Write the tour as it would be traveled if starting and ending at A. Give the total travel time of this tour.

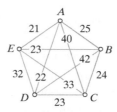

FIGURE 6-42 .

37. The Brute-Force Bandits is a rock band planning a five-city concert tour. The cities and the distances (in miles) between them are given in the weighted graph shown in Fig. 6-43. The tour must start and end at A. The cost of the chartered bus in which the band is traveling is $8 per mile.

   (a) Find the nearest-neighbor tour with starting vertex A. Give the cost (in $) of this tour.

   (b) Find the nearest-neighbor tour with starting vertex B. Write the tour as it would be traveled by the band, starting and ending at A. Give the cost (in $) of this tour.

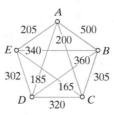

FIGURE 6-43

38. A space mission is scheduled to visit the moons Callisto (*C*), Ganymede (*G*), Io (*I*), Mimas (*M*), and Titan (*T*) to collect rock samples at each and then return to Earth (*E*). The travel times (in years) are given in the weighted graph shown in Fig. 6-44. (*Note*: This is the interplanetary TSP discussed in Example 6.11.)

(a) Find the nearest-neighbor tour with starting vertex *E*. Give the total travel time of this tour.

(b) Find the nearest-neighbor tour with starting vertex *T*. Write the tour as it would be traveled by an expedition starting and ending at *E*. Give the total travel time of this tour.

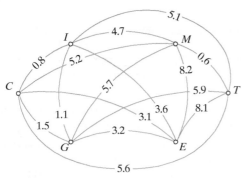

FIGURE 6-44

39. This exercise refers to the furniture truck TSP introduced in Exercise 29 (see Fig. 6-39).

(a) Find the nearest-neighbor tour starting at *A*.

(b) Find the nearest-neighbor tour starting at *B*, and give the answer using *A* as the starting/ending city.

40. This exercise refers to the social worker TSP introduced in Exercise 30 (see Fig. 6-40).

(a) Find the nearest-neighbor tour starting at *A*.

(b) Find the nearest-neighbor tour starting at *C*, and give the answer using *A* as the starting/ending city.

41. Darren is a sales rep whose territory consists of the six cities in the mileage chart shown in Fig. 6-45. Darren wants to visit customers at each of the cities, starting and ending his

Mileage Chart

	Atlanta	Columbus	Kansas City	Minneapolis	Pierre	Tulsa
Atlanta	*	533	798	1068	1361	772
Columbus	533	*	656	713	1071	802
Kansas City	798	656	*	447	592	248
Minneapolis	1068	713	447	*	394	695
Pierre	1361	1071	592	394	*	760
Tulsa	772	802	248	695	760	*

FIGURE 6-45

trip in his home city of Atlanta. His travel costs (gas, insurance, etc.) average $0.75 per mile.

(a) Find the nearest-neighbor tour with Atlanta as the starting city. What is the total cost of this tour?

(b) Find the nearest-neighbor tour using Kansas City as the starting city. Write the tour as it would be traveled by Darren, who must start and end the trip in Atlanta. What is the total cost of this tour?

42. The Platonic Cowboys are a country and western band based in Nashville. The Cowboys are planning a concert tour to the seven cities in the mileage chart shown in Fig. 6-46.

(a) Find the nearest-neighbor tour with Nashville as the starting city. What is the total length of this tour?

(b) Find the nearest-neighbor tour using St. Louis as the starting city. Write the tour as it would be traveled by the band, which must start and end the tour in Nashville. What is the total length of this tour?

Mileage Chart

	Boston	Dallas	Houston	Louisville	Nashville	Pittsburgh	St. Louis
Boston	*	1748	1804	941	1088	561	1141
Dallas	1748	*	243	819	660	1204	630
Houston	1804	243	*	928	769	1313	779
Louisville	941	819	928	*	168	388	263
Nashville	1088	660	769	168	*	553	299
Pittsburgh	561	1204	1313	388	553	*	588
St. Louis	1141	630	779	263	299	588	*

FIGURE 6-46

43. Find the repetitive nearest-neighbor tour (and give its cost) for the furniture truck TSP discussed in Exercises 29 and 39 (see Fig. 6-39).

44. Find the repetitive nearest-neighbor tour for the social worker TSP discussed in Exercises 30 and 40 (see Fig. 6-40).

45. This exercise is a continuation of Darren's sales trip problem (Exercise 41). Find the repetitive nearest-neighbor tour, and give the total cost for this tour. Write the answer using Atlanta as the starting city.

46. This exercise is a continuation of the Platonic Cowboys concert tour (Exercise 42). Find the repetitive nearest-neighbor tour, and give the total mileage for this tour. Write the answer using Nashville as the starting city.

47. Suppose that in solving a TSP you use the nearest-neighbor algorithm and find a nearest-neighbor tour with a total cost of $13,500. Suppose that you later find out that the cost of an optimal tour is $12,000. What was the relative error of your nearest-neighbor tour? Express your answer as a percentage, rounded to the nearest tenth of a percent.

Mileage Chart

	Atlanta	Boston	Buffalo	Chicago	Columbus	Dallas	Denver	Houston	Kansas City	Louisville	Memphis
Atlanta	*	1037	859	674	533	795	1398	789	798	382	371
Boston	1037	*	446	963	735	1748	1949	1804	1391	941	1293
Buffalo	859	446	*	522	326	1346	1508	1460	966	532	899
Chicago	674	963	522	*	308	917	996	1067	499	292	530
Columbus	533	735	326	308	*	1028	1229	1137	656	209	576
Dallas	795	1748	1346	917	1028	*	781	243	489	819	452
Denver	1398	1949	1508	996	1229	781	*	1019	600	1120	1040
Houston	789	1804	1460	1067	1137	243	1019	*	710	928	561
Kansas City	798	1391	966	499	656	489	600	710	*	520	451
Louisville	382	941	532	292	209	819	1120	928	520	*	367
Memphis	371	1293	899	530	576	452	1040	561	451	367	*

FIGURE 6-54

70. Julie is the marketing manager for a small software company based in Boston. She is planning a sales trip to Michigan to visit customers in each of the nine cities shown on the mileage chart in Fig. 6-55. She can fly from Boston to any one of the cities and fly out of any one of the cities back to Boston for the same price (call the arrival city A and the departure city D). Her plan is to pick up a rental car at A, drive to each of the other cities, and drop off the rental car at the last city D. Slightly complicating the situation is that Michigan has two separate peninsulas—an upper peninsula and a lower peninsula—and the only way to get from one to the other is through the Mackinaw Bridge connecting Cheboygan to Sault Ste. Marie. (There is a $3 toll to cross the bridge in either direction.)

(a) Suppose that the rental car company charges 39 cents per mile plus a drop off fee of $250 if A and D are different cities (there is no charge if $A = D$). Find the optimal (cheapest) route and give the total cost.

(b) Suppose that the rental car company charges 49 cents per mile but the car can be returned to any city without a drop off fee. Find the optimal route and give the total cost.

RUNNING

71. Complete bipartite graphs. A complete bipartite graph is a graph with the property that the vertices can be divided into two sets A and B and each vertex in set A is adjacent to each of the vertices in set B. There are no other edges! If there are m vertices in set A and n vertices in set B, the complete bipartite graph is written as $K_{n,n}$. Figure 6-56 shows a generic bipartite graph.

(a) For $n > 1$, the complete bipartite graphs of the form $K_{m,n}$ all have Hamilton circuits. Explain why.

Mileage Chart

	Detroit	Lansing	Grand Rapids	Flint	Cheboygan	Sault Ste. Marie	Marquette	Escanaba	Menominee
Detroit	*	90	158	68	280				
Lansing	90	*	68	56	221				
Grand Rapids	158	68	*	114	233				
Flint	68	56	114	*	215				
Cheboygan	280	221	233	215	*	78			
Sault Ste. Marie					78	*	164	174	227
Marquette						164	*	67	120
Escanaba						174	67	*	55
Menominee						227	120	55	*

FIGURE 6-55

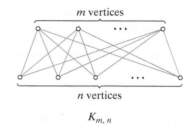

m vertices

n vertices

$K_{m,n}$

FIGURE 6-56

(b) If the difference between m and n is exactly 1 (i.e., $|m - n| = 1$), the complete bipartite graph $K_{m,n}$ has a Hamilton path. Explain why.

(c) When the difference between m and n is more than 1, then the complete bipartite graph $K_{m,n}$ has neither a Hamilton circuit nor a Hamilton path. Explain why.

72. m by n grid graphs. An m by n grid graph represents a rectangular street grid that is m blocks by n blocks, as indicated in Fig. 6-57. (You should try Exercises 63 through 66 before you try this one.)

(a) If m and n are both odd, then the m by n grid graph has a Hamilton circuit. Describe the circuit by drawing it on a generic graph.

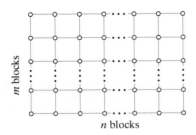

m blocks

n blocks

FIGURE 6-57

(b) If either m or n is even and the other one is odd, then the m by n grid graph has a Hamilton circuit. Describe the circuit by drawing it on a generic graph.

(c) If m and n are both even, then the m by n grid graph does not have a Hamilton circuit. Explain why a Hamilton circuit is impossible.

73. Ore's theorem. A connected graph with N vertices is said to satisfy *Ore's condition* if $\deg(X) + \deg(Y) \geq N$ for every pair of vertices X and Y of the graph. Ore's theorem states that *if a graph satisfies Ore's condition, then it has a Hamilton circuit.*

(a) Explain why the complete bipartite graph $K_{n,n}$ (see Exercise 71) satisfies Ore's condition.

(b) Explain why for $m \neq n$, the complete bipartite graph $K_{m,n}$ (see Exercise 71) does *not* satisfy Ore's condition.

(c) Ore's condition is sufficient to guarantee that a connected graph has a Hamilton circuit but is not a necessary condition. Give an example of a graph that has a Hamilton circuit but does not satisfy Ore's condition.

74. Dirac's theorem. If G is a connected graph with N vertices and $\deg(X) \geq \frac{N}{2}$ for every vertex X, then G has a Hamilton circuit. Explain why Dirac's theorem is a direct consequence of Ore's theorem.

PROJECTS AND PAPERS

1 The Nearest-Insertion Algorithm

The *nearest-insertion algorithm* is another approximate algorithm used for tackling TSPs. The basic idea of the algorithm is to start with a subcircuit (a circuit that includes some, but not all, of the vertices) and enlarge it, one step at a time, by adding an extra vertex—the one that is closest to some vertex in the circuit. By the time we have added all of the vertices, we have a full-fledged Hamilton circuit.

In this project, you should prepare a class presentation on the nearest-insertion algorithm. Your presentation should include a detailed description of the algorithm, at least two carefully worked-out examples, and a comparison of the nearest-insertion and the nearest-neighbor algorithms.

2 Computing with DNA

DNA is the basic molecule of life—it encodes the genetic information that characterizes all living organisms. Due to the recent great advances in biochemistry, scientists can now snip, splice, and recombine segments of DNA almost at will. In 1994, Leonard Adleman, a professor of computer science at the University of Southern California, was able to encode a graph representing seven cities into a set of DNA segments and to use the chemical reactions of the DNA fragments to uncover the existence of a Hamilton path in the graph. Basically, he was able to use the biochemistry of DNA to solve a graph theory problem. While the actual problem solved was insignificant, the idea was revolutionary, as it opened the door for the possibility of someday using DNA computers to solve problems beyond the reach of even the most powerful of today's electronic computers.

Write a research paper telling the story of Adleman's landmark discovery. How did he encode the graph into DNA? How did he extract the mathematical solution (Hamilton path) from the chemical solution? What other kinds of problems might be solved using DNA computing? What are the implications of Adleman's discovery for the future of computing?

3 Ant Colony Optimization

An individual ant is, by most standards, a dumb little creature, but collectively an entire ant colony can perform surprising feats of teamwork (such as lifting and carrying large leaves or branches) and self-organize to solve remarkably complex problems (finding the shortest route to a food source, optimizing foraging strategies, managing a smooth and steady traffic flow in congested ant highways). The ability of ants and other social insects to perform sophisticated group tasks goes by the name of *swarm intelligence*. Since ants don't talk to each other and don't have bosses telling them what to do, swarm intelligence is a decentralized, spontaneous type of intelligence that has many potential applications at the human scale. In recent years, computer scientists have been able to approach many difficult optimization problems (including TSPs) using *ant colony optimization* software (i.e., computer programs that use *virtual ants* to imitate the problem-solving strategies of real ants).

Write a research paper describing the concept of swarm intelligence and some of the recent developments in ant colony optimization methods and, in particular, the use of virtual ant algorithms for solving TSPs.

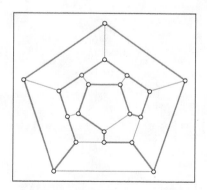

Solution to Hamilton's Icosian game
(Fig. 6-5, page 179).

7 The Mathematics of Networks

The Cost of Being Connected

What do Facebook, the Internet, your family, the electrical power grid, the interstate highway system, and the veins and arteries in your body have in common? They all share the same fundamental structure—they are *networks*.

While the word network is used today in many different contents (*social network, computer network, telecommunications network,* etc.), there is a common thread to all of them—a network *connects* things. So, for the purposes of this chapter we will use the term *network* to mean a *connected graph*.

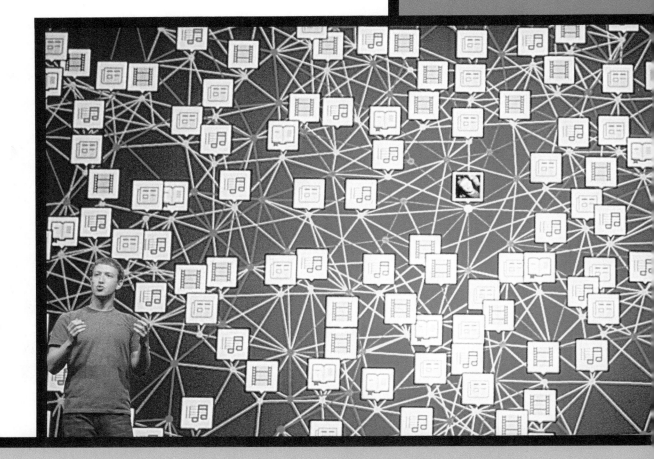

W hether we want to or not, we all belong to many different networks. Some are good (our families); some are not so good (the alumni association calling for a donation every other week); some are useful (the Internet); some are addictive (Facebook). Because of the ubiquitous role networks play in our lives, the study of networks has flourished in the last 20 years. Sociologists, economists, engineers, and urban planners all study different aspects of the theory of networks, but when you peel off all their layers, networks are basically mathematical structures.

The purpose of this chapter is to give a very general introduction to the mathematics of networks and related structures such as trees and spanning trees. Section 7.1 starts with several real-life examples of *networks*. By necessity, the size of the networks discussed is scaled down, but the general ideas can be applied at much bigger scales. Section 7.1 also introduces an important type of network called a *tree*. Section 7.2 introduces the concept of a *spanning tree* of a network. In the spirit of Chapters 5 and 6, Section 7.2 deals with optimization questions: What is a *minimum spanning tree* (MST) in a *weighted* network? What is a *maximum spanning tree* (MaxST)? *Why do we care*? We conclude the chapter with a discussion of *Kruskal's algorithm* (Sec. 7.3). Kruskal's algorithm is a simple method for finding minimum and maximum spanning trees in weighted networks. The algorithm works efficiently on networks regardless of their size, it always gives an optimal solution, and, most important, it is extremely easy to implement. When it comes to optimization problems one can't ask for better karma.

7.1 Networks and Trees

Networks

A **network** is a just another name for a *connected graph*. (In the context of networks, vertices are often called *nodes* and edges are called *links*.) Most of the networks we will consider in this chapter will be *simple networks* (i.e., without loops or multiple edges), but we do not make this a requirement. In some applications, a network can have loops, multiple edges, or both.

Our first example illustrates how social networks evolve. Social networks—such as Facebook, Twitter, and Instagram—are networks that connect people through some sort of social relationship—friendship, business, etc. The example is small, but you can imagine the same idea working on a much larger scale.

EXAMPLE 7.1 SOCIAL NETWORKS

Imagine 15 students (named *A* through *O*) enrolled in a very popular seminar called *The Mathematics of Social Networks*. One of the goals in a small seminar like this one is to get the students to connect with each other and exchange ideas as much as possible, in other words, to "network." For the purposes of this example we will say that two students in the seminar have *connected* if they have exchanged phone numbers or email addresses (presumably for the purposes of intellectual exchange, but we won't really dwell into their reasons for doing so). We can best visualize the interconnections among students in the seminar by means of a *connections graph*: the vertices (nodes) of the graph are the students, and pairs of students are linked by an edge if they have connected according to our definition of the term.

Figure 7-1(a) shows one possible version of the connections graph. In this scenario the graph is not a network but rather three separate, disconnected networks. Looking at this graph would not make the instructor happy. Figure 7-1(b) shows the new connections graph after two additional connections have been added: *EG* and *CH*. Now the graph becomes a true social network. The instructor is much happier—all students can connect, either directly or through intermediaries.

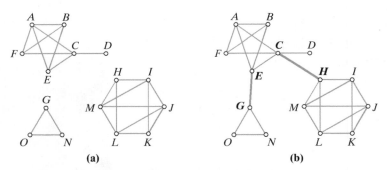

(a) **(b)**

FIGURE 7-1 (a) The graph of connections with three separate components. (b) The graph of connections becomes a network.

Because a network is a connected graph, there are paths going from any vertex to any other vertex—at least one but usually many more. We are usually interested in the *shortest path* connecting a pair of vertices—in other words, a path whose length is as small as possible. We will call the length of a shortest path joining two vertices in a network the **degree of separation** of the two vertices.

EXAMPLE 7.2 DEGREES OF SEPARATION

Consider again the network in Fig. 7-1(b). Let's look at degrees of separation between different pairs of students.

- *A* and *B* are joined by an edge, so we will say there is *one* degree of separation between them.

- *A* and *G* are not directly connected, but there is a path of length 2 connecting them: *A, E, G.* We will say that there are *two* degrees of separation between *A* and *G.*

- *A* and *K* are connected by the path *A, C, H, M, L, K* of length 5, but this is not as short as possible. The path *A, C, H, L, K* has length 4. Can we do even better? No. There is a second path of length 4 (*A, C, H, I, K*), but there are no paths of length 3 or less (to connect *A* and *K* one must go through *H*—that requires at least two edges; to connect *H* and *K* requires at least two more edges.) It follows that the degree of separation between *A* and *K* is *four.*

- *N* and *M* are pretty far apart—the shortest possible path connecting them is *N, G, E, C, H, M.* There you are—five degrees of separation.

- There are several pairs of students in this seminar with six degrees of separation between them. Can you find a couple?

Social networks such as Facebook, Twitter, and LinkedIn are examples of *organic* networks—networks that evolve and change on their own without any organized or centralized planning. In contrast to these, there are *planned* networks that are designed with a specific purpose in mind. Our next example illustrates on a very small scale one of the most important planned networks in modern life—the electrical power grid.

EXAMPLE 7.3 | POWER GRIDS

Figure 7-2(a) shows a map of the main Texas power grid. Figure 7-2(b) shows a small section of the power grid connecting 14 small towns labeled *A* through *N.* In this graph a small section of the vertices represent the towns and the edges represent the main power lines that carry electricity to the various towns. The graph is connected, so it is indeed a network—any town can draw power from the grid. In addition, there is a weight associated with each edge of the network. In this case the weight of an edge represents the length (in miles) of the power line connecting the two towns. [Figure 7-2(b) is not drawn to exact scale but is close. The reason for this is that the length of the power line is usually close to, but not necessarily the same, as the distance between the towns.]

We will return to this example in Section 7.3.

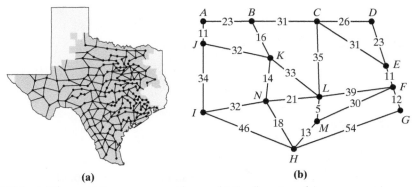

(a)   (b)

FIGURE 7-2   (a) The main Texas power grid map. (b) Small section of the power grid.

The network in Fig. 7.2 is an example of what we call a **weighted network**. Each edge has a *weight* that we will generally think of as representing a *cost* (either money, time, or distance). We will deal with weighted networks later in the chapter. In almost all weighted network problems the weights are positive numbers, but later in this chapter we will make an exception and consider weighted networks where the weights are negative numbers.

Trees

The second important concept in this chapter is that of a *tree*. We all know that trees are important, as they provide shade and help clean up our air, but in the context of this chapter the term **tree** means *a network that has no circuits.*

EXAMPLE 7.4 | TREES AND ROOTS

Figure 7-3 shows three networks.

- The network shown in Fig. 7-3(a) has the circuit A, B, G, F, E, D, H, A. It *is not* a tree.

- The network in Fig. 7-3(b) has no circuits. It *is* a tree. (What might look like a circuit in the picture is not—the crossing points of edge HD with edges BG and CG are just crossing points and not vertices.) This tree may not look very tree-like, but we can fix that easily.

- It is obvious that the network in Fig. 7-3(c) has no circuits. It is a tree, and it looks the part. Surprisingly, this tree is the same tree as the one shown in Fig. 7-3(b). We just picked one of the vertices to be the "root" of the tree (in this case B) and built the "branches" of the tree up from the root. We can do this with any tree: Pick any vertex to be the root and build the tree up from there. Figure 7-4 shows two more versions of the same tree—in Fig. 7-4(a) the tree is rooted at A; in Fig. 7-4(b) the tree is rooted at D. (Both trees are shown sideways with the root on the left—just trying to not waste space on the page . . . and save some real trees!)

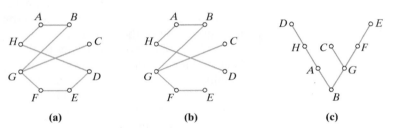

(a)	(b)	(c)

FIGURE 7-3   (a) A network with circuits is not a tree. (b) A tree. (c) The same tree with B as the "root."

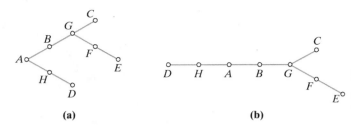

(a)	(b)

FIGURE 7-4   (a) Tree rooted at A. (b) Same tree rooted at D.

Trees have three key properties that distinguish them from ordinary networks. We will introduce the three properties first, illustrate them with an example, and conclude this section with a more formal version of these properties.

- **The single-path property.** In a tree, there is *only one path connecting two vertices.* If there were two paths connecting a pair of vertices, those two paths would create a circuit, as illustrated in Fig. 7-5. Conversely, a network that is not a tree must have at least one circuit, and that circuit will always provide alternative paths between its vertices. Look at Fig. 7-5 again: Given a circuit and two vertices (X and Y) in the circuit, there are at least two different paths (red and blue) connecting X and Y.

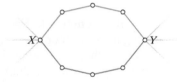

FIGURE 7-5   Two different paths joining X and Y make a circuit.

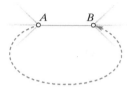

FIGURE 7-6 If *AB* is not a bridge, then it must be part of a circuit.

■ **The all-bridges property.** In a tree, *every edge is a bridge*. Essentially this means that a tree has no edges to spare—if we were to delete *any* edge, the tree would become disconnected and would no longer be a network. Figure 7-6 illustrates why every edge must be a bridge: Imagine an edge *AB* that is *not* a bridge. Then there would have to be an alternate path from *A* to *B* (shown as the dashed red curve). But *AB* together with the alternate path from *A* to *B* would form a circuit, and a tree doesn't have circuits. Conversely, if every edge of the network is a bridge then the network must be a tree.

■ **The $N-1$ edges property.** A tree with N vertices has $N-1$ edges. Always. This means that no matter what the shape of the tree is, the number of edges is one less than the number of vertices. The tree in Fig. 7-4 has $N=8$ vertices. We don't even have to check—the number of edges must be 7. Conversely, a network with N vertices and $N-1$ edges must be a tree.

From the above properties of trees we inherit the following key property of networks: In a network with N vertices and M edges, $M \geq N-1$ (i.e., the number of edges is at least $N-1$). When $M = N-1$ the network is a tree; when $M > N-1$ the network has circuits. The difference between the number of edges M and the minimum possible number of edges $N-1$ is an important number called the **redundancy** of the network.

■ **Redundancy of a Network.** In a network with N vertices and M edges, the redundancy R is given by $R = M - (N-1)$. [$R = 0$ means the network is a tree; $R > 0$ means the network is not a tree.]

| **EXAMPLE 7.5** | CONNECT THE DOTS (AND THEN STOP) |

Imagine the following "connect-the-dots" game: Start with eight isolated vertices. The object of the game is to create a network connecting the vertices by adding edges, one at a time. You are free to create any network you want. In this game, bridges are good and circuits are bad. (Imagine, for example, that for each bridge in your network you get a $10 reward, but for each circuit in your network you pay a $10 penalty.)

So grab a marker and start playing. We will let M denote the number of edges you have added at any point in time. In the early stages of the game ($M = 1, 2, \ldots, 6$) the graph is disconnected [Figs. 7-7(a) through (d)].

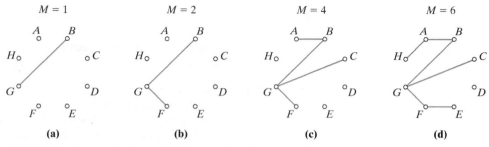

FIGURE 7-7 For small values of M, the graph is disconnected.

As soon as you get to $M = 7$ (and if you stayed away from forming any circuits) the graph becomes connected. Some of the possible configurations are shown in Fig. 7-8. Each of these networks has redundancy $R = 0$ and is, therefore, a tree, and now each of the seven edges is a bridge. Stop here and you will come out $70 richer.

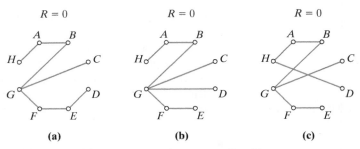

FIGURE 7-8   When $M = 7$, we have a tree $(R = 0)$.

Interestingly, this is as good as it will get. When $M = 8$ $(R = 1)$, the graph will have a circuit—it just can't be avoided. In addition, none of the edges in that circuit can be bridges of the graph. As a consequence, the larger the circuit that we create, the fewer the bridges left in the graph. [The graph in Fig. 7-9(a) has a circuit and five bridges, the graph in Fig. 7-9(b) has a circuit and two bridges, and the graph in Fig. 7-9(c) has a circuit and only one bridge.] As the redundancy increases, the number of circuits goes up (very quickly) and the number of bridges goes down [Figs. 7-10(a), (b), and (c)].

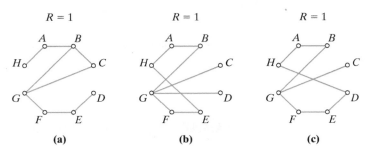

FIGURE 7-9   When $M = 8$ $(R = 1)$ we have a network with a circuit.

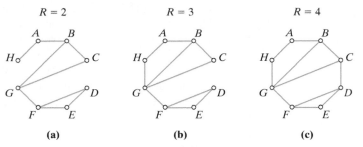

FIGURE 7-10   For larger values of R, we have a network with lots of circuits.

Our preceding discussion of trees and networks can be rephrased and summarized in the following two key observations (and respective conclusions):

- A tree is a *minimally connected* network. This means that every edge of the tree is needed to keep it connected—in a tree every edge is a bridge, and there are no redundant edges (zero redundancy). This also means that the number of edges is always one less than the number of vertices ($R = 0$ implies $M = N - 1$). *Conclusion 1: If you want to minimize the number of edges in a network, build a tree.*

- A network that is not a tree must have some redundant edges (positive redundancy). The redundant edges form circuits, and the higher the redundancy the more circuits in the network. Each circuit creates additional paths for connecting vertices in the circuit, so the more circuits the more ways there are to get around in the network. *Conclusion 2: If you want to have lots of alternative routes to get around in a network, increase its redundancy.*

7.2 Spanning Trees, MSTs, and MaxSTs

Spanning Trees

A **spanning tree** in a network is a *subtree* of the network that *spans* all the vertices. The easiest way to explain the meaning of this definition is with a few examples.

EXAMPLE 7.6 SUBTREES AND SPANNING TREES

Figure 7-11(a) shows a small network with 8 vertices and 9 edges. Figure 7-11(b) shows (in red) a *subtree* of the network. The name *subtree* comes from the fact that the red tree has its vertices and edges inside the network. The subtree in Fig. 7-11(b) does not include all the vertices, but the one in Fig. 7-11(c) does. We say that the subtree in Fig. 7-11(c) *spans* the network, and we call such subtrees *spanning trees* of the network. The spanning tree in Fig. 7-11(c) has 7 edges, and any other spanning tree of this network will have 7 edges as well.

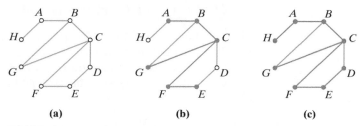

FIGURE 7-11   (a) The original network. (b) A subtree (in red). Vertices *H* and *D* are not in the subtree. (c) A spanning subtree.

EXAMPLE 7.7 COUNTING SPANNING TREES

The network in Fig. 7-12(a) has $N = 8$ vertices and $M = 8$ edges. The redundancy of the network is $R = 1$. To find a spanning tree we will have to "discard" one edge. Five of these edges are bridges of the network, and they *will have to be part of any spanning tree*. The other three edges (*BC*, *CG*, and *GB*) form a circuit of length 3, and if we exclude any one of the three edges, then we will have a spanning tree. Thus, the network has three different spanning trees [Figs. 7-12(b), (c), and (d)].

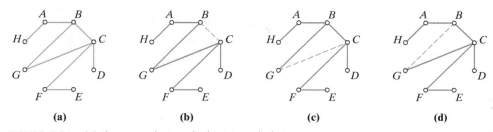

FIGURE 7-12   (a) The original network. (b), (c), and (d) Spanning trees.

The network in Fig. 7-13(a) is the same network as the one in Fig. 7-11(a). The redundancy of the network is $R = 2$, so to find a spanning tree we will have to "discard" two edges. Edges *AB* and *AH* are bridges of the network, so they will have to be part of any spanning tree. The other seven edges are split into two separate circuits (*B, C, G, B* of length 3 and *C, D, E, F, C* of length 4). A spanning tree can be found by "busting" each of the two circuits. This means excluding any one of the three edges of circuit *B, C, G, B* and any one of the four edges of circuit

C, D, E, F, C. For example, if we exclude BC and CD, we get the spanning tree shown in Fig. 7-13(b). We could also exclude BC and DE and get the spanning tree shown in Fig. 7-13(c), and so on. Given that there are $3 \times 4 = 12$ different ways to choose an edge from the circuit of length 3 and an edge from the circuit of length 4, we will not show all 12 spanning trees. [Figs. 7-13(b) through (e) show some of them.]

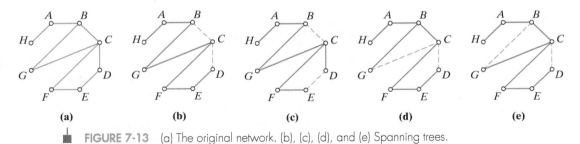

FIGURE 7-13   (a) The original network. (b), (c), (d), and (e) Spanning trees.

EXAMPLE 7.8   MORE COUNTING OF SPANNING TREES

The network in Fig. 7-14(a) is another network with 8 vertices and redundancy $R = 2$. The difference between this network and the one in Fig. 7-13(a) is that here the circuits B, C, G, B and C, D, E, G, C share a common edge CG. Determining which pairs of edges can be excluded in this case is a bit more complicated.

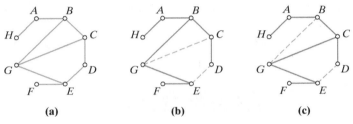

FIGURE 7-14   (a) The original network. (b) and (c) Spanning trees.

If one of the excluded edges is the common edge CG, then the other excluded edge can be any other edge in a circuit. There are five choices (BC, CD, DE, EG, and GB), and each choice will result in a different spanning tree [one of these is shown in Fig. 7-14(b)]. The alternative scenario is to exclude two edges neither of which is the common edge CG. In this case one excluded edge has to be either BC or BG (to "bust" circuit B, C, G, B), and the other excluded edge has to be either CD, DE, or EG (to "bust" circuit C, D, E, G, C). There are $2 \times 3 = 6$ possible spanning trees that can be formed this way [one of these is shown in Fig. 7-14(c)]. Combining the two scenarios gives a total of 11 possible spanning trees for the network in Fig. 7-14(a).

As the redundancy of a network grows, the number of spanning trees gets very large. In our next couple of examples we consider spanning trees in weighted networks of high redundancy.

EXAMPLE 7.9   THE AMAZONIAN CABLE NETWORK

The Amazonia Telephone Company is contracted to provide telephone, cable, and Internet service to the seven small mining towns shown in Fig. 7-15(a). These towns are located deep in the heart of the Amazon jungle, which makes the project particularly difficult and expensive. In this environment the most practical and environmentally friendly option is to create a network of underground fiber-optic cable lines connecting the towns. In addition, it makes sense to bury the underground cable lines along the already existing roads connecting the towns. The existing network of roads is shown in Fig. 7-15(a). Figure 7-15(b) is a network model of all the possible connections between the towns. The vertices of the network represent the towns, the edges represent the existing roads, and the weight of each edge represents the cost (in millions of dollars) of creating a fiber-optic cable connection along that particular edge.

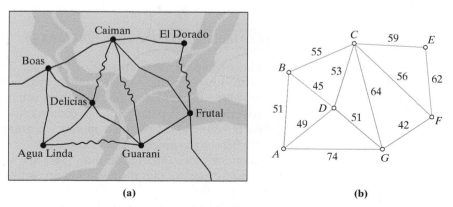

FIGURE 7-15 (a) Network of roads connecting seven towns. (b) Network model showing the cost (in millions) of each connection.

The problem facing the engineers and planners of the Amazonia Telephone Company is how to design a cable network that connects all the towns using the existing network of roads and that costs as little as possible to build—in other words, a *minimum cost* network. The first thing we can say about a minimum cost network is that it must be a *spanning tree* of the original network of roads shown in Fig. 7-15(a). (To connect all the towns means that the cable network must *span* all the vertices; to eliminate redundant connections means that it will have redundancy $R = 0$, and that means a *tree*.) But in this example there are costs involved, and not all spanning trees will have the same cost, so rather than finding any old spanning tree, we need to find the spanning tree with least total weight. We call such a spanning tree a *minimum spanning tree*.

One way to find a minimum spanning tree is to list all possible spanning trees, find the total cost of each, and pick the one with least cost. (This is the same approach we described in Chapter 6 as the *brute-force algorithm*.) The problem is that the network in Fig. 7-15(b) has high redundancy ($R = 6$) and hundreds of possible spanning trees. Sifting through all of them to find the one with least cost is not a good plan. In Section 7.3 we will discuss a better way of finding a minimum spanning tree in the Amazon jungle.

Example 7.9 was our introduction to the concept of a *minimum spanning tree*. We now give it a formal definition:

■ **Minimum Spanning Tree.** In a weighted network, a **minimum spanning tree (MST)** is *a* spanning tree with least total weight.

Sometimes there is only one MST and we can refer to it as *the* MST, but we can't assume this to be true in general. (For example, if all the weights in the network are the same, then every spanning tree is an MST.)

In most applications, the weights of the network represent *costs*—money, time, or distance. In these cases the goal is to *minimize*. There are some applications, however, where the weights represent *profits*. Profits (or other types of *gains* such as *higher bandwidth* on Internet connections or *increased flows* in pipelines) are things we want more of, rather than less, so instead of minimizing we should be maximizing. This leads to our next definition.

- ■ Maximum Spanning Tree. In a weighted network, a **maximum spanning tree (MaxST)** is *a* spanning tree with highest total weight.

Our next example illustrates a MaxST application.

| **EXAMPLE 7.10** | THE AMAZON MAX PROFIT NETWORK |

This example is the flip side of Example 7.9. The problem is still to connect the seven towns in the Amazon jungle with a cable network, but the circumstances are quite different. Imagine that there are two parties involved: one party—say the government—is paying for the construction costs of the cable network; the other party—say the telephone company—is going to operate and run the network.

The government insists on building a network with zero redundancy (i.e., a spanning tree). Other than that, there are no restrictions on the choice of spanning tree (we assume that the cost of construction is the same no matter which spanning tree gets built, so to the paying party any spanning tree will do). On the other hand, to the telephone company the choice of spanning tree is very important—as is the case with any company, it wants to maximize profit, so building the most profitable spanning tree is the name of the game.

Let's assume that the weight of each edge of the network in Fig. 7-16 represents the expected annual *profits* (in millions) to the phone company for operating that segment of the network. (You may have noticed that we are using exactly the same weighted network as that in Example 7.9. As you will see in the next section, this is not a coincidence.) To the phone company, the problem now becomes finding the MaxST of the original network. We will learn how to do this in the next section.

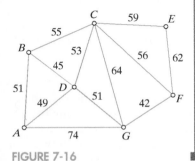

FIGURE 7-16

7.3 Kruskal's Algorithm

Unlike the situation with TSPs (see Chapter 6) there are several *efficient* and *optimal* algorithms for finding minimum spanning trees. Moreover, any algorithm that finds minimum spanning trees can be tweaked to find maximum spanning trees as well. In this section we will introduce one such algorithm—a simple algorithm called *Kruskal's algorithm* after American mathematician Joseph Kruskal.

Kruskal's algorithm is very similar to the *cheapest-link algorithm* used for solving TSPs in Chapter 6. The minimum spanning tree gets built one edge at a time by choosing at each step the cheapest available edge. The only restriction in choosing the edges is that one should never choose an edge that creates a circuit. Having three or more edges coming out of a vertex, however, is now OK. Continue choosing edges this way until $N - 1$ edges are chosen. At that point one has an MST.

The following is a formal description of Kruskal's algorithm. (For simplicity, we use "cheapest" to denote "of least weight.")

┌─■ **KRUSKAL'S ALGORITHM** ─────────────────────

- ■ **Step 1.** Pick the *cheapest edge* available. (In case of a tie, pick one at random.) Mark it (say in red).
- ■ **Step 2.** Pick the next cheapest edge available and mark it.
- ■ **Steps 3, 4, . . . , N − 1.** Continue picking and marking the cheapest unmarked edge available that does not create a circuit. After step $N - 1$ you are done.

EXAMPLE 7.11 THE AMAZONIAN CABLE NETWORK AND KRUSKAL'S ALGORITHM

In Example 7.9 we raised the following question: What is the optimal fiber-optic cable network connecting the seven towns shown in Fig. 7-17(a)? The weight of each edge is the cost (in millions of dollars) of laying the cable along that segment of the network.

The answer, as we now know, is to find the minimum spanning tree of the network in Fig. 7.17(a). We will use Kruskal's algorithm to do it. Here are the details:

- **Step 1.** We start by choosing the cheapest edge of the network. In this case we choose *GF*, and mark it in red (or any other color) as shown in Fig. 7-17(b). (Note that this does not have to be the first link actually built—we are putting the network together on paper only. On the ground, the schedule of construction is a different story, and there are many other factors that need to be considered.)

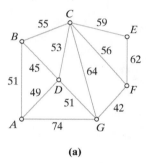 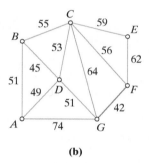 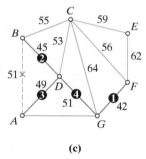 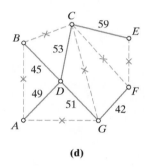

    (a)   (b)   (c)   (d)

FIGURE 7-17 (a) The original network. (b) Start. (c) First four steps. (d) The MST.

- **Step 2.** The next cheapest edge available is *BD* at $45 million. We choose it for the MST and mark it in red.

- **Step 3.** The next cheapest edge available is *AD* at $49 million. Again, we choose it for the MST and mark it in red.

- **Step 4.** For the next cheapest edge there is a tie between *AB* and *DG*, both at $51 million. But we can rule out *AB*—it would create a circuit in the MST, and we can't have that! (For bookkeeping purposes it is a good idea to erase or cross out the edge.) The edge *DG*, on the other hand, is just fine, so we mark it in red and make it part of the MST.

  Figure 7-17(c) shows how things look at this point.

- **Step 5.** The next cheapest edge available is *CD* at $53 million. No problems here, so again, we mark it in red and make it part of the MST.

- **Step 6.** The next cheapest edge available is *BC* at $55 million, but this edge would create a circuit, so we cross it out. The next possible choice is *CF* at $56 million, but once again, this choice creates a circuit so we must cross it out. The next possible choice is *CE* at $59 million, and this is one we do choose. We mark it in red and make it part of the MST.

- **Step. . . .** Wait a second—we are finished! Even without looking at a picture, we can tell we are done—six links is exactly what is needed for an MST on seven vertices.

  Figure 7-17(d) shows the MST in red. The total cost of the network is $299 million.

Any algorithm that can find an MST can also be used to find a MaxST by means of a simple modification: *Change the signs of the weights* in the network. We call the network that we get when we change the signs of all the weights the **negative** of the original network. Switching the signs of the weights switches MaxSTs into MSTs and vice versa. *A MaxST of a network is an MST of the negative network.* This follows from the simple fact that changing the signs of numbers reverses their inequality relationships ($74 > 45$ implies that $-74 < -45$). We will illustrate this idea by returning to the MaxST problem introduced in Example 7.10.

EXAMPLE 7.12   THE AMAZON MAX PROFIT AND KRUSKAL'S ALGORITHM

Figure 7-18(a) shows the *negative* network for the original network in Example 7.10 (Fig. 7-16). We'll use Kruskal's algorithm to find the MST of this negative network. This will be the MaxST that we are looking for.

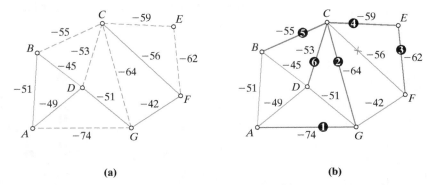

FIGURE 7-18   (a) The *negative* network. (b) The MST of the negative network.

- Step 1. The cheapest edge in the negative network is AG, with a weight of -74. We choose it and mark it in red.
- Step 2. The next cheapest edge is CG, with a weight of -64. We choose it and mark it in red.
- Step 3. The next cheapest edge is EF, with a weight of -62. We choose it and mark it in red.
- Step 4. The next cheapest edge is CE, with a weight of -59. We choose it and mark it in red.
- Step 5. The next cheapest edge is CF, with a weight of -56. We choose it and . . . oops! Can't do that. Choosing CF would create a red circuit. Spanning trees don't have circuits. We rule out CF, and move on to the next cheapest edge, CB, with a weight of -55. No circuits with this one, so we choose it for the MST.
- Step 6. The next cheapest edge is CD, with a weight of -53. No problems here, so we choose it and mark it in red.

At Step 6 we are done! We have our MST for the negative network, shown in Fig. 7-18(b). This network is the MaxST we were looking for in the original network. The total profits that can be expected from this MaxST are given by the sum of the original weights: $74 + 64 + 62 + 59 + 55 + 53 = 367$ million.

EXAMPLE 7.13   FINDING MSTs IN POWER GRIDS USING KRUSKAL'S ALGORITHM

In many rural areas electricity transmission lines are old. Old transmission lines carry lower voltages, leak more power, and are more sensitive to bad weather than modern transmission lines, so a common infrastructure project is to update the older parts of the grid with new transmission lines. The problem is how to choose the newer transmission lines so that they carry power to as many customers as possible while at the same time keeping the cost of the project down. The least costly solution often involves finding an MST.

Figure 7-19(a) shows a section of the electrical power grid connecting 14 rural towns in central Texas. This is the network introduced in Example 7.3. The weight of each edge represents the length (in miles) of that particular segment of the grid. When the terrain is flat—as is in central Texas—the cost of replacing a transmission line is proportional to the length of the line (for high-voltage, modern transmission lines it is about $500,000 per mile), so when we minimize length we are also minimizing cost. It follows that the MST of the grid in Fig. 7-19(a) is going to give the cheapest spanning tree of updated power lines for the grid.

We'll find the MST using Kruskal's algorithm. [As a heads-up, we know ahead of time that in this network Kruskal's algorithm will require 13 steps (the network has 14 vertices), so we'll be brief and to the point.]

- **Step 1.** Choose *LM* (5) and mark it in red.
- **Step 2.** Choose *AJ* (11) and mark it in red.
- **Step 3.** Choose *EF* (11) and mark it in red.
- **Step 4.** Choose *FG* (12) and mark it in red.
- **Step 5.** Choose *HM* (13) and mark it in red.
- **Step 6.** Choose *NK* (14) and mark it in red.
- **Step 7.** Choose *BK* (16) and mark it in red.
- **Step 8.** Choose *HN* (18) and mark it in red.
- **Step 9.** Skip *NL* (21) because it closes a circuit. Choose *AB* (23) and mark it in red.
- **Step 10.** Choose *DE* (23) and mark it in red.
- **Step 11.** Choose *CD* (26) and mark it in red.
- **Step 12.** Choose *FM* (30) and mark it in red.
- **Step 13.** Skip *CE* (31), *BC* (31), and *JK* (32) because they all close circuits. Choose *IN* (32) and mark it in red. That's it—we are done.

Figure 7-19(b) shows the MST. The total length of the MST is 232 miles. At an average cost of $500,000 per mile, the total cost of the infrastructure update is $117 million.

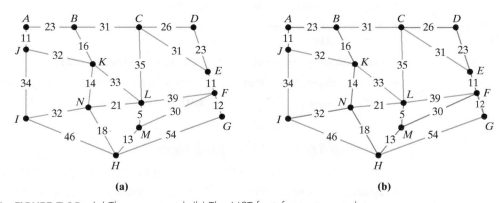

(a)   **(b)**

FIGURE 7-19   (a) The power grid. (b) The MST for infrastructure update.

Conclusion

A typical real-world network connects *things* (people, computers, cities, etc.) to each other, making possible the free flow of some *commodity* (communication, information, electricity, etc.) between the different nodes of the network. From the perspective of the people being served by the network, the *more* connected the network is, the better—connections increase the ways the commodity can flow among the nodes, thus improving convenience, reliability, and performance. On the other hand, from the perspective of those planning or servicing the network, the *less* connected the network is, the better—connections can be expensive to build and maintain. As is usually the case, there are tradeoffs that must be made between convenience and cost. When convenience is important, or when costs are low, networks tend to be highly connected and have a lot of redundancy. When costs are high, convenience becomes less of a consideration and networks tend to have little or no redundancy.

In this chapter we discussed networks in general and some of the mathematical concepts associated with building good networks—redundancy, trees, spanning trees, weighted networks, MSTs, and MaxSTs. This was just a small peek into the mathematics of networks, a deep and important topic with obvious applications to our ever more connected lives. If you don't believe that, think about going without electricity or Internet access for a few days or even worse, imagine Facebook or Twitter being down—for just a day.

KEY CONCEPTS

7.1 Networks and Trees

- **network:** a connected graph, **208**
- **degree of separation:** the length of the shortest path connecting two vertices of a network, **208**
- **weighted network:** a network with weights associated with the edges, **209**
- **tree:** a network with no circuits, **210**
- **single-path property:** in a tree there is one and only one path connecting any two vertices, **210**
- **all-bridges property:** in a tree all edges are bridges, **211**
- **$N - 1$ edges property:** a tree with N vertices has $N - 1$ edges, **211**
- **redundancy (R):** in a network with N vertices and M edges $R = M - (N - 1)$, **211**

7.2 Spanning Trees, MSTs, and MaxSTs

- **subtree:** a set of vertices and edges in a network that form a tree, **213**
- **spanning tree:** a subtree whose vertices are *all* the vertices of the network, **213**
- **minimum spanning tree (MST):** in a weighted network, a spanning tree with smallest total weight, **215**
- **maximum spanning tree (MaxST):** in a weighted network, a spanning tree with largest total weight, **216**

7.3 Kruskal's Algorithm

- **Kruskal's algorithm:** finds an MST of a weighted network; at each step, it chooses the cheapest available edge that does not form a circuit, **216**

- **negative network:** the network obtained by changing the signs of the weights in the original network, **217**

- **Kruskal's algorithm for MaxSTs:** applies Kruskal's algorithm for MSTs to the negative network, **218**

 # EXERCISES

WALKING

7.1 Networks and Trees

1. A computer lab has seven computers labeled A through G. The connections between computers are as follows:

   - A is connected to D and G
   - B is connected to C, E, and F
   - C is connected to B, E, and F
   - D is connected to A and G
   - E is connected to B and C
   - F is connected to B and C
   - G is connected to A and D

   Is the lab set-up a computer network? Explain why or why not.

2. The following is a list of the electrical power lines connecting eight small towns labeled A through H.

   - A power line connecting A and D
   - A power line connecting B and C
   - A power line connecting B and E
   - A power line connecting B and G
   - A power line connecting C and G
   - A power line connecting D and F
   - A power line connecting D and H
   - A power line connecting E and G

   Do the power lines form a network? Explain why or why not.

3. Consider the network shown in Fig. 7-20.

   (a) How many degrees of separation are there between C and E?

   (b) How many degrees of separation are there between A and E?

   (c) How many degrees of separation are there between A and H?

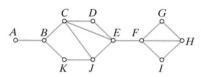

FIGURE 7-20

4. Consider the network shown in Fig. 7-21.

   (a) How many degrees of separation are there between D and J?

   (b) How many degrees of separation are there between A and L?

   (c) How many degrees of separation are there between A and K?

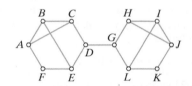

FIGURE 7-21

5. Consider the tree shown in Fig. 7-22 on the next page.

   (a) How many degrees of separation are there between A and J?

   (b) How many degrees of separation are there between E and L?

   (c) How many degrees of separation are there between M and P?

   (d) What is the largest degree of separation between a pair of vertices?

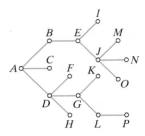

FIGURE 7-22

6. Consider the tree shown in Fig. 7-23.

(a) How many degrees of separation are there between A and P?

(b) How many degrees of separation are there between E and P?

(c) How many degrees of separation are there between L and P?

(d) What is the largest degree of separation between a pair of vertices?

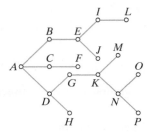

FIGURE 7-23

In Exercises 7 through 20 you are given information about a network. Choose one of the following three options: (A) the network is definitely a tree; (B) the network is definitely not a tree; (C) the network may or may not be a tree (more information is needed). Accompany your answer with a brief explanation for your choice.

7. The network has 15 vertices and 16 edges.

8. The network has 23 vertices and no bridges.

9. The network has 16 vertices and 15 edges.

10. The network has 23 vertices and 22 bridges.

11. The network has redundancy $R = 1$.

12. The network has redundancy $R = 0$.

13. The network has 10 vertices (A through J), and there is only one path connecting A and J.

14. The network has 10 vertices (A through J) and there are two paths connecting C and D.

15. The network has five vertices, no loops, and no multiple edges, and every vertex has degree 4.

16. The network has five vertices, no loops, and no multiple edges, and every vertex has degree 2.

17. The network has five vertices, no loops, and no multiple edges, and has one vertex of degree 4 and four vertices of degree 1.

18. The network has five vertices, no loops, and no multiple edges, and has two vertices of degree 1 and three vertices of degree 2.

19. The network has all vertices of even degree. (*Hint*: You will need to use some concepts from Chapter 5 to answer this question.)

20. The network has two vertices of odd degree and all the other vertices of even degree. (*Hint*: You will need to use some concepts from Chapter 5 to answer this question.)

7.2　Spanning Trees, MSTs, and MaxSTs

21. Consider the network shown in Fig. 7-24.

(a) Find a spanning tree of the network.

(b) Calculate the redundancy of the network.

(c) What is the largest degree of separation between a pair of vertices in the network?

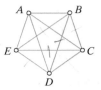

FIGURE 7-24

22. Consider the network shown in Fig. 7-25.

(a) Find a spanning tree of the network.

(b) Calculate the redundancy of the network.

(c) What is the largest degree of separation between a pair of vertices in the network?

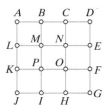

FIGURE 7-25

23. Consider the network shown in Fig. 7-26.

(a) Find a spanning tree of the network.

(b) Calculate the redundancy of the network.

(c) What is the largest degree of separation between a pair of vertices in the network?

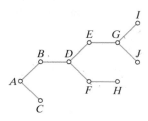

FIGURE 7-26

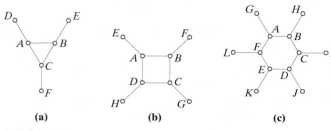

(a)   (b)   (c)

FIGURE 7-29

24. Consider the network shown in Fig. 7-27.

(a) Find a spanning tree of the network.

(b) Calculate the redundancy of the network.

(c) What is the largest degree of separation between a pair of vertices in the network?

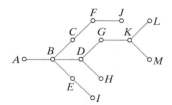

FIGURE 7-27

25. (a) Find all the spanning trees of the network shown in Fig. 7-28(a).

(b) Find all the spanning trees of the network shown in Fig. 7-28(b).

(c) How many different spanning trees does the network shown in Fig. 7-28(c) have?

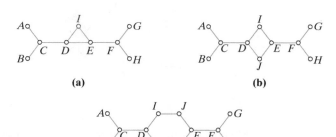

(a)   (b)

(c)

FIGURE 7-28

26. (a) Find all the spanning trees of the network shown in Fig. 7-29(a).

(b) Find all the spanning trees of the network shown in Fig. 7-29(b).

(c) How many different spanning trees does the network shown in Fig. 7-29(c) have?

27. (a) How many different spanning trees does the network shown in Fig. 7-30(a) have?

(b) How many different spanning trees does the network shown in Fig. 7-30(b) have?

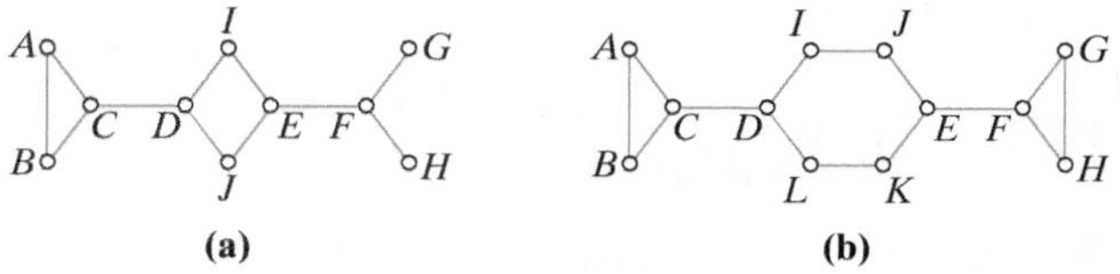

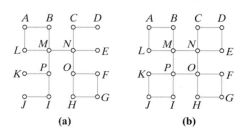

(a)   (b)

FIGURE 7-30

28. (a) How many different spanning trees does the network shown in Fig. 7-31(a) have?

(b) How many different spanning trees does the network shown in Fig. 7-31(b) have?

A   B   C   D   A   B   C   D

L   M   N   E   L   M   N   E

K   P   O   F   K   P   O   F

J   I   H   G   J   I   H   G

(a)   (b)

FIGURE 7-31

29. Consider the network shown in Fig. 7-32.

(a) How many different spanning trees does this network have?

(b) Find the spanning tree that has the largest degree of separation between H and G.

(c) Find a spanning tree that has the smallest degree of separation between H and G.

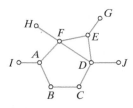

FIGURE 7-32

30. Consider the network shown in Fig. 7-33.

   (a) How many different spanning trees does this network have?

   (b) Find a spanning tree that has the largest degree of separation between H and J.

   (c) Find a spanning tree that has the smallest degree of separation between K and G.

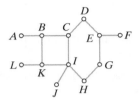

FIGURE 7-33

7.3 Kruskal's Algorithm

31. The 3 by 4 grid shown in Fig. 7-34 represents a network of streets (3 blocks by 4 blocks) in a small subdivision. For landscaping purposes, it is necessary to get water to each of the corners by laying down a system of pipes along the streets. The cost of laying down the pipes is $40,000 per mile, and each block of the grid is exactly half a mile long. Find the cost of the cheapest network of pipes connecting all the corners of the subdivision. Explain your answer. (*Hint*: First determine the number of blocks in the MST.)

FIGURE 7-34

32. The 4 by 5 grid shown in Fig. 7-35 represents a network of streets (4 blocks by 5 blocks) in a small subdivision. For landscaping purposes, it is necessary to get water to each of the corners by laying down a system of pipes along the streets. The cost of laying down the pipes is $40,000 per mile, and each block of the grid is exactly half a mile long. Find the cost of the cheapest network of pipes connecting all the corners of the subdivision. Explain your answer. (*Hint*: First determine the number of blocks in the MST.)

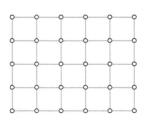

FIGURE 7-35

33. Find the MST of the network shown in Fig. 7-36 using Kruskal's algorithm, and give its weight.

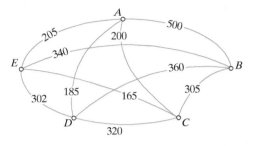

FIGURE 7-36

34. Find the MST of the network shown in Fig. 7-37 using Kruskal's algorithm, and give its weight.

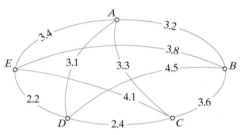

FIGURE 7-37

35. Find the MST of the network shown in Fig. 7-38 using Kruskal's algorithm, and give its weight.

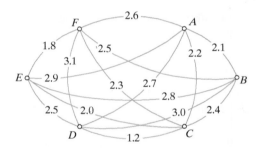

FIGURE 7-38

36. Find the MST of the network shown in Fig. 7-39 using Kruskal's algorithm, and give its weight.

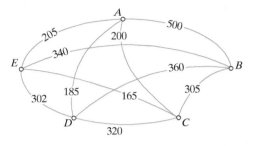

FIGURE 7-39

37. Find the MaxST of the network shown in Fig. 7-36 using Kruskal's algorithm and give its weight.

38. Find the MaxST of the network shown in Fig. 7-37 using Kruskal's algorithm and give its weight.

39. Find the MaxST of the network shown in Fig. 7-38 using Kruskal's algorithm and give its weight.

40. Find the MaxST of the network shown in Fig. 7-39 using Kruskal's algorithm and give its weight.

JOGGING

41. The mileage chart in Fig. 7-40 shows the distances between Atlanta, Columbus, Kansas City, Minneapolis, Pierre, and Tulsa. Working directly from the mileage chart use Kruskal's algorithm to find the MST connecting the six cities. (*Hint*: See Example 6.15 for the use of an auxiliary graph.)

Mileage Chart

	Atlanta	Columbus	Kansas City	Minneapolis	Pierre	Tulsa
Atlanta	*	533	798	1068	1361	772
Columbus	533	*	656	713	1071	802
Kansas City	798	656	*	447	592	248
Minneapolis	1068	713	447	*	394	695
Pierre	1361	1071	592	394	*	760
Tulsa	772	802	248	695	760	*

FIGURE 7-40

42. The mileage chart in Fig. 7-41 shows the distances between Boston, Dallas, Houston, Louisville, Nashville, Pittsburgh, and St. Louis. Working directly from the mileage chart use Kruskal's algorithm to find the MST connecting the seven cities. (*Hint*: See Example 6.15 for the use of an auxiliary graph.)

Mileage Chart

	Boston	Dallas	Houston	Louisville	Nashville	Pittsburgh	St. Louis
Boston	*	1748	1804	941	1088	561	1141
Dallas	1748	*	243	819	660	1204	630
Houston	1804	243	*	928	769	1313	779
Louisville	941	819	928	*	168	388	263
Nashville	1088	660	769	168	*	553	299
Pittsburgh	561	1204	1313	388	553	*	588
St. Louis	1141	630	779	263	299	588	*

FIGURE 7-41

43. Figure 7-42(a) shows a network of roads connecting cities *A* through *G*. The weights of the edges represent the cost (in millions of dollars) of putting underground fiber-optic lines along the roads, and the MST of the network is shown in red. Figure 7-42(b) shows the same network except that one additional road (connecting *E* and *G*) has been added. Let *x* be the cost (in millions) of putting fiber-optic lines along this new road.

(a) Describe the MST of the network in Fig. 7-42(b) in the case $x > 59$. Explain your answer.

(b) Describe the MST of the network in Fig. 7-42(b) in the case $x < 59$. Explain your answer.

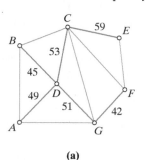 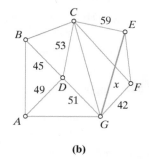

(a)   (b)

FIGURE 7-42

44. Consider a network with *M* edges. Let *k* denote the number of bridges in the network.

(a) If $M = 5$, list all the possible values of *k*.

(b) If $M = 123$, describe the set of all possible values of *k*.

45. **(a)** Let *G* be a tree with *N* vertices. Find the sum of the degrees of all the vertices in *G*.

(b) Explain why a tree must have at least two vertices of degree 1. (A vertex of degree 1 in a tree is called a *leaf*.)

(c) Explain why in a tree with three or more vertices the degrees of the vertices cannot all be the same.

46. Explain why in a network with no loops or multiple edges, the maximum redundancy is given by $R = \frac{(N^2 - 3N + 2)}{2}$. (*Hint*: The maximum redundancy occurs when the network is K_N.)

47. This exercise refers to weighted networks where all the weights in the network are different. Explain why these networks have only one MST and one MaxST. (*Hint*: Think of Kruskal's algorithm.)

48. This exercise refers to weighted networks where the weights in the network are *not* all different (i.e., there are at least two edges with the same weight).

(a) Give an example of a network of this type that has only one MST.

(b) Give an example of a network of this type that has more than one MST.

49. Suppose that in a weighted network there is just one edge (call it *XY*) with the *smallest* weight. Explain why the edge *XY* must be in every MST of the network.

50. Suppose that in a weighted network there is just one edge (call it *XY*) with the *largest* weight.

    (a) Give an example of a network with more than one MST and such that *XY* must be in every MST.

    (b) Give an example of a network with more than one MST and such that *XY* is in none of the MSTs.

51. Suppose *G* is a disconnected graph with *N* vertices, *M* edges, and no circuits.

    (a) How many components does the graph have when $N = 9$ and $M = 6$?

    (b) How many components does the graph have when $N = 240$ and $M = 236$? Explain your answer.

52. Suppose *G* is a disconnected graph with no circuits. Let *N* denote the number of vertices, *M* the number of edges, and *K* the number of components. Explain why $M = N - K$. (*Hint*: Try Exercise 51 first.)

53. Cayley's theorem. Cayley's theorem says that the number of spanning trees in a complete graph with *N* vertices is given by N^{N-2}.

    (a) List the $4^2 = 16$ spanning trees of K_4.

    (b) Which is larger, the number of Hamilton circuits or the number of spanning trees in a complete graph with *N* vertices? Explain.

RUNNING

54. Show that if a tree has a vertex of degree *K*, then there are at least *K* vertices in the tree of degree 1.

55. A *bipartite graph* is a graph with the property that the vertices of the graph can be divided into two sets *A* and *B* so that every edge of the graph joins a vertex from *A* to a vertex from *B* (Fig. 7-43). Explain why trees are always bipartite graphs.

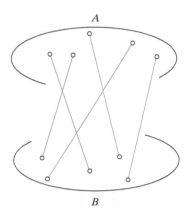

FIGURE 7-43

56. Suppose that there is an edge in a network that must be included in any spanning tree. Give an algorithm for finding the minimum spanning tree that includes a given edge. (*Hint*: Modify Kruskal's algorithm.)

 PROJECTS AND PAPERS

1 Other Algorithms for MSTs and MaxSTs

Kruskal's algorithm is not the only good algorithm for finding MSTs and MaxSTs in a weighted network—two other well-known algorithms that are used to solve the same problem are *Prim's algorithm* and *Boruvka's algorithm*. Prepare a presentation on Prim's and Boruvka's algorithms. Describe both algorithms, and demonstrate how they work using one of the examples from the chapter. Compare Prim's and Boruvka's algorithms to Kruskal's algorithm, and discuss their similarities and differences.

2 Dijkstra's Shortest-Path Algorithm

In a network, there is at least one, but often many, paths connecting two vertices *X* and *Y*. When the network is an ordinary network, the "shortest path" between *X* and *Y* is defined as the path with the fewest number of edges (and the number of edges in a shortest path is called the *degree of separation* between *X* and *Y*). On the other hand, when the network is a *weighted* network the "shortest path" between *X* and *Y* has a different defini-

tion: Among all paths connecting *X* and *Y*, it is the path of *least total weight*.

Finding the *shortest path* between pairs of vertices in a weighted network is a problem that has many similarities to the problem of finding a *minimum spanning tree* of the network, and there is a nice algorithm that solves the problem optimally and efficiently. The algorithm, known as *Dijkstra's algorithm*, is named after the Dutch computer scientist Edsger Dijkstra, who first proposed the algorithm in 1959. In this project you are asked to prepare a presentation on Dijkstra's algorithm. At the very least you should carefully describe the algorithm, discuss some of its applications to real-world problems, and illustrate the algorithm with a couple of examples. Dijkstra's algorithm is a well-known algorithm, and you will find plenty of resources for this project on the Web.

3 Social Networks and Privacy

There is an inverse relation between connectedness and privacy. In general, the more connected you are the less privacy you have. The problem gets worse when it comes to social networks, where losses of privacy are involuntary and invisible. When you sign up for Facebook, Twitter, Instagram, or other social media you are making a lot of your personal information available to others. How much privacy are you losing? How are you losing it? What steps can you take to minimize invasions of your privacy from the social networks you use? Write a paper discussing these issues. This is a much-discussed topic, and there are plenty of resources available on the Web. You may also want to take a look at the recent book by Lori Andrews that deals entirely with this subject (*I Know Who You Are and I Saw What You Did: Social Networks and the Death of Privacy*, Free Press, 2012).

8 The Mathematics of Scheduling

Chasing the Critical Path

Typically, it takes between four and nine months to build an average American home—rarely less than 120 days. But when a crowd of over 400 workers and volunteers got together the morning of October 1, 2005, in an empty lot in Tyler, Texas, they had a different idea in mind—the crazy thought that they would build a decent-sized, good quality house in less than *three* hours. Two hours and 52 minutes later—a world record—a 2249 square-foot, 3-bedroom, 2-bath house with a two-car garage was standing in the middle of the lot and ready for occupancy.

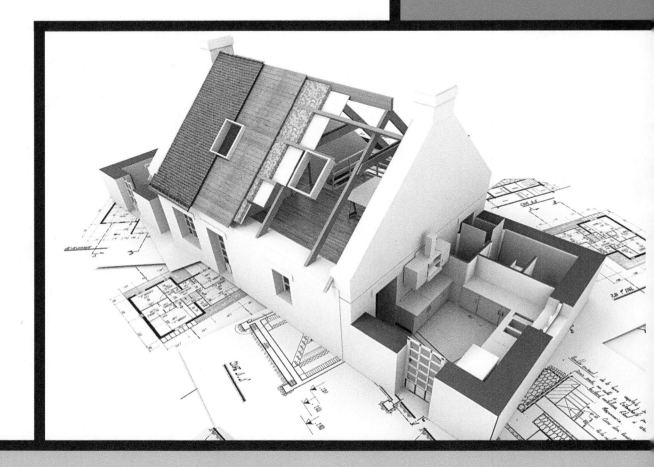

How was this tremendous feat of human ingenuity accomplished? Obviously, having hundreds of workers was essential to setting the record, but unleashing hordes of workers on a construction site is not enough—as a matter of fact, it is usually counterproductive. As is often said, *too many cooks can spoil the broth*. Most of the credit for the success of the project goes to what was accomplished before the physical work ever started: the creation of a seamless and critically coordinated system of assignments that told every worker what to do and when to do it, so that not a single second would be wasted. In other words, the creation of a master *schedule*.

Building a house in world record time using hundreds of workers is an extreme example of something that we do more often than we realize: When facing a complex project, we break up the project into small tasks, and then plan and execute those individual tasks in a *coordinated and organized* way. We do this when we have to throw a party, repair a car, cook a fancy dinner, or write a book.

This chapter is about the *coordination and organization* part of the story, or, to put it more formally, about *scheduling*. The chapter starts with an introduction to the key elements in any scheduling problem—*processors, tasks, processing times*, and *precedence relations* (Section 8.1). Scheduling problems are best modeled using a special type of graph called a *directed graph* (or digraph for short)—we discuss digraphs and some of their basic properties in Section 8.2. In Section 8.3 we will discuss the general rules for creating schedules—the key concept here is that of a *priority list*. The two most commonly used algorithms for "solving" a scheduling problem are the *decreasing-time* and the *critical-path algorithms*—we discuss these in Sections 8.4 and 8.5.

8.1 An Introduction to Scheduling

We will now introduce the principal characters in any scheduling story.

- **The processors.** Every job requires workers. We will use the term **processors** to describe the "workers" who carry out the work. While the word *processor* may sound cold and impersonal, it does underscore an important point: processors need not be human beings. In scheduling, a processor could just as well be a robot, a computer, an automated teller machine, and so on. We will use N to represent the number of processors and P_1, P_2, $P_3, \ldots, P_N$ to denote the processors. We will assume throughout the chapter that $N \geq 2$ (scheduling a job with just one processor is trivial and not very interesting).

- **The tasks.** In every complex project there are individual pieces of work, often called "jobs" or "tasks." We will need to be a little more precise than that, however. We will define a **task** as an indivisible unit of work that (either by nature or by choice) cannot be broken up into smaller units. Thus, by definition a task cannot be shared—it is always *carried out by a single processor*. In general, we will use capital letters $A, B, C, \ldots$, to represent the tasks, although in specific situations it is convenient to use abbreviations (such as *WE* for "wiring the electrical system" or *PL* for "plumbing").

At a particular moment in time a task can be in one of four possible states: (1) *ineligible* (the task cannot be started because some of the prerequisites for the task have not yet been completed), (2) *ready* (the task has not been started but could be started at this time), (3) *in execution* (the task is being carried out by one of the processors), or (4) *completed*.

- **The processing times.** The **processing time** of a task is the amount of time, without interruption, required by *one processor* to execute that task. When dealing with human processors, there are many variables (ability, attitude, work ethic, etc.) that can affect the processing time of a task, and this adds another layer of complexity to an already complex situation. On the other hand, if we assume a "robotic" interpretation of the processors (either because they are indeed machines or because they are human beings trained to work in a very standardized and uniform way), then scheduling becomes somewhat more manageable.

To keep things simple we will work under the following three assumptions:

1. *Versatility:* Any processor can execute any task.

2. *Uniformity:* The processing time for a task is the same regardless of which processor is executing the task.

3. *Persistence:* Once a processor starts a task, it will complete it without interruption.

Under the preceding assumptions, the concept of *processing time* for a task (we will sometimes call it the *P*-time) makes good sense—and we can conveniently incorporate this information by including it inside parentheses next to the name of the task. Thus, the notation $X(5)$ tells us that the task called X has a processing time of 5 units (be it minutes, hours, days, or any other unit of time) *regardless of which processor is assigned to execute the task*.

- **The precedence relations.** Precedence relations are formal restrictions on the order in which the tasks can be executed, much like those course prerequisites in the school catalog that tell you that you can't take course Y until you have completed course X. In the case of tasks, these prerequisites are called **precedence relations**. A typical precedence relation is of the form *task X precedes task Y* (we also say X is *precedent* to Y), and it means that *task Y cannot be started until task X has been completed*. A precedence relation can be conveniently abbreviated by writing $X \rightarrow Y$, or described graphically as shown in Fig. 8-1(a). A single scheduling problem can have hundreds or even thousands of precedence relations, each adding another restriction on the scheduler's freedom.

At the same time, it also happens fairly often that there are no restrictions on the order of execution between two tasks in a project. When a pair of tasks X and Y have no precedence requirements between them (neither $X \rightarrow Y$ nor $Y \rightarrow X$), we say that the tasks are **independent**. When two tasks are independent, either one can be started before the other one, or they can both be started at the same time. Graphically, we can tell that two tasks are independent if there are no arrows connecting them [Fig. 8-1(b)].

Two final comments about precedence relations are in order. First, precedence relations are *transitive*: If $X \rightarrow Y$ and $Y \rightarrow Z$, then it must be true that $X \rightarrow Z$. In a sense, the last precedence relation is implied by the first two, and it is really unnecessary to mention it [Fig. 8-1(c)]. Thus, we will make a distinction between two types of precedence relations: *basic* and *implicit*. Basic precedence relations are the ones that come with the problem and that we must follow in the process of creating a schedule. If we do this, the implicit precedence relations will be taken care of automatically.

The second observation is that *precedence relations cannot form a cycle!* Imagine having to schedule the tasks shown in Fig. 8-1(d): X precedes Y, which precedes Z, which precedes W, which in turn precedes X. Clearly, this is logically impossible. From here on, we will always assume that there are no cycles of precedence relations among the tasks.

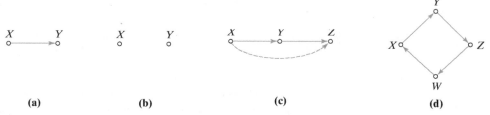

(a)	**(b)**	**(c)**	**(d)**

FIGURE 8-1 (a) X is precedent to Y. (b) X and Y are independent tasks. (c) When $X \rightarrow Y$ and $Y \rightarrow Z$ then $X \rightarrow Z$ is implied. (d) These tasks cannot be scheduled because of the cyclical nature of the precedence relations.

Processors, tasks, processing times, and *precedence relations* are the basic ingredients that make up a scheduling problem. They constitute, in a manner of speaking, the hand that is dealt to us. But how do we play such a hand? To get a small inkling of what's to come, let's look at the following simple example.

EXAMPLE 8.1   REPAIRING A WRECK

Imagine that you just wrecked your car, but thank heavens you are OK, and the insurance company will pick up the tab. You take the car to the best garage in town, operated by the Tappet brothers Click and Clack (we'll just call them P_1 and P_2). The repairs on the car can be broken into four different tasks: (A) exterior body work (4 hours), (B) engine repairs (5 hours), (C) painting and exterior finish work (7 hours), and (D)

transmission repair (3 hours). The only precedence relation for this set of tasks is that the painting and exterior finish work cannot be started until the exterior body work has been completed ($A \rightarrow C$). The two brothers always work together on a repair project, but each takes on a different task (so they won't argue with each other). Under these assumptions, how should the different tasks be scheduled? Who should do what and when?

Even in this simple situation, there are many different ways to schedule the repair. Figure 8-2 shows several possible schedules, each one illustrated by means of a timeline. Figure 8-2(a) shows a schedule that is very inefficient. All the short tasks are assigned to one processor (P_1) and all the long tasks to the other processor (P_2)—obviously not a very clever strategy. Under this schedule, the project **finishing time** (the duration of the project from the start of the first task to the completion of the last task) is 12 hours. (We will use *Fin* to denote the project finishing time, so for this project we can write *Fin* = 12 hours.)

Figure 8-2(b) shows what looks like a much better schedule, but it violates the precedence relation $A \rightarrow C$ (as much as we would love to, we cannot start task C until task A is completed). On the other hand, if we force P_2 to be idle for one hour, waiting for the green light to start task C, we get a perfectly good schedule, shown in Fig. 8-2(c). Under this schedule the finishing time of the project is *Fin* = 11 hours.

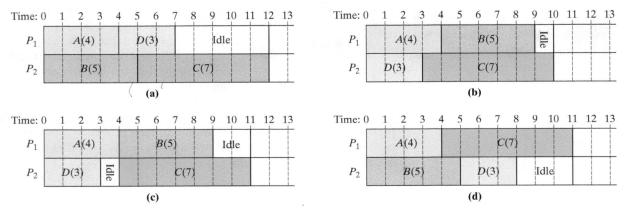

FIGURE 8-2 (a) A legal schedule with *Fin* = 12 hours. (b) An *illegal* schedule (the precedence relation $A \rightarrow C$ is violated). (c) An optimal schedule (*Opt* = 11 hours). (d) A different optimal schedule.

The schedule shown in Fig. 8-2(c) is an improvement over the first schedule. Can we do even better? No! No matter how clever we are and no matter how many processors we have at our disposal, the precedence relation $A(4) \rightarrow C(7)$ implies that 11 hours is a minimum barrier that we cannot break—it takes 4 hours to complete A, 7 hours to complete C, and *we cannot start C until A is completed!* Thus, the schedule shown in Fig. 8-2(c) is an **optimal schedule** and the finishing time of *Fin* = 11 hours is the **optimal finishing time**. (From now on we will use *Opt* instead of *Fin* when we are referring to the optimal finishing time.) Figure 8-2(d) shows a different optimal schedule with finishing time *Opt* = 11 hours.

As scheduling problems go, Example 8.1 was a fairly simple one. But even from this simple example, we can draw some useful lessons. First, notice that even though we had only four tasks and two processors, we were able to create several different schedules. The four we looked at were just a sampler—there are other possible schedules that we didn't bother to discuss. Imagine what would happen if we had hundreds of tasks and dozens of processors—the number of possible schedules to consider would be overwhelming. In looking for a good, or even an optimal, schedule, we are going to need a systematic way to sort through the many possibilities. In other words, we are going to need some good *scheduling algorithms*.

The second useful thing we learned in Example 8.1 is that when it comes to the finishing time of a project, there is an *absolute minimum* time that no schedule can break, no matter how good an algorithm we use or how many processors we put to work. In Example 8.1 this absolute minimum was 11 hours, and, as luck would have it, we easily found a schedule [actually two—Figs. 8-2(c) and (d)] with a finishing time to match it. Every project, no matter how simple or complicated, has such an absolute minimum (called the *critical time*) that depends on the processing times and precedence relations for the tasks and not on the number of processors used. We will return to the concept of critical time in Section 8.5.

To set the stage for a more formal discussion of scheduling algorithms, we will introduce the most important example of this chapter. While couched in what seems like science fiction terms, the situation it describes is not totally farfetched—in fact, this example is a simplified version of the types of scheduling problems faced by home builders in general.

EXAMPLE 8.2 BUILDING THAT DREAM HOME (IN MARS)

It is the year 2050, and several human colonies have already been established on Mars. Imagine that you accept a job offer to work in one of these colonies. What will you do about housing?

Like everyone else on Mars, you will be provided with a living pod called a Martian Habitat Unit (MHU). MHUs are shipped to Mars in the form of prefabricated kits that have to be assembled on the spot—an elaborate and unpleasant job if you are going to do it yourself. A better option is to use specialized "construction" robots that can do all the assembly tasks much more efficiently than human beings can. These construction robots can be rented by the hour at the local Rent-a-Robot outlet.

The assembly of an MHU consists of 15 separate tasks, and there are 17 different precedence relations among these tasks that must be followed. The tasks, their respective processing times, and their precedent tasks are all shown in Table 8-1.

Task	Label (*P*-time)	Precedent tasks
Assemble pad	*AP*(7)	
Assemble flooring	*AF*(5)	
Assemble wall units	*AW*(6)	
Assemble dome frame	*AD*(8)	
Install floors	*IF*(5)	*AP, AF*
Install interior walls	*IW*(7)	*IF, AW*
Install dome frame	*ID*(5)	*AD, IW*
Install plumbing	*PL*(4)	*IF*
Install atomic power plant	*IP*(4)	*IW*
Install pressurization unit	*PU*(3)	*IP, ID*
Install heating units	*HU*(4)	*IP*
Install commode	*IC*(1)	*PL, HU*
Complete interior finish work	*FW*(6)	*IC*
Pressurize dome	*PD*(3)	*HU*
Install entertainment unit	*EU*(2)	*PU, HU*

■ **TABLE 8-1** Tasks, *P*-times, and precedence relations for Example 8.2

Here are some of the questions we will address later in the chapter: How can you get your MHU built quickly? How many robots should you rent to do the job? How do you create a suitable work schedule that will get the job done? (A robot will do whatever it is told, but someone has to tell it what to do and when.)

8.2 Directed Graphs

A directed graph, or **digraph** for short, is a graph in which the edges have a direction associated with them, typically indicated by an arrowhead. Digraphs are particularly useful when we want to describe **asymmetric relationships** (X related to Y does not imply that Y must be related to X.

The classic example of an asymmetric relationship is romantic love: Just because X is in love with Y, there is no guarantee that Y reciprocates that love. Given two individuals X and Y and some asymmetric relationship (say love), we have four possible scenarios: Neither loves the other [Fig. 8-3(a)], X loves Y but Y does not love X [Fig. 8-3(b)], Y loves X but X does not love Y [Fig. 8-3(c)], and they love each other [Fig. 8-3(d)].

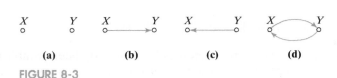

FIGURE 8-3

To distinguish digraphs from ordinary graphs, we use slightly different terminology.

- In a digraph, instead of talking about edges we talk about **arcs**. Every arc is defined by its *starting vertex* and its *ending vertex*, and we respect that order when we write the arc. Thus, if we write XY, we are describing the arc in Fig. 8-3(b) as opposed to the arc YX shown in Fig. 8-3(c).

- A list of all the arcs in a digraph is called the **arc-set** of the digraph. The digraph in Fig. 8-3(d) has arc-set $\mathcal{A} = \{XY, YX\}$.

- If XY is an arc in the digraph, we say that vertex X is **incident to** vertex Y, or, equivalently, that Y is **incident from** X.

- The arc YZ is said to be **adjacent** to the arc XY if the starting point of YZ is the ending point of XY. (Essentially, this means one can go from X to Z by way of Y.)

- In a digraph, a **path** from vertex X to vertex W ($W \neq X$) consists of a sequence of arcs $XY, YZ, ZU, \ldots, VW$ such that each arc is adjacent to the one before it and no arc appears more than once in the sequence—it is essentially a trip from X to W along the arcs in the digraph. The best way to describe the path is by listing the vertices in the order of travel: X, Y, Z, and so on.

- When the path starts and ends at the same vertex, we call it a **cycle** of the digraph. Just like circuits in a regular graph, cycles in digraphs can be written in more than one way—the cycle X, Y, Z, X is the same as the cycles Y, Z, X, Y and Z, X, Y, Z.

- In a digraph, the notion of the degree of a vertex is replaced by the concepts of *indegree* and *outdegree*. The **outdegree** of X is the number of arcs that have X as their *starting point* (outgoing arcs); the **indegree** of X is the number of arcs that have X as their *ending point* (incoming arcs).

The following example illustrates some of the above concepts.

EXAMPLE 8.3 DIGRAPH BASICS

The digraph in Fig. 8-4 has **vertex-set** $\mathcal{V} = \{A, B, C, D, E\}$ and arc-set $\mathcal{A} = \{AB, AC, BD, CA, CD, CE, EA, ED\}$. In this digraph, A is *incident to* B and C, but not to E. By the same token, A is *incident from* E as well as from C. The indegree of

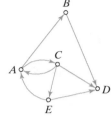

FIGURE 8-4

vertex A is 2, and so is the outdegree. The indegree of vertex D is 3, and the outdegree is 0. We leave it to the reader to find the indegrees and outdegrees of each of the other vertices of the graph.

In this digraph, there are several paths from A to D, such as A, C, D; A, C, E, D; A, B, D; and even A, C, A, B, D. On the other hand, A, E, D is not a path from A to D (because you can't travel directly from A to E). There are two cycles in this digraph: A, C, E, A (which can also be written as C, E, A, C and E, A, C, E) and A, C, A. Notice that there is no cycle passing through D because D has outdegree 0 and, thus, is a "dead-end," and there is no cycle passing through B because from B you can only go to D, and once there you are stuck.

While love is not to be minimized as a subject of study, there are many other equally important applications of digraphs:

- **The World Wide Web.** The Web is a giant digraph, where the vertices are Web pages and an arc from X to Y indicates that there is a *hyperlink* (informally called a *link*) on Web page X that allows you to jump directly to Web page Y. Web linkages are asymmetric—there may be a link on X that sends you to Y but no link in Y that sends you to X.

- **Traffic flow.** In most cities some streets are one-way streets and others are two-way streets. In this situation, digraphs allow us to visualize the flow of traffic through the city's streets. The vertices are intersections, and the *arcs* represent one-way streets. (To represent a two-way street, we use two arcs, one for each direction.)

- **Telephone traffic.** To track and analyze the traffic of telephone calls through their network, telephone companies use "call digraphs." In these digraphs the vertices are telephone numbers, and an arc from X to Y indicates that a call was initiated from telephone number X to telephone number Y.

- **Tournaments.** Digraphs are frequently used to describe certain types of tournaments, with the vertices representing the teams (or individual players) and the arcs representing the outcomes of the games played in the tournament (the arc XY indicates that X defeated Y). Tournament digraphs can be used in any sport in which the games cannot end in a tie (basketball, tennis, etc.).

- **Organization charts.** In any large organization (a corporation, the military, a university, etc.) it is important to have a well-defined chain of command. The best way to describe the chain of command is by means of a digraph often called an *organization chart*. In this digraph the *vertices* are the individuals in the organization, and an *arc* from X to Y indicates that X is Y's immediate boss (i.e., Y takes orders directly from X).

As you probably guessed by now, digraphs are also used in scheduling. There is no better way to visualize the tasks, processing times, and precedence relations in a project than by means of a digraph in which the vertices represent the tasks (with their processing times indicated in parentheses) and the arcs represent the precedence relations.

EXAMPLE 8.4   PROJECT DIGRAPH FOR THE MARTIAN HOME

Let's return to the scheduling problem first discussed in Example 8.2. We can take the tasks and precedence relations given in Table 8-1 and create a digraph like the one shown in Fig. 8-5(a). It is helpful to try to place the vertices of the

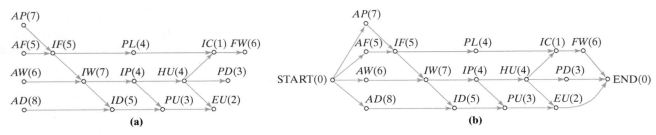

FIGURE 8-5

digraph so that the arcs point from left to right, and this can usually be done with a little trial-and-error. After this is done, it is customary to add two fictitious tasks called START and END, where START indicates the imaginary task of getting the project started (cutting the red ribbon, so to speak) and END indicates the imaginary task of declaring the project complete [Fig. 8-5(b)]. By giving these fictitious tasks zero processing time, we avoid affecting the time calculations for the project.

A diagraph having the tasks (and completion times) as vertices, the precedence relations as arcs, and with the fictitious tasks START (0) and END (0) representing the beginning and end of the project, respectively, is called a **project digraph**. The project digraph allows us to better visualize the execution of the project as a flow, moving from left to right.

8.3 Priority-List Scheduling

The project digraph is the basic graph model used to package all the information in a scheduling problem, but there is nothing in the project digraph itself that specifically tells us how to create a schedule. We are going to need something else, some set of instructions that indicates the order in which tasks should be executed. We can accomplish this by the simple act of prioritizing the tasks in some specified order, called a *priority list*.

A **priority list** is a list of all the tasks prioritized in the order we prefer to execute them. If task X is ahead of task Y in the priority list, then X gets priority over Y. This means that when it comes to a choice between the two, *X is executed ahead of Y*. However, if X is not yet *ready* for execution, then *we skip over it and move on to the first ready task after X in the priority list*. If there are no ready tasks after X in the priority list, the free processors must sit idle and wait until a task becomes ready.

The process of scheduling tasks using a priority list and following these basic rules is known as the *priority-list model* for scheduling. The priority-list model is a completely general model for scheduling—every priority list produces a schedule, and any schedule can be created from some (usually more than one) "parent" priority list. The trick is going to be to figure out *which* priority lists give us good schedules and which don't. We will come back to this topic in Sections 8.4 and 8.5.

Since each time we change the order of the tasks we get a different priority list, there are as many priority lists as there are ways to order the tasks. For three tasks, there are six possible priority lists; for 4 tasks, there are 24 priority lists; for 10 tasks, there are more than 3 million priority lists; and for 100 tasks, there are more priority lists than there are molecules in the universe.

Clearly, a shortage of priority lists is not going to be our problem. If this sounds familiar, it's because we have seen the idea before—priority lists are nothing more than *permutations of the tasks*. Like sequential coalitions (Chapter 2) and Hamilton circuits (Chapter 6), the number of priority lists is given by a factorial.

For a review of permutations and factorials, see Section 2.4.

NUMBER OF PRIORITY LISTS ─────────────

The number of possible priority lists in a project consisting of M tasks is
$$M! = M \times (M-1) \times \cdots \times 2 \times 1$$

Before we proceed, we will illustrate how the priority-list model for scheduling works with a few small but important examples. Even with such small examples, there is a lot to keep track of, and you are well advised to have pencil and paper in front of you as you follow the details.

EXAMPLE 8.5 PREPARING FOR LAUNCH: PART 1

Immediately preceding the launch of a satellite into space, last-minute system checks need to be performed by the on-board computers, and it is important to complete these system checks as quickly as possible—for both cost and safety reasons. Suppose that there are five system checks required: $A(6), B(5), C(7), D(2)$, and $E(5)$, with the numbers in parentheses representing the hours it takes one computer to perform that system check. In addition, there are precedence relations: D cannot be started until both A and B have been finished, and E cannot be started until C has been finished. The project digraph is shown in Fig. 8-6.

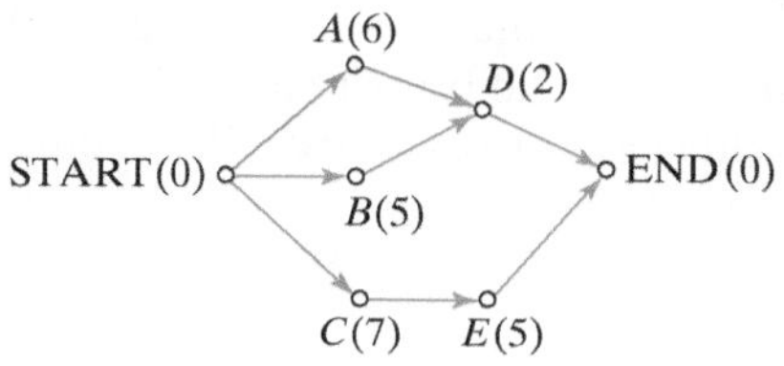

Let's assume that there are two identical computers on board (P_1 and P_2) that will carry out the individual system checks. How do we use the priority-list model to create a schedule for these two processors?

For starters, we will need a priority list. Suppose that the priority list is given by listing the system checks in alphabetical order, and let's follow the evolution of the project under the priority-list model. We will use T to indicate the elapsed time in hours.

START(0) ○ ─── ○ A(6) ─── D(2) ○ ─── ○ END(0)
B(5) ── C(7) ── E(5)

FIGURE 8-6

Priority list: $A(6), B(5), C(7), D(2), E(5)$

- $T = 0$ (START). $A(6), B(5)$, and $C(7)$ are the only *ready* tasks. Following the priority list, we assign $A(6)$ to P_1 and $B(5)$ to P_2.
- $T = 5$. P_1 is still *busy* with $A(6)$; P_2 has just *completed* $B(5)$. $C(7)$ is the only available *ready* task. We assign $C(7)$ to P_2.
- $T = 6$. P_1 has just *completed* $A(6)$; P_2 is *busy* with $C(7)$. $D(2)$ has just become a *ready* task (A and B have been completed). We assign $D(2)$ to P_1.
- $T = 8$. P_1 has just *completed* $D(2)$; P_2 is still *busy* with $C(7)$. There are no *ready* tasks at this time for P_1, so P_1 has to sit *idle*.

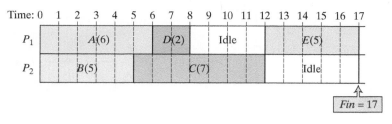

Time: 0 1 2 3 4 5 6 7 8 9 10 11 12 13 14 15 16 17

P_1	A(6) D(2) Idle E(5)
P_2	B(5) C(7) Idle

Fin = 17

FIGURE 8-7

- $T = 12$. P_1 is *idle*; P_2 has just *completed* $C(7)$. Both processors are *ready* for work. $E(5)$ is the only ready task, so we assign $E(5)$ to P_1, P_2 sits *idle*. (Note that in this situation, we could have just as well assigned $E(5)$ to P_2 and let P_1 sit idle. The processors don't get tired and don't care if they are working or idle, so the choice is random.)

- $T = 17$ (END). P_1 has just *completed* $E(5)$, and, therefore, the project is completed.

The evolution of the entire project together with the project finishing time ($Fin = 17$) are captured in the timeline shown in Fig. 8-7. Is this a good schedule? Given the excessive amount of idle time (a total of 9 hours), one might suspect this is a rather bad schedule. How could we improve it? We might try changing the priority list.

EXAMPLE 8.6   PREPARING FOR LAUNCH: PART 2

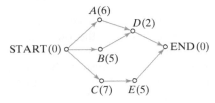

FIGURE 8-8

We are going to schedule the satellite launch system checks with the same two processors but with a different priority list. The project digraph is shown once again in Fig. 8-8. (When scheduling, it's really useful to have the project digraph right in front of you.)

This time let's try a reverse alphabetical order for the priority list. Why? Why not—at this point we are just shooting in the dark! (Don't worry—we will become a lot more enlightened later in the chapter.)

Priority list: $E(5), D(2), C(7), B(5), A(6)$

- $T = 0$ (START). $C(7)$, $B(5)$, and $A(6)$ are the only *ready* tasks. Following the priority list, we assign $C(7)$ to P_1 and $B(5)$ to P_2.

- $T = 5$. P_1 is still *busy* with $C(7)$; P_2 has just *completed* $B(5)$. $A(6)$ is the only available ready task. We assign $A(6)$ to P_2.

- $T = 7$. P_1 has just *completed* $C(7)$; P_2 is *busy* with $A(6)$. $E(5)$ has just become a *ready* task, and we assign it to P_1.

- $T = 11$. P_2 has just *completed* $A(6)$; P_1 is *busy* with $E(5)$. $D(2)$ has just become a *ready* task, and we assign it to P_2.

- $T = 12$. P_1 has just *completed* $E(5)$; P_2 is *busy* with $D(2)$. There are no tasks left, so P_1 sits idle.

- $T = 13$. (END). P_2 has just *completed* the last task, $D(2)$. Project is completed.

The timeline for this schedule is shown in Fig. 8-9. The project finishing time is $Fin = 13$ hours.

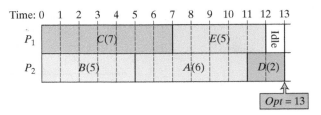

FIGURE 8-9

Clearly, this schedule is a lot better than the one obtained in Example 8.5. In fact, we were pretty lucky—this schedule turns out to be an optimal schedule for two processors. [Two processors cannot finish this project in less than 13 hours because there is a total of 25 hours worth of work (the sum of all processing times), which implies that in the best of cases it would take 12.5 hours to finish the project. But since the processing times are all whole numbers and tasks cannot be split, the finishing time cannot be less than 13 hours! Thus, *Opt* = 13 hours.]

Thirteen hours is still a long time for the computers to go over their system checks. Since that's the best we can do with two computers, the only way to speed things up is to add a third computer to the "workforce." Adding another computer to the satellite can be quite expensive, but perhaps it will speed things up enough to make it worth it. Let's see.

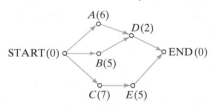

FIGURE 8-10

| **EXAMPLE 8.7** | PREPARING FOR LAUNCH: PART 3 |

We will now schedule the system checks using $N = 3$ computers (P_1, P_2, P_3). For the reader's convenience the project digraph is shown again in Fig. 8-10. We will use the "good" priority list we found in Example 8.6.

Priority list: $E(5), D(2), C(7), B(5), A(6)$

- $T = 0$ (START). $C(7)$, $B(5)$, and $A(6)$ are the *ready* tasks. We assign $C(7)$ to P_1, $B(5)$ to P_2, and $A(6)$ to P_3.

- $T = 5$. P_1 is *busy* with $C(7)$; P_2 has just *completed* $B(5)$; and P_3 is *busy* with $A(6)$. There are no available ready tasks for P_2 [$E(5)$ can't be started until $C(7)$ is done, and $D(2)$ can't be started until $A(6)$ is done], so P_2 sits idle until further notice.

- $T = 6$. P_3 has just *completed* $A(6)$; P_2 is *idle*; and P_1 is still *busy* with $C(7)$. $D(2)$ has just become a *ready* task. We randomly assign $D(2)$ to P_2 and let P_3 be idle, since there are no other ready tasks. [Note that we could have just as well assigned $D(2)$ to P_3 and let P_2 be idle.]

- $T = 7$. P_1 has just *completed* $C(7)$ and $E(5)$ has just become a *ready* task, so we assign it to P_1. There are no other tasks to assign, so P_3 continues to sit idle.

- $T = 8$. P_2 has just *completed* $D(2)$. There are no other tasks to assign, so P_2 and P_3 both sit *idle*.

- $T = 12$ (END). P_1 has just *completed* the last task, $E(5)$, so the project is completed.

The timeline for this schedule is shown in Fig. 8-11. The project finishing time is *Fin* = 12 hours, a pathetically small improvement over the two-processor schedule found in Example 8.6. The cost of adding a third processor doesn't seem to justify the benefit.

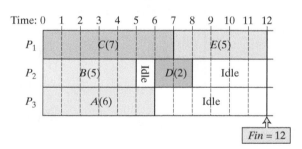

FIGURE 8-11

The Priority-List Model

The previous three examples give us a general sense of how to create a schedule from a project digraph *and* a priority list. We will now formalize the ground rules of the **priority-list model** for scheduling.

At any particular moment in time throughout a project, a processor can be either *busy* or *idle* and a task can be *ineligible, ready, in execution*, or *completed*. Depending on the various combinations of these, there are three different scenarios to consider:

- *All processors are busy.* In this case, there is nothing we can do but wait.
- *One processor is free.* In this case, we scan the priority list from left to right, looking for the first *ready* task in the priority list and assign it to the free processor. (Remember that for a task to be *ready*, all the tasks that are precedent to it must have been completed.) If there are no ready tasks at that moment, the processor stays idle until things change.
- *More than one processor is free.* In this case, the *first ready* task on the priority list is given to one free processor, the second ready task is given to another free processor, and so on. If there are more free processors than ready tasks, some of the processors will remain idle until one or more tasks become ready. Since the processors are identical and tireless, the choice of which free processor is assigned which ready task is completely arbitrary.

It's fair to say that the basic idea behind the priority-list model is not difficult, but there is a lot of bookkeeping involved, and that becomes critical when the number of tasks is large. At each stage of the schedule we need to keep track of the status of each task—which tasks are *ready* for processing, which tasks are *in execution*, which tasks have been *completed*, which tasks are still *ineligible*. One convenient recordkeeping strategy goes like this: On the priority list itself *ready* tasks are circled in red [Fig. 8-12(a)]. When a ready task is picked up by a processor and goes into *execution*, put a single red slash through the red circle [Fig. 8-12(b)]. When a task that has been in execution is completed, put a second red slash through the circle [Fig. 8-12(c)]. At this point, it is also important to check the project digraph to see if any new tasks have all of a sudden become eligible. Tasks that are *ineligible* remain unmarked [Fig. 8-12(d)].

As they say, the devil is in the details, so a slightly more substantive example will help us put everything together—the project digraph, the priority list model, and the bookkeeping strategy.

(a)   **(b)**   **(c)**   **(d)**

FIGURE 8-12 "Road" signs on a priority list. (a) Task *X* is *ready*. (b) Task *X* is *in execution*. (c) Task *X* is *completed*. (d) Task *X* is *ineligible*.

EXAMPLE 8.8 ASSEMBLING A MARTIAN HOME WITH A PRIORITY LIST

This is the third act of the Martian Habitat Unit (MHU) building project. We are finally ready to start the project of assembling that MHU, and, like any good scheduler, we will first work the entire schedule out with pencil and paper. Let's start with the assumption that maybe we can get by with just two robots (P_1 and P_2). For the reader's convenience, the project digraph is shown again in Fig. 8-13.

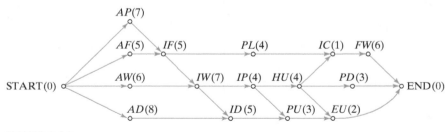

FIGURE 8-13

Let's start with a random priority list.

Priority list: $\widehat{AD(8)}$, $\widehat{AW(6)}$, $\widehat{AF(5)}$, $IF(5)$, $\widehat{AP(7)}$, $IW(7)$, $ID(5)$, $IP(4)$, $PL(4)$, $PU(3)$, $HU(4)$, $IC(1)$, $PD(3)$, $EU(2)$, $FW(6)$. (Ready tasks are circled in red.)

- $T = 0$ **(START).** Status of processors: P_1 starts AD; P_2 starts AW. We put a single red slash through AD and AW.

  Priority list: $\widehat{AD}$, $\widehat{AW}$, $\widehat{AF}$, IF, $\widehat{AP}$, IW, ID, IP, PL, PU, HU, IC, PD, EU, FW.

- $T = 6$. P_1 busy (executing AD); P_2 completed AW (put a second slash through AW) and starts AF (put a slash through AF).

  Priority list: $\widehat{AD}$, $\widehat{AW}$, $\widehat{AF}$, IF, $\widehat{AP}$, IW, ID, IP, PL, PU, HU, IC, PD, EU, FW.

- $T = 8$. P_1 completed AD and starts AP; P_2 is busy (executing AF).

  Priority list: $\widehat{AD}$, $\widehat{AW}$, $\widehat{AF}$, IF, $\widehat{AP}$, IW, ID, IP, PL, PU, HU, IC, PD, EU, FW.

- $T = 11$. P_1 busy (executing AP); P_2 completed AF, but since there are no ready tasks, it remains idle.

  Priority list: $\widehat{AD}$, $\widehat{AW}$, $\widehat{AF}$, IF, $\widehat{AP}$, IW, ID, IP, PL, PU, HU, IC, PD, EU, FW.

- $T = 15$. P_1 completed AP. IF becomes a ready task and goes to P_1; P_2 stays idle.

  Priority list: $\widehat{AD}$, $\widehat{AW}$, $\widehat{AF}$, $\widehat{IF}$, $\widehat{AP}$, IW, ID, IP, PL, PU, HU, IC, PD, EU, FW.

At this point, we will let you take over and finish the schedule. (Remember—the object is to learn how to keep track of the status of each task, and the only way to do this is with practice.)

After a fair amount of work, we obtain the final schedule shown in Fig. 8-14, with project finishing time $Fin = 44$ hours.

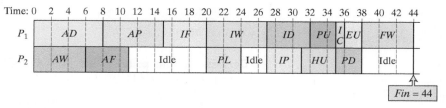

FIGURE 8-14

Scheduling with priority lists is a two-part process: (1) choose a priority list and (2) use the priority list and the ground rules of the priority-list model to come up with a schedule (Fig. 8-15). As we saw in the previous example, the second part is long and tedious, but purely mechanical—it can be done by anyone (or anything) that is able to follow a set of instructions, be it a meticulous student or a properly programmed computer. We will use the term *scheduler* to describe the entity (be it student or machine) that takes a priority list as input and produces the schedule as output.

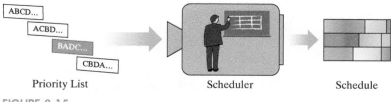

Priority List   Scheduler   Schedule

FIGURE 8-15

Ironically, it is the seemingly easiest part of this process—choosing a priority list—that is actually the most interesting. Among all the priority lists there is one (or more) that will give a schedule with the optimal finishing time. We will call these **optimal priority lists**. How do we find an optimal priority list? Short of that, how do we find "good" priority lists, that is, priority lists that give schedules with finishing times reasonably close to the optimal? These are both important questions, and some answers are coming up next.

8.4 The Decreasing-Time Algorithm

Our first attempt to find a good priority list is to formalize what is an intuitive and commonly used strategy: *Do the longer jobs first and leave the shorter jobs for last.* In terms of priority lists, this strategy is implemented by creating a priority list in which the tasks are listed in decreasing order of processing times—longest first, second longest next, and so on. (When there are two or more tasks with equal processing times, we order them randomly.)

A priority list in which the tasks are listed in decreasing order of processing times is called, not surprisingly, a **decreasing-time priority list**, and the process of creating a schedule using a decreasing-time priority list is called the **decreasing-time algorithm**.

EXAMPLE 8.9 THE DECREASING TIME ALGORITHM GOES TO MARS

Figure 8-16 shows, once again, the project digraph for the Martian Habitat Unit building project. To use the decreasing-time algorithm we first prioritize the 15 tasks in a decreasing-time priority list.

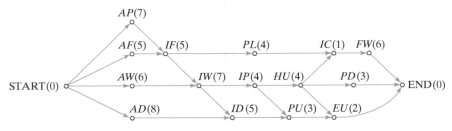

FIGURE 8-16

Decreasing-time priority list: $AD(8)$, $AP(7)$, $IW(7)$, $AW(6)$, $FW(6)$, $AF(5)$, $IF(5)$, $ID(5)$, $IP(4)$, $PL(4)$, $HU(4)$, $PU(3)$, $PD(3)$, $EU(2)$, $IC(1)$

Using the decreasing-time algorithm with $N = 2$ processors, we get the schedule shown in Fig. 8-17, with project finishing time $Fin = 42$ hours. (Table 8-2 shows the details of how this schedule came about, but you may want to try re-creating the schedule on your own.)

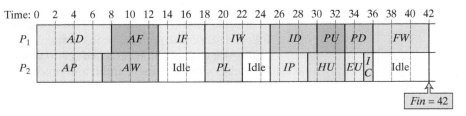

FIGURE 8-17

When looking at the finishing time under the decreasing-time algorithm, one can't help but feel disappointed. The sensible idea of prioritizing the longer jobs ahead of the shorter jobs turned out to be somewhat of a dud—at least in this example! What went wrong? If we work our way backward from the end, we can see that we made a bad choice at $T = 33$ hours. At this point there were three ready tasks [$PD(3)$, $EU(2)$, and $IC(1)$], and both processors were available. Based on the decreasing-time priority list, we chose the two "longer" tasks, $PD(3)$ and $EU(2)$, ahead of the short task, $IC(1)$. This was a bad move! $IC(1)$ is a much more *critical* task than the other two because we can't start task $FW(6)$ until we finish task $IC(1)$. Had we looked ahead at some of the tasks for which PD, EU, and IC are precedent tasks, we might have noticed this.

Step	Time	Priority-List Status	Schedule Status
1	$T = 0$	AD(8) AP(7) IW(7) AW(6) FW(6) AF(5) IF(5) ID(5) IP(4) PL(4) HU(4) PU(3) PD(3) EU(2) IC(1)	P_1: AD P_2: AP
2	$T = 7$	AD(8) AP(7) IW(7) AW(6) FW(6) AF(5) IF(5) ID(5) IP(4) PL(4) HU(4) PU(3) PD(3) EU(2) IC(1)	P_1: AD P_2: AP · AW
3	$T = 8$	AD(8) AP(7) IW(7) AW(6) FW(6) AF(5) IF(5) ID(5) IP(4) PL(4) HU(4) PU(3) PD(3) EU(2) IC(1)	P_1: AD · AF P_2: AP · AW
4	$T = 13$	AD(8) AP(7) IW(7) AW(6) FW(6) AF(5) IF(5) ID(5) IP(4) PL(4) HU(4) PU(3) PD(3) EU(2) IC(1)	P_1: AD · AF · IF P_2: AP · AW
5	$T = 18$	AD(8) AP(7) IW(7) AW(6) FW(6) AF(5) IF(5) ID(5) IP(4) PL(4) HU(4) PU(3) PD(3) EU(2) IC(1)	P_1: AD · AF · IF · IW P_2: AP · AW · Idle · PL
6	$T = 22$	AD(8) AP(7) IW(7) AW(6) FW(6) AF(5) IF(5) ID(5) IP(4) PL(4) HU(4) PU(3) PD(3) EU(2) IC(1)	P_1: AD · AF · IF · IW P_2: AP · AW · Idle · PL
7	$T = 25$	AD(8) AP(7) IW(7) AW(6) FW(6) AF(5) IF(5) ID(5) IP(4) PL(4) HU(4) PU(3) PD(3) EU(2) IC(1)	P_1: AD · AF · IF · IW · ID P_2: AP · AW · Idle · PL · Idle · IP
8	$T = 29$	AD(8) AP(7) IW(7) AW(6) FW(6) AF(5) IF(5) ID(5) IP(4) PL(4) HU(4) PU(3) PD(3) EU(2) IC(1)	P_1: AD · AF · IF · IW · ID P_2: AP · AW · Idle · PL · Idle · IP · HU
9	$T = 30$	AD(8) AP(7) IW(7) AW(6) FW(6) AF(5) IF(5) ID(5) IP(4) PL(4) HU(4) PU(3) PD(3) EU(2) IC(1)	P_1: AD · AF · IF · IW · ID · PU P_2: AP · AW · Idle · PL · Idle · IP · HU
10	$T = 33$	AD(8) AP(7) IW(7) AW(6) FW(6) AF(5) IF(5) ID(5) IP(4) PL(4) HU(4) PU(3) PD(3) EU(2) IC(1)	P_1: AD · AF · IF · IW · ID · PU · PD P_2: AP · AW · Idle · PL · Idle · IP · HU · EU
11	$T = 35$	AD(8) AP(7) IW(7) AW(6) FW(6) AF(5) IF(5) ID(5) IP(4) PL(4) HU(4) PU(3) PD(3) EU(2) IC(1)	P_1: AD · AF · IF · IW · ID · PU · PD P_2: AP · AW · Idle · PL · Idle · IP · HU · EU · IC
12	$T = 36$	AD(8) AP(7) IW(7) AW(6) FW(6) AF(5) IF(5) ID(5) IP(4) PL(4) HU(4) PU(3) PD(3) EU(2) IC(1)	P_1: AD · AF · IF · IW · ID · PU · PD · FW P_2: AP · AW · Idle · PL · Idle · IP · HU · EU · IC
13	$T = 42$	AD(8) AP(7) IW(7) AW(6) FW(6) AF(5) IF(5) ID(5) IP(4) PL(4) HU(4) PU(3) PD(3) EU(2) IC(1)	P_1: AD · AF · IF · IW · ID · PU · PD · FW P_2: AP · AW · Idle · PL · Idle · IP · HU · EU · IC · Idle

Time scale across schedule: 0 2 4 6 8 10 12 14 16 18 20 22 24 26 28 30 32 34 36 38 40 42

■ TABLE 8-2   Scheduling the assembly of the Martian Habitat Unit with the decreasing-time algorithm

An even more blatant example of the weakness of the decreasing-time algorithm occurs at the very start of this schedule, when the algorithm fails to take into account that task $AF(5)$ should have a very high priority. Why? $AF(5)$ is one of the two tasks that must be finished before $IF(5)$ can be started, and $IF(5)$ must be finished before $IW(7)$ can be started, which must be finished before $IP(4)$ and $ID(5)$ can be started, and so on down the line.

<table>
<tr><td>8.5</td><td></td></tr>
</table>

Critical Paths and the Critical-Path Algorithm

When there is a long path of tasks in the project digraph, it seems clear that the first task along that path should be started as early as possible. This idea leads to the following informal rule: *The greater the total amount of work that lies ahead of a task, the sooner that task should be started.*

To formalize these ideas, we will introduce the concepts of *critical paths* and *critical times*.

■ **Critical path (time) for a vertex.** For a given vertex X of a project digraph, the *critical path for X* is the path *from X to END* with *longest* processing time. (The *processing time* of a path is defined to be the sum of the processing times of all the tasks along the path.) When we add the processing times of all the tasks along the critical path for a vertex X, we get the *critical time for X*. (By definition, the critical time of END is 0.)

■ **Critical path (time) for a project.** The path with longest processing time from START to END is called the *critical path for the project*, and the total processing time for this critical path is called the *critical time for the project*.

EXAMPLE 8.10   **CRITICAL PATHS IN THE MARTIAN DIGRAPH**

Figure 8-18 shows the project digraph for assembling the Martian Habitat Unit. We will find critical paths and critical times for several vertices of the project digraph.

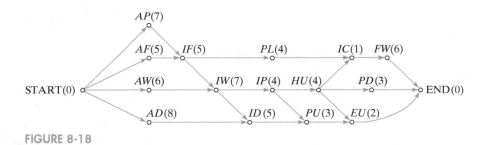

FIGURE 8-18

■ Let's start with a relatively easy case — the vertex HU. A quick look at Fig. 8-18 should convince you that there are only three paths from HU to END, namely,

1. HU, IC, FW, END, with processing time $4 + 1 + 6 = 11$ hours,

2. HU, PD, END, with processing time $4 + 3 = 7$ hours, and

3. HU, EU, END, with processing time $4 + 2 = 6$ hours.

Of the three paths, (1) has the longest processing time, so HU, IC, FW, END is the *critical path* for vertex HU. The *critical time* for HU is 11 hours.

- Next, let's find the critical path for vertex *AD*. There is only one path from *AD* to END, namely *AD*, *ID*, *PU*, *EU*, END, which makes the decision especially easy. Since this is the only path, it is automatically the longest path and, therefore, the *critical path* for *AD*. The *critical time* for *AD* is $8 + 5 + 3 + 2 = 18$ hours.
- To find the critical path for the project, we need to find the path from START to END with longest processing time. Since there are dozens of paths from START to END, let's just eyeball the project digraph for a few seconds and take our best guess. . . .
- OK, if you guessed START, *AP*, *IF*, *IW*, *IP*, *HU*, *IC*, *FW*, END, you have good eyes. This is indeed the *critical path*. It follows that the *critical time* for the Martian Habitat Unit project is 34 hours.

We will soon discuss the special role that the critical time and the critical path play in scheduling, but before we do so, let's address the issue of how to find critical paths. In a large project digraph there may be thousands of paths from START to END, and the "eyeballing" approach we used in Example 8.10 is not likely to work. What we need here is an efficient algorithm, and fortunately there is one—it is called the **backflow algorithm**.

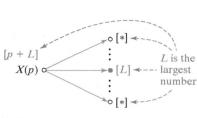

FIGURE 8-19

■ **THE BACKFLOW ALGORITHM**

- **Step 1.** Find the critical time for every vertex of the project digraph. This is done by starting at END and working backward toward START according to the following rule: *The critical time for a task X equals the processing time of X plus the largest critical time among the vertices incident from X.* The general idea is illustrated in Fig. 8-19. [To help with the recordkeeping, it is suggested that you write the critical time of the vertex in square brackets [ ] to distinguish it from the processing time in parentheses ( ).]
- **Step 2.** Once we have the critical time for every vertex in the project digraph, critical paths are found by just following the *path along largest critical times*. In other words, the critical path for any vertex *X* (and that includes START) is obtained by starting at *X* and moving to the adjacent vertex with largest critical time, and from there to the adjacent vertex with largest critical time, and so on.

While the backflow algorithm sounds a little complicated when described in words, it is actually pretty easy to implement in practice, as we will show in the next example.

EXAMPLE 8.11   THE BACKFLOW ALGORITHM AND THE MARTIAN DIGRAPH

We are now going to use the backflow algorithm to find the critical time for each of the vertices of the Martian Habitat Unit project digraph (Fig. 8-20).

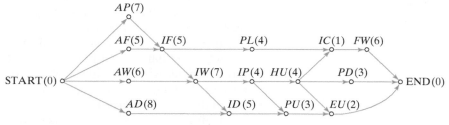

FIGURE 8-20

- **Step 1.**
    - Start at END. The critical time of END is 0, so we add a $[0]$ next to END(0).
    - The backflow now moves to the three vertices that are incident to END, namely, $FW(6)$, $PD(3)$, and $EU(2)$. In each case the critical time is the processing time plus 0, so the critical times are $FW[6]$, $PD[3]$, and $EU[2]$. We add this information to the project digraph.
    - From $FW[6]$, the backflow moves to $IC(1)$. The vertex $IC(1)$ is incident only to $FW[6]$, so the critical time for IC is $1 + 6 = 7$. We add a $[7]$ next to IC in the project digraph.
    - The backflow now moves to $HU(4)$, $PL(4)$, and $PU(3)$. There are three vertices $HU(4)$ is incident to ($IC[7]$, $PD[3]$, and $EU[2]$). Of the three, the one with the largest critical time is $IC[7]$. This means that the critical time for HU is $4 + 7 = 11$. $PL(4)$ is only incident to $IC[7]$, so its critical time is $4 + 7 = 11$. $PU(3)$ is only incident to $EU[2]$, so its critical time is $3 + 2 = 5$. Add $[11]$, $[11]$, and $[5]$ next to HU, PL, and PU, respectively.
    - The backflow now moves to $IP(4)$ and $ID(5)$. $IP(4)$ is incident to $HU[11]$ and $PU[5]$, so the critical time for IP is $4 + 11 = 15$. $ID(5)$ is only incident to $PU(5)$, so its critical time is $5 + 5 = 10$. We add $[15]$ next to IP, and $[10]$ next to ID.
    - The backflow now moves to $IW(7)$. The critical time for IW is $7 + 15 = 22$. (Please verify that this is correct!)
    - The backflow now moves to $IF(5)$. The critical time for IF is $5 + 22 = 27$. (Ditto.)
    - The backflow now moves to $AP(7)$, $AF(5)$, $AW(6)$, and $AD(8)$. Their respective critical times are $7 + 27 = 34$, $5 + 27 = 32$, $6 + 22 = 28$, and $8 + 10 = 18$.
    - Finally, the backflow reaches START(0). We still follow the same rule — the critical time is $0 + 34 = 34$. This is the critical time for the project!
- **Step 2.** The critical time for every vertex of the project digraph is shown in red numbers in Fig. 8-21. We can now find the critical path by following the trail of largest critical times: START, AP, IF, IW, IP, HU, IC, FW, END.

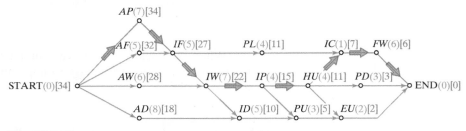

FIGURE 8-21

Why are the critical path and critical time of a project of special significance? We saw earlier in the chapter that for every project there is a theoretical time barrier below which a project cannot be completed, regardless of how clever the scheduler is or how many processors are used. Well, guess what? This theoretical barrier *is the project's critical time.*

If a project is to be completed in the optimal completion time, it is absolutely essential that all the tasks in the critical path be done at the earliest possible time. Any delay in starting up one of the tasks in the critical path will necessarily delay the finishing time of the entire project. (By the way, this is why this path is called *critical*.)

Unfortunately, it is not always possible to schedule the tasks on the critical path one after the other, bang, bang, bang without delay. For one thing, processors are not always free when we need them. (Remember that a processor cannot stop in the middle of one task to start a new task.) Another reason is the problem of uncompleted precedent tasks. We cannot concern ourselves only with tasks along the critical path and disregard other tasks that might affect them through precedence relations. There is a whole web of interrelationships that we need to worry about. Optimal scheduling is extremely complex.

The Critical-Path Algorithm

The concept of critical paths can be used to create very good (although not necessarily optimal) schedules. The idea is to use *critical times* rather than processing times to prioritize the tasks. The priority list we obtain when we write the tasks in decreasing order of *critical times* (with ties broken randomly) is called the **critical-time priority list**, and the process of creating a schedule using the critical-time priority list is called the **critical-path algorithm**.

◼ CRITICAL-PATH ALGORITHM ─────────────────

- **Step 1: Find critical times.** Using the backflow algorithm, find the *critical time* for every task in the project.
- **Step 2: Create priority list.** Using the critical times obtained in Step 1, create a *priority list* with the tasks listed in decreasing order of critical times (i.e., a critical-time priority list).
- **Step 3: Create schedule.** Using the critical-time priority list obtained in Step 2, create the *schedule*.

There are, of course, plenty of small details that need to be attended to when carrying out the critical-path algorithm, especially in Steps 1 and 3. Fortunately, everything that needs to be done we now know how to do.

EXAMPLE 8.12   THE CRITICAL-PATH ALGORITHM GOES TO MARS

We will now describe the process for scheduling the assembly of the Martian Habitat Unit using the critical-path algorithm and $N = 2$ processors.

We took care of Step 1 in Example 8.11. The critical times for each task are shown in red in Fig. 8-22.

Step 2 follows directly from Step 1. The critical-time priority list for the project is $AP[34]$, $AF[32]$, $AW[28]$, $IF[27]$, $IW[22]$, $AD[18]$, $IP[15]$, $PL[11]$, $HU[11]$, $ID[10]$, $IC[7]$, $FW[6]$, $PU[5]$, $PD[3]$, $EU[2]$.

Step 3 is a lot of busywork—the details are left to the reader.

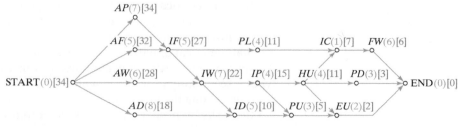

FIGURE 8-22

The timeline for the resulting schedule is given in Fig. 8-23. The project finishing time is *Fin* = 36 hours. This is a very good schedule, but it is not an optimal schedule. (Figure 8-24 shows the timeline for an *optimal schedule* with finishing time *Opt* = 35 hours.)

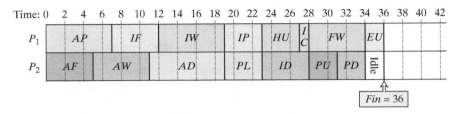

FIGURE 8-23   Timeline for the MHU building project under the critical-path algorithm (*N* = 2).

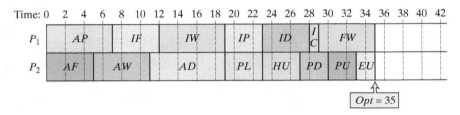

FIGURE 8-24   Timeline for an *optimal schedule* for the MHU building project (*N* = 2).

The critical-path algorithm is an excellent *approximate* algorithm for scheduling a project, but as Example 8.12 shows, it does not always give an optimal schedule. In this regard, scheduling problems are like TSPs (Chapter 6)—there are *efficient approximate* algorithms for scheduling, but no *efficient optimal* algorithm is currently known. Of the standard scheduling algorithms, the critical-path algorithm is by far the most commonly used. Other, more sophisticated algorithms have been developed in the last 40 years, and under specialized circumstances they can outperform the critical-path algorithm, but as an all-purpose algorithm for scheduling, the critical-path algorithm is hard to beat.

Conclusion

In one form or another, the scheduling of human (and nonhuman) activity is a pervasive and fundamental problem of modern life. At its most informal, it is part and parcel of the way we organize our everyday living (so much so that we are often scheduling things without realizing we are doing so). In its more formal incarnation, the systematic scheduling of a set of activities for the purposes of saving either time or money is a critical issue in management science. Business, industry, government, education—wherever there is a big project, there is a schedule behind it.

By now, it should not surprise us that at their very core, scheduling problems are mathematical in nature and that the mathematics of scheduling can range from the simple to the extremely complex. In this chapter we focused on a very specific type of scheduling problem in which we are given a set of *tasks*, a set of *precedence relations* among the tasks, and a set of identical *processors*. The objective is to schedule the tasks by properly assigning tasks to processors so that the *project finishing time* is as small as possible.

To tackle these scheduling problems systematically, we first developed a graph model of the problem, called the *project digraph*, and a general framework by means of which we can create, compare, and analyze schedules, called the *priority-list model*. Within the priority-list model, many strategies can be followed (with each strategy leading to the creation of a specific priority list). In this chapter, we considered two basic strategies for creating schedules. The first was the *decreasing-time algorithm*, a strategy that intuitively makes a lot of sense but that in practice often results in inefficient schedules. The second strategy, called the *critical-path algorithm*, is generally a big improvement over the decreasing-time algorithm, but it falls short of the ideal goal of guaranteeing an optimal schedule. The critical-path algorithm is by far the best known and most widely used algorithm for scheduling in business and industry.

Much like TSPs, scheduling problems are deceptively difficult. No optimal and efficient algorithm for scheduling is currently known, so when facing very large scheduling problems we must settle for *suboptimal* solutions.

KEY CONCEPTS

8.1 An Introduction to Scheduling

- **processor:** a worker (individual or machine) assigned to carry out a task, **230**
- **task:** an indivisible unit of work that is not broken up or shared, **230**
- **processing time (*P*-time):** for a task, the amount of time required by anyone processor to fully execute the task, **230**
- **precedence relation:** a prerequisite indicating that a task cannot be started before another task is complete, **231**
- **independent tasks:** a pair of tasks not bound by any precedence relations, **231**
- **finishing time (*Fin*):** the total time elapsed between the start and the end of a project, **232**
- **optimal schedule:** a schedule with the smallest possible finishing time, **232**
- **optimal finishing time (*Opt*):** the finishing time under an optimal schedule, **232**

8.2 Directed Graphs

- **asymmetric relationship:** a relationship between pairs of objects that need not be reciprocal, **234**
- **digraph:** a graph with directed edges (arcs) used to describe an asymmetric relationship between objects, **234**
- **arc:** an arc XY ($X \rightarrow Y$) indicates that the relationship goes from X to Y, **234**
- **arc-set:** a list of all the arcs in a digraph, **234**
- **incident to (from):** given an arc XY, X is *incident to* Y; Y is *incident from* X, **234**
- **adjacent arcs:** arc AB is adjacent to arc XY if and only if $B = X$, **234**
- **path:** from X to Z; a sequence of distinct adjacent arcs, starting at X and ending at a different vertex Z, **234**
- **cycle:** a sequence of distinct adjacent arcs that starts and ends at the same vertex, **234**
- **outdegree:** for a vertex X, the number of arcs having X as their starting vertex, **234**
- **indegree:** for a vertex Y, the number of arcs having Y as their ending vertex, **234**
- **project digraph:** a digraph having the tasks (including the imaginary tasks START and END) as vertices and the precedence relations as arcs. The processing times are included with the tasks for convenience, **236**

EXERCISES

WALKING

8.1 An Introduction to Scheduling

No exercises for this section.

8.2 Directed Graphs

1. For the digraph shown in Fig. 8-25, give

(a) the arc-set.

(b) the sum of the indegrees of all the vertices.

(c) the sum of the outdegrees of all the vertices.

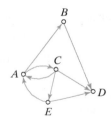

FIGURE 8-25

2. For the digraph shown in Fig. 8-26, give

(a) the arc-set.

(b) the sum of the indegrees of all the vertices.

(c) the sum of the outdegrees of all the vertices.

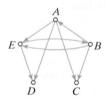

FIGURE 8-26

3. For the digraph in Fig. 8-25 (page 250), find

(a) all the possible paths from A to D.

(b) all the cycles in the digraph.

4. For the digraph in Fig. 8-26, find

(a) all the possible paths from B to E.

(b) all the cycles in the digraph.

5. For the digraph in Fig. 8-25 (page 250), find

(a) all vertices that are incident *to A*.

(b) all vertices that are incident *from A*.

(c) all vertices that are incident *to D*.

(d) all vertices that are incident *from D*.

(e) all the arcs adjacent to *AC*.

(f) all the arcs adjacent to *CD*.

6. For the digraph in Fig. 8-26, find

(a) all vertices that are incident *to A*.

(b) all vertices that are incident *from A*.

(c) all vertices that are incident *to D*.

(d) all vertices that are incident *from D*.

(e) all the arcs adjacent to *BA*.

(f) all the arcs adjacent to *BC*.

7. (a) Draw a digraph with vertex-set $V = \{A, B, C, D\}$ and arc-set $A = \{AB, AC, AD, BD, DB\}$.

(b) Draw a digraph with vertex-set $V = \{A, B, C, D, E\}$ and arc-set $A = \{AC, AE, BD, BE, CD, DC, ED\}$.

(c) Draw a digraph with vertex-set $V = \{W, X, Y, Z\}$ and such that W is incident to X and Y, X is incident to Y and Z, Y is incident to Z and W, and Z is incident to W and X.

8. (a) Draw a digraph with vertex-set $V = \{A, B, C, D\}$ and arc-set $A = \{AB, AC, AD, BC, BD, DB, DC\}$.

(b) Draw a digraph with vertex-set $V = \{V, W, X, Y, Z\}$ and arc-set $A = \{VW, VZ, WZ, XV, XY, XZ, YW, ZY, ZW\}$.

(c) Draw a digraph with vertex-set $V = \{W, X, Y, Z\}$ and such that every vertex is incident to every other vertex.

9. Consider the digraph with vertex-set $V = \{A, B, C, D, E\}$ and arc-set $A = \{AB, AE, CB, CE, DB, EA, EB, EC\}$. Without drawing the digraph, determine

(a) the outdegree of A.

(b) the indegree of A.

(c) the outdegree of D.

(d) the indegree of D.

10. Consider the digraph with vertex-set $V = \{V, W, X, Y, Z\}$ and arc-set $A = \{VW, VZ, WZ, XY, XZ, YW, ZY, ZW\}$. Without drawing the digraph, determine

(a) the outdegree of V.

(b) the indegree of V.

(c) the outdegree of Z.

(d) the indegree of Z.

11. Consider the digraph with vertex-set $V = \{A, B, C, D, E, F\}$ and arc-set $A = \{AB, BD, CF, DE, EB, EC, EF\}$.

(a) Find a path from vertex A to vertex F.

(b) Find a Hamilton path from vertex A to vertex F. (*Note*: A Hamilton path is a path that passes through every vertex of the graph once.)

(c) Find a cycle in the digraph.

(d) Explain why vertex F cannot be part of any cycle.

(e) Explain why vertex A cannot be part of any cycle.

(f) Find all the cycles in this digraph.

12. Consider the digraph with vertex-set $V = \{A, B, C, D, E\}$ and arc-set $A = \{AB, AE, CB, CD, DB, DE, EB, EC\}$.

(a) Find a path from vertex A to vertex D.

(b) Explain why the path you found in (a) is the only possible path from vertex A to vertex D.

(c) Find a cycle in the digraph.

(d) Explain why vertex A cannot be part of a cycle.

(e) Explain why vertex B cannot be part of a cycle.

(f) Find all the cycles in this digraph.

13. The White Pine subdivision is a rectangular area six blocks long and two blocks wide. Streets alternate between one way and two way as shown in Fig. 8-27. Draw a digraph that represents the traffic flow in this neighborhood.

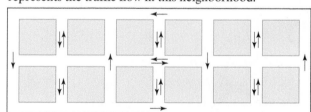

FIGURE 8-27

14. A mathematics textbook consists of 10 chapters. Although many of the chapters are independent of the others, some chapters require that previous chapters be covered first. The following list describes all the chapter dependences: Chapter 1 is a prerequisite to Chapters 3 and 5; Chapters 2 and 9 are both prerequisites to Chapter 10; Chapter 3 is a prerequisite to Chapter 6; and Chapter 4 is a prerequisite to Chapter 7, which in turn is a prerequisite to Chapter 8. Draw a digraph that describes the dependences among the chapters in the book.

15. The digraph in Fig. 8-28 is a *respect* digraph. That is, the vertices of the digraph represent members of a group and an arc *XY* represents that *X* respects *Y*.

(a) If you had to choose one person to be the leader of the group, whom would you pick? Explain.

(b) Who would be the worst choice to be the leader of the group? Explain.

(c) Assume that you know the respect digraph of a group of individuals, and that is the only information available to you. Which individual would be the most reasonable choice for leader of the group?

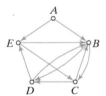

FIGURE 8-28

16. The digraph in Fig. 8-29 is an example of a *tournament* digraph. In this example the vertices of the digraph represent five volleyball teams in a round-robin tournament (i.e., every team plays every other team). An arc *XY* represents that *X* defeated *Y* in the tournament. (*Note:* There are no ties in volleyball.)

(a) Which team won the tournament? Explain.

(b) Which team came in last in the tournament? Explain.

(c) Suppose that you are given the tournament digraph of some tournament. What does the *indegree* of a vertex represent? What does the *outdegree* of a vertex represent?

(d) If *T* denotes the tournament digraph for a round-robin tournament with *N* teams, then for any vertex *X* in *T*, the indegree of *X* plus the outdegree of *X* = *N* − 1. Explain why.

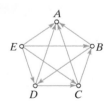

FIGURE 8-29

17. As part of its extended concert tour around the United States, the famous rock band Angelface will be giving a concert at the Smallville Bowl next month. This is a big event for Smallville, and the whole town is buzzing. The digraph in Fig. 8-30 shows the hyperlinks connecting the following six Web sites: (1) www.angelface.com (the rock band's Web site), (2) www.ticketmonster.com (the Web site for TicketMonster, the only ticket agency licensed to sell tickets to the concert), (3) www.knxrock.com (the Web site of Smallville rock station KNXR), (4) www .joetheblogger.com (the personal blog of Joe Fan, a local rock and roll aficionado), and (5) and (6) www.Smallville Inn.com and www.SmallvilleSuites.com (the Web sites of two local sister hotels owned by the same company and both offering a special rate for out-of-town fans coming to the concert).

(a) Make an educated guess as to which vertex is the most likely to represent (1), the rock band's Web site, and explain the reasoning behind your answer.

(b) Make an educated guess as to which vertex is the most likely to represent (2), the TicketMonster Web site, and explain the reasoning behind your answer.

(c) Make an educated guess as to which vertex is the most likely to represent (3), the Web site of rock station KNXR, and explain the reasoning behind your answer.

(d) Make an educated guess as to which vertex is the most likely to represent (4), Joe Fan's blog, and explain the reasoning behind your answer.

(e) Make an educated guess as to which two vertices are the most likely to represent (5) and (6), the two Smallville sister hotel Web sites.

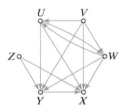

FIGURE 8-30

18. Wobble, a start-up company, is developing a search engine for the Web. Given a particular search word, say Angelface (the name of a rock band), Wobble's strategy is to find all the Web sites containing the term *Angelface,* and then look at Web sites to which those Web sites link, to obtain a ranked list of search results. In other words, if there are lots of links pointing to Web site *X* from Web sites that mention Angelface, then it is likely that *X* contains lots of useful information about Angelface. In the digraph shown in Fig. 8-31, the vertices represent Web pages that contain the word *Angelface* and the arcs represent hyperlinks from one Web site to another.

(a) Which Web sites would show up first, second, and third in the search results? Explain your answer.

(b) One of the vertices of the digraph is the official Angel-face Web site. Which do you think it is? Explain your answer.

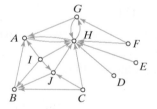

FIGURE 8-31

19. A project consists of eight tasks labeled *A* through *H*. The processing time (*P*-time) and precedence relations for each task are given in Table 8-3. Draw the project digraph.

Task	P-time	Precedent tasks
A	3	
B	10	*C, F, G*
C	2	*A*
D	4	*G*
E	5	*C*
F	8	*A, H*
G	7	*H*
H	5	

■ TABLE 8-3

20. A project consists of eight tasks labeled *A* through *H*. The processing time (*P*-time) and precedence relations for each task are given in Table 8-4. Draw the project digraph.

Task	P-time	Precedent tasks
A	5	*C*
B	5	*C, D*
C	5	
D	2	*G*
E	15	*A, B*
F	6	*D*
G	2	
H	2	*G*

■ TABLE 8-4

21. Eight experiments need to be carried out. One of the experiments requires 10 hours to complete, two of the experiments require 7 hours each to complete, two more require 12 hours each to complete, and three of the experiments require 20 hours each to complete. In addition, none of the 20-hour experiments can be started until both of the 7-hour experiments have been completed, and the 10-hour experiment cannot be started until both of the 12-hour experiments have been completed. Draw a project digraph for this scheduling problem.

22. Every fifty thousand miles an aircraft undergoes a complete inspection that involves 10 different diagnostic "checks." Three of the checks require 4 hours each to complete, three more require 7 hours each to complete, and four of the checks require 15 hours each to complete. Moreover, none of the 15-hour checks can be started until all the 4-hour checks have been completed. Draw a project digraph for this scheduling problem.

23. Apartments Unlimited is an apartment maintenance company that refurbishes apartments before new tenants move in. Table 8-5 shows the tasks for refurbishing a one-bedroom apartment, their processing times (in hours), and their precedent tasks. Draw a project digraph for the project.

Tasks	Label (*P*-time)	Precedent tasks
Bathrooms (clean)	*B*(2)	*P*
Carpets (shampoo)	*C*(1)	*S, W*
Filters (replace)	*F*(0.5)	
General cleaning	*G*(2)	*B, F, K*
Kitchen (clean)	*K*(3)	*P*
Lights (replace bulbs)	*L*(0.5)	
Paint	*P*(6)	*L*
Smoke detectors (battery)	*S*(0.5)	*G*
Windows (wash)	*W*(1)	*G*

■ TABLE 8-5

24. A ballroom is to be set up for a large wedding reception. Table 8-6 shows the tasks to be carried out, their processing times (in hours), and their precedent tasks. Draw a project digraph for the project of setting up for the wedding reception.

Tasks	Label (*P*-time)	Precedent tasks
Set up tables and chairs	TC(1.5)	
Set tablecloths and napkins	TN(0.5)	TC
Make flower arrangements	FA(2.2)	
Unpack crystal, china, and flatware	CF(1.2)	
Put place settings on table	PT(1.8)	TN, CF
Arrange table decorations	TD(0.7)	FA, PT
Set up the sound system	SS(1.4)	
Set up the bar	SB(0.8)	TC

■ **TABLE 8-6**

25. Preparing a banquet for a large number of people requires careful planning and the execution of many individual tasks. Imagine preparing a four-course dinner for a party of 20 friends. Suppose that the project is broken down into 10 individual tasks. The tasks and their processing times (in hours) are as follows: $A(1.5)$, $B(1)$, $C(0.5)$, $D(1.25)$, $E(1.5)$, $F(1)$, $G(3)$, $H(2.5)$, $I(2)$, and $J(1.25)$. The precedence relations are as follows: B cannot be started until A and D have been completed, C cannot be started until B and J have been completed, E cannot be started until D and G have been completed, F cannot be started until E and J have been completed, H cannot be started until F and C have been completed, and J cannot be started until I has been completed. Draw a project digraph for this culinary project.

26. Speedy Landscape Service has a project to landscape the garden of a new model home. The tasks that must be performed and their processing times (in hours) are: collect and deliver rocks, $R(4)$; collect and deliver soil (two loads), $S_1(3)$ and $S_2(3)$; move and position rocks, $RM(4)$; grade soil, $SG(5)$; seed lawn, $SL(3)$; collect and deliver bushes and trees, $B(2)$; plant bushes and trees, $BP(1)$; water the new plantings, $W(1)$; and lay mulch, $M(2)$. The precedence relations between tasks are $R \rightarrow RM$, $RM \rightarrow SG$, $S_1 \rightarrow SG$, $S_2 \rightarrow SG$, $SG \rightarrow SL$, $SG \rightarrow B$, $B \rightarrow BP$, $SL \rightarrow W$, $BP \rightarrow W$, and $BP \rightarrow M$. Draw a project digraph for this landscaping project.

8.3 Priority-List Scheduling

Exercises 27 through 30 refer to a project consisting of 11 tasks (A through K) with the following processing times (in hours): $A(10)$, $B(7)$, $C(11)$, $D(8)$, $E(9)$, $F(5)$, $G(3)$, $H(6)$, $I(4)$, $J(7)$, $K(5)$.

27. (a) A schedule with $N = 3$ processors produces finishing time $Fin = 31$ hours. What is the total idle time for all the processors?

(b) Explain why a schedule with $N = 3$ processors must have finishing time $Fin \geq 25$ hours.

28. (a) A schedule with $N = 5$ processors has finishing time $Fin = 19$ hours. What is the total idle time for all the processors?

(b) Explain why a schedule with $N = 5$ processors must have finishing time $Fin \geq 15$ hours.

29. Explain why a schedule with $N = 6$ processors must have finishing time $Fin \geq 13$ hours.

30. (a) Explain why a schedule with $N = 10$ processors must have finishing time $Fin \geq 11$ hours.

(b) Explain why it doesn't make sense to put more than 10 processors on this project.

Exercises 31 and 32 refer to the Martian Habitat Unit scheduling project with $N = 2$ processors discussed in Example 8.8. The purpose of these exercises is to fill in some of the details left out in Example 8.8.

31. For the priority list in Example 8.8, show the priority-list status at time $T = 26$.

32. For the priority list in Example 8.8, show the priority-list status at time $T = 32$.

33. Consider the project digraph shown in Fig. 8-32(a). (Processing times not relevant to this question have been omitted.) Suppose the project is to be scheduled with two processors, P_1 and P_2, and the priority list is *A, B, C, D, E, F, G, H*. The schedule starts as shown in Fig. 8-32(b).

(a) Can C be the next task assigned to P_1 at $T = 4$? If not, explain why not.

(b) Can D be the next task assigned to P_1 at $T = 4$? If not, explain why not.

(c) Can H be the next task assigned to P_1 at $T = 4$? If not, explain why not.

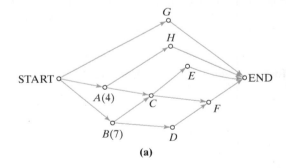

(a)

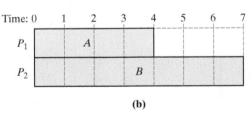

(b)

FIGURE 8-32

34. Consider the project digraph shown in Fig. 8-33(a). (Processing times not relevant to this question have been omitted.) Suppose the project is to be scheduled with two processors, P_1 and P_2, and the priority list is *A, B, C, D, E, F, G, H, I*. The schedule starts as shown in Fig. 8-33(b).

(a) Can *D* be the next task assigned to P_1 at $T = 6$? If not, explain why not.

(b) Can *E* be the next task assigned to P_1 at $T = 6$? If not, explain why not.

(c) Can *G* be the next task assigned to P_1 at $T = 6$? If not, explain why not.

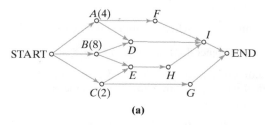

(a)

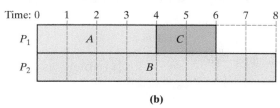

(b)

FIGURE 8-33

35. Using the priority list *D, C, A, E, B, G, F*, schedule the project described by the project digraph shown in Fig. 8-34 using $N = 2$ processors. Show the project timeline and give its finishing time.

36. Using the priority list *G, F, E, D, C, B, A*, schedule the project described by the project digraph shown in Fig. 8-34 using $N = 2$ processors. Show the project timeline and give its finishing time.

37. Using the priority list *D, C, A, E, B, G, F*, schedule the project described by the project digraph shown in Fig. 8-34 using $N = 3$ processors. Show the project timeline and give its finishing time.

38. Using the priority list *G, F, E, D, C, B, A*, schedule the project described by the project digraph shown in Fig. 8-34 using $N = 3$ processors. Show the project timeline and give its finishing time.

39. Explain why the priority lists *A, B, D, F, C, E, G* and *F, D, A, B, G, E, C* produce the same schedule for the project shown in Fig. 8-34.

40. Explain why the priority lists *E, G, C, B, A, D, F* and *G, C, E, F, D, B, A* produce the same schedule for the project shown in Fig. 8-34.

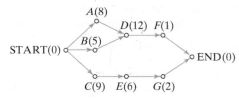

FIGURE 8-34

8.4 The Decreasing-Time Algorithm

41. Use the decreasing-time algorithm to schedule the project described by the project digraph shown in Fig. 8-34 using $N = 2$ processors. Show the timeline for the project, and give the project finishing time.

42. Use the decreasing-time algorithm to schedule the project described by the project digraph shown in Fig. 8-34 using $N = 3$ processors. Show the timeline for the project, and give the project finishing time.

43. Use the decreasing-time algorithm to schedule the project described by the project digraph shown in Fig. 8-35 using $N = 3$ processors. Show the timeline for the project, and give the project finishing time.

44. Use the decreasing-time algorithm to schedule the project described by the project digraph shown in Fig. 8-35 using $N = 2$ processors. Show the timeline for the project, and give the project finishing time.

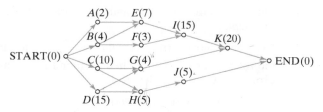

FIGURE 8-35

45. Consider the project described by the project digraph shown in Fig. 8-36, and assume that you are to schedule this project using $N = 2$ processors.

(a) Use the decreasing-time algorithm to schedule the project. Show the timeline for the project and the finishing time *Fin*.

(b) Find an optimal schedule and the optimal finishing time *Opt*.

(c) Use the relative error formula $\varepsilon = \frac{Fin - Opt}{Opt}$ to find the relative error of the schedule found in (a), and express your answer as a percent.

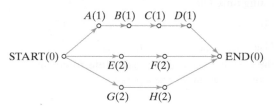

FIGURE 8-36

46. Consider the project described by the project digraph shown in Fig. 8-37, and assume that you are to schedule this project using $N = 2$ processors.

(a) Use the decreasing-time algorithm to schedule the project. Show the timeline for the project and the finishing time *Fin*.

(b) Find an optimal schedule and the optimal finishing time *Opt*.

(c) Use the relative error formula $\varepsilon = \frac{Fin - Opt}{Opt}$ to find the relative error of the schedule found in (a), and express your answer as a percent.

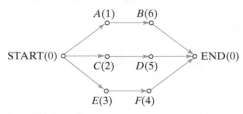

FIGURE 8-37

47. Consider the project described by the project digraph shown in Fig. 8-38, and assume that you are to schedule this project using $N = 3$ processors.

(a) Use the decreasing-time algorithm to schedule the project. Show the timeline for the project and the finishing time *Fin*.

(b) Find an optimal schedule and the optimal finishing time *Opt*.

(c) Use the relative error formula $\varepsilon = \frac{Fin - Opt}{Opt}$ to find the relative error of the schedule found in (a), and express your answer as a percent.

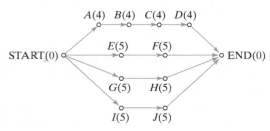

FIGURE 8-38

48. Consider the project described by the project digraph shown in Fig. 8-39, and assume that you are to schedule this project using $N = 4$ processors.

(a) Use the decreasing-time algorithm to schedule the project. Show the timeline for the project and the finishing time *Fin*.

(b) Find an optimal schedule. (*Hint*: *Opt* = 17.)

(c) Use the relative error formula $\varepsilon = \frac{Fin - Opt}{Opt}$ to find the relative error of the schedule found in (a), and express your answer as a percent.

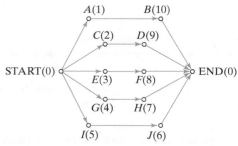

FIGURE 8-39

8.5 Critical Paths and the Critical-Path Algorithm

49. Consider the project digraph shown in Fig. 8-40.

(a) Use the backflow algorithm to find the critical time for each vertex.

(b) Find the critical path for the project.

(c) Schedule the project with $N = 2$ processors using the critical-path algorithm. Show the timeline, and give the project finishing time.

(d) Explain why the schedule obtained in (c) is optimal.

50. Consider the project digraph shown in Fig. 8-40.

(a) Schedule the project with $N = 3$ processors using the critical-path algorithm. Show the timeline, and give the project finishing time.

(b) Explain why the schedule obtained in (a) is optimal.

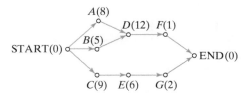

FIGURE 8-40

51. Consider the project digraph shown in Fig. 8-41.

(a) Find the critical path for the project.

(b) Schedule the project with $N = 3$ processors using the critical-path algorithm. Show the timeline, and give the project finishing time.

52. Consider the project digraph shown in Fig. 8-41.

(a) Use the backflow algorithm to find the critical time for each vertex.

(b) Schedule the project with $N = 2$ processors using the critical-path algorithm. Show the timeline, and give the project finishing time.

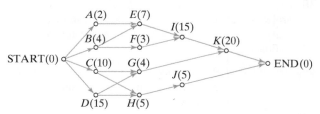

FIGURE 8-41

53. Schedule the Apartments Unlimited project given in Exercise 23 (Table 8-5) with $N = 2$ processors using the critical-path algorithm. Show the timeline, and give the project finishing time. (Note that the project digraph was done in Exercise 23.)

54. Schedule the project given in Exercise 24, Table 8-6 (setting up a ballroom for a wedding) with $N = 3$ processors using the critical-path algorithm. Show the timeline, and give the project finishing time. (Note that the project digraph was done in Exercise 24.)

55. Consider the project described by the project digraph shown in Fig. 8-42.

(a) Find the critical path and critical time for the project.

(b) Find the critical-time priority list.

(c) Schedule the project with $N = 2$ processors using the critical-path algorithm. Show the timeline and the project finishing time.

(d) Find an optimal schedule for $N = 2$ processors.

(e) Use the relative error formula $\varepsilon = \dfrac{Fin - Opt}{Opt}$ to find the relative error of the schedule found in (c).

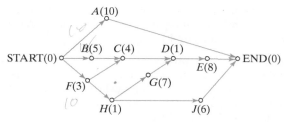

FIGURE 8-42

56. Consider the project digraph shown in Fig. 8-43, with the processing times given in hours.

(a) Find the critical path and critical time for the project.

(b) Find the critical-time priority list.

(c) Schedule the project with $N = 2$ processors using the critical-path algorithm. Show the timeline and the project finishing time.

(d) Explain why any schedule for $N = 2$ processors with finishing time $Fin = 22$ must be an optimal schedule.

(e) Schedule the project with $N = 3$ processors using the critical-path algorithm. Show the timeline and the project finishing time.

(f) Explain why the schedule found in (e) is an optimal schedule for three processors.

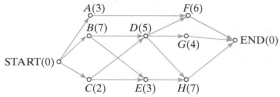

FIGURE 8-43

JOGGING

57. Explain why, in any digraph, the sum of all the indegrees must equal the sum of all the outdegrees.

58. Symmetric and totally asymmetric digraphs. A digraph is called *symmetric* if, whenever there is an arc from vertex X to vertex Y, there is *also* an arc from vertex Y to vertex X. A digraph is called *totally asymmetric* if, whenever there is an arc from vertex X to vertex Y, there *is not* an arc from vertex Y to vertex X. For each of the following, state whether the digraph is symmetric, totally asymmetric, or neither.

(a) A digraph representing the streets of a town in which all streets are one-way streets.

(b) A digraph representing the streets of a town in which all streets are two-way streets.

(c) A digraph representing the streets of a town in which there are both one-way and two-way streets.

(d) A digraph in which the vertices represent a group of men, and there is an arc from vertex X to vertex Y if X is a brother of Y.

(e) A digraph in which the vertices represent a group of men, and there is an arc from vertex X to vertex Y if X is the father of Y.

59. For the schedule shown in Fig. 8-44, find a priority list that generates the schedule. (*Note:* There is more than one possible answer.)

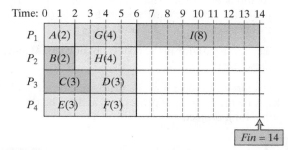

FIGURE 8-44

Exercises 60 through 62 introduce three paradoxes that can occur in scheduling. In all three exercises we will use the project described by the project digraph shown in Fig. 8-45. Assume that processing times are given in hours. [Source: Garey, M.R. et al. "Performance Guarantees for Scheduling Algorithms." Operations Research, 26 (1978)]

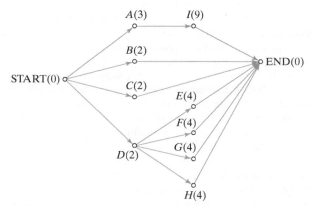

FIGURE 8-45

60. (a) Using the priority list $A, B, C, D, E, F, G, H, I$, schedule the project shown in Fig. 8-45 using $N = 3$ processors.

(b) Using the same priority list as in (a), schedule the project using $N = 4$ processors.

(c) There is a paradox in the results obtained in (a) and (b). Describe the paradox.

61. (a) Using the priority list $A, B, C, D, E, F, G, H, I$, schedule the project shown in Fig. 8-45 using $N = 3$ processors.

[This is the same question as in 60(a). If you already answered 60(a), you can recycle the answer.]

(b) Imagine that the processors are fine-tuned so that the processing times for all the tasks are shortened by 1 hour [i.e., the tasks now are $A(2)$, $B(1)$, ..., $H(3)$]. Using the same priority list as in (a), schedule this project using $N = 3$ processors.

(c) There is a paradox in the results obtained in (a) and (b). Describe the paradox.

62. (a) Using the priority list $A, B, C, D, E, F, G, H, I$, schedule the project shown in Fig. 8-45 using $N = 3$ processors. [Same question again as 60(a) and 61(a). You're getting your money's worth on this one!]

(b) Suppose that the precedence relations $D \to E$ and $D \to F$ are no longer required. All other precedence relations and processing times are as in the original project. Using the same priority list as in (a), schedule this project with $N = 3$ processors.

(c) There is a paradox in the results obtained in (a) and (b). Describe the paradox.

63. Let W represent the sum of the processing times of all the tasks, N be the number of processors, and Fin be the finishing time for a project.

(a) Explain the meaning of the inequality $Fin \geq W/N$ and why it is true for any schedule.

(b) Under what circumstances is $Fin = W/N$?

(c) What does the value $N \times Fin - W$ represent?

RUNNING

64. You have $N = 2$ processors to process M independent tasks (i.e., there are no precedence relations at all) with processing times $1, 2, 3, \ldots, M$. Find the optimal schedule, and give the optimal completion time Opt in terms of M. (*Hint*: Consider four separate cases based on the remainder when N is divided by 4.)

65. You have $N = 3$ processors to process M independent tasks with processing times $1, 2, 3, \ldots, M$. Find the optimal schedule, and give the optimal completion time Opt in terms of M. (*Hint*: Consider six separate cases based on the remainder when N is divided by 6.)

66. You have $N = 2$ processors to process $M + 1$ independent tasks with processing times $1, 2, 4, 8, 16, \ldots, 2^M$. Find the optimal schedule, and give the optimal completion time Opt in terms of M.

PROJECTS AND PAPERS

1 Worst-Case Analysis of Scheduling Algorithms

We saw in this chapter that when creating schedules there is a wide range of possibilities, from *very bad schedules* to *optimal* (best possible) schedules. Our focus was on creating good (if possible optimal) schedules, but the study of bad schedules is also of considerable importance in many applications. In the late 1960s and early 1970s, Ronald Graham of AT&T Bell Labs pioneered the study of worst-case scenarios in scheduling, a field known as *worst-case analysis*. As the name suggests, the issue in worst-case analysis is to analyze how bad a schedule can get. This research was motivated by a deadly serious question—how would the performance of the antiballistic missile defense system of the United States be affected by a failure in the computer programs that run the system?

In his research on worst-case analysis in scheduling, Graham made the critical discovery that there is a limit on how bad a schedule can be—no matter how stupidly a schedule is put together, the project finishing time Fin must satisfy the inequality $Fin \leq Opt \left(2 - \frac{1}{N}\right)$, where N is the number of processors and Opt is the optimal completion time of the project.

Prepare a presentation explaining Graham's worst-case analysis result and its implications. Give examples comparing optimal schedules and the worst possible schedules for projects involving $N = 2$ and $N = 3$ processors.

2 Dijkstra's Shortest-Path Algorithm

Just as there are weighted graphs, there are also *weighted digraphs*. A weighted digraph is a digraph in which each arc has a weight (distance, cost, time) associated with it. Weighted digraphs are used to model many important optimization problems in vehicle routing, pipeline flows, and so on. (Note that a weighted digraph is not the same as a project digraph—in the project digraph the vertices rather than the edges are the ones that have weights.) A fundamental question when working with weighted digraphs is finding the shortest path from a given vertex X to a given vertex Y. (Of course, there may be no path at all from X to Y, in which case the question is moot.) The classic algorithm for finding the shortest path between two vertices in a digraph is known as *Dijkstra's algorithm*, named after the Dutch computer scientist Edsger Dijkstra, who first proposed the algorithm in 1959.

Prepare a presentation describing Dijkstra's algorithm. Describe the algorithm carefully, and illustrate how the algorithm works with a couple of examples. Discuss why Dijkstra's algorithm is important. Is it efficient? Optimal? Discuss some possible applications of the algorithm.

3 Tournaments

In the language of graph theory, a *tournament* is a digraph whose underlying graph is a complete graph. In other words, to create a tournament you can start with K_N (the complete graph on N vertices) and then change each edge into an arc by putting an arbitrary direction on it. The reason these graphs are called tournaments is that they can be used to describe the results of a tournament in which every player plays against every other player (no ties allowed).

Write a paper on the mathematics of tournaments (as defined previously). If you studied Chapter 1, you should touch on the connection between tournaments and the results of elections decided under the *method of pairwise comparisons*.

PART 4

Shape
and
Form

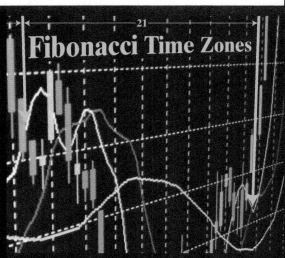

11 The Mathematics of Symmetry

Beyond Reflection

If you are a good skateboarder, you can do a 360. If you are a great skateboarder, you can do a 720. If you are the world's best, you can do a 900. But no matter how great you are, you can't do a 920.

When Tony Hawk—considered by most to be the greatest skateboarder of his generation—set a world record in 1999 by doing a 900 (2 ½ rotations in the air while launching from a half-pipe), few people thought the record could be broken. But 13 years later, on March 26, 2012, Tom Schaar, a skateboarder from Malibu, California, pulled off an amazing feat—the first 1080 in skateboarding history. The fact that Tom Schaar was a 12-year-old sixth-grader makes the feat even more amazing.

Rigid Motions

The act of taking an object and moving it from some starting position to some ending position *without altering its shape or size* is called a **rigid motion** (and sometimes an *isometry*). If, in the process of moving the object, we stretch it, tear it, or generally alter its shape or size, the motion is *not* a rigid motion. Since in a rigid motion the size and shape of an object are not altered, distances between points are preserved: *The distance between any two points X and Y in the starting position is the same as the distance between the same two points in the ending position.* Figure 11-2 illustrates the difference between a motion that is rigid and one that is not. In (a), the motion does not change the shape of the object; only its position in space has changed. In (b), both position *and* shape have changed.

| (a) | (b) |

FIGURE 11-2   (a) A rigid motion preserves distances between points. (b) If the shape is altered, the motion is not rigid.

In defining rigid motions we are completely result oriented. We are only concerned with the *net effect* of the motion—where the object started and where the object ended. What happens during the "trip" is irrelevant. This implies that a rigid motion is completely defined by the starting and ending positions of the object being moved, and two rigid motions that move an object from the same starting position to the same ending position are **equivalent rigid motions**—never mind the details of how they go about it (Fig. 11-3).

| (a) | (b) |

FIGURE 11-3   Equivalent rigid motions (a) and (b) move an object from the same starting position to the same ending position.

A rigid motion of the plane—let's call it $\mathcal{M}$—moves each point in the plane from its starting position P to an ending position P', also in the plane. (From here on we will use script letters such as $\mathcal{M}$ and $\mathcal{N}$ to denote rigid motions, which should eliminate any possible confusion between the point M and the rigid motion $\mathcal{M}$.) We will call the point P' the **image** of the point P under the rigid motion $\mathcal{M}$ and describe this informally by saying that $\mathcal{M}$ *moves P to P'*. (We will also stick to the convention that the image point has the same label as the original point but with a prime symbol added.) It may happen that a point P is moved back to itself under $\mathcal{M}$, in which case we call P a **fixed point** of the rigid motion $\mathcal{M}$.

When it comes to how a rigid motion can move an object, the number of possibilities is surprisingly small. In the case of two-dimensional objects moving in a plane, there are only *four* possibilities. The four types of rigid motions (called **basic rigid motions**) are (1) *reflections*, (2) *rotations*, (3) *translations*, and (4) *glide reflections*. There are no other possibilities. Essentially, this means that when you move a two-dimensional object in the plane, no matter how complicated the motion might be, the net result is equivalent to one, and only one, of these four basic types. (If you are curious, in the case of three-dimensional objects moving in space, there are six basic types of rigid motions: *reflections, rotations, translations, glide reflections,* and two new types called *rotary reflections* and *screw displacements*.)

We will now discuss each of the four basic rigid motions of the plane in a little more detail.

11.2   Reflections

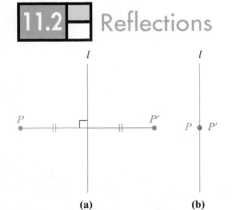

(a)

FIGURE 11-4

A **reflection** in the plane is a rigid motion that moves an object into a new position that is a mirror image of the starting position. In two dimensions, the "mirror" is a line called the **axis** of reflection.

From a purely geometric point of view, a reflection can be defined by showing how it moves a generic point P in the plane. This is shown in Fig. 11-4: The image of any point P is found by drawing a line through P perpendicular to the axis of reflection l and finding the point P' on the opposite side of l at the same distance as P from l. Points on the axis itself are *fixed points* of the reflection [Fig. 11-4(b)].

(b)

EXAMPLE 11.2   REFLECTIONS OF A TRIANGLE

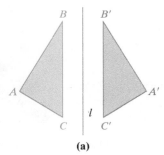

(a)

FIGURE 11-5

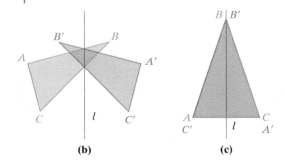

(b)   **(c)**

Figure 11-5 shows three cases of reflection of a triangle ABC. In all cases the original triangle ABC is shaded in blue and the reflected triangle $A'B'C'$ is shaded in red. In (a), the axis of reflection l does not intersect the triangle ABC. In (b), the axis of reflection l cuts through the triangle ABC—here the points where l intersects the triangle are fixed points of the triangle. In (c), the reflected triangle $A'B'C'$ falls on top of the original triangle ABC. The vertex B is a fixed point of the triangle, but the vertices A and C swap positions under the reflection.

The following are simple but useful properties of a reflection.

1. *A reflection is completely determined by its axis l.* If we know the axis of reflection, we can find the image of any point P under the reflection (just drop a perpendicular to the axis through P and find the point on the other side of the axis that is at an equal distance).

2. *A reflection is completely determined by two points (a point and its image).* If we know a point P and its image P' under the reflection (and assuming P' is different from P), we can find the axis l of the reflection (it is the perpendicular bisector of the segment PP'). Once we have the axis l of the reflection, we can find the image of any other point (property 1).

3. *A reflection has infinitely many fixed points.* The *fixed points* of a reflection are all the points on the axis *l*. Points not on the axis of reflection are never fixed.

4. *Reflections are improper rigid motions.* An **improper rigid motion** is one that changes the *left-right* and *clockwise-counterclockwise* orientations of objects. This property is the reason a left hand reflected in a mirror looks like a right hand and the hands of a clock reflected in a mirror move counterclockwise.

5. *Under a reflection, the image of the image is the original object.* For any point *P*, if *P'* is its image then the image of *P'* is *P*. This means that when we apply the same reflection twice, every point ends up in its original position and the rigid motion is equivalent to *not having moved the object at all.*

A rigid motion that is equivalent to not moving the object at all is called the **identity** motion. At first blush it may seem somewhat silly to call the identity motion a motion (after all, nothing moves), but there are very good mathematical reasons to do so, and we will soon see how helpful this convention is for studying and classifying symmetries.

The five properties of reflections listed above can be summarized as follows.

■ PROPERTIES OF REFLECTIONS ────────────────

- ■ A reflection is completely determined by its axis *l*.
- ■ A reflection is completely determined by a single point-image pair *P* and *P'* (as long as *P' ≠ P*).
- ■ A reflection has infinitely many fixed points (all points on *l*).
- ■ A reflection is an *improper* rigid motion.
- ■ When the same reflection is applied twice, we get the *identity* motion.

11.3 Rotations

FIGURE 11-7

Informally, a **rotation** in the plane is a rigid motion that pivots or swings an object around a fixed point *O*. A rotation is defined by two pieces of information: (1) the **rotocenter** (the point *O* that acts as the center of the rotation) and (2) the **angle of rotation** (actually the *measure* of an angle indicating the amount of rotation). (We will describe angle measures using degrees, but converting degrees to radians or radians to degrees is easy if you just remember that 180 degrees equals π radians.) In addition, it is necessary to specify the direction (clockwise or counterclockwise) associated with the angle of rotation.

Figure 11-7 illustrates geometrically how a *clockwise* rotation with rotocenter *O* and angle of rotation α moves a point *P* to the point *P'*.

EXAMPLE 11.3 ROTATIONS OF A TRIANGLE

Figure 11-8 illustrates three cases of rotation of a triangle *ABC*. In all cases the original triangle *ABC* is shaded in blue and the reflected triangle *A'B'C'* is shaded in red. In (a), the rotocenter *O* lies outside the triangle *ABC*. The 90° *clockwise* rotation moved the triangle from the "12 o'clock position" to the "3 o'clock position." (Note that a 90° *counterclockwise* rotation would have moved the triangle *ABC* to the "9 o'clock position.") In (b), the rotocenter *O* is at the center of the triangle *ABC*. The 180° rotation turns the triangle "upside down." For obvious reasons, a 180° rotation is often called a *half-turn*. (With half-turns the result is the same whether we rotate clockwise or counterclockwise, so it is unnecessary to specify a direction.) In (c), the 360° rotation moves every point back to its original position—from the rigid motion point of view it's as if the triangle had not moved.

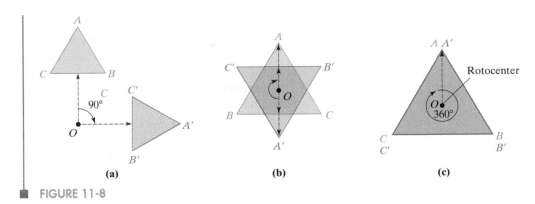

FIGURE 11-8

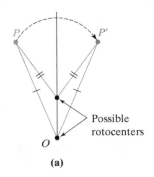

(a)

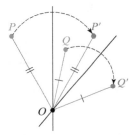

(b)

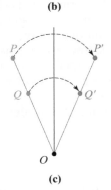

(c)

FIGURE 11-9

The following are some important properties of a rotation.

1. *A rotation is completely determined by four points (two points and their respective images).* Unlike a reflection, a rotation *cannot* be determined by a single point-image pair P and P'; it takes a second point-image pair Q and Q' to nail down the rotation. The reason is that infinitely many rotations can move P to P': Any point located on the perpendicular bisector of the segment PP' can be a rotocenter for such a rotation, as shown in Fig. 11-9(a). Given a second pair of points Q and Q' we can identify the rotocenter O as the point where the perpendicular bisectors of PP' and QQ' meet, as shown in Fig. 11-9(b). Once we have identified the rotocenter O, the angle of rotation α is given by the measure of angle POP' (or for that matter QOQ'—they are the same). [*Note*: In the special case where PP' and QQ' happen to have the same perpendicular bisector, as in Fig. 11-9(c), the rotocenter O is the intersection of PQ and $P'Q'$.]

2. *The rotocenter is the only fixed point of a rotation.* This is true for all rotations except for the identity (where all points are fixed points).

3. *A rotation is a proper rigid motion.* A **proper rigid motion** is one where the left-right and clockwise-counterclockwise orientations are preserved. A rotated left hand remains a left hand, and the hands of a rotated clock still move in the clockwise direction.

   A common misconception is to confuse a 180° rotation with a reflection, but we can see that they are very different from just observing that the reflection is an improper rigid motion, whereas the 180° rotation is a proper rigid motion.

4. *A 360° rotation is the identity motion.* A 360° rotation is equivalent to a 0° rotation, and a 0° rotation is just the identity motion. (The expression "going around full circle" is the well-known colloquial version of this property.)

   It follows that all rotations can be described using an angle of rotation between 0° and 360°. For angles larger than 360° we divide the angle by 360° and just use the remainder (for example, a clockwise rotation by 759° is equivalent to a clockwise rotation by 39°; the remaining 720° count as 0°). In addition, we can describe a rotation using clockwise or counterclockwise orientations (for example, a clockwise rotation by 39° is equivalent to a counterclockwise rotation by 321°).

The four properties of rotations listed above can be summarized as follows.

■ **PROPERTIES OF ROTATIONS** ――――――――――――――

- A rotation is completely determined by *two* point-image pairs P, P' and Q, Q'.
- A rotation that is not the identity motion has only *one* fixed point, its rotocenter.
- A rotation is a *proper* rigid motion.
- A 360° rotation is equivalent to the *identity* motion.

11.4 Translations

FIGURE 11-10

A **translation** consists of essentially dragging an object in a specified *direction* and by a specified amount (the *length* of the translation). The two pieces of information (direction and length of the translation) are combined in the form of a **vector of translation** (usually denoted by *v*). The vector of translation is represented by an arrow—the arrow points in the direction of translation and the length of the arrow is the length of the translation. A very good illustration of a translation in a two-dimensional plane is the dragging of the cursor on a computer screen (Fig. 11-10). Regardless of what happens in between, the net result when you drag an icon on your screen is a translation in a specific direction and by a specific length.

| EXAMPLE 11.4 | TRANSLATION OF A TRIANGLE

Figure 11-11 illustrates the translation of a triangle *ABC*. Two "different" arrows are shown in the figure, but they both have the same length and direction, so they describe the same vector of translation *v*. As long as the arrow points in the proper direction and has the right length, the placement of the arrow in the picture is immaterial.

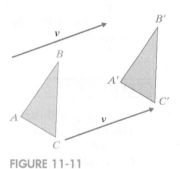

FIGURE 11-11

The following are some important properties of a translation.

1. *A translation is completely determined by two points (a point and its image).* If we are given a point *P* and its image *P'* under a translation, the arrow joining *P* to *P'* gives the vector of the translation. Once we know the vector of the translation, we know where the translation moves any other point. Thus, a single point-image pair *P* and *P'* is all we need to completely determine the translation.

2. *A translation has no fixed points.* In a translation, every point gets moved some distance and in some direction, so there can't be any fixed points.

3. *A translation is a proper rigid motion.* When an object is translated, left-right and clockwise-counterclockwise orientations are preserved: A translated left hand is still a left hand, and the hands of a translated clock still move in the clockwise direction (Fig. 11-12).

FIGURE 11-12

4. *A translation followed by the same translation in the opposite direction is the identity.* The effect of a translation with vector *v* can be undone by a translation of the same length but in the opposite direction (Fig. 11-13). The vector for this opposite translation can be conveniently described as −*v*. Thus, a translation with vector *v* followed with a translation with vector −*v* is equivalent to the identity motion.

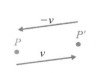

FIGURE 11-13

The four properties of translations listed above can be summarized as follows.

■ PROPERTIES OF TRANSLATIONS —————————————————

- A translation is completely determined by a single point-image pair P and P'.
- A translation has *no* fixed points.
- A translation is a *proper* rigid motion.
- A translation with vector v followed by the translation with vector $-v$ is equivalent to the *identity* motion.

11.5 Glide Reflections

A **glide reflection** is a rigid motion obtained by combining a translation (the glide) with a reflection. Moreover, the axis of reflection *must* be parallel to the direction of translation. Thus, a glide reflection is described by two things: the vector of the translation v and the axis of the reflection l, and these two *must* be parallel. The footprints left behind by someone walking on soft sand (Fig. 11-14) are a classic example of a glide reflection: right and left footprints are images of each other under the combined effects of a reflection (left foot–right foot) and a translation (the step).

FIGURE 11-14

EXAMPLE 11.5   GLIDE REFLECTION OF A TRIANGLE

Figure 11-15 illustrates the result of applying the glide reflection with vector v and axis l to the triangle ABC. We can do this in two different ways, but the final result will be the same. In Fig. 11-15(a), the translation is applied first, moving triangle ABC to the intermediate position $A*B*C*$. The reflection is then applied to $A*B*C*$, giving the final position $A'B'C'$. If we apply the reflection first, the triangle ABC gets moved to the intermediate position $A*B*C*$ [Fig. 11-15(b)] and then translated to the final position $A'B'C'$.

Notice that any point and its image under the glide reflection [for example, A and A' in Fig. 11-15(a)] are on opposite sides but equidistant from the axis l. This implies that the midpoint of the segment joining a point and its image under a glide reflection *must* fall on the axis l [point M in Fig. 11-15(a)].

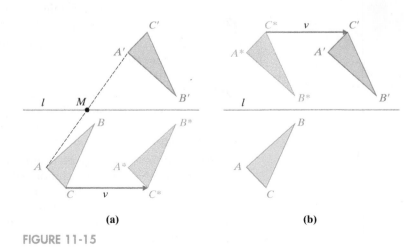

(a)   **(b)**

FIGURE 11-15

The following are a few basic properties of a glide reflection.

1. *A glide reflection is completely determined by four points (two points and their respective images).* Given a point-image pair P and P' under a glide reflection, we do not have enough information to determine the glide reflection, but we do know that the axis l must pass through the midpoint of the line segment PP'. Given a second point-image pair Q and Q', we can determine the axis of the reflection: It is the line passing through the points M (midpoint of the line segment PP') and N (midpoint of the line segment QQ'), as shown in Fig. 11-16(a). Once we find the axis of reflection l, we can find the image of one of the points—say P'—under the reflection. This gives the intermediate point $P*$, and the vector that moves P to $P*$ is the vector of translation v, as shown in Fig. 11-16(b). [In the event that the midpoints of PP' and QQ' are the same point M, as shown in Fig. 11-16(c), we can still find the axis l by drawing a line perpendicular to the line PQ passing through the common midpoint M.]

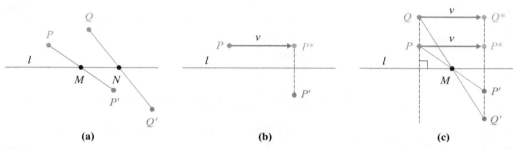

(a)   **(b)**   **(c)**

FIGURE 11-16

2. *A glide reflection has no fixed points.* A fixed point of a glide reflection would have to be a point that ends up exactly where it started after it is first translated and then reflected. This cannot happen because the translation moves every point and the reflection cannot undo the action of the translation.

3. *A glide reflection is an improper rigid motion.* A glide reflection is a combination of a proper rigid motion (the translation) and an improper rigid motion (the reflection). Since the translation preserves left-right and clockwise-counterclockwise orientations but the reflection reverses them, the net result under a glide reflection is that orientations are reversed.

4. *A glide reflection followed by the same glide reflection in the opposite direction is the identity.* To be more precise, if we move an object under a glide reflection with vector of translation v and axis of reflection l and then follow it with another glide reflection with vector of translation $-v$ and axis of reflection still l, we get the identity motion. It is as if the object was not moved at all.

The four properties of glide reflections listed above can be summarized as follows.

■ PROPERTIES OF GLIDE REFLECTIONS ─────────────

- A glide reflection is completely determined by *two* point-image pairs P, P' and Q, Q'.
- A glide reflection has *no* fixed points.
- A glide reflection is an *improper* rigid motion.
- When a glide reflection with vector v and axis of reflection l is followed with a glide reflection with vector $-v$ and the same axis of reflection l we get the *identity* motion.

11.6 Symmetries and Symmetry Types

With an understanding of the four basic rigid motions and their properties, we can now look at the concept of symmetry in a much more precise way. Here, finally, is a good definition of *symmetry*, one that probably would not have made much sense at the start of this chapter: A **symmetry** of an object is a rigid motion that moves the object back onto itself.

One useful way to think of a symmetry is this: You observe the position of an object, and then, while you are not looking, the object is moved. If you can't tell that the object was moved, the rigid motion is a symmetry. It is important to note that this does not necessarily force the rigid motion to be the identity motion. Individual points may be moved to different positions, even though the whole object is moved back into itself. And, of course, the identity motion is itself a symmetry, one possessed by every object and that from now on we will simply call the *identity*.

Since there are only four basic kinds of rigid motions of two-dimensional objects in two-dimensional space, there are also only four possible types of symmetries: *reflection symmetries, rotation symmetries, translation symmetries*, and *glide reflection symmetries*.

> **EXAMPLE 11.6** THE SYMMETRIES OF A SQUARE
>
> What are the possible rigid motions that move the square in Fig. 11-17(a) back onto itself? First, there are *reflection symmetries*. For example, if we use the line l_1 in Fig. 11-17(b) as the axis of reflection, the square falls back into itself with points A and B interchanging places and C and D interchanging places. It is not hard to think of three other reflection symmetries, with axes l_2, l_3, and l_4 as shown in Fig. 11-17(b). Are there any other types of symmetries? Yes—the square has *rotation symmetries* as well. Using the center of the square O as the rotocenter, we can rotate the square by an angle of 90°. This moves the upper-left corner A to the upper-right corner B, B to the lower-right corner C, C to the lower-left corner D, and D to the upper-right corner A. Likewise, rotations with rotocenter O and angles of 180°, 270°, and 360°, respectively, are also symmetries of the square. Notice that the 360° rotation is just the identity.

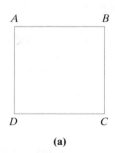
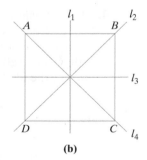
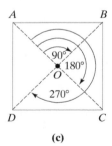

FIGURE 11-17   (a) The original square, (b) reflection symmetries (axes l_1, l_2, l_3, and l_4), and (c) rotation symmetries (rotocenter O and angles of 90°, 180°, 270°, and 360°, respectively).

All in all, we have easily found eight symmetries for the square in Fig. 11-17(a): Four of them are reflections, and the other four are rotations. Could there be more? What if we combined one of the reflections with one of the rotations? A symmetry combined with another symmetry, after all, has to be itself a symmetry. It turns out that the eight symmetries we listed are all there are—no matter how we combine them we always end up with one of the eight (see Exercise 74).

EXAMPLE 11.7 THE SYMMETRIES OF A PROPELLER

Let's now consider the symmetries of the shape shown in Fig. 11-18(a)—a two-dimensional version of a boat propeller (or a ceiling fan if you prefer) with four blades. Once again, we have a shape with four reflection symmetries [the axes of reflection are l_1, l_2, l_3, and l_4 as shown in Fig. 11-18(b)] and four rotation symmetries [with rotocenter located at the center of the propeller and angles of 90°, 180°, 270°, and 360°, respectively, as shown in Fig. 11-18(c)]. And, just as with the square, there are no other possible symmetries.

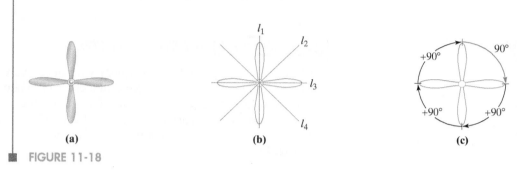

(a)   (b)   (c)

FIGURE 11-18

An important lesson lurks behind Examples 11.6 and 11.7: *Two different-looking objects can have exactly the same set of symmetries.* A good way to think about this is that the square and the propeller, while certainly different objects, are members of the same "symmetry family" and carry exactly the same symmetry genes. Formally, we will say that two objects or shapes are of the same **symmetry type** if they have *exactly* the same set of symmetries. The propeller in Fig. 11-18 and a square both have the same symmetry type called D_4 (shorthand for four reflections plus four rotations). The four-point star, the four-leaf clover, and the decorative tile shown in Fig. 11-19 also have four reflection and four rotation symmetries and, therefore, have symmetry type D_4.

(a)   (b)   (c)

FIGURE 11-19 Objects with symmetry type D_4.

EXAMPLE 11.8 THE SYMMETRY TYPE Z_4

Let's consider now the propeller shown in Fig. 11-20(a). This propeller is only slightly different from the one in Example 11.7, but from the symmetry point of view the difference is significant—here we still have the four rotation symmetries (90°, 180°, 270°, and 360°), but there are no reflection symmetries! [This makes sense because the individual blades of the propeller have no reflection symmetry. As can be seen in Fig. 11-20(c), a vertical reflection is not a symmetry, and neither are any of the other reflections.] This object belongs to a new symmetry family called Z_4 (shorthand for the symmetry type of objects having four rotations only).

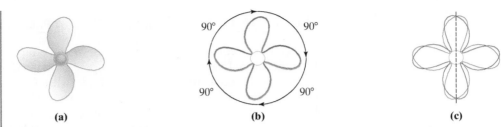

FIGURE 11-20   A propeller with symmetry type Z_4 (four rotation symmetries, no reflection symmetries).

EXAMPLE 11.9   THE SYMMETRY TYPE Z_2

Here is one last propeller example. Every once in a while a propeller looks like the one in Fig. 11-21(a), which is kind of a cross between Figs. 11-20(a) and 11-19(a)—only opposite blades are the same. This figure has no reflection symmetries, and a 90° rotation won't work either [Fig. 11-20(b)]. The only symmetries of this shape are a half-turn (i.e., 180° rotation) and the identity (i.e., a 360° rotation), as shown in Fig. 11-20(c).

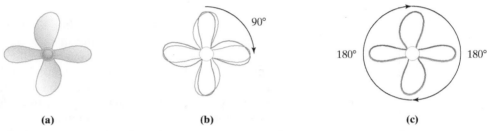

FIGURE 11-21   A propeller with symmetry type Z_2 (two rotation symmetries, no reflection symmetries).

An object having only two rotation symmetries (the identity and a half-turn) is said to be of symmetry type Z_2. Figure 11-22 shows a few additional examples of shapes and objects with symmetry type Z_2.

FIGURE 11-22   Objects with symmetry type Z_2. (a) The letter Z, (b) the letter S (in some fonts but not in others), and (c) the queen of spades (and many other cards in the deck).

EXAMPLE 11.10   THE SYMMETRY TYPE D_1

One of the most common symmetry types occurring in nature is that of objects having a single reflection symmetry plus a single rotation symmetry (the identity). This symmetry type is called D_1. Figure 11-23 shows several examples of shapes and objects having symmetry type D_1. Notice that it doesn't matter if the axis of reflection is vertical, horizontal, or slanted.

- D_N. This is the symmetry type of shapes with both rotation and reflection symmetries. The subscript N ($N = 1, 2, 3$, etc.) denotes the number of reflection symmetries, which is always equal to the number of rotation symmetries. (The rotations are an automatic consequence of the reflections—an object can't have reflection symmetries without having an equal number of rotation symmetries.)
- Z_N. This is the symmetry type of shapes with rotation symmetries only. The subscript N ($N = 1, 2, 3$, etc.) denotes the number of rotation symmetries.
- D_∞. This is the symmetry type of a circle and of circular objects such as rings and washers, the only possible two-dimensional shapes or objects with an infinite number of rotations and reflections.

11.7 Patterns

Well, we've come a long way, but we have yet to see examples of shapes having translation or glide reflection symmetry. If we think of objects as being finite, translation symmetry is impossible: A slide will always move the object to a new position different from its original position! But if we broaden our horizons and consider infinite "objects," translation and glide reflection symmetries are indeed possible.

We will formally define a **pattern** as an infinite "object" consisting of an infinitely repeating basic design called the **motif** of the pattern. The reason we have "object" in quotation marks is that a pattern is really an abstraction—in the real world there are no infinite objects as such, although the idea of an infinitely repeating motif is familiar to us from such everyday objects as pottery, textiles, and tile designs (Fig. 11-27).

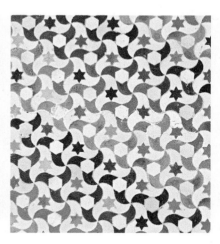

FIGURE 11-27   Patterns in pottery, textiles, and tile designs.

Just like finite shapes, *patterns* can be classified by their symmetries. The classification of patterns according to their symmetry type is of fundamental importance in the study of molecular and crystal organization in chemistry, so it is not surprising that some of the first people to investigate the symmetry types of patterns were crystallographers. Archaeologists and anthropologists have also found that analyzing the symmetry types used by a particular culture in their textiles and pottery helps them gain a better understanding of that culture.

We will briefly discuss the symmetry types of *border* and *wallpaper* patterns. A comprehensive study of patterns is beyond the scope of this book, so we will not go into as much detail as we did with finite shapes.

Border Patterns

Border patterns (also called *linear* patterns) are patterns in which a basic *motif* repeats itself indefinitely in a single direction (or creates the illusion of doing so), as in a decorative fabric, a ribbon, or a ceramic pot (Fig. 11-28).

The most common direction in a border pattern (what we will call the *direction of the pattern*) is horizontal, but in general a border pattern can be in any direction (vertical, slanted 45°, etc.). (For typesetting in a book, it is much more convenient to display a border pattern horizontally, so you will only see examples of horizontal border patterns.)

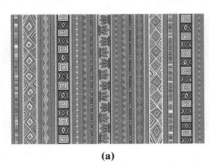
(a)

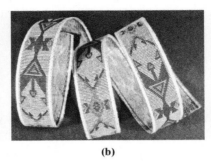
(b)

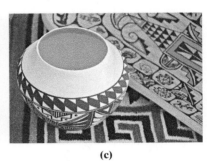
(c)

FIGURE 11-28   (a) African textile patterns, (b) ribbon with Navajo pattern, and (c) Hopi Pueblo pot.

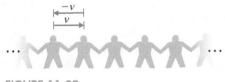

FIGURE 11-29

We will now discuss what kinds of symmetries are possible in a border pattern. Fortunately, the number of possibilities is quite small.

- **Translations.** A border pattern always has *translation symmetries* —they come with the territory. There is a *basic* translation symmetry v (v moves each copy of the motif one unit to the right), the opposite translation $-v$, and any multiple of v or $-v$ (Fig. 11-29).

- **Reflections.** A border pattern can have (a) no reflection symmetry [Fig. 11-30(a)], (b) *horizontal* reflection symmetry only [Fig. 11-30(b)], (c) *vertical* reflection symmetries only [Fig. 11-30(c)], or (d) both *horizontal* and *vertical* reflection symmetries [Fig. 11-30(d)]. In this last case the border pattern automatically picks up a half-turn symmetry as well. In terms of reflection symmetries, Fig. 11-30 illustrates the only four possibilities for reflection symmetry in a border pattern.

··· J J J J J J ···   ··· B·B·B·B·B·B ···   ··· A A A A A A ···   ··· X X X X X X ···
(a)   (b)   (c)   (d)

FIGURE 11-30

- **Rotations.** Like with any other object, the identity is a rotation symmetry of every border pattern, so every border pattern has at least one rotation symmetry. The only other possible rotation symmetry of a border pattern is a 180° rotation. Clearly, no other angle of rotation can take a horizontal pattern and move it back onto itself. Thus, in terms of rotation symmetry there are two kinds of border patterns: those whose only rotation symmetry is the identity and those having a half-turn (180° rotation) symmetry in addition to the identity. The former are border patterns that have a right side "up" [Fig. 11-31(a)]; the latter are border patterns that have no "up" or "down"—they look the same either way [Fig. 11-31(b)].

··· A A A A A ···   ··· Z Z Z Z Z ···
(a)   (b)

FIGURE 11-31

■ *Glide reflections.* A border pattern can have a *glide reflection symmetry*, but there is only one way this can happen: The axis of reflection *has* to be a line along the center of the pattern, and the *reflection part of the glide reflection is not by itself a symmetry of the pattern.* This means that a border pattern having horizontal reflection symmetry such as the one shown in Fig. 11-32(a) is not considered to have glide reflection symmetry. On the other hand, the border pattern shown in Fig. 11-32(b) does not have horizontal reflection symmetry (the footprints do not get reflected into footprints), but a glide by the vector *w* combined with a reflection along the axis *l* result in an honest-to-goodness glide reflection symmetry. (An important property of the glide reflection symmetry is that the vector *w* is always half the length of the basic translation symmetry *v*. This implies that two consecutive glide reflection symmetries are equivalent to the basic translation symmetry.) The border pattern in Fig. 11-32(c) has vertical reflection symmetry as well as glide reflection symmetry. In these cases half-turn symmetry (rotocenter *O*) comes free in the bargain.

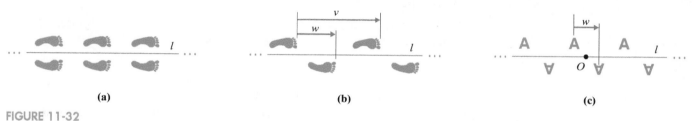

(a) (b) (c)

FIGURE 11-32

Combining the preceding observations, we get the following list of possible symmetries of a border pattern. (For simplicity, we assume that the border pattern is in a horizontal direction.)

1. The *identity:* Everything has identity symmetry.
2. *Translation:* By definition all border patterns have translation symmetry (Fig. 11-29).
3. *Horizontal reflection:* Some border patterns have it, some don't. There is only one possible horizontal axis of reflection, and it must run through the middle of the pattern [Fig. 11-30(b)].
4. *Vertical reflection:* Some border patterns have it, some don't. Vertical axes of reflection (i.e., axes perpendicular to the direction of the pattern) can run through the middle of a motif or between two motifs [Fig. 11-30(c)].
5. *Half-turn:* Some border patterns have it, some don't. Rotocenters can be located at the center of a motif or between two motifs [Fig. 11-31(b)].
6. *Glide reflection:* Some border patterns have it, some don't. Neither the reflection nor the glide can be symmetries on their own. The length of the glide is half that of the basic translation. The axis of the reflection runs through the middle of the pattern [Figs. 11-32(b) and (c)].

Based on the various possible combinations of these symmetries, border patterns can be classified into just *seven different symmetry types,* which we list next. (Since all border patterns have identity symmetry and translation symmetry, we will only make reference to the additional symmetries.)

■ Type 11. This symmetry type represents border patterns that have no symmetries beyond the identity and translation symmetry. The pattern of J's in Fig. 11-30(a) is an example of this symmetry type.
■ Type 1m. This symmetry type represents border patterns with just horizontal reflection symmetry. The pattern of B's in Fig. 11-30(b) is an example of this symmetry type.

■ The oddball, two-symbol codes are a classification scheme originally developed by crystallographers called the *standard crystallographic notation*. The first symbol is either an *m* (indicating that the pattern has vertical reflections) or a 1 (indicating no vertical reflections). The second symbol specifies the existence of a horizontal reflection (*m*), a glide reflection (*g*), a half-turn (2), or none of these (1).

- **Type m1.** This symmetry type represents border patterns with *just vertical reflection symmetry*. The pattern of A's in Fig. 11-30(c) is an example of this symmetry type.

- **Type mm.** This symmetry type represents border patterns with *both a horizontal and a vertical reflection symmetry*. When both of these symmetries are present, there is also *half-turn symmetry*. The pattern of X's in Fig. 11-30(d) is an example of this symmetry type.

- **Type 12.** This symmetry type represents border patterns with *only half-turn symmetry*. The pattern of Z's in Fig. 11-31(b) is an example of this symmetry type.

- **Type 1g.** This symmetry type represents border patterns with *only glide reflection symmetry*. The pattern of footprints in Fig. 11-32(b) is an example of this symmetry type.

- **Type mg.** This symmetry type represents border patterns with *vertical reflection and glide reflection symmetry*. When both of these symmetries are present, there is also *half-turn symmetry*. The pattern in Fig. 11-32(c) is an example of this symmetry type.

Table 11-1 summarizes the symmetries for each of the seven border pattern symmetry types.

	Translation	Horizontal reflection	Vertical reflection	Half-turn	Glide reflection	Example
11	Yes	No	No	No	No	Fig. 11-30(a)
1m	Yes	Yes	No	No	No	Fig. 11-30(b)
m1	Yes	No	Yes	No	No	Fig. 11-30(c)
mm	Yes	Yes	Yes	Yes	No	Fig. 11-30(d)
12	Yes	No	No	Yes	No	Fig. 11-31(b)
1g	Yes	No	No	No	Yes	Fig. 11-32(b)
mg	Yes	No	Yes	Yes	Yes	Fig. 11-32(c)

■ **TABLE 11-1**   The Seven Symmetry Types of Border Patterns

Wallpaper Patterns

Wallpaper patterns are patterns that cover the plane by repeating a *motif* indefinitely along *two or more* nonparallel directions. Typical examples of such patterns can be found in wallpaper (of course), carpets, and textiles.

With wallpaper patterns things get a bit more complicated, so we will skip the details. The possible symmetries of a wallpaper pattern are as follows:

- **Translations.** Every wallpaper pattern has translation symmetry in at least two different (nonparallel) directions (Fig. 11-33).

- **Reflections.** A wallpaper pattern can have (a) no reflections, (b) reflections in only one direction, (c) reflections in two nonparallel directions, (d) reflections in three nonparallel directions, (e) reflections in four nonparallel directions, and (f) reflections in six nonparallel directions. There are no other possibilities. (Note that it is not possible for a wallpaper pattern to have reflections in exactly five different directions.)

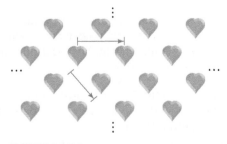

FIGURE 11-33

 **MyMathLab®**
The 17 symmetry types of wallpaper patterns are listed and illustrated in *The 17 Wallpaper Symmetry Types* chart in the online Appendix in MyMathLab.*

■ **Rotations.** In terms of rotation symmetries, a wallpaper pattern can have (a) the identity only, (b) two rotations (identity and 180°), (c) three rotations (identity, 120°, and 240°), (d) four rotations (identity, 90°, 180°, and 270°), and (e) six rotations (identity, 60°, 120°, 180°, 240°, and 300°). There are no other possibilities. (Once again, note that a wallpaper pattern cannot have just five different rotations.)

■ **Glide reflections.** A wallpaper pattern can have (a) no glide reflections, (b) glide reflections in only one direction, (c) glide reflections in two nonparallel directions, (d) glide reflections in three nonparallel directions, (e) glide reflections in four nonparallel directions, and (f) glide reflections in six nonparallel directions. There are no other possibilities.

In the early 1900s, it was shown mathematically that there are *only 17 possible symmetry types for wallpaper patterns.* This is quite a surprising fact—it means that the hundreds and thousands of wallpaper patterns one can find at a decorating store all fall into just 17 different symmetry families.

Conclusion

FIGURE 11-34

There is no doubt that a *Z* and a queen of spades are two very different things (Fig. 11-34)—they look different and they serve completely different purposes. In a very fundamental way, however, they share a very important characteristic: They have exactly the same set of symmetries (identity and half-turn). Understanding the symmetries of an object and being able to sort and classify the objects in our physical world by their symmetries is a rare but useful skill, and artists, designers, architects, archaeologists, chemists, and mathematicians often rely on it. In this chapter we explored some of the basic ideas behind the mathematical study of symmetry.

Although we live in a three-dimensional world inhabited by mostly three-dimensional objects and shapes, in this chapter we restricted ourselves to studying the symmetries of two-dimensional objects and shapes for the simple reason that it is a lot easier.

A first important step in understanding symmetries is to understand the different kinds of *rigid motions*—motions that move an object while preserving its original shape. It is somewhat surprising that despite the infinite freedom we have to move an object, for two-dimensional objects there are just four basic types of rigid motions: *reflections, rotations, translations,* and *glide reflections.* In other words, no matter how complicated or convoluted the actual "trip" taken by the object might appear to be, in the final analysis the motion is equivalent to a single reflection, a single rotation, a single translation, or a single glide reflection.

From the four different kinds of rigid motions in the plane we inherit the four different possible kinds of symmetry in the plane—*reflection, rotation, translation,* and *glide reflection.* Finite objects can only have rotations, or reflections *and* rotations (in an equal number). Patterns can have a little more flexibility in their combinations of the four symmetries but not as much as one would think—only seven symmetry types are possible in the case of border patterns and only 17 symmetry types are possible in the case of wallpaper patterns.

* MyMathLab code required.

KEY CONCEPTS

11.1 Rigid Motions

- **rigid motion:** a motion that moves an object without altering its shape or size, **327**
- **equivalent rigid motions:** two rigid motions that move an object from the same starting position to the same ending position, regardless of what happens in-between, **327**
- **image:** the ending position of a point or object after a rigid motion is applied, **327**
- **fixed point:** any point that is not moved by the rigid motion, **327**

11.2 Reflections

- **reflection:** a rigid motion that moves a point to the opposite side and at the same distance from the axis of reflection, **328**
- **improper rigid motion:** a rigid motion that changes the left-right and clockwise-counterclockwise orientations of objects, **329**
- **identity rigid motion:** the rigid "motion" that does not move an object at all, **329**

11.3 Rotations

- **rotation:** a rigid motion that swings or pivots an object around a fixed point, **329**
- **rotocenter:** the fixed point or center of the rotation, **329**
- **proper rigid motion:** a rigid motion that preserves the left-right and clockwise- . counterclockwise orientations of objects, **330**

11.4 Translations

- **translation:** a rigid motion that moves an object in a specified direction and by a specified length, **331**
- **vector of translation:** an arrow showing the direction and length of the translation, **331**

11.5 Glide Reflections

- **glide reflection:** a rigid motion that combines a translation and a reflection (the axis of the reflection must be parallel to the vector of the translation), **332**

11.6 Symmetries and Symmetry Types

- **symmetry:** a rigid motion that moves an object back onto itself, **334**
- **symmetry type:** a classification of objects based on their symmetries (objects that have the same set of symmetries have the same symmetry type), **335**
- D_N: the symmetry type of objects having N reflection symmetries and N rotation symmetries, **339**
- Z_N: the symmetry type of objects having N rotation symmetries (and *no* reflection symmetries), **339**

11.7 Patterns

- **pattern:** an infinite "object" consisting of an infinitely repeating basic motif, **339**
- **motif:** the infinitely repeating basic building block of a pattern, **339**
- **border pattern:** a pattern where the motif repeats itself in a single direction, **340**
- **wallpaper pattern:** a pattern that fills the plane by repeating a motif in two or more nonparallel directions, **342**

EXERCISES

WALKING

11.1 Rigid Motions

No exercises for this section.

11.2 Reflections

1. In Fig. 11-35, indicate which point is the image of P under

  (a) the reflection with axis l_1.

  (b) the reflection with axis l_2.

  (c) the reflection with axis l_3.

  (d) the reflection with axis l_4.

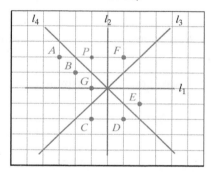

FIGURE 11-35

2. In Fig. 11-36, indicate which point is the image of P under

  (a) the reflection with axis l_1.

  (b) the reflection with axis l_2.

  (c) the reflection with axis l_3.

  (d) the reflection with axis l_4.

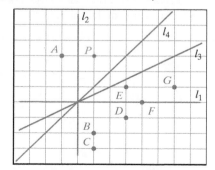

FIGURE 11-36

3. In Fig. 11-37, A' is the image of A under a reflection.

  (a) Find the axis of the reflection.

  (b) Find the image of A' under the reflection.

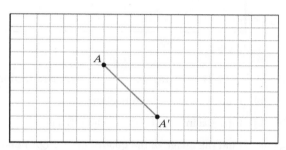

FIGURE 11-37

4. In Fig. 11-38, P' is the image of P under a reflection.

  (a) Find the axis of the reflection.

  (b) Find the image of P' under the reflection.

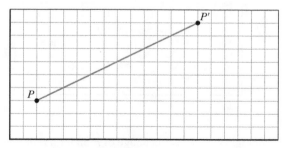

FIGURE 11-38

5. In Fig. 11-39, l is the axis of reflection.

  (a) Find the image of S under the reflection.

  (b) Find the image of quadrilateral $PQRS$ under the reflection.

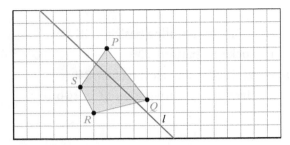

FIGURE 11-39

6. In Fig. 11-40, *l* is the axis of reflection.

   (a) Find the image of *P* under the reflection.

   (b) Find the image of the parallelogram *PQRS* under the reflection.

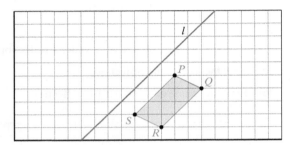

FIGURE 11-40

7. In Fig. 11-41, *P′* is the image of *P* under a reflection.

   (a) Find the axis of the reflection.

   (b) Find the image of *S* under the reflection.

   (c) Find the image of the quadrilateral *PQRS* under the reflection.

   (d) Find a point on the quadrilateral *PQRS* that is a fixed point of the reflection.

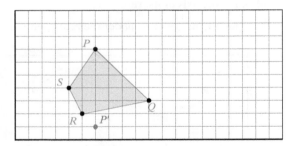

FIGURE 11-41

8. In Fig. 11-42, *P′* is the image of *P* under a reflection.

   (a) Find the axis of the reflection.

   (b) Find the image of *S* under the reflection.

   (c) Find the image of the quadrilateral *PQRS* under the reflection.

   (d) Find a point on the quadrilateral *PQRS* that is a fixed point of the reflection.

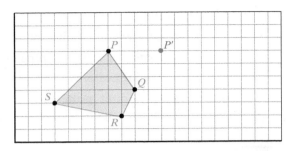

FIGURE 11-42

9. In Fig. 11-43, *P′* is the image of *P* under a reflection.

   (a) Find the axis of the reflection.

   (b) Find the image of the shaded arrow under the reflection.

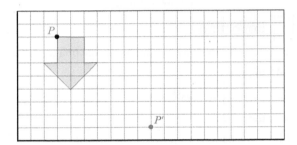

FIGURE 11-43

10. In Fig. 11-44, *R′* is the image of *R* under a reflection.

   (a) Find the axis of reflection.

   (b) Find the image of the shaded arrow under the reflection.

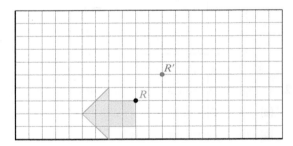

FIGURE 11-44

11. In Fig. 11-45, *A* and *B* are fixed points of a reflection. Find the image of the shaded region under the reflection.

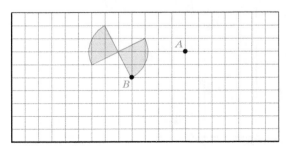

FIGURE 11-45

12. In Fig. 11-46, A and B are fixed points of a reflection. Find the image of the shaded region under the reflection.

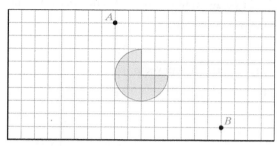

FIGURE 11-46

11.3 Rotations

13. In Fig. 11-47, indicate which point is

(a) the image of B under a 90° clockwise rotation with rotocenter A.

(b) the image of A under a 90° clockwise rotation with rotocenter B.

(c) the image of D under a 60° clockwise rotation with rotocenter B.

(d) the image of D under a 120° clockwise rotation with rotocenter B.

(e) the image of I under a 3690° clockwise rotation with rotocenter A.

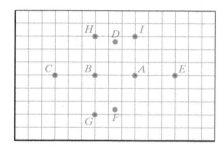

FIGURE 11-47

14. In Fig. 11-47, indicate which point is

(a) the image of C under a 90° counterclockwise rotation with rotocenter B.

(b) the image of F under a 60° clockwise rotation with rotocenter A.

(c) the image of F under a 120° clockwise rotation with rotocenter B.

(d) the image of I under a 90° clockwise rotation with rotocenter H.

(e) the image of G under a 3870° counterclockwise rotation with rotocenter B.

15. In each case, give an answer between 0° and 360°.

(a) A clockwise rotation by an angle of 710° is equivalent to a counterclockwise rotation by an angle of _____.

(b) A clockwise rotation by an angle of 710° is equivalent to a clockwise rotation by an angle of _____.

(c) A counterclockwise rotation by an angle of 7100° is equivalent to a clockwise rotation by an angle of _____.

(d) A clockwise rotation by an angle of 71,000° is equivalent to a clockwise rotation by an angle of _____.

16. In each case, give an answer between 0° and 360°.

(a) A clockwise rotation by an angle of 500° is equivalent to a clockwise rotation by an angle of _____.

(b) A clockwise rotation by an angle of 500° is equivalent to a counterclockwise rotation by an angle of _____.

(c) A clockwise rotation by an angle of 5000° is equivalent to a clockwise rotation by an angle of _____.

(d) A clockwise rotation by an angle of 50,000° is equivalent to a counterclockwise rotation by an angle of _____.

17. In Fig. 11-48, a rotation moves B to B' and C to C'.

(a) Find the rotocenter.

(b) Find the image of triangle ABC under the rotation.

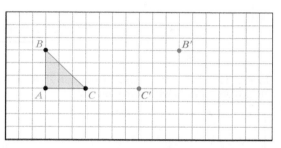

FIGURE 11-48

18. In Fig. 11-49, a rotation moves A to A' and B to B'.

(a) Find the rotocenter O.

(b) Find the image of the shaded arrow under the rotation.

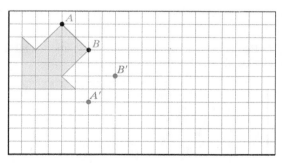

FIGURE 11-49

19. In Fig. 11-50, a rotation moves A to A' and B to B'.

(a) Find the rotocenter O.

(b) Find the image of the shaded arrow under the rotation.

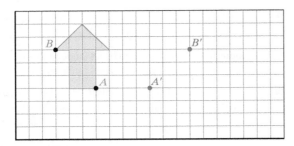

FIGURE 11-50

20. In Fig. 11-51, a rotation moves Q to Q' and R to R'.

(a) Find the rotocenter.

(b) Find the angle of rotation.

(c) Find the image of quadrilateral $PQRS$ under the rotation.

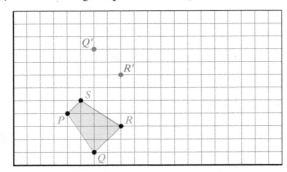

FIGURE 11-51

21. In Fig. 11-52, find the image of triangle ABC under a 60° clockwise rotation with rotocenter O.

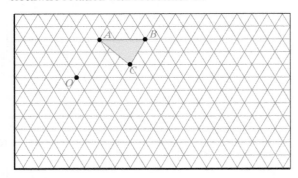

FIGURE 11-52

22. In Fig. 11-53, find the image of $ABCD$ under a 60° counter-clockwise rotation with rotocenter O.

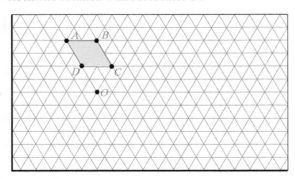

FIGURE 11-53

11.4 Translations

23. In Fig. 11-54, indicate which point is the image of P under

(a) the translation with vector v_1.

(b) the translation with vector v_2.

(c) the translation with vector v_3.

(d) the translation with vector v_4.

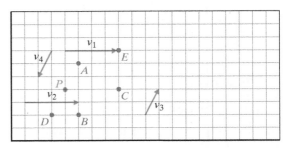

FIGURE 11-54

24. In Fig. 11-55, indicate which point is the image of P under

(a) the translation with vector v_1.

(b) the translation with vector v_2.

(c) the translation with vector v_3.

(d) the translation with vector v_4.

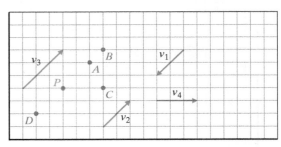

FIGURE 11-55

25. In Fig. 11-56, E' is the image of E under a translation.

(a) Find the image of A under the translation.

(b) Find the image of the shaded figure under the translation.

(c) Draw a vector for the translation.

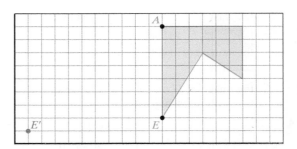

FIGURE 11-56

26. In Fig. 11-57, Q' is the image of Q under a translation.

   (a) Find the image of P under the translation.

   (b) Find the image of the shaded quadrilateral under the translation.

   (c) Draw a vector for the translation.

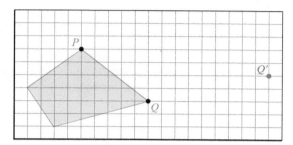

FIGURE 11-57

27. In Fig. 11-58, D' is the image of D under a translation. Find the image of the shaded trapezoid under the translation.

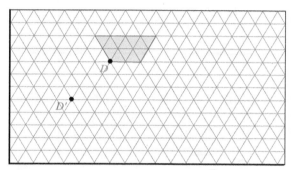

FIGURE 11-58

28. In Fig. 11-59, Q' is the image of Q under a translation. Find the image of the shaded region under the translation.

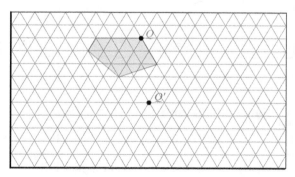

FIGURE 11-59

11.5   Glide Reflections

29. Given a glide reflection with vector v and axis l as shown in Fig. 11-60, find the image of the triangle ABC under the glide reflection.

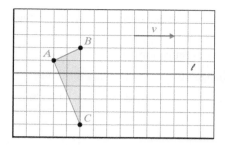

FIGURE 11-60

30. Given a glide reflection with vector v and axis l as shown in Fig. 11-61, find the image of the quadrilateral $ABCD$ under the glide reflection.

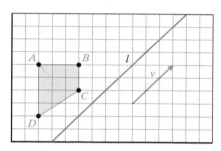

FIGURE 11-61

31. In Fig. 11-62, D' is the image of D under a glide reflection having axis l. Find the image of the polygon $ABCDE$ under the glide reflection.

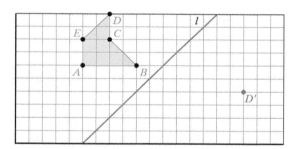

FIGURE 11-62

32. In Fig. 11-63, P' is the image of P under a glide reflection having axis l. Find the image of the quadrilateral $PQRS$ under the glide reflection.

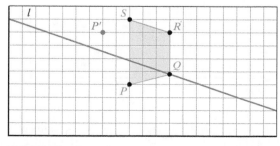

FIGURE 11-63

33. In Fig. 11-64, B' is the image of B and D' is the image of D under a glide reflection.

   (a) Find the axis of reflection.

   (b) Find the image of A under the glide reflection.

   (c) Find the image of the shaded figure under the glide reflection.

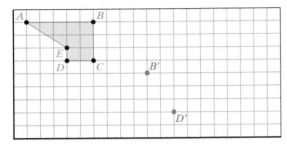

FIGURE 11-64

34. In Fig. 11-65, A' is the image of A and C' is the image of C under a glide reflection.

   (a) Find the axis of reflection.

   (b) Find the image of B under the glide reflection.

   (c) Find the image of the shaded figure under the glide reflection.

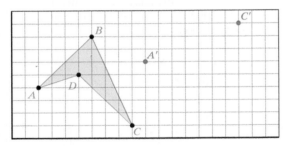

FIGURE 11-65

35. In Fig. 11-66, P' is the image of P and Q' is the image of Q under a glide reflection. Find the image of the shaded figure under the glide reflection.

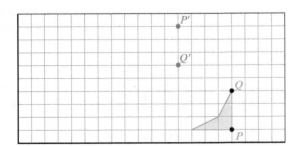

FIGURE 11-66

36. In Fig. 11-67, P' is the image of P and Q' is the image of Q under a glide reflection. Find the image of the shaded figure under the glide reflection.

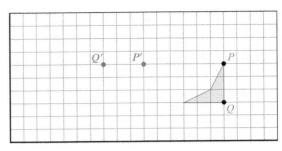

FIGURE 11-67

37. In Fig. 11-68, D' is the image of D and C' is the image of C under a glide reflection. Find the image of the shaded figure under the glide reflection.

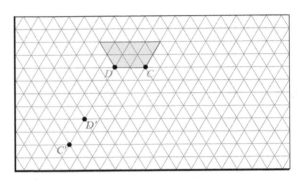

FIGURE 11-68

38. In Fig. 11-69, A' is the image of A and D' is the image of D under a glide reflection. Find the image of the shaded figure under the glide reflection.

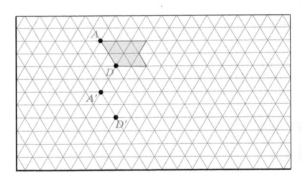

FIGURE 11-69

11.6 **Symmetries and Symmetry Types**

39. List the symmetries of each object shown in Fig. 11-70. (Describe each symmetry by giving specifics—the axes of reflection, the centers and angles of rotation, etc.)

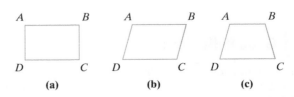

FIGURE 11-70

40. List the symmetries of each object shown in Fig. 11-71. (Describe each symmetry by giving specifics—the axes of reflection, the centers and angles of rotation, etc.)

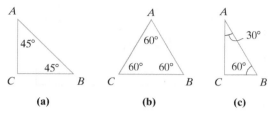

    (a)   (b)   (c)

FIGURE 11-71

41. List the symmetries of each object shown in Fig. 11-72. (Describe each symmetry by giving specifics—the axes of reflection, the centers and angles of rotation, etc.)

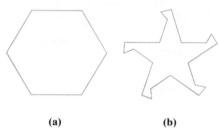

    (a)   (b)

FIGURE 11-72

42. List the symmetries of each object shown in Fig. 11-73. (Describe each symmetry by giving specifics—the axes of reflection, the centers and angles of rotation, etc.)

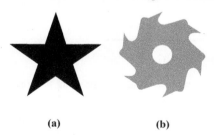

    (a)   (b)

FIGURE 11-73

43. For each of the objects in Exercise 39, give its symmetry type.

44. For each of the objects in Exercise 40, give its symmetry type.

45. For each of the objects in Exercise 41, give its symmetry type.

46. For each of the objects in Exercise 42, give its symmetry type.

47. Find the symmetry type for each of the following letters.

  (a) A   **(b)** D

  (c) L   **(d)** Z

  (e) H   **(f)** N

48. Find the symmetry type for each of the following symbols.

  (a) \$ **(b)** @

  (c) %   **(d)** ×

  (e) &

49. Give an example of a capital letter of the alphabet that has symmetry type

  (a) Z_1. **(b)** D_1.

  (c) Z_2. **(d)** D_2.

50. Give an example of a one- or two-digit number that has symmetry type

  (a) Z_1. **(b)** D_1.

  (c) Z_2. **(d)** D_2.

11.7 Patterns

51. Classify each border pattern by its symmetry type. Use the standard crystallographic notation (mm, mg, m1, 1m, 1g, 12, or 11).

  (a) ... A A A A A ...
  (b) ... D D D D D ...
  (c) ... Z Z Z Z Z ...
  (d) ... L L L L L ...

52. Classify each border pattern by its symmetry type. Use the standard crystallographic notation (mm, mg, m1, 1m, 1g, 12, or 11).

  (a) ...J J J J J...
  (b) ...H H H H H...
  (c) ...W W W W W...
  (d) ...N N N N N...

53. Classify each border pattern by its symmetry type. Use the standard crystallographic notation (mm, mg, m1, 1m, 1g, 12, or 11).

  (a) ...qpqpqpqp...
  (b) ...pdpdpdpd...
  (c) ...pbpbpbpb...
  (d) ...pqbdpqbd...

54. Classify each border pattern by its symmetry type. Use the standard crystallographic notation (mm, mg, m1, 1m, 1g, 12, or 11).

  (a) ...qbqbqbqb...
  (b) ...qdqdqdqd...
  (c) ...dbdbdbdb...
  (d) ...qpdbqpdb...

55. If a border pattern consists of repeating a motif of symmetry type Z_2, what is the symmetry type of the border pattern?

56. If a border pattern consists of repeating a motif of symmetry type Z_1, what is the symmetry type of the border pattern?

57. Imagine a border pattern of type m1 placed between parallel lines l_1 and l_2 (Fig. 11-74). Create a new border pattern twice the height by reflecting a copy of the original pattern about l_2. What is the symmetry type of the new border pattern?

FIGURE 11-74

58. Imagine a border pattern of type 12 placed between parallel lines l_1 and l_2 (Fig. 11-74). Create a new border pattern twice the height by rotating a copy of the original pattern 180 degrees and gluing both copies along line l_2. What is the symmetry type of this new border pattern?

JOGGING

59. The minute hand of a clock is pointing at the number 9, and it is then wound clockwise 7080 degrees.

(a) How many full hours has the hour hand moved?

(b) At what number on the clock does the minute hand point at the end?

60. Name the rigid motion (translation, reflection, glide reflection, or rotation) that moves footprint 1 onto footprint

(a) 2   (b) 3

(c) 4   (d) 5

FIGURE 11-75

61. In each case, determine whether the rigid motion is a reflection, rotation, translation, or glide reflection or the identity motion.

(a) The rigid motion is proper and has exactly one fixed point.

(b) The rigid motion is proper and has infinitely many fixed points.

(c) The rigid motion is improper and has infinitely many fixed points.

(d) The rigid motion is improper and has no fixed points.

*Exercises 62 through 69 deal with combining rigid motions. Given two rigid motions $\mathcal{M}$ and $\mathcal{N}$, we can combine the two rigid motions by first applying $\mathcal{M}$ and then applying $\mathcal{N}$ to the result. The rigid motion defined by combining $\mathcal{M}$ and $\mathcal{N}$ ($\mathcal{M}$ goes first, $\mathcal{N}$ goes second) is called the **product** of $\mathcal{M}$ and $\mathcal{N}$.*

62. In Fig. 11-76, l_1, l_2, l_3, and l_4 are axes of reflection. In each case, indicate which point is the image of P under

(a) the product of the reflection with axis l_1 and the reflection with axis l_2.

(b) the product of the reflection with axis l_2 and the reflection with axis l_1.

(c) the product of the reflection with axis l_2 and the reflection with axis l_3.

(d) the product of the reflection with axis l_3 and the reflection with axis l_2.

(e) the product of the reflection with axis l_1 and the reflection with axis l_4.

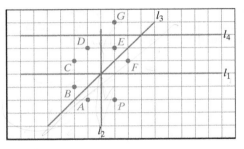

FIGURE 11-76

63. In Fig. 11-77, indicate which point is the image of P under

(a) the product of the reflection with axis l and the 90° clockwise rotation with rotocenter A.

(b) the product of the 90° clockwise rotation with rotocenter A and the reflection with axis l.

(c) the product of the reflection with axis l and the 180° rotation with rotocenter A.

(d) the product of the 180° rotation with rotocenter A and the reflection with axis l.

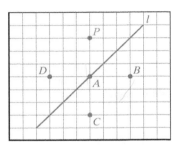

FIGURE 11-77

64. In each case, state whether the rigid motion $\mathcal{M}$ is proper or improper.

(a) $\mathcal{M}$ is the product of a proper rigid motion and an improper rigid motion.

(b) $\mathcal{M}$ is the product of an improper rigid motion and an improper rigid motion.

(c) $\mathcal{M}$ is the product of a reflection and a rotation.

(d) $\mathcal{M}$ is the product of two reflections.

65. Suppose that a rigid motion $\mathcal{M}$ is the product of a reflection with axis l_1 and a reflection with axis l_2, where l_1 and l_2 intersect at a point C. Explain why $\mathcal{M}$ must be a rotation with center C.

66. Suppose that the rigid motion $\mathcal{M}$ is the product of the reflection with axis l_1 and the reflection with axis l_3, where l_1 and l_3 are parallel. Explain why $\mathcal{M}$ must be a translation.

67. In Fig. 11-78, l_1 and l_2 intersect at C, and the angle between them is α.

(a) Give the rotocenter, angle, and direction of rotation of the product of the reflection with axis l_1 and the reflection with axis l_2.

(b) Give the rotocenter, angle, and direction of rotation of the product of the reflection with axis l_2 and the reflection with axis l_1.

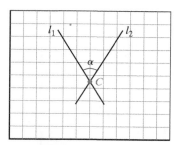

FIGURE 11-78

68. In Fig. 11-79, l_1 and l_3 are parallel and the distance between them is d.

(a) Give the length and direction of the vector of the translation that is the product of the reflection with axis l_1 and the reflection with axis l_3.

(b) Give the length and direction of the vector of the translation that is the product of the reflection with axis l_3 and the reflection with axis l_1.

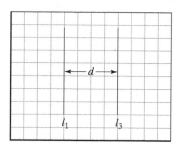

FIGURE 11-79

69. In Fig. 11-80, P' is the image of P under a translation $\mathcal{M}$ and Q' is the image of Q under a translation $\mathcal{N}$.

(a) Find the images of P and Q under the product of $\mathcal{M}$ and $\mathcal{N}$.

(b) Show that the product of $\mathcal{M}$ and $\mathcal{N}$ is a translation. Give a geometric description of the vector of the translation.

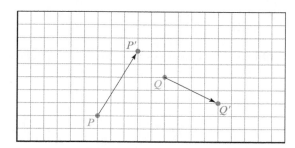

FIGURE 11-80

70. (a) Explain why a border pattern cannot have a reflection symmetry along an axis forming a 45° angle with the direction of the pattern.

(b) Explain why a border pattern can have only horizontal and/or vertical reflection symmetry.

71. A rigid motion $\mathcal{M}$ moves the triangle PQR into the triangle $P'Q'R'$ as shown in Fig. 11-81. Explain why the rigid motion $\mathcal{M}$ must be a glide reflection.

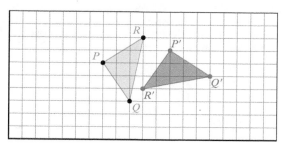

FIGURE 11-81

RUNNING

72. Construct border patterns for each of the seven symmetry types using copies of the symbol ♥ (and rotated versions of it).

73. Let the six symmetries of the equilateral triangle ABC shown in Fig. 11-82 be denoted as follows: r_1 denotes the reflection with axis l_1; r_2 denotes the reflection with axis l_2; r_3 denotes the reflection with axis l_3; R_1 denotes the 120° clockwise rotation with rotocenter O; R_2 denotes the 240° clockwise rotation with rotocenter O; I denotes the identity symmetry. Complete the symmetry "multiplication table" by entering, in each row and column of the table, the product of the row and the column (i.e., the result of applying first the symmetry in the row and then the symmetry in the column). For example, the entry in row r_1 and column r_2 is R_1 because the product of the reflection r_1 and the reflection r_2 is the rotation R_1.

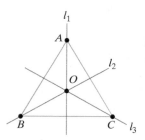

FIGURE 11-82

	r_1	r_2	r_3	R_1	R_2	I
r_1		R_1				
r_2						
r_3						
R_1						
R_2						
I						

74. Let the eight symmetries of the square $ABCD$ shown in Fig. 11-83 be denoted as follows: r_1 denotes the reflection with axis l_1; r_2 denotes the reflection with axis l_2; r_3 denotes the reflection with axis l_3; r_4 denotes the reflection with axis l_4; R_1 denotes the 90° clockwise rotation with rotocenter O; R_2 denotes the 180° clockwise rotation with rotocenter O; R_3 denotes the 270° clockwise rotation with rotocenter O; I denotes the identity symmetry.

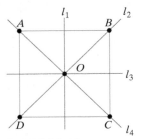

FIGURE 11-83

Complete the symmetry multiplication table below (*Hint*: Try Exercise 73 first.)

	r_1	r_2	r_3	r_4	R_1	R_2	R_3	I
r_1								
r_2								
r_3								
r_4								
R_1								
R_2								
R_3								
I								

75. List all the symmetries of the wallpaper pattern shown in Fig. 11-84.

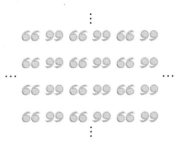

FIGURE 11-84

76. List all the symmetries of the wallpaper pattern shown in Fig. 11-85.

FIGURE 11-85

77. List all the symmetries of the wallpaper pattern shown in Fig. 11-86.

FIGURE 11-86

78. List all the symmetries of the wallpaper pattern shown in Fig. 11-87.

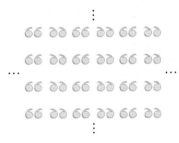

FIGURE 11-87

79. List all the symmetries of the wallpaper pattern shown in Fig. 11-88.

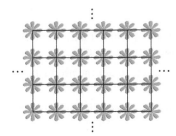

FIGURE 11-88

80. List all the symmetries of the wallpaper pattern shown in Fig. 11-89.

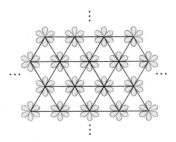

FIGURE 11-89

PROJECTS AND PAPERS

1 Patterns Everywhere

Border patterns can be found in many objects from the real world—ribbons, wallpaper borders, and architectural friezes. Even ceramic pots and woven baskets exhibit border patterns (when the pattern goes around in a circle it can be unraveled as if it were going on a straight line). Likewise, wallpaper patterns can be found in wallpapers, textiles, neckties, rugs, and gift-wrapping paper. Patterns are truly everywhere.

This project consists of two separate subprojects.

Part 1. Find examples from the real world of each of the seven possible border-pattern symmetry types. Do not use photographs from a book or designs you have just downloaded from some Web site. This part is not too hard, and it is a warm-up for Part 2, the real challenge.

Part 2. Find examples from the real world of each of the 17 wallpaper-pattern symmetry types. (The 17 symmetry types for wallpaper patterns are listed in *The 17 Wallpaper Symmetry Types* chart in the online Appendix in MyMathLab.*). The same rules apply as for Part 1.

*MyMathLab code required.

Notes: (1) Your best bet is to look at wallpaper patterns and borders at a wallpaper store or gift-wrapping paper and ribbons at a paper store. You will have to do some digging—a few of the wallpaper-pattern symmetry types are hard to find. (2) For ideas, you may want to visit Steve Edwards's excellent Web site *Tiling Plane and Fancy* at *http://www2.spsu.edu/math/tile/index.htm*.

2 Three-Dimensional Rigid Motions

For two-dimensional objects, we have seen that every rigid motion is of one of four basic types. For three-dimensional objects moving in three-dimensional space, there are *six* possible types of rigid motion. Specifically, every rigid motion in three-dimensional space is equivalent to a *reflection*, a *rotation*, a *translation*, a *glide reflection*, a *rotary reflection*, or a *screw displacement*.

Prepare a presentation on the six possible types of rigid motions in three-dimensional space. For each one give a precise definition of the rigid motion, describe its most important properties, and give illustrations as well as real-world examples.

12 Fractal Geometry

The Kinky Nature of Nature

Romanesco broccoli (also known as *Roman cauliflower* and often called *Romanesco* for short) is an edible flower and a close cousin of both broccoli and cauliflower. Romanesco is not a staple of the American diet—if you are lucky, you might find it occasionally in the vegetable section of one of your better supermarkets—which is too bad: Romanesco is nutritious, delicious (milder and nuttier than cauliflower), and beautiful to behold. It is also kinky. Very, very kinky.

Kinky is a word that means different things in different contexts, and in the context of this chapter we use "kinky" to mean the opposite of "smooth." The kind of kinkiness exhibited by Romanesco is of particular interest to us because it is the result of a special property called *self-similarity*. Self-similarity is the characteristic of an object that looks like parts of itself, and these parts in turn look like even smaller parts of themselves, and so on (at least for a while). Self-similarity is an extremely useful property, and many things in nature have some form of it—trees, clouds, mountains, rivers, our system of veins and arteries, etc.

> 66 Nature is a mutable cloud which is always and never the same. 99
>
> – *Ralph Waldo Emerson*

Whatever nature creates, man wants to imitate. By and large, this is a good idea (nature usually knows what it is doing), but imitating nature is easier said than done. How do you imitate the kinky structure of a tree, a cloud, or a mountain? The first step in this direction is the development of a new type of geometry called *fractal geometry* and the creation of super-kinky geometric shapes called *fractals*. These remarkable shapes are made possible only by incorporating self-similarity into the structure of their geometry. This chapter is an introduction to the basic ideas of fractal geometry.

The chapter is organized around a series of classic examples of geometric fractals— the *Koch snowflake* (followed by a general discussion of *self-similarity*) in Section 12.1, the *Sierpinski gasket* (followed by the *chaos game*) in Section 12.2, the *twisted Sierpinski gasket* in Section 12.3, and the *Mandelbrot set* in Section 12.4. As we discuss each of these examples, we will explore the connection between fractal geometry and the organized kinkiness exhibited by many objects in nature.

◄ Computer-generated fractal Romanesco. Image courtsey of Aleksandar Rodić.

357

12.1 The Koch Snowflake and Self-Similarity

Our first example of a *geometric fractal* is an object known as the *Koch snowflake*, named after the Swedish mathematician Helge von Koch (1870–1954). Like other geometric fractals we will discuss in this chapter, the Koch snowflake is constructed by means of a *recursive process*, a process in which the same set of rules is applied repeatedly in an infinite feedback loop—the output at one stage becomes the input at the next stage. (We have seen examples of recursive processes in earlier chapters—recursive ranking methods in Chapter 1 and recursive definitions of sequences in Chapter 9.)

The construction of the **Koch snowflake** proceeds as follows:

- **Start.** Start with a shaded *equilateral* triangle [Fig. 12-1(a)]. We will refer to this starting triangle as the *seed* of the Koch snowflake. The size of the seed triangle is irrelevant, so for simplicity we will assume that the sides are of length 1.

- **Step 1.** To the middle third of each of the sides of the seed add an equilateral triangle with sides of length $\frac{1}{3}$, as shown in Fig. 12-1(b). The result is the 12-sided "snowflake" shown in Fig. 12-1(c)—a shape just a tad kinkier than the seed triangle.

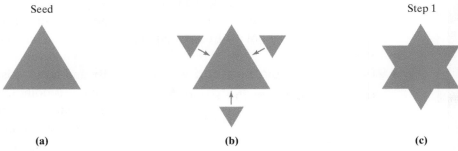

(a)   (b)   (c)

FIGURE 12-1   First step of the construction.

- **Step 2.** To the middle third of each of the 12 sides of the "snowflake" in Step 1 add an equilateral triangle with sides of length one-third the length of that side. The result is a "snowflake" with 48 sides (12×4), each of length $\left(\frac{1}{3}\right)^2 = \frac{1}{9}$, as shown in Fig. 12-2(a). (The snowflake got kinkier.)

  For ease of reference, we will call the procedure of adding an equilateral triangle to the middle third of each side of the figure *procedure KS*. This will make the rest of the construction a lot easier to describe. Notice that every time we apply *procedure KS* the snowflake gets kinkier—each side "crinkles" into four new sides and the sides get shorter by a factor of one-third.

- **Step 3.** Apply *procedure KS* to the "snowflake" in Step 2. This gives the more elaborate "snowflake" shown in Fig. 12-2(b), with 192 sides (48×4), each of length $\left(\frac{1}{3}\right)^3 = \frac{1}{27}$.

- **Step 4.** Apply *procedure KS* to the "snowflake" in Step 3. This gives the "snowflake" shown in Fig. 12-2(c). (You definitely don't want to do this by hand—there are 192 tiny little equilateral triangles that are being added!)

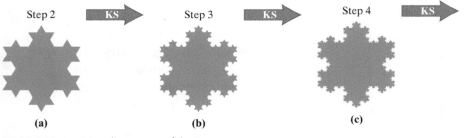

(a)   (b)   (c)

FIGURE 12-2   Next three steps of the construction.

■ MyMathLab®
For a step-by-step view of the process that generates a Koch snowflake, see the applet *Geometric Fractals* in MyMathLab.*

■ **Steps 5, 6, etc.** At each step apply *procedure KS* to the "snowflake" obtained in the previous step.

At every step of this recursive process the rules that define procedure KS generate a new "snowflake," but after a while it's hard to tell that there are any changes. There is already a very small difference between the snowflakes in Figs. 12-2(b) and (c), and after a few more steps the images become *visually stable*—to the naked eye there is no difference between one snowflake and the next. For all practical purposes what we are seeing is a rendering of a *Koch snowflake* [Fig. 12-3(a)].

Because the Koch snowflake is constructed in an infinite sequence of steps, a perfect rendering of it is impossible—Fig. 12-3(a) is only an approximation. This is no reason to be concerned or upset—the Koch snowflake is an abstract shape that we can study and explore by looking at imperfect pictures of it (much like we do in high school geometry when we study circles even though it is impossible to draw a perfect circle).

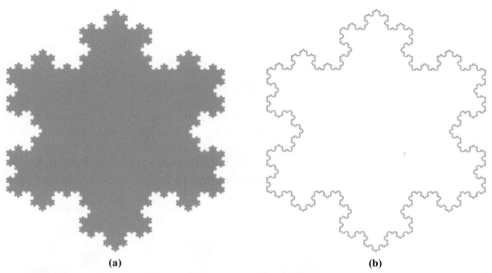

(a)   (b)

FIGURE 12-3   (a) Koch snowflake. (b) Koch curve.

The most "happening" part of the Koch snowflake is its boundary (that's where all the kinkiness occurs), so it is often more convenient to only look at the boundary and forget about the interior. If we do that, we get the **Koch curve** (sometimes called the *snowflake curve*) shown in Fig. 12-3(b). From now on, our discussion will alternate between the Koch snowflake (a region, with an *area*) and the Koch curve (a closed curve, with a *length*).

One advantage of recursive processes is that they allow for very simple and efficient definitions, even when the objects being defined are quite complicated. The Koch curve, for example, is a fairly complicated shape, but we can define it in two lines using a form of shorthand we will call a **replacement rule**—a scale-independent rule that specifies how to substitute one piece for another.

Koch curve replacement rule:

■ **Start:** Start with an equilateral triangle.
■ **Replacement rule:** In each step replace any line segment ——— with the "crinkled" version ＿／＼＿ .

One of the most remarkable facts about the Koch snowflake is that it occupies a relatively small area and yet its boundary is infinitely long—a notion that seems to defy common sense.

* MyMathLab code required.

To compute the length of the boundary let's first compute the perimeter of the "snowflakes" obtained in the first few steps of the construction (Fig. 12-4). The seed triangle has perimeter $P_0 = 3$. In Step 1, each side of length 1 is replaced by four sides of length $\frac{1}{3}$: The perimeter is $P_1 = 3 \times \left(\frac{4}{3}\right) = 4$. In Step 2, each side of length $\frac{1}{3}$ is replaced by four sides of length $\frac{1}{9}$: The perimeter is $P_2 = 3 \times \left(\frac{4}{3}\right)^2 = \frac{48}{9}$. As the replacement process continues, at each step we replace a side by four sides that are $\frac{1}{3}$ as long. Thus, at any given step the perimeter p is $\frac{4}{3}$ times the perimeter at the preceding step. This implies that the perimeters keep growing with each step, and growing very fast indeed. After infinitely many steps the perimeter is infinite.

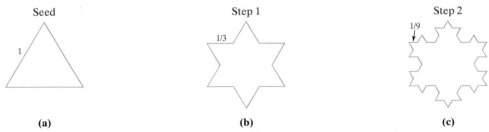

FIGURE 12-4   (a) Three sides of length 1 $(P_0 = 3)$. (b) Twelve sides of length $\frac{1}{3}$ $(P_1 = 4)$. (c) 48 sides of length $\frac{1}{9}$ $\left(P_2 = \frac{48}{9} = 5\frac{1}{3}\right)$.

Computing the exact area of the Koch snowflake is considerably more difficult, and we will not discuss the details here, but it is not hard to convince oneself that the Koch snowflake has a finite area, not larger than the area of the circle that circumscribes the seed triangle (Fig. 12-5). Indeed, we can be much more specific: The area of the Koch snowflake is exactly $\frac{8}{5}$ (or 1.6) times the area of the seed triangle.

FIGURE 12-5   At every step the snowflakes remain inside the circle that circumscribes the seed triangle.

The following is a summary of the key properties of the Koch snowflake and the Koch curve.

- **Replacement rule.** In each step replace any line segment ——— with the "crinkled" version ⎽⎽/\⎽⎽.
- **Boundary (Koch curve).** Infinitely long boundary.
- **Area.** Finite area [equal to $(1.6)A$, where A denotes the area of the seed triangle].
- **Self-similarity.** *Exact*, *infinite*, and *universal* self-similarity. We will define precisely what this means next.

Self-Similarity

The most important characteristic shared by the shapes and objects, which we will see in this chapter, is that they are all *self-similar*. In broad terms, we say that an object is **self-similar** when it is similar to some part of itself. In other words, parts of the object are similar to the whole object. The self-similarity can occur at many different scales and in many different ways, and we will discuss the many variations on the theme of self-similarity next.

We start with a closer look at our new friend, *the Koch curve*. Figure 12-6(a) shows a section of the Koch curve. We do know that the curve is pretty kinky, but to get a better idea of how kinky it really is we will look at it with an imaginary microscope. When we choose to look at a little piece of the original curve and magnify it, we get a surprise (or maybe not)—nothing has changed! The little piece is an exact replica of the larger piece but at a smaller scale [Fig. 12-6(b)]. And, if we crank up the magnification and choose to look at an even smaller piece it happens again—we get a copy of the original piece at an even smaller scale [Fig. 12-6(c)]. Frustrated, we continue cranking the magnification and looking at smaller and smaller bits of the curve, but nothing changes—more of the same at smaller and smaller scales. Boring, you say? Not once you understand how useful this can be.

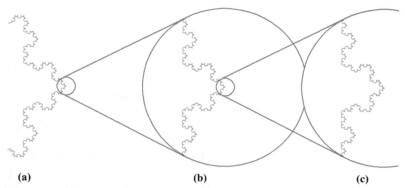

(a)   (b)   (c)

FIGURE 12-6   (a) A small piece of the Koch curve. (b) The piece in (a) magnified ×9. (c) The same piece magnified ×81.

The kind of self-similarity exhibited by the Koch curve has three key properties—it is *exact*, *infinite*, and *universal*.

- **Exact self-similarity.** An object or shape has *exact self-similarity* if different parts of the object look *exactly* the same at different scales. (Using the microscope analogy, this means that as you crank up the microscope's magnification you continue seeing parts that are identical in shape.)
- **Infinite self-similarity.** An object or shape has *infinite self-similarity* if the self-similarity occurs at infinitely many different scales. (This means that if you were able to continue cranking up your microscope's magnification indefinitely, the self-similar parts would continue showing up indefinitely.)
- **Universal self-similarity.** An object or shape has *universal self-similarity* if the self-similarity occurs in every part of the object. (Again using the microscope analogy, you don't have to point the microscope in a specific direction—no matter where you zoom you will eventually find self-similar pieces.)

For a different perspective on self-similarity, let's take another look at Romanesco. We start with a full head of Romanesco [Fig. 12-7(a)]—for convenience, we will call it the "mother." The mother is made up of a series of buds of various sizes (the "first generation"). Figure 12-7(b) is a close-up of some of the first generation buds at the center of the original picture. These buds all look very much like the mother but they are not identical to it. Let's say that they are approximately (but not exactly) self-similar. Figure 12-7(c) is a close-up of some of the first-generation buds. We can clearly see now the "second-generation" buds, looking just as Romanesque as the mother and the first-generation buds but not identical to any. The self-similar replication continues but only for another three generations. Figure 12-7(d) shows the "fifth generation," and we can see that the self-similar replication is beginning to break down. These buds no longer look like the mother or like earlier generations. It is also worth noting that the buds of a Romanesco head are spatially arranged in a very special way—the first-generation buds form a spiral arrangement inside the

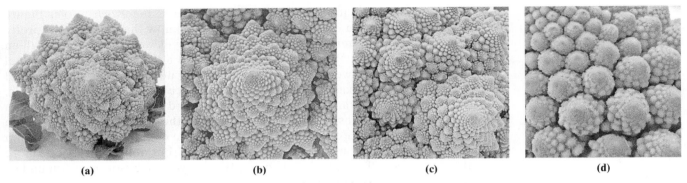

FIGURE 12-7 (a) Romanesco broccoli. (b) Close-up. (c) Close-up. (d) Close-up.

mother, each second-generation bud is part of a spiral inside its parent bud, and so on. Because of this spiral arrangement, the self-similarity is not universal—it occurs only along certain directions.

What happened with the Romanesco head is the typical kind of self-similarity that can be found in nature—*approximate*, *finite*, and *local* (the alternatives to exact, infinite, and universal).

- **Approximate self-similarity.** An object or shape has *approximate self-similarity* if different parts of the object share the same structure as the whole object and look *approximately* (but not exactly) the same at different scales.
- **Finite self-similarity.** An object or shape has *finite self-similarity* if the self-similarity occurs at multiple scales but eventually stops.
- **Local self-similarity.** An object or shape has *local self-similarity* if the self-similarity occurs in some parts of the object but not everywhere.

We can find self-similarity in many shapes in nature: trees, leaves, lightning, seashells, rivers, mountains, clouds, our circulatory system, our lungs, etc. Figure 12-8 illustrates a few examples of nature's affinity for self-similar shapes. In all cases, the self-similarity is *approximate*, *finite*, and *local*, and for some unexplained reason, quite beautiful.

FIGURE 12-8

The appeal of self-similarity transcends natural shapes, and self-similarity is often used in man-made objects and images: Russian dolls, cake decorations, product labels, abstract art, and so on (Fig. 12-9). Typically, the implied message that these man-made creations try to convey is that the self-similar replication is infinite and that the images keep repeating forever at smaller and smaller scales, but obviously this is an illusion—the self-similarity is *finite* and has to stop after a few iterations (it is impossible for the human hand to draw or physically create an infinite repetition).

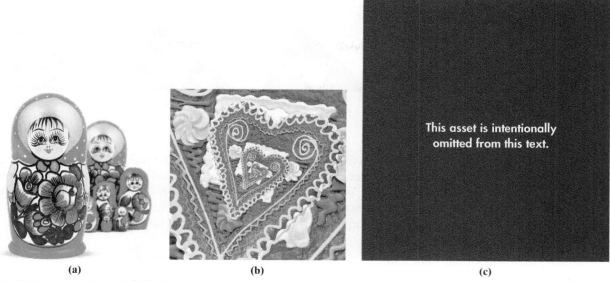

FIGURE 12-9   (a) Russian dolls. (b) Gingerbread heart. (c) www.mcescher.com, *Butterflies*

For infinite self-similarity we need to think in abstract, mathematical terms and create virtual objects and shapes (such as the Koch snowflake) that can only be seen in the mind's eye. We will study several of these in the remainder of this chapter.

12.2 The Sierpinski Gasket and the Chaos Game

With the insight gained by our study of the Koch snowflake, we will now look at another well-known geometric fractal called the *Sierpinski gasket*, named after the Polish mathematician Waclaw Sierpinski (1882–1969).

Just like with the Koch snowflake, the construction of the **Sierpinski gasket** starts with a solid triangle, but this time, instead of repeatedly *adding* smaller and smaller versions of the original triangle, we will *remove* them according to the following procedure:

- Start. Start with a seed—the solid triangle *ABC* [Fig. 12-10(a)].
- Step 1. Remove the triangle connecting the midpoints of the sides of the seed triangle. This gives the shape shown in Fig. 12-10(b)—consisting of three solid triangles, each a half-scale version of the seed and a hole where the middle triangle used to be.

  For convenience, we will call this process of hollowing out the middle triangle of a solid triangle *procedure SG*.

- Step 2. Apply *procedure SG* to each of the three solid triangles in Fig. 12-10(b). The result is the "gasket" shown in Fig. 12-10(c) consisting of nine solid triangles, each at one-fourth the scale of the seed triangle, plus three small holes of the same size and one larger hole in the middle.

- Step 3. Apply *procedure SG* to each of the nine solid triangles in Fig. 12-10(c). The result is the "gasket" shown in Fig. 12-10(d) consisting of 27 solid triangles, each at one-eighth the scale of the original triangle, nine small holes of the same size, three medium-sized holes, and one large hole in the middle.

- Steps 4, 5, etc. Apply *procedure SG* to each solid triangle in the "gasket" obtained in the previous step.

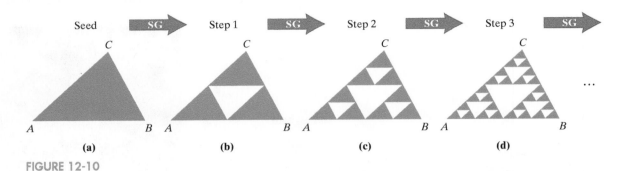

FIGURE 12-10

After a few more steps the figure becomes visually stable—the naked eye cannot tell the difference between the gasket obtained at one step and the gasket obtained at the next step. At this point we have a good rendering of the Sierpinski gasket itself. In your mind's eye you can think of Fig. 12-11 as a picture of the Sierpinski gasket (in reality, it is the gasket obtained at Step 7 of the construction).

FIGURE 12-11

The Sierpinski gasket is clearly a fairly complicated geometric shape, and yet it can be defined in two lines using the following recursive *replacement rule*.

Sierpinski gasket replacement rule:

- **Start:** Start with a shaded seed triangle.
- **Replacement rule:** In each step replace any solid triangle ▲ with the "hollowed" version ▲▲.

Looking at Fig. 12-11, we might think that the Sierpinski gasket is made of a huge number of tiny triangles, but this is just an optical illusion—there are no solid triangles in the Sierpinski gasket, just specks of the original triangle surrounded by a sea of white triangular holes. If we were to magnify any small part of the Sierpinski gasket [Fig. 12-12(a)], we would see more of the same—specks surrounded by white triangles [Fig. 12-12(b)]. This, of course, is another example of *self-similarity*. As with the Koch curve, the self-similarity of the Sierpinski gasket is *exact*, *infinite*, and *universal*.

As a geometric object existing in the plane, the Sierpinski gasket should have an area, but it turns out that its area is infinitesimally small, smaller than any positive quantity. Paradoxical as it may first seem, the mathematical formulation of this fact is that the Sierpinski gasket has *zero area*. At the same time, the boundary of the "gaskets" obtained at each step of the construction grows without bound, which implies that the Sierpinski gasket has an infinitely long boundary (see Exercises 21 and 22).

* MyMathLab code required.

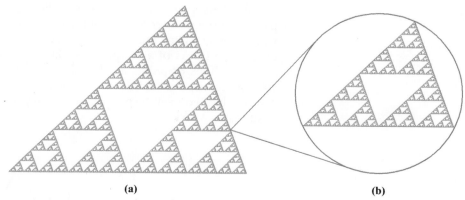

(a)   **(b)**

FIGURE 12-12   (a) Sierpinski gasket. (b) Sierpinski gasket detail (magnification ×256).

The following is a summary of the key properties of the Sierpinski gasket:

- **Replacement rule.** In each step replace any solid triangle ▲ with the "hollowed" version ◮.
- **Boundary.** Infinitely long boundary.
- **Area.** Infinitely small (zero area).
- **Self-similarity.** Exact, infinite, and universal self-similarity.

The Chaos Game

For a change of pace, we will now play a game of chance called the *chaos game*. All we need to play the chaos game is a single six-sided die and an arbitrary triangle with vertices labeled A, B, and C [Fig. 12-13(a)].

The purpose of the die is to randomly choose one of the three vertices of the triangle with equal probability. We can do this in many different ways. For example, if we roll a 1 or a 2, we choose A; if we roll a 3 or a 4, we choose B; and if we roll a 5 or a 6, we choose C. Here now are the rules for the **chaos game**:

- **Start.** Roll the die and mark the chosen vertex. Say we roll a 5. This puts us at vertex C [Fig. 12-13(b)].
- **Step 1.** Roll the die again. Say we roll a 2, so the new chosen vertex is A. We now *move to the point M_1 halfway between the previous position C and the winning vertex A.* Mark the new position M_1 [Fig. 12-13(c)].
- **Step 2.** Roll the die again, and *move to the point halfway between the last position M_1 and the new chosen vertex.* [Say we roll a 3—the move then is to M_2 halfway between M_1 and B as shown in Fig. 12-13(d).] Mark a point at the new position M_2.
- **Steps 3, 4, etc.** Continue rolling the die, each time *moving to a point halfway between the last position and the chosen vertex* and marking that point.

■ MyMathLab®
For an easy way to play the chaos game online see the applet *Geometric Fractals* in MyMathLab.*

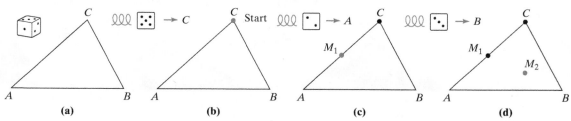

(a)   **(b)**   **(c)**   **(d)**

FIGURE 12-13   The chaos game: Always move from the previous position toward the chosen vertex and stop halfway.

* MyMathLab code required.

What happens after you roll the die a few times? Figure 12-14(a) shows the pattern of points after 50 rolls of the die—just a bunch of scattered dots—but when you continue rolling the die, a pattern emerges [Fig. 12-14(b), (c), and (d)]: the unmistakable tracks of a Sierpinski gasket! The longer we play the chaos game, the more the track of points left behind looks like a Sierpinski gasket. After 100,000 rolls of the die, it would be impossible to tell the difference between the two. (You can convince yourself by playing the chaos game with the applet *Geometric Fractals* available in MyMathLab.)

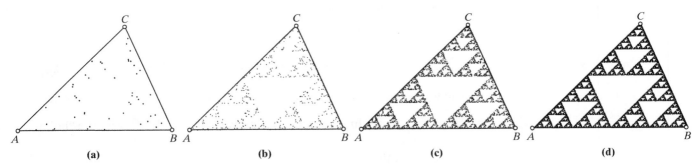

FIGURE 12-14   The "footprint" of the chaos game after (a) 50 rolls, (b) 500 rolls, (c) 5000 rolls, (d) 10,000 rolls.

This is a truly surprising turn of events. The chaos game is ruled by the laws of chance; thus, we would expect that essentially a random pattern of points would be generated. Instead, we get an approximation to the Sierpinski gasket, and the longer we play the chaos game, the better the approximation gets. An important implication of this is that it is possible to generate geometric fractals using simple rules based on the laws of chance.

12.3 The Twisted Sierpinski Gasket

Our next construction is a variation of the original Sierpinski gasket. For lack of a better name, we will call it the *twisted Sierpinski gasket*.

The construction starts out exactly like the one for the regular Sierpinski gasket, with a solid seed triangle [Fig. 12-15(a)] from which we cut out the middle triangle, [whose vertices we will call M, N, and L as shown in Fig. 12-15(b)]. The next move (which we will call the "twist") is new. Each of the points M, N, and L is moved a small amount in a random direction—as if jolted by an earthquake—to new positions M', N', and L'. One possible resulting shape is shown in Fig. 12-15(c).

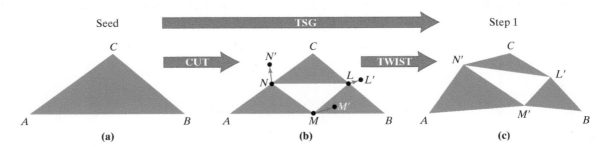

FIGURE 12-15   The two moves in *procedure TSG*: (b) the *cut* and (c) the *twist*.

* MyMathLab code required.

For convenience, we will use the term *procedure TSG* to describe the combination of the two moves ("cut" and then "twist").

- **Cut.** Remove the "middle" of the triangle [Fig. 12-15(b)].
- **Twist.** Translate each of the midpoints of the sides by a small random amount and in a random direction [Fig. 12-15(c)].

When we repeat *procedure TSG* in an infinite recursive process, we get the **twisted Sierpinski gasket**:

- **Start.** Start with a solid seed triangle [Fig. 12-16(a)].
- **Step 1.** Apply *procedure TSG* to the seed triangle. This gives the "twisted gasket" shown in Fig. 12-16(b), with three twisted solid triangles and a triangular hole in the middle.
- **Step 2.** To each of the three solid triangles in Fig. 12-16(b) apply *procedure TSG*. The result is the "twisted gasket" shown in Fig. 12-16(c), consisting of nine twisted solid triangles and four triangular holes of various sizes.
- **Steps 3, 4, etc.** Apply *procedure TSG* to each shaded triangle in the "twisted gasket" obtained in the previous step.

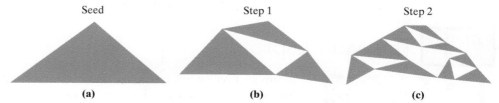

Seed	Step 1	Step 2
(a)	(b)	(c)

FIGURE 12-16   First two steps in the construction of the twisted Sierpinski gasket.

Figure 12-17(a) shows a twisted Sierpinski gasket by the time you get to Step 7 of the construction. Past this point the figure will remain unchanged to the naked eye. Notice the striking resemblance to a snow-covered mountain. With a few of the standard tools of computer graphics—color, lighting, and shading—a twisted Sierpinski gasket can be morphed to give a very realistic-looking mountain. In Figs. 12-17(b) and (c), one of them is photo of a real mountain, the other is a computer generated image created using a three-dimensional version of the twisted Sierpinski gasket construction. Can you tell which one is which? (If you are dying to find out, check the photo credits at the back of the book.)

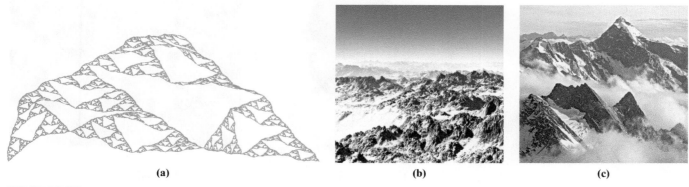

(a)	(b)	(c)

FIGURE 12-17

We find approximate self-similarity most commonly in nature (trees, rivers, mountains, etc.), but the twisted Sierpinski gasket is the rare example of a man-made geometric shape having approximate self-similarity—when we magnify any part of the gasket we see similar, but not identical, images (Fig. 12-18).

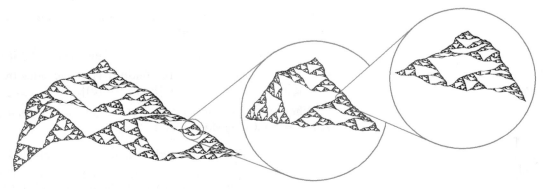

FIGURE 12-18 Approximate self-similarity in the twisted Sierpinski gasket.

The following is a summary of the key properties of the twisted Sierpinski gasket:

- **Self-similarity.** Approximate, infinite, and universal self-similarity.
- **Boundary.** Infinitely long boundary.
- **Replacement rule.** Whenever you have a solid triangle, apply *procedure TSG* to it (i.e., first "cut" it, then "twist" it).
- **Area.** Infinitely small.

12.4 The Mandelbrot Set

Benoit Mandelbrot (1924–2010)

In this section we will introduce one of the most interesting and beautiful geometric fractals ever created, an object called the *Mandelbrot set* after the Polish-American mathematician Benoit Mandelbrot. Some of the mathematics behind the Mandelbrot set goes a bit beyond the level of this book, so we will describe the overall idea and try not to get bogged down in the details.

We will start this section with a brief visual tour. The **Mandelbrot set** is the shape shown in Fig. 12-19(a), a strange-looking blob of black. Using a strategy we will describe later, the different regions outside the Mandelbrot set can be colored according to their mathematical properties, and when this is done [Fig. 12-19(b)], the Mandelbrot set comes to life like a switched-on neon sign.

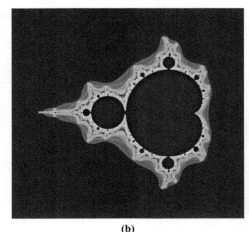

(a) **(b)**

FIGURE 12-19 (a) The Mandelbrot set (black) on a white background. (b) The Mandelbrot set comes to life when color is added to the outside.

In the wild imagination of some, the Mandelbrot set looks like some sort of bug—an exotic extraterrestrial flea. The "flea" is made up of a heart-shaped body (called a *cardioid*), a head, and an antenna coming out of the middle of the head. A careful look at Fig. 12-19 shows that the flea has many "smaller fleas that prey on it," but we can only begin to understand the full extent of the infestation when we look at Fig. 12-20(a)—a

> So Natr'alists observe, A Flea Hath smaller Fleas that on him prey and these have smaller Fleas to bite'em and so proceed, ad infinitum.
>
> *– Jonathan Swift*

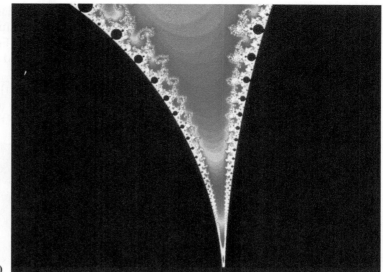

(a)

(b)

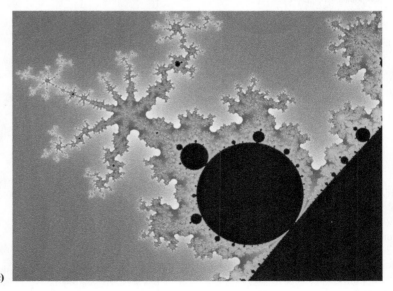

(c)

FIGURE 12-20 (a) Detailed close-up of a small region on the boundary. (b) An even tighter close-up of the boundary. (c) A close-up of one of the secondary "fleas."

finely detailed close-up of the boundary of the Mandelbrot set. When we magnify the view around the boundary even further, we can see that these secondary fleas also have fleas that "prey" on them [Figs. 12-20(b) and (c)], and further magnification would show this repeats itself ad infinitum. Clearly, Jonathan Swift was onto something!

Looking carefully at Figs. 12-20(a), (b), and (c), it appears that the Mandelbrot set has some strange form of *infinite* and *approximate* self-similarity—at infinitely many levels of magnification we see the same theme—similar but never identical

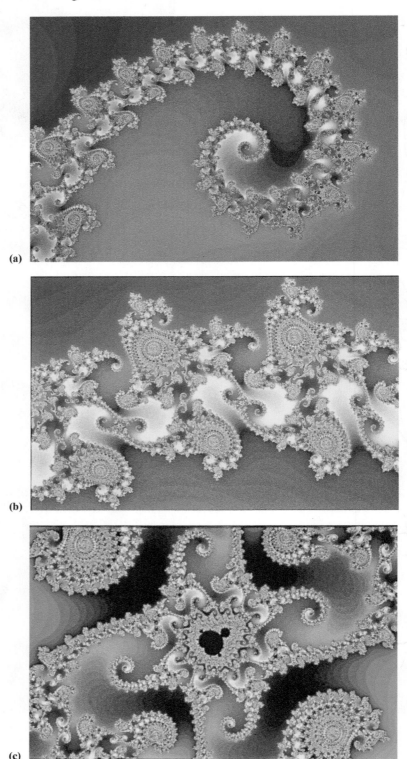

(a)

(b)

(c)

FIGURE 12-21 (a) A close-up of one of the "seahorse tails" in Fig. 12-20(b) (×100 magnification). (b) A further close-up of a section of Fig. 12-21(a) shows the fine detail and more seahorse tails (×200 magnification). (c) At infinitely many levels of magnification, old themes ⌐vels in new settings (×10,000

fleas surrounded by similar smaller fleas. At the same time, we can see that there is tremendous variation in the regions surrounding the individual fleas. The images we see are a peek into a psychedelic coral reef—a world of strange "urchins" and "seahorse tails" in Fig. 12-20(b), "anemone" and "starfish" in Fig. 12-20(c). Further magnification shows an even more exotic and beautiful landscape. Figure 12-21(a) is a close-up of one of the seahorse tails in Fig. 12-20(b). A further close-up of a section of Fig. 12-21(a) is shown in Fig. 12-21(b), and an even further magnification of it is seen in Fig. 12-21(c), revealing a tiny copy of the Mandelbrot set surrounded by a beautiful arrangement of swirls, spirals, and seahorse tails. [The magnification for Fig. 12-21(c) is approximately 10,000 times the original.]

What we see in these pictures is a truly amazing form of approximate self-similarity—anywhere we choose to look we will find (if we crank up the magnification enough) copies of the original Mandelbrot set, always surrounded by an infinitely changing, but always stunning, background. The infinite, approximate self-similarity of the Mandelbrot set manages to blend infinite repetition and infinite variety, creating a landscape as consistently exotic and diverse as nature itself.

Complex Numbers and Mandelbrot Sequences

How does this magnificent mix of beauty and complexity called the Mandelbrot set come about? Incredibly, the Mandelbrot set itself can be described mathematically by a recursive process involving simple computations with *complex numbers*.

You may recall having seen complex numbers in high school algebra. Among other things, complex numbers allow us to take square roots of negative numbers and solve quadratic equations of any kind. The basic building block for complex numbers is the number $i = \sqrt{-1}$. Starting with i we can build all other complex numbers using the general form $a + bi$, where a and b are real numbers. For example, $3 + 2i$, $-0.125 + 0.75i$, and even $1 + 0i = 1$ or $-0.75 + 0i = -0.75$. Just like real numbers, complex numbers can be added, multiplied, divided, and squared. (For a quick review of the basic operations with complex numbers, see Exercises 41 through 44.)

For our purposes, the most important fact about complex numbers is that they have a geometric interpretation: The complex number $(a + bi)$ can be identified with the point (a, b) in a Cartesian coordinate system, as shown in Fig. 12-22. This identification means that every complex number can be thought of as a point in the plane and that operations with complex numbers have geometric interpretations (see Exercises 45 and 46).

The key concept in the construction of the Mandelbrot set is that of a *Mandelbrot sequence*. A *Mandelbrot sequence* is an infinite sequence of complex numbers that starts with an arbitrary complex number s we call the *seed*, and then each successive term in the sequence is obtained recursively by *adding the seed s to the square of the previous term*. Figure 12-23 shows a schematic illustration of how a generic Mandelbrot sequence is generated. [Notice that the only complex number operations involved are squaring a complex number and adding two complex numbers. If you know how to do these two things, you can compute Mandelbrot sequences.]

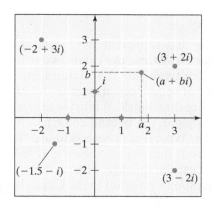

FIGURE 12-22 Every complex number is a point in the Cartesian plane; every point in the Cartesian plane is a complex number.

FIGURE 12-23 A Mandelbrot sequence with seed s. The red arrow is shorthand for "square the number and add the seed."

Much like a Koch snowflake and a Sierpinski gasket, a **Mandelbrot sequence** can be defined by means of a recursive rule.

Mandelbrot sequence recursive rule:

- Start: Choose an arbitrary complex number s. We will call s the seed of the Mandelbrot sequence. Set the seed s to be the initial term of the sequence $(s_0 = s)$.

- Recursive Rule: To find the next term in the sequence, square the preceding term and add the seed $\left[s_{N+1} = (s_N)^2 + s \right]$.

The following set of examples will illustrate the different patterns of growth exhibited by Mandelbrot sequences as we vary the seeds. These different patterns of growth are going to tell us how to generate the Mandelbrot set itself and the incredible images that we saw in our visual tour. The idea goes like this: Each point in the Cartesian plane is a complex number and thus the seed of some Mandelbrot sequence. The pattern of growth of that Mandelbrot sequence determines whether the seed is inside the Mandelbrot set (black point) or outside (nonblack point). In the case of nonblack points, the color assigned to the point is also determined by the pattern of growth of the corresponding Mandelbrot sequence. Let's try it.

EXAMPLE 12.1   ESCAPING MANDELBROT SEQUENCES

Figure 12-24 shows the first few terms of the Mandelbrot sequence with seed $s = 1$. (Since integers and decimals are also complex numbers, they make perfectly acceptable seeds.) The pattern of growth of this Mandelbrot sequence is clear—the terms are getting larger and larger, and they are doing so very quickly. Geometrically, it means that the points in the Cartesian plane that represent the numbers in this sequence are getting farther and farther away from the origin. For this reason, we call this sequence an *escaping* Mandelbrot sequence.

Seed   Step 1   Step 2   Step 3   Step 4

$s = 1$ ➡ $s_1 = 1^2 + 1$ $= 2$ ➡ $s_2 = 2^2 + 1$ $= 5$ ➡ $s_3 = 5^2 + 1$ $= 26$ ➡ $s_4 = 26^2 + 1$ $= 677$ ···

FIGURE 12-24   Mandelbrot sequence with seed $s = 1$ *(escaping very quickly)*.

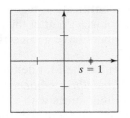

FIGURE 12-25   The seed $s = 1$ is assigned a "cool" color (blue).

In general, when the points that represent the terms of a Mandelbrot sequence move farther and farther away from the origin, we will say that the Mandelbrot sequence is **escaping**. The basic rule that defines the Mandelbrot set is that seeds of escaping Mandelbrot sequences are *not* in the Mandelbrot set and must be assigned some color other than black. While there is no specific rule that tells us what color should be assigned, the overall color palette is based on how fast the sequence is escaping. The typical approach is to use "hot" colors such as reds, yellows, and oranges for seeds that escape slowly and "cool" colors such as blues and purples for seeds that escape quickly. The seed $s = 1$, for example, escapes very quickly, and the corresponding point in the Cartesian plane is painted blue (Fig. 12-25).

EXAMPLE 12.2   PERIODIC MANDELBROT SEQUENCES

Figure 12-26 shows the first few terms of the Mandelbrot sequence with seed $s = -1$. The pattern that emerges here is also clear—the numbers in the sequence alternate between 0 and -1. In this case, we say that the Mandelbrot sequence is *periodic*.

Seed   Step 1   Step 2   Step 3

$s = -1$ ➡ $s_1 = (-1)^2 + (-1)$ $= 0$ ➡ $s_2 = 0^2 + (-1)$ $= -1$ ➡ $s_3 = (-1)^2 + (-1)$ $= 0$ ···

FIGURE 12-26   Mandelbrot sequence with seed $s = -1$ *(periodic)*.

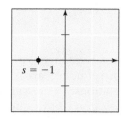

FIGURE 12-27 The seed $s = -1$ is in the Mandelbrot set (black point).

In general, a Mandelbrot sequence is said to be **periodic** if at some point the numbers in the sequence start repeating themselves in a cycle. When the Mandelbrot sequence is periodic, the seed is a point of the Mandelbrot set and, thus, is assigned the color black (Fig. 12-27).

EXAMPLE 12.3 ATTRACTED MANDELBROT SEQUENCES

Figure 12-28 shows the first few terms in the Mandelbrot sequence with seed $s = -0.75$. Here the growth pattern is not obvious, and additional terms of the sequence are needed. Further computation (a calculator will definitely come in handy) shows that as we go farther and farther out in this sequence, the terms get closer and closer to the value -0.5 (see Exercise 58). In this case, we will say that the sequence is *attracted* to the value -0.5.

FIGURE 12-28   Mandelbrot sequence with seed $s = -0.75$ (attracted).

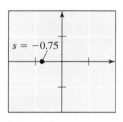

FIGURE 12-29 The seed $s = -0.75$ is in the Mandelbrot set (black point).

In general, when the terms in a Mandelbrot sequence get closer and closer to a fixed complex number a, we say that a is an **attractor** for the sequence or, equivalently, that the sequence is **attracted** to a. Just as with periodic sequences, when a Mandelbrot sequence is attracted, the seed s is in the Mandelbrot set and is colored black (Fig. 12-29).

So far, all our examples have been based on rational number seeds (mostly to keep things simple), but the truly interesting cases occur when the seeds are complex numbers. The next two examples deal with complex number seeds.

EXAMPLE 12.4 A PERIODIC MANDELBROT SEQUENCE WITH COMPLEX TERMS

In this example we will examine the growth of the Mandelbrot sequence with seed $s = i$. Starting with $s = i$ (and using that $i^2 = -1$), we get $s_1 = i^2 + i = -1 + i$. If we now square s_1 and add i, we get $s_2 = (-1 + i)^2 + i = -i$, and repeating the process gives $s_3 = (-i)^2 + i = -1 + i$. At this point we notice that $s_3 = s_1$, which implies $s_4 = s_2, s_5 = s_1$, and so on (Fig. 12-30). This, of course, means that this Mandelbrot sequence is *periodic*, with its terms alternating between the complex numbers $-1 + i$ (odd terms) and $-i$ (even terms).

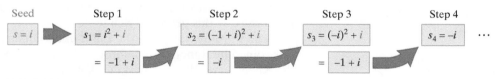

FIGURE 12-30   Mandelbrot sequence with seed $s = i$ (periodic).

The key conclusion from the preceding computations is that the seed i is a black point inside the Mandelbrot set (Fig. 12-31).

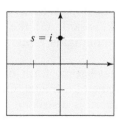

FIGURE 12-31 The seed $s = i$ is in the Mandelbrot set (black point).

The next example illustrates the case of a Mandelbrot sequence with three complex attractors.

EXAMPLE 12.5 A MANDELBROT SEQUENCE WITH THREE COMPLEX ATTRACTORS

In this example we examine the growth of the Mandelbrot sequence with seed $s = -0.125 + 0.75i$. The first few terms of the Mandelbrot sequence are shown. We leave it to the enterprising reader to check these calculations. (You will need a scientific calculator that handles complex numbers. If you don't have one, you can download a free virtual calculator for doing complex number arithmetic from *http://www.calc3D.com* or other similar Web sites.)

$s_0 = -0.125 + 0.75i$ $s_1 = -0.671875 + 0.5625i$ $s_2 = 0.0100098 - 0.00585938i$

$s_3 = -0.124934 + 0.749883i$ $s_4 = -0.671716 + 0.562628i$ $s_5 = 0.00965136 - 0.00585206i$

$s_6 = -0.124941 + 0.749887i$ $s_7 = -0.67172 + 0.562617i$ $s_8 = 0.00967074 - 0.00584195i$

We can see that the terms in this Mandelbrot sequence are complex numbers that essentially cycle around in sets of three and are approaching three different attractors. Since this Mandelbrot sequence is attracted, the seed $s = -0.125 + 0.75i$ represents another point in the Mandelbrot set.

The Mandelbrot Set

Given all the previous examples and discussion, a formal definition of the **Mandelbrot set** using seeds of Mandelbrot sequences sounds incredibly simple: If the Mandelbrot sequence is *periodic* or *attracted*, the seed is a point of the Mandelbrot set and assigned the color black; if the Mandelbrot sequence is *escaping*, the seed is a point outside the Mandelbrot set and assigned a color that depends on the speed with which the sequence is escaping (hot colors for slowly escaping sequences, cool colors for quickly escaping sequences). There are a few technical details that we omitted, but essentially these are the key ideas behind the amazing pictures that we saw in Figs. 12-20 and 12-21. In addition, of course, a computer is needed to carry out the computations and generate the images.

Because the Mandelbrot set provides a bounty of aesthetic returns for a relatively small mathematical investment, it has become one of the most popular mathematical playthings of our time. Hundreds of software programs that allow one to explore the beautiful landscapes surrounding the Mandelbrot set are available, and many of these programs are freeware. You can find plenty of these by Googling the term "Mandelbrot set." There are also many exploratory zooms into the depths of the Mandelbrot set available in YouTube.

 Conclusion

The study of fractals and their geometry has become a hot mathematical topic. It is a part of mathematics that combines complex and interesting theories, beautiful graphics, and extreme relevance to the real world. In this chapter we only scratched the surface of this deep and rich topic.

The word **fractal** (from the Latin *fractus*, meaning "broken up or fragmented") was coined by Benoit Mandelbrot in the mid-1970s to describe objects as diverse as the Koch curve, the Sierpinski gasket, the twisted Sierpinski gasket, and the Mandelbrot set, as well as many shapes in nature, such as clouds, mountains, trees, rivers, and Romanesco broccoli.

These objects share one key characteristic: They all have some form of self-similarity. (Self-similarity is not the only defining characteristic of a fractal. Others, such as *fractional dimension*, are discussed in Project 1.) There is a striking difference between the kinky geometry of self-similar shapes and the smooth geometry of traditional lines, circles, spheres, and so on. This difference is most apparent when we compare the look and texture of natural objects with those of man-made objects.

- **attracted Mandelbrot sequence:** a Mandelbrot sequence with the property that at some point the terms of the sequence start to get closer and closer to one or several attractors, **373**
- **Mandelbrot set:** a geometric shape defined by points in the Cartesian plane representing complex numbers with the property that the Mandelbrot sequences they generate are either periodic or attracted, **368**

 # EXERCISES

WALKING

12.1 The Koch Snowflake and Self-Similarity

1. Consider the construction of a Koch snowflake starting with a seed triangle having sides of length 81 cm. Let M denote the number of sides, L the length of each side, and P the perimeter of the "snowflake" obtained at the indicated step of the construction. Complete the missing entries in Table 12-1.

	M	L	P
Start	3	81 cm	243 cm
Step 1	12	27 cm	324 cm
Step 2			
Step 3			
Step 4			
Step 5			

■ TABLE 12-1

2. Consider the construction of a Koch snowflake starting with a seed triangle having sides of length 18 cm. Let M denote the number of sides, L the length of each side, and P the perimeter of the "snowflake" obtained at the indicated step of the construction. Complete the missing entries in Table 12-2.

	M	L	P
Start	3	18 cm	54 cm
Step 1	12	6 cm	72 cm
Step 2			
Step 3			
Step 4			
Step 5			

■ TABLE 12-2

3. Consider the construction of a Koch snowflake starting with a seed triangle having area $A = 81$. Let R denote the number of triangles added at a particular step, S the area of each added triangle, T the total new area added, and Q the area of the "snowflake" obtained at a particular step of the construction. Complete the missing entries in Table 12-3.

	R	S	T	Q
Start	0	0	0	81
Step 1	3	9	27	108
Step 2	12	1	12	120
Step 3				
Step 4				
Step 5				

■ TABLE 12-3

4. Consider the construction of a Koch snowflake starting with a seed triangle having area $A = 729$. Let R denote the number of triangles added at a particular step, S denote the area of each added triangle, T the total new area added, and Q the area of the "snowflake" obtained at a particular step of the construction. Complete the missing entries in Table 12-4.

	R	S	T	Q
Start	0	0	0	729
Step 1	3	81	243	972
Step 2	12	9	108	1080
Step 3				
Step 4				
Step 5				

■ TABLE 12-4

*Exercises 5 through 8 refer to a variation of the Koch snowflake called the **quadratic Koch fractal**. The construction of the quadratic Koch fractal is similar to that of the Koch snowflake, but it uses squares instead of equilateral triangles as the shape's building blocks. The following recursive construction rule defines the quadratic Koch fractal:*

Quadratic Koch Fractal

- Start. *Start with a solid seed square [Fig. 12-32(a)].*
- Step 1. *Attach a smaller square (sides one-third the length of the sides of the seed square) to the middle third of each side [Fig. 12-32(b)].*
- Step 2. *Attach a smaller square (sides one-third the length of the sides of the previous side to the middle third of each side [Fig. 12-32(c)]. (Call this procedure QKF.)*
- Steps 3, 4, etc. *At each step, apply procedure QKF to the figure obtained in the preceding step.*

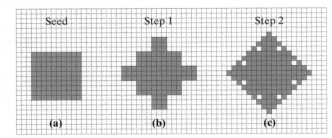

FIGURE 12-32

5. Assume that the seed square of the *quadratic Koch fractal* has sides of length 81 cm. Let M denote the number of sides, L the length of each side, and P the perimeter of the shape obtained at the indicated step of the construction. Complete the missing entries in Table 12-5.

	M	L	P
Start	4	81 cm	324 cm
Step 1	20	27 cm	540 cm
Step 2			
Step 3			
Step 40			

TABLE 12-5

6. Assume that the seed square of the *quadratic Koch fractal* has sides of length L. Let M denote the number of sides, l the length of each side, and P the perimeter of the shape obtained at the indicated step of the construction. Complete the missing entries in Table 12-6.

	M	L	P
Start	4	1	4
Step 1	20	$\frac{1}{3}$	$\frac{20}{3}$
Step 2			
Step 3			
Step 4			

TABLE 12-6

7. Assume that the seed square of the *quadratic Koch fractal* has area $A = 81$. Let R denote the number of squares added at a particular step, S the area of each added square, T the total new area added, and Q the area of the shape obtained at a particular step of the construction. Complete the missing entries in Table 12-7.

	R	S	T	Q
Start	0	0	0	81
Step 1	4	9	36	117
Step 2	20	1	20	137
Step 3				
Step 4				

TABLE 12-7

8. Assume that the seed square of the *quadratic Koch fractal* has area $A = 243$. Let R denote the number of squares added at a particular step, S the area of each added square, T the total new area added, and Q the area of the shape obtained at a particular step of the construction. Complete the missing entries in Table 12-8.

	R	S	T	Q
Start	0	0	0	243
Step 1	4	27	108	351
Step 2	20	3	60	411
Step 3				
Step 4				

TABLE 12-8

*Exercises 9 through 12 refer to a variation of the Koch snowflake called the **Koch antisnowflake**. The Koch antisnowflake is much like the Koch snowflake, but it is based on a recursive rule that removes equilateral triangles. The recursive replacement rule for the Koch antisnowflake is as follows:*

Koch Antisnowflake

- Start: *Start with a solid seed equilateral triangle [Fig. 12-33(a)].*

■ Replacement rule: *In each step replace any boundary line segment* ——— *with a* ∨ . *[Figures 12-33(b) and (c) show the figures obtained at Steps 1 and 2, respectively.]*

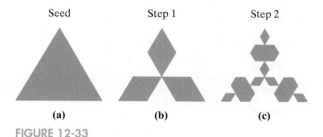

Seed (a)   Step 1 (b)   Step 2 (c)

FIGURE 12-33

9. Assume that the seed triangle of the *Koch antisnowflake* has sides of length 81 cm. Let M denote the number of sides, L the length of each side, and P the perimeter of the shape obtained at the indicated step of the construction. Complete the missing entries in Table 12-9.

	M	L	P
Start	3	81 cm	243 cm
Step 1	12	27 cm	324 cm
Step 2			
Step 3			
Step 4			
Step 5			

■ TABLE 12-9

10. Assume that the seed triangle of the *Koch antisnowflake* has sides of length 18 cm. Let M denote the number of sides, L the length of each side, and P the perimeter of the shape obtained at the indicated step of the construction. Complete the missing entries in Table 12-10.

	M	L	P
Start	3	18 cm	54 cm
Step 1	12	6 cm	72 cm
Step 2			
Step 3			
Step 4			
Step 5			

■ TABLE 12-10

11. Assume that the seed triangle of the *Koch antisnowflake* has area $A = 81$. Let R denote the number of triangles subtracted at a particular step, S the area of each subtracted triangle, T the total area subtracted, and Q the area of the shape obtained at a particular step of the construction. Complete the missing entries in Table 12-11.

	R	S	T	Q
Start	0	0	0	81
Step 1	3	9	27	54
Step 2	12	1	12	42
Step 3				
Step 4				
Step 5				

■ TABLE 12-11

12. Assume that the seed triangle of the *Koch antisnowflake* has area $A = 729$. Let R denote the number of triangles subtracted at a particular step, S the area of each subtracted triangle, T the total area subtracted, and Q the area of the shape obtained at a particular step of the construction. Complete the missing entries in Table 12-12.

	R	S	T	Q
Start	0	0	0	729
Step 1	3	81	243	486
Step 2	12	9	108	378
Step 3				
Step 4				
Step 5				

■ TABLE 12-12

Exercises 13 through 16 refer to the construction of the **quadratic Koch island**. *The quadratic Koch island is defined by the following recursive replacement rule.*

Quadratic Koch Island

■ Start: *Start with a seed square [Fig. 12-34(a)]. (Notice that here we are only dealing with the boundary of the square.)*

■ Replacement rule: *In each step replace any horizontal boundary segment with the "sawtooth" version shown in Fig. 12-34(b) and any vertical line segment with the "sawtooth" version shown in Fig. 12-34(c).*

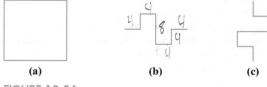

(a)   (b)   (c)

FIGURE 12-34

13. Assume that the seed square of the *quadratic Koch island* has sides of length 16.

    (a) Carefully draw the figures obtained in Steps 1 and 2 of the construction. (*Hint:* Use graph paper and make the seed square a 16 by 16 square.)

    (b) Find the perimeter of the figure obtained in Step 1 of the construction.

    (c) Find the perimeter of the figure obtained in Step 2 of the construction.

    (d) Explain why the quadratic Koch island has infinite perimeter.

14. Assume that the seed square of the *quadratic Koch island* has sides of length a.

    (a) Carefully draw the figures obtained in Steps 1 and 2 of the construction. (*Hint:* Use graph paper and make the seed square a 16 by 16 square.)

    (b) Find the perimeter of the figure obtained in Step 1 of the construction.

    (c) Find the perimeter of the figure obtained in Step 2 of the construction.

    (d) Explain why the quadratic Koch Island has infinite perimeter.

15. This exercise is a continuation of Exercise 13.

    (a) Find the area of the figure obtained in Step 1 of the construction.

    (b) Find the area of the figure obtained in Step 2 of the construction.

    (c) Explain why the area of the quadratic Koch Island is the same as the area of the seed square.

16. This exercise is a continuation of Exercise 14.

    (a) Find the area of the figure obtained in Step 1 of the construction.

    (b) Find the area of the figure obtained in Step 2 of the construction.

    (c) Explain why the area of the quadratic Koch Island is the same as the area of the seed square.

12.2 The Sierpinski Gasket and the Chaos Game

17. Consider the construction of a Sierpinski gasket starting with a seed triangle of area $A = 64$. Let R denote the number of triangles removed at a particular step, S the area of each removed triangle, T the total area removed, and Q the area of the "gasket" obtained at a particular step of the construction. Complete the missing entries in Table 12-13.

	R	S	T	Q
Start	0	0	0	64
Step 1	1	16	16	48
Step 2	3	4	12	36
Step 3				
Step 4				
Step 5				

■ TABLE 12-13

18. Consider the construction of a Sierpinski gasket starting with a seed triangle of area $A = 1$. Let R denote the number of triangles removed at a particular step, S the area of each removed triangle, T the total area removed, and Q the area of the "gasket" obtained at a particular step of the construction. Complete the missing entries in Table 12-14.

	R	S	T	Q
Start	0	0	0	1
Step 1	1	$\frac{1}{4}$	$\frac{1}{4}$	$\frac{3}{4}$
Step 2	3	$\frac{1}{16}$	$\frac{3}{16}$	$\frac{9}{16}$
Step 3				
Step 4				
Step 5				

■ TABLE 12-14

19. Assume that the seed triangle of the *Sierpinski gasket* has perimeter of length $P = 8$ cm. Let U denote the number of shaded triangles at a particular step, V the perimeter of each shaded triangle, and W the length of the boundary of the "gasket" obtained at a particular step of the construction. Complete the missing entries in Table 12-15.

	U	V	W
Start	1	8 cm	8 cm
Step 1	3	4 cm	12 cm
Step 2			
Step 3			
Step 4			
Step 5			

■ TABLE 12-15

20. Assume that the seed triangle of the *Sierpinski gasket* has perimeter $P = 20$. Let U denote the number of shaded triangles at a particular step, V the perimeter of each shaded triangle, and W the length of the boundary of the "gasket" obtained at a particular step of the construction. Complete the missing entries in Table 12-16.

	U	V	W
Start	1	20	20
Step 1	3	10	30
Step 2			
Step 3			
Step 4			
Step 5			

■ TABLE 12-16

21. Let A denote the area of the seed triangle of the *Sierpinski gasket*.

(a) Find the area of the gasket at step N of the construction expressed in terms of A and N. (*Hint*: Try Exercises 17 and 18 first.)

(b) Explain why the area of the Sierpinski gasket is infinitesimally small (i.e., smaller than any positive quantity).

22. Let P denote the perimeter of the seed triangle of the *Sierpinski gasket*.

(a) Find the perimeter of the gasket at step N of the construction expressed in terms of P and N. (*Hint*: Try Exercises 19 and 20 first.)

(b) Explain why the Sierpinski gasket has an infinitely long perimeter.

Exercises 23 through 26 refer to a square version of the Sierpinski gasket called the **Sierpinski carpet.** *The Sierpinski carpet is defined by the following recursive construction rule.*

Sierpinski Carpet

■ *Start. Start with a solid seed square [Fig. 12-35(a)].*

■ *Step 1. Subdivide the seed square into nine equal sub-squares and remove the central subsquare [Fig. 12-35(b)].*

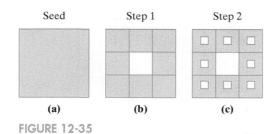

Seed   Step 1   Step 2

(a)   (b)   (c)

FIGURE 12-35

■ *Step 2. Subdivide each of the remaining solid squares into nine subsquares and remove the central subsquare [Fig. 12-35(c)]. (Call the procedure of subdividing a solid square into nine subsquares and removing the middle square procedure SC.)*

■ *Steps 3, 4, etc. Apply procedure SC to each solid square of the "carpet" obtained in the previous step.*

23. Assume that the seed square of the *Sierpinski carpet* has area $A = 1$.

(a) Carefully draw the "carpet" obtained in Step 3 of the construction. [*Hint:* Use a piece of graph paper with a small grid and make the seed square a 27-by-27 square. Use Fig. 12-35(c) as your starting point.]

(b) Find the area of the "carpet" obtained in Step 1 of the construction.

(c) Find the area of the "carpet" obtained in Step 2 of the construction. (*Hint:* Your best bet is to think of the carpet in Step 2 as made of eight identical one-third scale versions of the carpet in Step 1.)

(d) Find the area of the "carpet" obtained in Step 3 of the construction.

(e) Find the area of the "carpet" obtained in Step N of the construction expressed in terms of N.

24. Assume that the seed square of the *Sierpinski carpet* has area A.

(a) Carefully draw the "carpet" obtained in Step 3 of the construction. [*Hint:* Use a piece of graph paper with a small grid and make the seed square a 27-by-27 square. Use Fig. 12-35(c) as your starting point.]

(b) Find the area of the "carpet" obtained in Step 1 of the construction.

(c) Find the area of the "carpet" obtained in Step 2 of the construction. (*Hint:* Your best bet is to think of the gasket in Step 2 as made of eight identical one-third scale versions of the gasket in Step 1.)

(d) Find the area of the "carpet" obtained in Step 3 of the construction.

(e) Find the area of the "carpet" obtained in Step N of the construction expressed in terms of A and N.

25. Assume that the seed square of the *Sierpinski carpet* has sides of length 1.

(a) Find the length of the boundary of the "carpet" obtained in Step 1 of the construction.

(b) Find the length of the boundary of the "carpet" obtained in Step 2 of the construction. (*Hint:* It is the length of the boundary of the carpet in the previous step plus the perimeter of the "small" white holes introduced in this step.)

(c) Find the length of the boundary of the "carpet" obtained in Step 3 of the construction.

26. Assume that the seed square of the *Sierpinski carpet* has sides of length L.

(a) Find the length of the boundary of the "carpet" obtained in Step 1 of the construction.

(b) Find the length of the boundary of the "carpet" obtained in Step 2 of the construction. (*Hint*: It is the length of the boundary of the carpet in the previous step plus the perimeter of the "small" white holes introduced in this step.)

(c) Find the length of the boundary of the "carpet" obtained in Step 3 of the construction.

Exercises 27 through 30 refer to the **Sierpinski ternary gasket**, *a variation of the Sierpinski gasket defined by the following recursive replacement rule.*

Sierpinski Ternary Gasket

■ Start: *Start with a solid seed equilateral triangle [Fig. 12-36(a)].*

■ Replacement rule: *In each step replace any solid triangle* ▲ *with a* ⟁. *[Figures 12-36(b) and (c) show Steps 1 and 2, respectively.]*

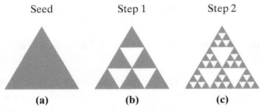

Seed	Step 1	Step 2
(a)	(b)	(c)

FIGURE 12-36

27. Assume that the seed triangle of the *Sierpinski ternary gasket* has area $A = 1$. Let R denote the number of triangles removed at a particular step, S the area of each removed triangle, T the total area removed, and Q the area of the "ternary gasket" obtained at a particular step of the construction. Complete the missing entries in Table 12-17.

	R	S	T	Q
Start	0	0	0	1
Step 1	3	$\frac{1}{9}$	$\frac{1}{3}$	$\frac{2}{3}$
Step 2				
Step 3				
Step 4				
Step N				

■ TABLE 12-17

28. Assume that the seed triangle of the *Sierpinski ternary gasket* has area $A = 81$. Let R denote the number of triangles removed at a particular step, S the area of each removed triangle, T the total area removed, and Q the area of the "gasket" obtained at a particular step of the construction. Complete the missing entries in Table 12-18.

	R	S	T	Q
Start	0	0	0	81
Step 1	3	9	27	54
Step 2				
Step 3				
Step 4				
Step N				

■ TABLE 12-18

29. Assume that the seed triangle of the *Sierpinski ternary gasket* has perimeter of length $P = 9$ cm. Let U denote the number of shaded triangles at a particular step, V the perimeter of each shaded triangle, and W the length of the boundary of the "ternary gasket" obtained at a particular step of the construction. Complete the missing entries in Table 12-19.

	U	V	W
Start	1	9 cm	9 cm
Step 1	6	3 cm	18 cm
Step 2			
Step 3			
Step 4			
Step N			

■ TABLE 12-19

30. Assume that the seed triangle of the *Sierpinski ternary gasket* has perimeter P. Let U denote the number of shaded triangles at a particular step, V the perimeter of each shaded triangle, and W the length of the boundary of the "gasket" obtained at a particular step of the construction. Complete the missing entries in Table 12-20.

	U	V	W
Start	1	P	P
Step 1	6	$\frac{P}{3}$	$2P$
Step 2			
Step 3			
Step 4			
Step N			

■ TABLE 12-20

Exercises 31 and 32 refer to a variation of the Sierpinski gasket called the **box fractal**. The box fractal is defined by the following recursive rule:

- **Start.** Start with a solid seed square [Fig. 12-37(a)].

- **Step 1.** Subdivide the seed square into nine equal subsquares, and remove the center subsquare along each of the sides [Fig. 12-37(b)].

- **Step 2.** Subdivide each of the remaining solid squares into nine subsquares, and remove the center subsquare along each side [Fig. 12-37(c)]. Call this process (subdividing a solid square into nine subsquares and removing the central subsquares along the four sides) procedure BF.

- **Steps 3, 4, etc.** Apply procedure BF to each solid square of the "carpet" obtained in the previous step.

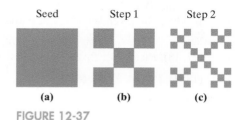

Seed   Step 1   Step 2

(a)   (b)   (c)

FIGURE 12-37

31. Assume that that the seed square for the *box fractal* has area $A = 1$.

(a) Find the area of the figure obtained in Step 1 of the construction.

(b) Find the area of the figure obtained in Step 2 of the construction.

(c) Find the area of the figure obtained in Step N of the construction.

32. Assume that the seed square for the *box fractal* has sides of length 1.

(a) Find the perimeter of the figure obtained in Step 1 of the construction.

(b) Find the perimeter of the figure obtained in Step 2 of the construction.

(c) Find the perimeter of the figure obtained in Step N of the construction.

Exercises 33 through 36 refer to the chaos game as described in Section 12.2. You should use graph paper for these exercises. Start with an isosceles right triangle ABC with $AB = AC = 32$, as shown in Fig. 12-38. Choose vertex A for a roll of 1 or 2, vertex B for a roll of 3 or 4, and vertex C for a roll of 5 or 6.

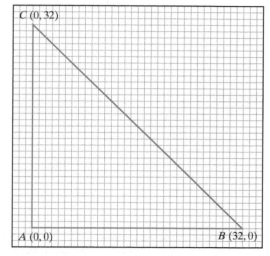

FIGURE 12-38

33. Suppose that the die is rolled six times and that the outcomes are 3, 1, 6, 4, 5, and 5. Carefully draw the points P_1 through P_6 corresponding to these outcomes. (*Note:* Each of the points P_1 through P_6 falls on a grid point of the graph. You should be able to identify the location of each point without using a ruler.)

34. Suppose that the die is rolled six times and that the outcomes are 2, 6, 1, 4, 3, and 6. Carefully draw the points P_1 through P_6 corresponding to these outcomes. (*Note:* Each of the points P_1 through P_6 falls on a grid point of the graph. You should be able to identify the location of each point without using a ruler.)

35. Using a rectangular coordinate system with A at $(0, 0)$, B at $(32, 0)$, and C at $(0, 32)$, complete Table 12-21.

Roll	Point	Coordinates
3	P_1	$(32, 0)$
1	P_2	$(16, 0)$
2	P_3	
3	P_4	
5	P_5	
5	P_6	

■ TABLE 12-21

36. Using a rectangular coordinate system with A at $(0, 0)$, B at $(32, 0)$, and C at $(0, 32)$, complete Table 12-22.

Roll	Point	Coordinates
2	P_1	$(0, 0)$
6	P_2	$(0, 16)$
5	P_3	
1	P_4	
3	P_5	
6	P_6	

■ TABLE 12-22

Exercises 37 through 40 refer to a variation of the chaos game. In this game you start with a square ABCD with sides of length 27 as shown in Fig. 12-39 and a fair die that you will roll many times. When you roll a 1, choose vertex A; when you roll a 2, choose vertex B; when you roll a 3, choose vertex C; and when you roll a 4 choose vertex D. (When you roll a 5 or a 6, disregard the roll and roll again.) A sequence of rolls will generate a sequence of points $P_1, P_2, P_3, \ldots$ inside or on the boundary of the square according to the following rules.

- ■ *Start. Roll the die. Mark the chosen vertex and call it P_1.*
- ■ *Step 1. Roll the die again. From P_1 move two-thirds of the way toward the new chosen vertex. Mark this point and call it P_2.*
- ■ *Steps 2, 3, etc. Each time you roll the die, mark the point two-thirds of the way between the previous point and the chosen vertex.*

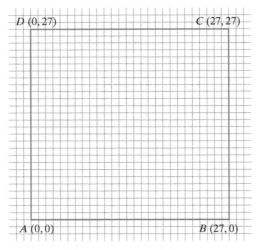

FIGURE 12-39

37. Using graph paper, find the points P_1, P_2, P_3, and P_4 corresponding to

(a) the sequence of rolls 4, 2, 1, 2.

(b) the sequence of rolls 3, 2, 1, 2.

(c) the sequence of rolls 3, 3, 1, 1.

38. Using graph paper, find the points P_1, P_2, P_3, and P_4 corresponding to

(a) the sequence of rolls 2, 2, 4, 4.

(b) the sequence of rolls 2, 3, 4, 1.

(c) the sequence of rolls 1, 3, 4, 1.

39. Using a rectangular coordinate system with A at $(0, 0)$, B at $(27, 0)$, C at $(27, 27)$, and D at $(0, 27)$, find the sequence of rolls that would produce the given sequence of marked points.

(a) P_1: $(0, 27)$, P_2: $(18, 9)$, P_3: $(6, 3)$, P_4: $(20, 1)$

(b) P_1: $(27, 27)$, P_2: $(9, 9)$, P_3: $(3, 3)$, P_4: $(19, 19)$

(c) P_1: $(0, 0)$, P_2: $(18, 18)$, P_3: $(6, 24)$, P_4: $(20, 8)$

40. Using a rectangular coordinate system with A at $(0, 0)$, B at $(27, 0)$, C at $(27, 27)$, and D at $(0, 27)$, find the sequence of rolls that would produce the given sequence of marked points.

(a) P_1: $(27, 0)$, P_2: $(27, 18)$, P_3: $(9, 24)$, P_4: $(3, 8)$

(b) P_1: $(0, 27)$, P_2: $(18, 9)$, P_3: $(24, 3)$, P_4: $(8, 19)$

(c) P_1: $(27, 27)$, P_2: $(9, 9)$, P_3: $(21, 3)$, P_4: $(7, 19)$

12.3 The Twisted Sierpinski Gasket

No exercises for this section.

12.4 The Mandelbrot Set

Exercises 41 through 46 are a review of complex number arithmetic. Recall that (1) to add two complex numbers you simply add the real parts and the imaginary parts: e.g., $(2 + 3i) + (5 + 2i) = 7 + 5i$; (2) to multiply two complex numbers you multiply them as if they were polynomials and use the fact that $i^2 = -1$: e.g., $(2 + 3i)(5 + 2i) = 10 + 4i + 15i + 6i^2 = 4 + 19i$. Finally, if you know how to multiply two complex numbers then you also know how to square them, since $(a + bi)^2 = (a + bi)(a + bi)$.

41. Simplify each expression.

(a) $(-i)^2 + (-i)$

(b) $(-1 - i)^2 + (-i)$

(c) $i^2 + (-i)$

42. Simplify each expression.

(a) $(1 + i)^2 + (1 + i)$

(b) $(1 + 3i)^2 + (1 + i)$

(c) $(-7 + 7i)^2 + (1 + i)$

43. Simplify each expression. (Give your answers rounded to three significant digits.)

(a) $(-0.25 + 0.25i)^2 + (-0.25 + 0.25i)$

(b) $(-0.25 - 0.25i)^2 + (-0.25 - 0.25i)$

44. Simplify each expression. (Give your answers rounded to three significant digits.)

(a) $(-0.25 + 0.125i)^2 + (-0.25 + 0.125i)$

(b) $(-0.2 + 0.8i)^2 + (-0.2 + 0.8i)$

45. (a) Plot the points corresponding to the complex numbers $(1 + i)$, $i(1 + i)$, $i^2(1 + i)$, and $i^3(1 + i)$.

(b) Plot the points corresponding to the complex numbers $(3 - 2i)$, $i(3 - 2i)$, $i^2(3 - 2i)$, and $i^3(3 - 2i)$.

(c) What geometric effect does multiplication by i have on a complex number?

46. (a) Plot the points corresponding to the complex numbers $(1 + i)$, $-i(1 + i)$, $(-i)^2(1 + i)$, and $(-i)^3(1 + i)$.

(b) Plot the points corresponding to the complex numbers $(0.8 + 1.2i)$, $-i(0.8 + 1.2i)$, $(-i)^2(0.8 + 1.2i)$, and $(-i)^3(0.8 + 1.2i)$.

(c) What geometric effect does multiplication by $-i$ have on a complex number?

47. Consider the Mandelbrot sequence with seed $s = -2$.

(a) Find s_1, s_2, s_3, and s_4.

(b) Find s_{100}.

(c) Is this Mandelbrot sequence *escaping*, *periodic*, or *attracted*? Explain.

48. Consider the Mandelbrot sequence with seed $s = 2$.

(a) Find s_1, s_2, s_3, and s_4.

(b) Is this Mandelbrot sequence *escaping*, *periodic*, or *attracted*? Explain.

49. Consider the Mandelbrot sequence with seed $s = -0.5$.

(a) Using a calculator find s_1 through s_5, rounded to four decimal places.

(b) Suppose you are given $s_N = -0.366$. Using a calculator find s_{N+1}, rounded to four decimal places.

(c) Is this Mandelbrot sequence *escaping*, *periodic*, or *attracted*? Explain.

50. Consider the Mandelbrot sequence with seed $s = -0.25$.

(a) Using a calculator find s_1 through s_{10}, rounded to six decimal places.

(b) Suppose you are given $s_N = -0.207107$. Using a calculator find s_{N+1}, rounded to six decimal places.

(c) Is this Mandelbrot sequence *escaping*, *periodic*, or *attracted*? Explain.

51. Consider the Mandelbrot sequence with seed $s = -i$.

(a) Find s_1 through s_5. (*Hint*: Try Exercise 41 first.)

(b) Is this Mandelbrot sequence *escaping*, *periodic*, or *attracted*? Explain.

52. Consider the Mandelbrot sequence with seed $s = 1 + i$. Find s_1, s_2, and s_3. (*Hint*: Try Exercise 42 first.)

JOGGING

53. Let H denote the total number of "holes" (i.e., white triangles) in the "gasket" obtained at a particular step of the construction of the Sierpinski gasket.

(a) Complete the entries in the following table.

	H
Start	0
Step 1	1
Step 2	$1 + 3$
Step 3	
Step 4	
Step 5	

(b) At Step N of the construction, the value of H is given by $\frac{(3^N - 1)}{2}$. Explain this formula. *Hint*: You will need to use the geometric sum formula

$$P + cP + c^2P + \cdots + c^{N-1}P = P\left(\frac{c^N - 1}{c - 1}\right).$$

Exercises 54 and 55 refer to the Menger sponge, a three-dimensional cousin of the Sierpinski carpet. (See Exercises 23–26.) The **Menger sponge** *is defined by the following recursive construction rule.*

Menger Sponge

■ **Start.** *Start with a solid seed cube [Fig. 12-40(a)].*

■ **Step 1.** *Subdivide the seed cube into 27 equal subcubes and remove the central cube and the six cubes in the centers of each face. This leaves a "sponge" consisting of 20 solid subcubes, as shown in Fig. 12-40(b).*

■ **Step 2.** *Subdivide each solid subcube into 27 subcubes and remove the central cube and the six cubes in the centers of each face. This gives the "sponge" shown in Fig. 12-40(c). (Call the procedure of removing the central cube and the cubes in the center of each face procedure MS.)*

■ **Steps 3, 4, etc.** *Apply procedure MS to each cube of the "sponge" obtained in the previous step.*

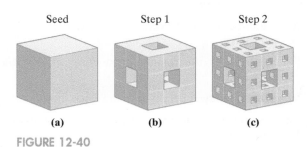

Seed	Step 1	Step 2
(a)	(b)	(c)

FIGURE 12-40

54. Assume that the seed cube of the Menger sponge has volume 1.

  (a) Let C denote the total number of cubes removed at a particular step of the construction, U the volume of each removed cube, and V the volume of the sponge at that particular step of the construction. Complete the entries in the following table.

	C	U	V
Start	0	0	1
Step 1	7	$\frac{1}{27}$	$\frac{20}{27}$
Step 2			
Step 3			
Step 4			
Step N			

  (b) Explain why the Menger sponge has infinitesimally small volume.

55. Let H denote total number of cubic holes in the "sponge" obtained at a particular step of the construction of the Menger sponge.

  (a) Complete the entries in the following table.

	H
Start	0
Step 1	7
Step 2	$7 + 20 \times 7$
Step 3	
Step 4	
Step 5	

  (b) Find a formula that gives the value of H for the "sponge" obtained at Step N of the construction. (*Hint:* You will need to use the geometric sum given in Exercise 53.)

Exercises 56 and 57 refer to reflection and rotation symmetries as discussed in Chapter 11 and, thus, require a good understanding of the material in that chapter.

56. (a) Describe all the reflection symmetries of the Koch snowflake.

  (b) Describe all the rotation symmetries of the Koch snowflake.

  (c) What is the symmetry type of the Koch snowflake?

57. This exercise refers to the Sierpinski carpet discussed in Exercises 23 through 26.

  (a) Describe all the reflection symmetries of the Sierpinski carpet.

  (b) Describe all the rotation symmetries of the Sierpinski carpet.

  (c) What is the symmetry type of the Sierpinski carpet?

58. Consider the Mandelbrot sequence with seed $s = -0.75$. Show that this Mandelbrot sequence is attracted to the value -0.5. (*Hint:* Consider the quadratic equation $x^2 - 0.75 = x$, and consider why solving this equation helps.)

59. Consider the Mandelbrot sequence with seed $s = 0.25$. Is this Mandelbrot sequence *escaping*, *periodic*, or *attracted*? If attracted, to what number? (*Hint:* Consider the quadratic equation $x^2 + 0.25 = x$, and consider why solving this equation helps.)

60. Consider the Mandelbrot sequence with seed $s = -1.25$. Is this Mandelbrot sequence *escaping*, *periodic*, or *attracted*? If attracted, to what number?

61. Consider the Mandelbrot sequence with seed $s = \sqrt{2}$. Is this Mandelbrot sequence *escaping*, *periodic*, or *attracted*? If attracted, to what number?

RUNNING

62. Suppose that we play the chaos game using triangle ABC and that M_1, M_2, and M_3 are the midpoints of the three sides of the triangle. Explain why it is impossible at any time during the game to land inside triangle $M_1M_2M_3$.

63. Consider the following variation of the chaos game. The game is played just like with the ordinary chaos game but with the following change in rules: If you roll a 1, 2, or 3, move halfway toward vertex A; if you roll a 4, move halfway toward vertex B; and if you roll a 5 or 6, move halfway toward vertex C. What familiar geometric fractal is approximated by repeated rolls in this game? Explain.

64. (a) Show that the complex number $s = -0.25 + 0.25i$ is in the Mandelbrot set.

  (b) Show that the complex number $s = -0.25 - 0.25i$ is in the Mandelbrot set. [*Hint:* Your work for (a) can help you here.]

65. Show that the Mandelbrot set has a reflection symmetry. (*Hint:* Compare the Mandelbrot sequences with seeds $a + bi$ and $a - bi$.)

*Exercises 66 through 68 refer to the concept of **fractal dimension**. The fractal dimension of a geometric fractal consisting of N self-similar copies of itself each reduced by a scaling factor of S is $D = \frac{\log N}{\log S}$. (The fractal dimension is described in a little more detail in Project 1 below.)*

66. Compute the fractal dimension of the *Koch curve*.

67. Compute the fractal dimension of the *Sierpinski carpet*. (The Sierpinski carpet is discussed in Exercises 23 through 26.)

68. Compute the fractal dimension of the *Menger sponge*. (The Menger sponge is discussed in Exercises 54 and 55.)

PROJECTS AND PAPERS

1 Fractal Dimension

The dimensions of a line segment, a square, and a cube are, as we all learned in school, 1, 2, and 3, respectively. But what is the dimension of the Sierpinski gasket?

The line segment of size 4 shown in Fig. 12-41(a) is made of four smaller copies of itself each scaled down by a factor of four; the square shown in Fig. 12-41(b) is made of $16 = 4^2$ smaller copies of itself each scaled down by a factor of four; and the cube shown in Fig. 12-41(c) is made of $64 = 4^3$ smaller copies of itself each scaled down by a factor of four. In all these cases, if N is the number of smaller copies of the object reduced by a scaling factor S, the dimension D is the exponent to which we need to raise S to get N (i.e., $N = S^D$). If we apply the same argument to the Sierpinski gasket shown in Fig. 12-41(d), we see that the Sierpinski gasket is made of $N = 3$ smaller copies of itself and that each copy has been reduced by a scaling factor $S = 2$. If we want to be consistent, the dimension of the Sierpinski gasket should be the exponent D in the equation $3 = 2^D$. To solve for D you have to use *logarithms*. When you do, you get $D = \frac{\log 3}{\log 2}$. Crazy but true: The dimension of the Sierpinski gasket is not a whole number, not even a rational number. It is the irrational number $\frac{\log 3}{\log 2}$ (about 1.585)!

For a geometric fractal with exact self-similarity, we will define its dimension as $D = \frac{\log N}{\log S}$, where N is the number of self-similar pieces that the parent fractal is built out of and S is the scale by which the pieces are reduced (if the pieces are one-half the size of the parent fractal $S = 2$, if the pieces are one-third the size of the parent fractal $S = 3$, and so on).

In this project you should discuss the meaning and importance of the concept of dimension as it applies to geometric fractals having exact self-similarity.

3 Book Review: *The Fractal Murders*

If you enjoy mystery novels, this project is for you.

The Fractal Murders by Mark Cohen (Muddy Gap Press, 2002) is a *whodunit* with a mathematical backdrop. In addition to the standard elements of a classic murder mystery (including a brilliant but eccentric detective), this novel has a fractal twist: The victims are all mathematicians doing research in the field of fractal geometry.

Read the novel and write a review of it. Include in your review a critique of both the literary and the mathematical merits of the book. To get some ideas as to how to write a good book review, you should check out the *New York Times Book Review* section, which appears every Sunday in the *New York Times* (*www.nytimes.com*).

4 Fractal Antennas

One of the truly innovative practical uses of fractals is in the design of small but powerful antennas that go inside wireless communication devices such as cell phones, wireless modems, and GPS receivers. The application of fractal geometry to antenna design follows from the discovery in 1999 by radio astronomers Nathan Cohen and Robert Hohlfeld of Boston University that an antenna that has a self-similar shape has the ability to work equally well at many different frequencies of the radio spectrum.

Write a paper discussing the application of the concepts of fractal geometry to the design of antennas.

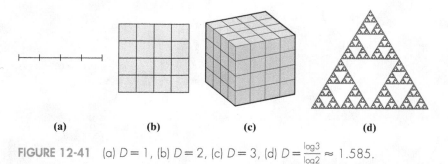

FIGURE 12-41 (a) $D = 1$, (b) $D = 2$, (c) $D = 3$, (d) $D = \frac{\log 3}{\log 2} \approx 1.585$.

2 Fractals and Music

The hallmark of a fractal shape is the property of *self-similarity*—there are themes that repeat themselves (either exactly or approximately) at many different scales. This type of repetition also works in music, and the application of fractal concepts to musical composition has produced many intriguing results.

Write a paper discussing the connections between fractals and music.

13 Fibonacci Numbers and the Golden Ratio

Tales of Rabbits and Gnomons

Fib retracements, arcs and fans, time zones, Elliott waves. Surfer's talk? No, Wall Street talk. All of the these terms describe some of the technical tools used by "chartists"—sophisticated traders who use the past up-and-down patterns in the chart of a stock market commodity to predict how the stock will perform in the future. Chartists live and die by their predictions: An accurate prediction is golden; a bad prediction can spell ruin. So it is quite remarkable that some of the most technical tools used by financial traders to predict market prices originated, more than 800 years ago, with, of all things, the behavior of a bunch of prolific bunny rabbits.

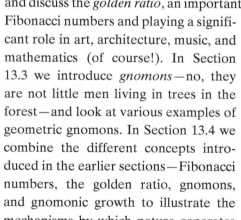

R ewind the clock to the year 1202. That's the year that a young Italian mathematician named Leonardo Pisano, known to the world as Fibonacci, published a book called *Liber Abaci* (literally translated as "The Book of Computation"). In *Liber Abaci*, Fibonacci introduced to the Europe of the Middle Ages the Hindu numerals and the Arabic algorithms for doing arithmetic and basic algebra—basically all of the school mathematics of today.

Because of its scope and influence, *Liber Abaci* was one of the most important books in the history of mathematics, but ironically, Fibonacci's modern fame (and the reason Wall Street traders talk about *Fibonacci time zones* and *Fibonacci analysis*) is a single example in the book involving a fairly simple rabbit–breeding problem:

> *A certain man put a pair of rabbits in a place surrounded in all sides by a wall. How many pairs of rabbits can be produced from that pair in a year if it is supposed that every month each pair begets a new pair, which from the second month on becomes productive?*

The numbers that give the general solution to this problem are now called the *Fibonacci numbers*, and, as they say, the rest is history.

This chapter starts by revisiting Fibonacci's rabbit-breeding problem (first discussed in Chapter 9, Example 9.5), followed by an introduction to the *Fibonacci numbers* and some of their mathematical properties. In Section 13.2 we introduce and discuss the *golden ratio*, an important irrational number closely connected to the Fibonacci numbers and playing a significant role in art, architecture, music, and mathematics (of course!). In Section 13.3 we introduce *gnomons*—no, they are not little men living in trees in the forest—and look at various examples of geometric gnomons. In Section 13.4 we combine the different concepts introduced in the earlier sections—Fibonacci numbers, the golden ratio, gnomons, and gnomonic growth to illustrate the mechanisms by which nature generates some of its beautiful spirals.

> **❝** Come forth into the light of things, let Nature be your teacher. **❞**
>
> *– William Wordsworth*

Leonardo Fibonacci (circa 1175–1250)

13.1 Fibonacci Numbers

We start this section with an abbreviated discussion of the Fibonacci rabbit problem. A much more detailed discussion of the problem was given in Example 9.5, page 265.

EXAMPLE 13.1 FIBONACCI'S RABBITS REVISITED

The key elements of Fibonacci's rabbit problem are as follows:

- **Start.** The population count starts with one pair of baby rabbits $(P_0 = 1)$. [*Note*: The rabbit count is by pairs, and each pair is assumed to be a male and a female.]
- **Month 1.** One month later the original pair is mature and able to produce offspring, but there is still one pair of rabbits: $P_1 = 1$.
- **Month 2.** The original pair produces a baby pair. There are now two pairs (one baby pair plus the parent pair): $P_2 = 1 + 1 = 2$.
- **Month 3.** The original pair produces another baby pair. There are now three pairs [the two pairs from the previous month (now both mature) plus the new baby pair]: $P_3 = 2 + 1 = 3$.
- **Month 4.** The two mature pairs in the previous month both have offspring. There are now five pairs [the three pairs from the previous month plus two new baby pairs]: $P_4 = 3 + 2 = 5$.
- **Month 5.** The three mature pairs in the previous month all have offspring. There are now eight pairs [the five pairs from the previous month plus three new baby pairs]: $P_4 = 5 + 3 = 8$.

  As long as the rabbits continue doing their thing and don't die, the pattern will continue: Each month the population will consist of the population in the previous month (mature pairs) plus the population in the previous previous month (baby pairs). It's a lot easier to express the idea in mathematical notation:

- **Month N.** $P_N = P_{N-1} + P_{N-2}$.

  The month-by-month sequence for the growth of the rabbit population is $1, 1, 2, 3, 5, 8, 13, 21, \ldots$.

If we forget about rabbits and think of the sequence $1, 1, 2, 3, 5, 8, 13, 21, \ldots$ as just an infinite sequence of numbers, we have what almost everyone calls *the Fibonacci sequence*.

- **Fibonacci sequence (infinite list form).** The *Fibonacci sequence* is the sequence

$$1, 1, 2, 3, 5, 8, 13, 21, 34, 55, 89, 144, \ldots.$$

The terms of this sequence are called the **Fibonacci numbers**. (The conventional notation is to use F_N to describe the Nth Fibonacci number and to start the count at F_1, so we write $F_1 = 1$, $F_2 = 1$, $F_3 = 2$, $F_4 = 3$, etc.)

- **Fibonacci numbers (recursive formula).** Starting with F_3, the Fibonacci numbers are given by the recursive formula $F_N = F_{N-1} + F_{N-2}$. (The first two numbers are by definition $F_1 = 1$ and $F_2 = 1$).

The recursive formula makes it very easy to find any Fibonacci number, as long as you know all the Fibonacci numbers that come before it. If you don't, you may have a problem.

EXAMPLE 13.2 FIBONACCI NUMBERS GET BIG FAST

Suppose you were given the following choice: You can have $100 billion or a sum equivalent to F_{100} pennies. Which one would you choose? Surely, this is a no brainer—how could you pass on the $100 billion? (By the way, that much money would make you considerably richer than Bill Gates.) But before you make a rash decision, let's see if we can figure out the dollar value of the second option. To do so, we need to compute F_{100}.

How could one find the value of F_{100}? With a little patience (and a calculator) we could use the recursive formula for the Fibonacci numbers as a "crank" that we repeatedly turn to ratchet our way up the Fibonacci sequence: From the seeds F_1 and F_2 we compute F_3, then use F_3 and F_2 to compute F_4, and so on. If all goes well, after many turns of the crank (we will skip the details) you will eventually get to

$$F_{97} = 83,621,143,489,848,422,977$$

and

$$F_{98} = 135,301,852,344,706,746,049$$

One more turn of the crank gives

$$F_{99} = F_{98} + F_{97} = 218,922,995,834,555,169,026$$

and the last turn gives

$$F_{100} = F_{99} + F_{98} = 354,224,848,179,261,915,075$$

Thus, the F_{100} cents can be rounded nicely to $3,542,248,481,792,619,150. How much money is that? If you take $100 billion for yourself and then divide what's left evenly among every man, woman, and child on Earth (about 6.7 billion people), each person would get more than *$500 million*!

The most obvious lesson to be drawn from Example 13.2 is that Fibonacci numbers grow very large very quickly. A more subtle lesson (less obvious because we cheated in Example 13.2 and skipped most of the work) is that computing Fibonacci numbers using the recursive formula takes an enormous amount of effort (each turn of the crank involves just one addition, but as we noted, the numbers being added get very large very quickly).

Is there a more convenient way to compute Fibonacci numbers—without the need to repeatedly turn the crank in the recursive formula? Yes and no. In 1736 Leonhard Euler (the same Euler behind the namesake theorems in Chapter 5) discovered a formula for the Fibonacci numbers that does not rely on previous Fibonacci numbers. The formula was lost and rediscovered 100 years later by French mathematician and astronomer Jacques Binet, who somehow ended up getting all the credit, as the formula is now known as *Binet's formula*. Now come the bad news.

■ **Binet's formula (original version).** The Nth Fibonacci number is given by

$$F_N = \left[\left(\frac{1 + \sqrt{5}}{2} \right)^N - \left(\frac{1 - \sqrt{5}}{2} \right)^N \right] \Big/ \sqrt{5}.$$

Admittedly, Binet's original formula is quite complicated and intimidating, and even with a good calculator you might have trouble finding an exact value when N is large, but there is a simplified version of the formula that makes the calculations a bit easier. In this simplified version we essentially disregard the second half of the numerator (it is a very small number) and make up for it by rounding to the nearest integer.

■ **Binet's formula (simplified version).** The *N*th Fibonacci number is given by

$$F_N = \left[\left(\frac{1+\sqrt{5}}{2}\right)^N \Big/ \sqrt{5}\right], \text{ where } [\ ] \text{ means "round to the nearest integer".}$$

Binet's simplified formula is an explicit formula (we don't have to know the previous Fibonacci numbers to use it), but it only makes sense to use it to compute very large Fibonacci numbers (for smaller Fibonacci numbers you are much better off using the recursive formula). For example, if you need to find F_{100} you might consider using Binet's simplified formula. To do so you will need a good calculator that can handle fairly large numbers. (A very good free online calculator that can handle very large numbers is *web2.0calc*, available at *http://web2.0calc.com*).

EXAMPLE 13.3 COMPUTING F_{100} WITH BINET'S SIMPLIFIED FORMULA

Binet's simplified formula for F_{100} is $F_{100} = \left[\left(\frac{1+\sqrt{5}}{2}\right)^{100} \Big/ \sqrt{5}\right]$.

The key step is to compute the number inside the double square brackets. The last step is to round the number to the nearest integer, which is trivial. For this example, *web2.0calc* is used for the calculation. Figure 13-1(a) shows a screen shot of the input prior to the calculation; Fig. 13-1(b) shows the answer given by *web2.0calc*. The last step is rounding the answer to the nearest integer, but in this case the calculator shows no decimal part to the answer, so no rounding is needed. We are done:

$$F_{100} = 354{,}224{,}848{,}179{,}261{,}915{,}075.$$

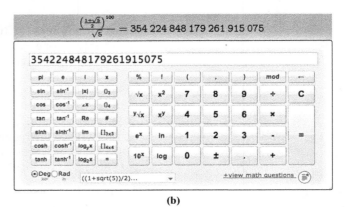

(a)   **(b)**

FIGURE 13-1 Computing F_{100} with Binet's simplified formula.

Fibonacci Numbers in Nature

One of the major attractions of the Fibonacci numbers is how often they show up in natural organisms, particularly flowers and plants that grow as spirals. The petal counts of most varieties of daisies are Fibonacci numbers—most often 3, 5, 8, 13, 21, 34, or 55 (but giant daisies with 89 petals also exist).

Figure 13-2 shows three varieties of daisies with 13, 21, and 34 petals, respectively. The bracts of a typical pinecone are arranged in 5, 8, and 13 spiraling rows depending on the direction you count [Figs. 13-3(a) and (b)]; and the seeds on a sunflower head are arranged in 21 and 34 spiraling rows [Figs. 13-3(c) and (d)]. Why Fibonacci numbers? It is a bit of a mystery, but definitely related to the spiraling nature of the growth. We will come back to spiral growth and the connection with Fibonacci numbers in the last section of this chapter.

FIGURE 13-2 (a) Yellow daisy (13 petals). (b) English daisy (21 petals). (c) Oxeye daisy (34 petals).

FIGURE 13-3 (a) and (b) Arrangement of bracts in a pinecone. (c) and (d) Arrangement of seeds in a sunflower head.

13.2 The Golden Ratio

In this section we will introduce a remarkable number known as the *golden ratio* (sometimes also called the *golden mean* or the *golden section*). We will use the Greek letter ϕ ("phi"; pronounced "fi" with a long "i") to denote this special irrational number.

Irrational numbers are numbers that have an infinite, nonrepeating decimal expansion. This is not an actual definition (a proper mathematical definition is quite complicated and beyond the scope of this book), but it will serve our purposes for the moment. While π is undoubtedly the best known of all irrational numbers, the easiest place to find a mother lode of irrational numbers is to look at the square roots of positive integers: When a positive integer is *not a perfect square its square root is an irrational number.* So for the record, $\sqrt{2}$, $\sqrt{3}$, $\sqrt{5}$, $\sqrt{6}$, and $\sqrt{7}$ are all examples of irrational numbers.

Irrational numbers don't mix well with rational numbers. Say you take $\sqrt{7}$, add 1 to it, and then divide the result by 2. What do you have? You have another irrational number, but there is no way to write it as a single numerical entity—it is simply "the number" $\frac{1 + \sqrt{7}}{2}$. There is one exception to this situation—the number $\frac{1 + \sqrt{5}}{2}$. This number is so special and important that it has its own symbol and name. This number is, in fact, the golden ratio ϕ.

- **The Golden Ratio.** The golden ratio is the irrational number $\phi = \frac{1 + \sqrt{5}}{2}$. A decimal approximation for ϕ accurate to 10 decimal places is $\phi \approx 1.6180339887$. (For the purposes of memorization, $\phi \approx 1.618$ is a convenient shortcut.)

What is it that makes the golden ratio such a special number? There are several different explanations, but in one way or another they all fall back to the following fact: $\phi^2 = \phi + 1$. For ease of reference we call this the *golden property.*

- **The Golden Property.** $\phi^2 = \phi + 1$. Restated in plain English, this property says that to square the golden ratio all you have to do is add one to it.

Our next example shows that the golden ratio is the only *positive* number satisfying the golden property.

EXAMPLE 13.4 SOLVING $x^2 = x + 1$

To find all numbers with the property that squaring the number is the same as adding one to it we set up the quadratic equation $x^2 = x + 1$. Solving this equation involves the use of the quadratic formula—standard fare in high school algebra. (For a review of the quadratic formula, see Exercises 25 through 28.)

To solve the equation we first rewrite it in the form $x^2 - x - 1 = 0$. The two solutions are $\frac{1 \pm \sqrt{5}}{2}$ [see Exercise 25(a)]. The positive solution is $\phi = \frac{1 + \sqrt{5}}{2} \approx 1.6180339887$. The second (negative) solution is $\frac{1 - \sqrt{5}}{2} \approx -0.6180339887$. Both approximations are accurate to 10 decimal places.

Notice that the two solutions appear to have identical decimal parts. This is not a coincidence, since one is positive, the other is negative, and their sum equals 1 [see Exercise 25(b)]. It follows that the negative solution can be written as $1 - \phi$.

Our next example illustrates why the golden property is relevant to our discussion.

EXAMPLE 13.5 THE DIVINE PROPORTION

Imagine that the line segment in Fig. 13-4(a) represents some undefined unit—a building, a work of art, a musical composition, whatever. This unit is to be split into two unequal sections in a nice, aesthetically pleasing and balanced proportion. Figure 13-4(b) shows a split that most of us would consider pretty unbalanced—the larger piece is too large and out of proportion in relation to the shorter piece.

What kind of split would make for an ideal proportion? The ancient Greeks—masters of both geometry and aesthetics—came up with a very clever answer: *Make the split in such a way that the ratio of the bigger piece to the smaller piece is equal to the ratio of the whole unit to the bigger piece.* They called this proportion *the divine proportion.*

If we let B and S stand for the sizes of the bigger and smaller pieces respectively [Fig. 13-4(c)], the divine proportion is satisfied when $\frac{B}{S} = \frac{B + S}{B}$, or equivalently, $\frac{B}{S} = 1 + \frac{S}{B}$. If we now let x denote the ratio $\frac{B}{S}$, then $\frac{B}{S} = 1 + \frac{S}{B}$ becomes the equation $x = 1 + \frac{1}{x}$, or equivalently, $x^2 = x + 1$. Since $x = \frac{B}{S}$ has to be positive (B and S are both

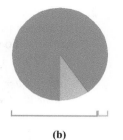
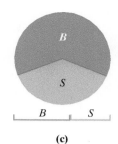

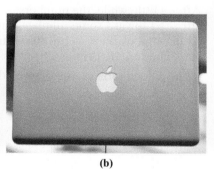

FIGURE 13-4　Searching for the golden split.

positive) and the only positive number satisfying $x^2 = x + 1$ is the golden ratio ϕ, we can conclude that $\frac{B}{S} = \phi$ (i.e., the divine proportion is satisfied only when the ratio of the bigger piece to the shorter piece equals the golden ratio ϕ).

Throughout history, many famous painters, sculptors, architects, and designers are said to have looked at the golden ratio $\phi = 1.618\ldots$ as the perfect ratio of big to small and used it in their works. How much of it is true and how much of it is hype is a matter of some debate, but there is no shortage of man-made structures and everyday objects having *approximately divine* proportions (longer side/shorter side $\approx 1.618 \approx \phi$). Figure 13-5 shows some random examples: A standard credit card measures 8.5 by 5.3 cm (aspect ratio of approximately 1.604); the screen of a MacBook Air measures 11.375 in by 7.1875 in (aspect ratio of approximately 1.583); the CN tower in Toronto (the tallest building in North America) has a height of 553 m with an observation deck located at a height of 342 m (a ratio of approximately 1.617). While none of these ratios is exactly the golden ratio, in the real world the difference between a ratio of 1.604 and 1.618... is invisible to the human eye—so who cares? We can think of these ratios as *imperfectly golden.*

FIGURE 13-5　Imperfectly golden proportions.

Fibonacci Numbers and the Golden Ratio

Other than the fact that the Fibonacci numbers and the golden ratio share equal billing in the title of this chapter, there is no particular reason to guess that they are connected in any way. But they are, and their relationship is very tight. In this section we will briefly discuss just a few of the many ways that the Fibonacci numbers and the golden ratio come together.

1. Binet's formula. Take another look at the original version of Binet's formula. The numerator has two numbers raised to the Nth power: $\frac{1 + \sqrt{5}}{2}$ and $\frac{1 - \sqrt{5}}{2}$. We now know that the first of these numbers is ϕ and the second is $1 - \phi$ (see Example 13.4). It follows that we can rewrite Binet's original formula in terms of ϕ: $F_N = [\phi^N - (1 - \phi)^N]/\sqrt{5}$. Binet's simplified formula takes an even nicer form: $F_N = [\phi^N/\sqrt{5}]$.

2. Golden power formula: $\phi^N = F_N\phi + F_{N-1}$. This formula is a generalization of the golden property. It expresses any power of ϕ in terms of ϕ and Fibonacci numbers. To see how this formula comes about, let's compute ϕ^2 through ϕ^5.

- $\phi^2 = \phi + 1$. [The golden property].

- $\phi^3 = 2\phi + 1$. [Multiply both sides of $\phi^2 = \phi + 1$ by ϕ and replace ϕ^2 by $\phi + 1$. This gives $\phi^3 = \phi^2 + \phi = (\phi + 1) + \phi = 2\phi + 1$.]

- $\phi^4 = 3\phi + 2$. [Multiply both sides of $\phi^3 = 2\phi + 1$ by ϕ and replace ϕ^2 by $\phi + 1$. This gives $\phi^4 = 2\phi^2 + \phi = 2(\phi + 1) + \phi = 3\phi + 2$.]

- $\phi^5 = 5\phi + 3$. [Multiply both sides of $\phi^4 = 3\phi + 2$ by ϕ and replace ϕ^2 by $\phi + 1$. This gives $\phi^5 = 3\phi^2 + 2\phi = 3(\phi + 1) + 2\phi = 5\phi + 3$.]

If you look at the pattern that is emerging, you will notice that for each power of ϕ the coefficients on the right-hand side are consecutive Fibonacci numbers: $\phi^2 = F_2\phi + F_1$, $\phi^3 = F_3\phi + F_2$, $\phi^4 = F_4\phi + F_3$, and $\phi^5 = F_5\phi + F_4$. The general version of this observation gives the golden power formula $\phi^N = F_N\phi + F_{N-1}$.

3. Ratio of consecutive Fibonacci numbers. Let's look at the sequence of numbers obtained by dividing a Fibonacci number by the preceding Fibonacci number (in other words, the sequence defined by the fractions $\frac{F_{N+1}}{F_N}$). Writing this sequence in fractional form doesn't give us anything that looks very interesting:

$$\frac{1}{1}, \frac{2}{1}, \frac{3}{2}, \frac{5}{3}, \frac{8}{5}, \frac{13}{8}, \frac{21}{13}, \frac{34}{21}, \frac{55}{34}, \frac{89}{55}, \frac{144}{89}, \frac{233}{144}, \frac{377}{233}, \frac{610}{377}, \frac{987}{610}, \frac{1597}{987}, \ldots$$

If we write the same numbers as decimals (rounded to six decimal places when needed), things look a lot more interesting:

1, 2, 1.5, 1.666667, 1.6, 1.625, 1.615385, 1.619048, 1.617647, 1.618182, 1.617978, 1.618056, 1.618026, 1.618037, 1.618033, 1.618034, . . .

After a little while, the numbers in this sequence start to look like they are being attracted toward some number, and yes, that number is ϕ. (In fact, rounded to six decimal places $\phi = 1.618034$, matching exactly the last number in our second list.) The fact that ratios of successive Fibonacci numbers get closer and closer to the golden ratio can be described symbolically by $\left(\frac{F_{N+1}}{F_N}\right) \to \phi$.

13.3 Gnomons

The most common usage of the word *gnomon* is to describe the pin of a sundial—the part that casts the shadow that shows the time of day. The original Greek meaning of the word *gnomon* is "one who knows," so it's not surprising that the word should find its way into the vocabulary of mathematics.

In this section we will discuss a different meaning for the word *gnomon*. Before we do so, we will do a brief review of a few facts from high school geometry.

Similarity

We know from geometry that two objects are said to be **similar** if one is a scaled version of the other. The following important facts about similarity of basic two-dimensional figures will come in handy later in the chapter:

- **Triangles:** Two triangles are similar if and only if the measures of their respective angles are the same. Alternatively, two triangles are similar if and only if corresponding

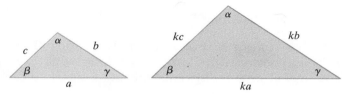

FIGURE 13-6   Similar triangles ($k = 1.6$).

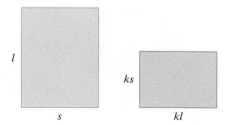

FIGURE 13-7   Similar rectangles ($k = 0.75$).

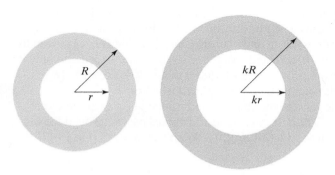

FIGURE 13-8   Similar rings $\left(k = 4/3\right)$.

sides are proportional. In other words, if triangle 1 has sides of length a, b, and c, then triangle 2 is similar to triangle 1 if and only if its sides have length ka, kb, and kc for some positive constant k called the *scaling factor*. When $k > 1$, triangle 2 is larger than triangle 1 (Fig. 13-6); when $0 < k < 1$, triangle 2 is smaller than triangle 1.

- **Squares:** Two squares are always similar.
- **Rectangles:** Two rectangles are similar if their corresponding sides are proportional (Fig. 13-7).
- **Circles and disks:** Two circles are always similar. Any circular disk (a circle plus all its interior) is similar to any other circular disk.
- **Circular rings:** Two circular rings are similar if and only if their inner and outer radii are proportional (Fig. 13-8).

Gnomons

We will now return to the main topic of this section—gnomons. In geometry, a **gnomon** G to a figure A is a connected figure that, when suitably *attached* to A, produces a new figure similar to A. By "attached," we mean that the two figures are coupled into one figure without any overlap. Informally, we will describe it this way: G is a gnomon to A if G & A *is similar to* A (Fig. 13-9). Here the symbol "&" should be taken to mean "attached in some suitable way."

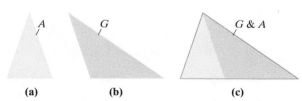

FIGURE 13-9   (a) The original object A. (b) The gnomon G. (c) G & A is similar to A.

EXAMPLE 13.6   GNOMONS TO SQUARES

Consider the square S in Fig. 13-10(a). The L-shaped figure G in Fig. 13-10(b) is a gnomon to the square—when G is attached to S as shown in Fig. 13-10(c), we get the square S'.

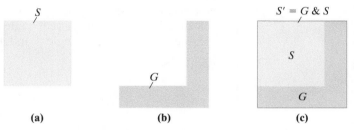

FIGURE 13-10   (a) A square S. (b) The gnomon G. (c) G & S form a larger square.

Note that the wording is *not* reversible. The square S *is not* a gnomon to the L-shaped figure G, since there is no way to attach the two to form an L-shaped figure similar to G.

EXAMPLE 13.7   GNOMONS TO CIRCULAR DISKS

Consider the circular disk C with radius r in Fig. 13-11(a). The O-ring G in Fig. 13-11(b) with inner radius r is a gnomon to C. Clearly, G & C form the circular disk C' shown in Fig. 13-11(c). Since all circular disks are similar, C' is similar to C.

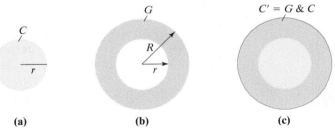

FIGURE 13-11   (a) A circular disk C. (b) The gnomon G. (c) G & C form a larger circular disk.

EXAMPLE 13.8   GNOMONS TO RECTANGLES

Consider a rectangle R of height h and base b as shown in Fig. 13-12(a). The L-shaped figure G shown in Fig. 13-12(b) can clearly be attached to R to form the larger rectangle R' shown in Fig. 13-12(c). This does not, in and of itself, guarantee that G is a gnomon to R. The rectangle R' [with height $(h + x)$ and base $(b + y)$] is similar to R if and only if their corresponding sides are proportional, which requires that $b/h = (b + y)/(h + x)$. With a little algebraic manipulation, this can be simplified to $b/h = y/x$.

There is a simple geometric way to determine if the L-shaped G is a gnomon to R— just extend the diagonal of R in G & R. If the extended diagonal passes through the outside corner of G, then G is a gnomon [Fig. 13-12(c)]; if it doesn't, then it isn't [Fig. 13-12(d)].

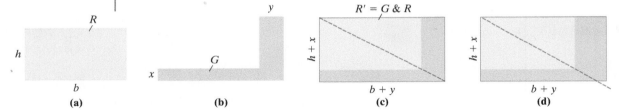

FIGURE 13-12   (a) A rectangle R. (b) A candidate for gnomon G. (c) G & R is similar to R. (d) G & R is not similar to R.

EXAMPLE 13.9   A GOLDEN TRIANGLE

In this example, we are going to do things a little bit backward. Let's start with an isosceles triangle T, with vertices B, C, and D whose angles measure 72°, 72°, and 36°, respectively, as shown in Fig. 13-13(a). On side CD we mark the point A so that BA is congruent to BC [Fig. 13-13(b)]. (A is the point of intersection of side CD and the circle of radius BC and center B.) Since T' is an isosceles triangle, angle BAC measures 72° and it follows that angle ABC measures 36°. This implies that triangle T' has equal angles as triangle T and, thus, they are similar triangles.

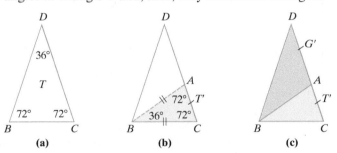

FIGURE 13-13   (a) A 72-72-36 isosceles triangle T. (b) T' is similar to T. (c) G' & $T' = T$.

"So what?" you may ask. Where is the gnomon to triangle T? We don't have one yet! But we *do* have a gnomon to triangle T'—it is triangle BAD, labeled G' in Fig. 13-13(c). After all, G' & T' give T—a triangle similar to T'. Note that G' is an isosceles triangle with angles that measure 36°, 36°, and 108°.

We now know how to find a gnomon not only to triangle T' but also to any 72-72-36 triangle, including the original triangle T: Attach a 36-36-108 triangle to one of the longer sides [Fig. 13-14(a)]. If we repeat this process indefinitely, we get a spiraling series of ever-increasing 72-72-36 triangles [Fig. 13-14(b)]. It's not too far-fetched to use a family analogy: Triangles T and G are the "parents," with T having the "dominant genes"; the "offspring" of their union looks just like T (but bigger). The offspring then has offspring of its own (looking exactly like its grandparent T), and so on ad infinitum.

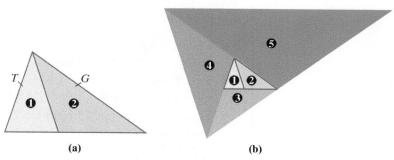

FIGURE 13-14   The process of adding a 36-36-108 gnomon G to a 72-72-36 triangle T can be repeated indefinitely, producing a spiraling chain of ever-increasing similar triangles.

Example 13.9 is of special interest to us for two reasons. First, this is the first time we have an example in which the figure and its gnomon are of the same type (isosceles triangles). Second, the isosceles triangles in this story (72-72-36 and 36-36-108) have a property that makes them unique: In both cases, the ratio of their sides (longer side over shorter side) is the golden ratio (see Exercise 66). These are the only two isosceles triangles with this property, and for this reason they are called **golden triangles**.

EXAMPLE 13.10   SQUARE GNOMONS TO RECTANGLES

We saw in Example 13.8 that *any* rectangle can have an L-shaped gnomon. Much more interesting is the case when a rectangle has a square gnomon. Not every rectangle can have a square gnomon, and the ones that do are quite special.

Consider a rectangle R with sides of length B and S [Fig. 13-15(a)], and suppose that the square G with sides of length B shown in Fig. 13-15(b) is a gnomon to R. If so, then the rectangle R' shown in Fig. 13-15(c) must be similar to R, which implies that their corresponding sides must be proportional: $\frac{B}{S} = \frac{B+S}{B}$. If this proportion looks familiar, it's because it is the *divine proportion* we first discussed in Example 13.5 and whose only possible solution is $B/S = \phi$.

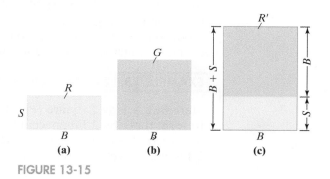

FIGURE 13-15

Example 13.10 tells us that the only way that a rectangle can have a square gnomon is if its sides are in a divine proportion (i.e., $B/S = \phi$ where B and S are the lengths of the bigger and shorter sides, respectively.

Golden and Fibonacci Rectangles

A rectangle whose sides are in the proportion of the golden ratio is called a **golden rectangle**. In other words, a golden rectangle is a rectangle with sides B and S satisfying $B/S = \phi$. A close relative to a golden rectangle is a **Fibonacci rectangle**—a rectangle whose sides are consecutive Fibonacci numbers.

EXAMPLE 13.11 GOLDEN AND ALMOST GOLDEN RECTANGLES

Figure 13-16 shows an assortment of rectangles (please note that the rectangles are not drawn to the same scale). Some are golden, some are close.

- The rectangle in Fig. 13-16(a) has $B = 1$ and $S = 1/\phi$. Since $B/S = 1/(1/\phi) = \phi$, this is a golden rectangle.
- The rectangle in Fig. 13-16(b) has $B = \phi + 1$ and $S = \phi$. Here $B/S = (\phi + 1)/\phi$. Since $\phi + 1 = \phi^2$, this is another golden rectangle.
- The rectangle in Fig. 13-16(c) has $B = 8$ and $S = 5$. This is a Fibonacci rectangle, since 5 and 8 are consecutive Fibonacci numbers. The ratio of the sides is $B/S = 8/5 = 1.6$, so this is not a golden rectangle. On the other hand, the ratio 1.6 is reasonably close to $\phi = 1.618\ldots$, so we will think of this rectangle as "imperfectly golden."
- The rectangle in Fig. 13-16(d) with $B = 89$ and $S = 55$ is another Fibonacci rectangle. Since $89/55 = 1.61818\ldots$, this rectangle is as good as golden—the ratio of the sides is the same as the golden ratio up to three decimal places.

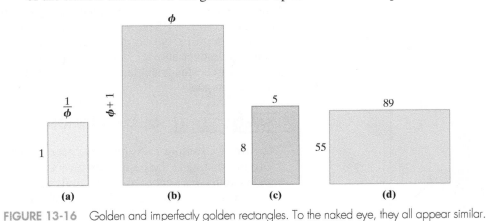

FIGURE 13-16   Golden and imperfectly golden rectangles. To the naked eye, they all appear similar.

13.4 Spiral Growth in Nature

In nature, where form usually follows function, the perfect balance of a golden rectangle shows up in spiral-growing organisms, often in the form of consecutive Fibonacci numbers. To see how this connection works, consider the following example, which serves as a model for certain natural growth processes.

EXAMPLE 13.12 STACKING SQUARES ON FIBONACCI RECTANGLES

Start with a 1 by 1 square [Fig. 13-17(a)] and attach to it another 1 by 1 square to form the 1 by 2 Fibonacci rectangle shown in Fig. 13-17(b). We will call this the "second-generation" rectangle. Next, add a 2 by 2 square. This gives the 3 by 2 Fibonacci rectangle shown in Fig. 13-17(c)—the "third generation" rectangle.

Next, add a 3 by 3 square as shown Fig. 13-17(d), giving a 3 by 5 Fibonacci rectangle—the "fourth generation". Next, add a 5 by 5 square as shown in Fig. 13-17(e) giving an 8 by 5 Fibonacci rectangle. You get the picture—we can keep doing this as long as we want.

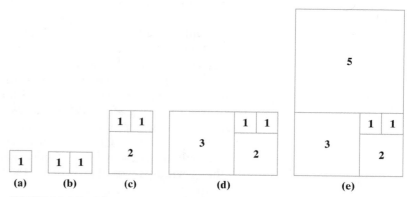

FIGURE 13-17   Fibonacci rectangles beget Fibonacci rectangles.

We might imagine these growing Fibonacci rectangles describing the growth of a living organism. In each generation, the organism grows by adding a square (a very simple, basic shape). The interesting feature of this growth is that as the Fibonacci rectangles grow larger, they become very close to golden rectangles, and as such, they become essentially similar to one another. This kind of growth—getting bigger while maintaining the same overall shape and proportion—is characteristic of the way many natural organisms grow.

The next example is a simple variation of Example 13.12.

EXAMPLE 13.13   THE GROWTH OF A "CHAMBERED" FIBONACCI RECTANGLE

Let's revisit the growth process of the previous example, except now let's create within each of the squares being added an interior "chamber" in the form of a quarter-circle. We need to be a little careful about how we attach the chambered square in each successive generation, but other than that, we can repeat the sequence of steps in Example 13.12 to get the sequence of shapes shown in Fig. 13-18. These figures depict the consecutive generations in the evolution of the *chambered Fibonacci rectangle*. The outer spiral formed by the circular arcs is often called a **Fibonacci spiral**, shown in Fig. 13-19.

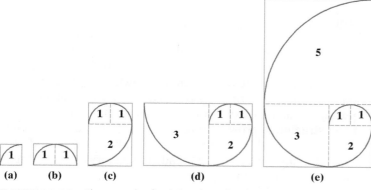

FIGURE 13-18   The growth of a "chambered" Fibonacci rectangle.

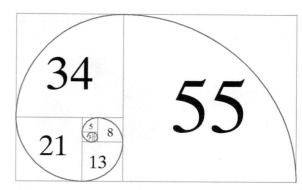

FIGURE 13-19   A Fibonacci spiral after 10 "generations."

Gnomonic Growth

Natural organisms grow in essentially two different ways. Humans, most animals, and many plants grow following what can informally be described as an *all-around growth* rule. In this type of growth, all living parts of the organism grow simultaneously—but not necessarily at the same rate. One characteristic of this type of growth is that there is no obvious way to distinguish between the newer and the older parts of the organism. In fact, the distinction between new and old parts does not make much sense. The historical record (so to speak) of the organism's growth is lost.

Contrast this with the kind of growth exemplified by the shell of a chambered nautilus, a ram's horn, or the trunk of a redwood tree (Fig. 13-20). These organisms grow following a *one-sided* or *asymmetric growth* rule, meaning that the organism has a new part added to it in such a way that the old organism together with the added part form the new organism. At any stage of the growth process, we can see not only the present form of the organism but also the organism's entire past. All the previous stages of growth are the building blocks that make up the present structure.

  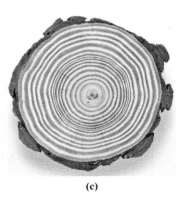

(a)   (b)   (c)

FIGURE 13-20   (a) Chambered nautilus. (b) Ram's horn. (c) Cross section of a redwood tree.

The other important aspect of natural growth is the principle of *self-similarity*: Organisms like to maintain their overall shape and proportions as they grow. This is where gnomons come into the picture. For the organism to retain its overall structure as it grows, the new growth must be a *gnomon* of the entire organism. We will call this kind of growth process **gnomonic growth**.

We have already seen abstract mathematical examples of gnomonic growth (Examples 13.12 and 13.13). Here is a pair of more realistic examples.

EXAMPLE 13.14   CIRCULAR GNOMONIC GROWTH

FIGURE 13-21   The growth rings in a redwood tree — an example of circular gnomonic growth.

We know from Example 13.7 that the gnomon to a circular disk is an O-ring with an inner radius equal to the radius of the circle. We can, thus, have circular gnomonic growth (Fig. 13-21) by the regular addition of O-rings. O-rings added one layer at a time to a starting circular structure preserve the circular shape throughout the structure's growth. When carried to three dimensions, this is a good model for the way the trunk of a redwood tree grows. And this is why we can "read" the history of a felled redwood tree by studying its rings.

EXAMPLE 13.15 SPIRAL GNOMONIC GROWTH

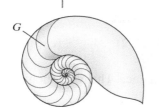

FIGURE 13-22 Gnomonic growth of a chambered nautilus.

Figure 13-22 shows a diagram of a cross section of the chambered nautilus. The chambered nautilus builds its shell in stages, each time adding another chamber to the already existing shell. At every stage of its growth, the shape of the chambered nautilus shell remains the same—the beautiful and distinctive spiral shown in Fig. 13-20(a). This is a classic example of gnomonic growth—each new chamber added to the shell is a gnomon of the entire shell. The gnomonic growth of the shell proceeds, in essence, as follows: Starting with its initial shell (a tiny spiral similar in all respects to the adult spiral shape), the animal builds a chamber (by producing a special secretion around its body that calcifies and hardens). The resulting, slightly enlarged spiral shell is similar to the original one. The process then repeats itself over many stages, each one a season in the growth of the animal. Each new chamber adds a gnomon to the shell, so the shell grows and yet remains similar to itself. This process is a real-life variation of the mathematical spiral-building process discussed in Example 13.13. The curve generated by the outer edge of a nautilus shell's cross section is called a *logarithmic spiral.*

More complex examples of gnomonic growth occur in sunflowers, daisies, pineapples, pinecones, and so on. Here, the rules that govern growth are somewhat more involved, but Fibonacci numbers and the golden ratio once again play a prominent role.

Conclusion

Some of the most beautiful shapes in nature arise from a basic principle of design: *form follows function.* The beauty of natural shapes is a result of their inherent elegance and efficiency, and imitating nature's designs has helped humans design and build beautiful and efficient structures of their own.

In this chapter, we examined a special type of growth—gnomonic growth—where an organism grows by the addition of gnomons, thereby preserving its basic shape even as it grows. Many beautiful spiral-shaped organisms, from seashells to flowers, exhibit this type of growth.

To us, understanding the basic principles behind spiral growth was relevant because it introduced us to some wonderful mathematical concepts that have been known and studied in their own right for centuries—*Fibonacci numbers, the golden ratio, the divine proportion*, and *gnomons*.

To humans, these abstract mathematical concepts have been, by and large, intellectual curiosities. To nature—the consummate artist and builder—they are the building tools for some of its most beautiful creations: flowers, plants, and seashells.

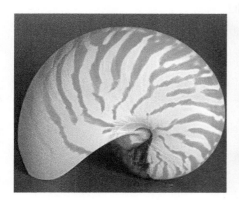

KEY CONCEPTS

13.1 Fibonacci Numbers

- **Fibonacci sequence:** the sequence 1, 1, 2, 3, 5, 8, 13, 21, 34, . . . (each term of the sequence is the sum of the two preceding terms), **390**

- **Fibonacci numbers:** the terms of the Fibonacci sequence. The Nth Fibonacci number is denoted by F_N, **390**

- **Binet's formula:** $F_N = \left[\left(\frac{1 + \sqrt{5}}{2}\right)^N - \left(\frac{1 - \sqrt{5}}{2}\right)^N \right] \Big/ \sqrt{5}$. A simplified version of the formula is given by $F_N = \left[\left(\frac{1 + \sqrt{5}}{2}\right)^N \Big/ \sqrt{5}\right]$ (where $[\ ]$ denotes round to the nearest integer), **391**

13.2 The Golden Ratio

- **golden ratio ϕ:** the irrational number $\frac{1 + \sqrt{5}}{2}$, **394**

- **golden property:** $\phi^2 = \phi + 1$, **394**

- **divine proportion:** $\frac{B}{S} = \frac{B + S}{B}$, where B and S are, respectively the bigger and smaller parts of a whole that has been split into two unequal parts, **394**

- **golden power formula:** $\phi^N = F_N\phi + F_{N-1}$, **396**

- **ratio of consecutive Fibonacci numbers:** As Fibonacci numbers get bigger and bigger, the ratios F_{N+1}/F_N get closer and closer to ϕ, **396**

13.3 Gnomons

- **gnomon (to a figure A):** a figure that, when suitably combined with A, produces a new figure that is similar to A, **397**

- **golden triangle:** an isosceles triangle with angles measuring 72°, 72°, and 36°, or alternatively, angles measuring 36°, 36°, and 108°, **398**

- **golden rectangle:** a rectangle with sides of length B and S where $B/S = \phi$, **400**

- **Fibonacci rectangle:** a rectangle having sides whose lengths are consecutive Fibonacci numbers, **400**

13.4 Spiral Growth in Nature

- **Fibonacci spiral:** a spiral obtained by forming a series of Fibonacci rectangles by adding squares and then connecting opposite corners of the squares in a continuous arc, **401**

- **gnomonic growth:** a type of growth where an organism grows by repeatedly adding new parts that are gnomons to the old organism, **402**

EXERCISES

WALKING

13.1 Fibonacci Numbers

1. Compute the value of each of the following.
   (a) F_{15} (b) $F_{15} - 2$
   (c) F_{15-2} (d) $\frac{F_{15}}{5}$
   (e) $F_{15/5}$

2. Compute the value of each of the following.
   (a) F_{16} (b) $F_{16} + 1$
   (c) F_{16+1} (d) $\frac{F_{16}}{4}$
   (e) $F_{16/4}$

3. Compute the value of each of the following.
   (a) $F_1 + F_2 + F_3 + F_4 + F_5$
   (b) $F_{1+2+3+4+5}$
   (c) $F_3 \times F_4$
   (d) $F_{3\times 4}$

4. Compute the value of each of the following.
   (a) $F_1 + F_3 + F_5 + F_7$
   (b) $F_{1+3+5+7}$
   (c) F_{10}/F_5
   (d) F_{10/F_5}

5. Describe in words what each of the expressions represents.
   (a) $3F_N + 1$ (b) $3F_{N+1}$
   (c) $F_{3N} + 1$ (d) F_{3N+1}

6. Describe in words what each of the expressions represents.
   (a) $F_{2N} - 3$ (b) F_{2N-3}
   (c) $2F_N - 3$ (d) $2F_{N-3}$

7. Given that $F_{36} = 14{,}930{,}352$ and $F_{37} = 24{,}157{,}817$,
   (a) find F_{38}.
   (b) find F_{39}.

8. Given that $F_{32} = 2{,}178{,}309$ and $F_{33} = 3{,}524{,}578$,
   (a) find F_{34}.
   (b) find F_{35}.

9. Given that $F_{36} = 14{,}930{,}352$ and $F_{37} = 24{,}157{,}817$,
   (a) find F_{35}.
   (b) find F_{34}.

10. Given that $F_{32} = 2{,}178{,}309$ and $F_{33} = 3{,}524{,}578$,
    (a) find F_{31}.
    (b) find F_{30}.

11. Using a good calculator (an online calculator if necessary) and Binet's simplified formula, compute F_{20}.

12. Using a good calculator (an online calculator if necessary) and Binet's simplified formula, compute F_{25}.

13. Consider the following sequence of equations involving Fibonacci numbers.

$$1 + 2 = 3$$
$$1 + 2 + 5 = 8$$
$$1 + 2 + 5 + 13 = 21$$
$$1 + 2 + 5 + 13 + 34 = 55$$
$$\vdots$$

(a) Write down a reasonable choice for the fifth equation in this sequence.

(b) Find the subscript that will make the following equation true.

$$F_1 + F_3 + F_5 + \cdots + F_{21} = F_?$$

(c) Find the subscript that will make the following equation true (assume N is odd).

$$F_1 + F_3 + F_5 + \cdots + F_N = F_?$$

14. Consider the following sequence of equations involving Fibonacci numbers.

$$2(2) - 3 = 1$$
$$2(3) - 5 = 1$$
$$2(5) - 8 = 2$$
$$2(8) - 13 = 3$$
$$\vdots$$

(a) Write down a reasonable choice for the fifth equation in this sequence.

(b) Find the subscript that will make the following equation true.

$$2(F_?) - F_{15} = F_{12}$$

(c) Find the subscript that will make the following equation true.

$$2(F_{N+2}) - F_{N+3} = F_?$$

15. Fact: *If we make a list of any four consecutive Fibonacci numbers, the first one times the fourth one is always equal to the third one squared minus the second one squared.*

    (a) Verify this fact for the list F_8, F_9, F_{10}, F_{11}.

    (b) Using the list F_N, F_{N+1}, F_{N+2}, F_{N+3}, write this fact as a mathematical formula.

16. Fact: *If we make a list of any 10 consecutive Fibonacci numbers, the sum of all these numbers divided by 11 is always equal to the seventh number on the list.*

    (a) Verify this fact for the list F_1, F_2, . . . , F_{10}.

    (b) Using the list F_N, F_{N+1}, . . . , F_{N+9}, write this fact as a mathematical formula.

17. Express each of the following as a single Fibonacci number.

    (a) $F_{N+1} + F_{N+2} =$

    (b) $F_N - F_{N-2} =$

    (c) $F_N + F_{N+1} + F_{N+3} + F_{N+5} =$

18. Express each of the following as a single Fibonacci number.

    (a) $F_{N-2} + F_{N-3} =$

    (b) $F_{N+2} - F_N =$

    (c) $F_{N-3} + F_{N-2} + F_N + F_{N+2} =$

19. Express each of the following as a ratio of two Fibonacci numbers.

    (a) $1 + \dfrac{F_N}{F_{N-1}} =$

    (b) $\dfrac{F_{N-1}}{F_N} - 1 =$

20. Express each of the following as a ratio of two Fibonacci numbers.

    (a) $1 + \dfrac{F_{N-1}}{F_N} =$

    (b) $1 - \dfrac{F_N}{F_{N-2}} =$

Exercises 21 through 24 refer to "Fibonacci-like" sequences. Fibonacci-like sequences are based on the same recursive rule as the Fibonacci sequence (from the third term on each term is the sum of the two preceding terms), but they are different in how they get started.

21. Consider the Fibonacci-like sequence $5, 5, 10, 15, 25, 40, \ldots$, and let A_N denote the Nth term of the sequence.

    (a) Find A_{10}.

    (b) Given that $F_{25} = 75{,}025$, find A_{25}.

    (c) Express A_N in terms of F_N.

22. Consider the Fibonacci-like sequence $2, 4, 6, 10, 16, 26, \ldots$, and let B_N denote the Nth term of the sequence.

    (a) Find B_9.

    (b) Given that $F_{20} = 6765$, find B_{19}.

    (c) Express B_N in terms of F_{N+1}.

23. Consider the Fibonacci-like sequence 1, 3, 4, 7, 11, 18, 29, 47, . . . , and let L_N denote the Nth term of the sequence. (*Note:* This sequence is called the *Lucas sequence*, and the terms of the sequence are called the *Lucas numbers*.)

    (a) Find L_{12}.

    (b) The Lucas numbers are related to the Fibonacci numbers by the formula $L_N = 2F_{N+1} - F_N$. Verify that this formula is true for $N = 1, 2, 3$, and 4.

    (c) Given that $F_{20} = 6765$ and $F_{21} = 10{,}946$, find L_{20}.

24. Consider the Fibonacci-like sequence $1, 4, 5, 9, 14, 23, 37, \ldots$, and let T_N denote the Nth term of the sequence.

    (a) Find T_{12}.

    (b) The numbers in this sequence are related to the Fibonacci numbers by the formula $T_N = 3F_{N+1} - 2F_N$. Verify that this formula is true for $N = 1, 2, 3$, and 4.

    (c) Given that $F_{20} = 6765$ and $F_{21} = 10{,}946$, find T_{20}.

13.2 The Golden Ratio

Exercises 25 through 29 involve solving quadratic equations using the quadratic formula. Here is an instant refresher on the **quadratic formula** *(for a more in-depth review, any high school algebra book should do):*

▪ *To use the quadratic formula the quadratic equation must be in the standard form $ax^2 + bx + c = 0$. If the equation is not in standard form, you need to get it into that form.*

▪ *The solutions of the quadratic equation $ax^2 + bx + c = 0$ are given by $x = \left(-b \pm \sqrt{b^2 - 4ac}\right)/2a$. The formula gives two different solutions unless $b^2 - 4ac = 0$.*

25. Consider the quadratic equation $x^2 = x + 1$.

    (a) Use the quadratic formula to find the two solutions of the equation. Give the value of each solution rounded to five decimal places.

    (b) Find the sum of the two solutions in (a).

    (c) Explain why the decimal part has to be exactly the same in both solutions.

26. Consider the quadratic equation $x^2 = 3x + 1$.

    (a) Use the quadratic formula to find the two solutions of the equation. Give the value of each solution rounded to five decimal places.

    (b) Find the sum of the two solutions in (a).

    (c) Explain why the decimal part has to be exactly the same in both solutions.

27. Consider the quadratic equation $3x^2 = 8x + 5$.

    (a) Use the quadratic formula to find the two solutions of the equation. Give the value of each solution rounded to five decimal places.

    (b) Find the sum of the two solutions found in (a).

28. Consider the quadratic equation $8x^2 = 5x + 2$.

    (a) Use the quadratic formula to find the two solutions of the equation. Give the value of each solution rounded to five decimal places.

    (b) Find the sum of the two solutions found in (a).

29. Consider the quadratic equation $55x^2 = 34x + 21$.

    (a) Without using the quadratic formula, show that $x = 1$ is one of the two solutions of the equation.

    (b) Without using the quadratic formula, find the second solution of the equation. (*Hint*: The sum of the two solutions of $ax^2 + bx + c = 0$ is given by $-b/a$.)

30. Consider the quadratic equation $89x^2 = 55x + 34$.

    (a) Without using the quadratic formula, show that $x = 1$ is one of the two solutions of the equation.

    (b) Without using the quadratic formula, find the second solution of the equation. (*Hint*: The sum of the two solutions of $ax^2 + bx + c = 0$ is given by $-b/a$.)

31. Consider the quadratic equation $21x^2 = 34x + 55$.

    (a) Without using the quadratic formula, show that $x = -1$ is one of the two solutions of the equation.

    (b) Without using the quadratic formula, find the second solution of the equation. (*Hint*: The sum of the two solutions of $ax^2 + bx + c = 0$ is given by $-b/a$.)

32. Consider the quadratic equation $34x^2 = 55x + 89$.

    (a) Without using the quadratic formula, show that $x = -1$ is one of the two solutions of the equation.

    (b) Without using the quadratic formula, find the second solution of the equation. (*Hint*: The sum of the two solutions of $ax^2 + bx + c = 0$ is given by $-b/a$.)

33. Consider the quadratic equation $(F_N)x^2 = (F_{N-1})x + F_{N-2}$, where F_{N-2}, F_{N-1}, and F_N are consecutive Fibonacci numbers.

    (a) Show that $x = 1$ is one of the two solutions of the equation. [*Hint*: Try Exercises 29(a) or 30(a) first.]

    (b) Find the second solution of the equation expressed in terms of Fibonacci numbers. [*Hint*: Try Exercises 29(b) or 30(b) first.]

34. Consider the quadratic equation $(F_{N-2})x^2 = (F_{N-1})x + F_N$, where F_{N-2}, F_{N-1}, and F_N are consecutive Fibonacci numbers.

    (a) Show that $x = -1$ is one of the two solutions of the equation. [*Hint*: Try Exercises 31(a) or 32(a) first.]

    (b) Find the second solution of the equation expressed in terms of Fibonacci numbers. [*Hint*: Try Exercises 31(b) or 32(b) first.]

35. The number $\frac{1}{\phi}$ is the *reciprocal* of the golden ratio.

    (a) Using a calculator, compute $\frac{1}{\phi}$ to 10 decimal places.

    (b) Explain why $\frac{1}{\phi}$ has exactly the same decimal part as ϕ. (*Hint*: Show that $\frac{1}{\phi} = \phi - 1$.)

36. The square of the golden ratio is the irrational number $\phi^2 = \left(\frac{1 + \sqrt{5}}{2}\right)^2 = \frac{3 + \sqrt{5}}{2}$.

    (a) Using a calculator, compute ϕ^2 to 10 decimal places.

    (b) Explain why ϕ^2 has exactly the same decimal part as ϕ.

37. Given that $F_{499} \approx 8.6168 \times 10^{103}$, find an approximate value for F_{500} in scientific notation. (*Hint*: $F_N/F_{N-1} \approx \phi$.)

38. Given that $F_{1002} \approx 1.138 \times 10^{209}$, find an approximate value for F_{1000} in scientific notation. (*Hint*: $F_N/F_{N-1} \approx \phi$.)

39. The *Fibonacci sequence of order 2* is the sequence of numbers $1, 2, 5, 12, 29, 70, \ldots$. Each term in this sequence (from the third term on) equals two times the term before it plus the term two places before it; in other words, $A_N = 2A_{N-1} + A_{N-2}$ ($N \geq 3$).

    (a) Compute A_7.

    (b) Use your calculator to compute to five decimal places the ratio A_7/A_6.

    (c) Use your calculator to compute to five decimal places the ratio A_{11}/A_{10}.

    (d) Guess the value (to five decimal places) of the ratio A_N/A_{N-1} when $N > 11$.

40. The *Fibonacci sequence of order 3* is the sequence of numbers $1, 3, 10, 33, 109, \ldots$. Each term in this sequence (from the third term on) equals three times the term before it plus the term two places before it; in other words, $A_N = 3A_{N-1} + A_{N-2}$ ($N \geq 3$).

    (a) Compute A_6.

    (b) Use your calculator to compute to five decimal places the ratio A_6/A_5.

    (c) Guess the value (to five decimal places) of the ratio A_N/A_{N-1} when $N > 6$.

13.3 Gnomons

41. R and R' are similar rectangles. Suppose that the width of R is a and the width of R' is $3a$.

    (a) If the perimeter of R is 41.5 in., what is the perimeter of R'?

    (b) If the area of R is 105 sq. in., what is the area of R'?

42. O and O' are similar O-rings. The inner radius of O is 5 ft, and the inner radius of O' is 15 ft.

    (a) If the circumference of the outer circle of O is 14π ft, what is the circumference of the outer circle of O'?

    (b) Suppose that it takes 1.5 gallons of paint to paint the O-ring O. If the paint is used at the same rate, how much paint is needed to paint the O-ring O'?

43. Triangles T and T' shown in Fig. 13-23 are similar triangles. (Note that the triangles are not drawn to scale.)

FIGURE 13-23

(a) If the perimeter of T is 13 in., what is the perimeter of T' (in meters)?

(b) If the area of T is 20 sq. in., what is the area of T' (in square meters)?

44. Polygons P and P' shown in Fig. 13-24 are similar polygons.

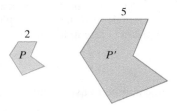

FIGURE 13-24

(a) If the perimeter of P is 10, what is the perimeter of P'?

(b) If the area of P is 30, what is the area of P'?

45. Find the value of c so that the shaded rectangle in Fig. 13-25 is a gnomon to the white 3 by 9 rectangle. (Figure is not drawn to scale.)

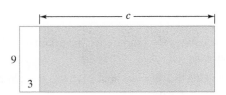

FIGURE 13-25

46. Find the value of x so that the shaded figure in Fig. 13-26 is a gnomon to the white rectangle. (Figure is not drawn to scale.)

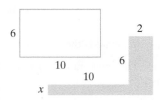

FIGURE 13-26

47. Find the value of x so that the shaded figure in Fig. 13-27 is a gnomon to the white rectangle. (Figure is not drawn to scale.)

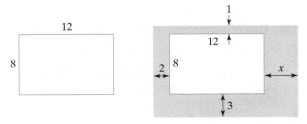

FIGURE 13-27

48. Find the value of x so that the shaded figure in Fig. 13-28 is a gnomon to the white rectangle. (Figure is not drawn to scale.)

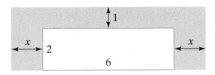

FIGURE 13-28

49. Rectangle A is 10 by 20. Rectangle B is a gnomon to rectangle A. What are the dimensions of rectangle B?

50. Find the value of x so that the shaded frame in Fig. 13-29 is a gnomon to the white x by 8 rectangle. (Figure is not drawn to scale.)

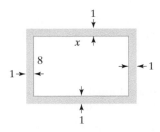

FIGURE 13-29

51. In Fig. 13-30 triangle BCA is a 36-36-108 triangle with sides of length ϕ and 1. Suppose that triangle ACD is a gnomon to triangle BCA.

(a) Find the measure of the angles of triangle ACD.

(b) Find the length of the three sides of triangle ACD.

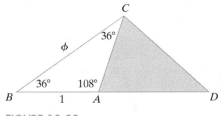

FIGURE 13-30

52. Find the values of x and y so that in Fig. 13-31 the shaded triangle is a gnomon to the white triangle ABC.

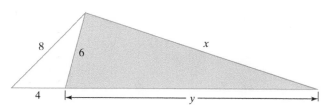

FIGURE 13-31

53. Find the values of x and y so that in Fig. 13-32 the shaded figure is a gnomon to the white triangle.

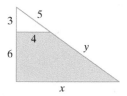

FIGURE 13-32

54. Find the values of x and y so that in Fig. 13-33 the shaded triangle is a gnomon to the white triangle.

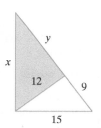

FIGURE 13-33

13.4 Spiral Growth in Nature

No exercises for this section.

JOGGING

55. Consider the sequence of ratios $\frac{F_N}{F_{N+1}}$.

(a) Using a calculator compute the first 14 terms of this sequence in decimal form (rounded to six decimal places when needed).

(b) Explain why $\left(\frac{F_N}{F_{N+1}}\right) \to \phi - 1$ (i.e., as N gets larger and larger, the ratios $\frac{F_N}{F_{N+1}}$ get closer and closer to $\phi - 1$).

56. Consider the sequence of ratios $\frac{F_{N+2}}{F_N}$.

(a) Using a calculator compute the first 15 terms of this sequence in decimal form (rounded to six decimal places when needed).

(b) Explain why $\left(\frac{F_{N+2}}{F_N}\right) \to \phi + 1$ (i.e., as N gets larger and larger, the ratios $\frac{F_{N+2}}{F_N}$ get closer and closer to $\phi + 1$).

57. Consider the sequence T given by the following recursive definition: $T_{N+1} = 1 + \frac{1}{T_N}$, and $T_1 = 1$.

(a) Find the first six terms of the sequence, and leave the terms in fractional form.

(b) Explain why $T_N \to \phi$ (i.e., as N gets larger and larger, T_N gets closer and closer to ϕ).

58. Consider the sequence U given by the following recursive definition: $U_{N+1} = \frac{1}{1 + U_N}$, and $U_1 = 1$. As N gets larger and larger, the terms of this sequence get closer and closer to some number. Give the number expressed in terms of the golden ratio ϕ. (*Hint:* Try Exercises 55 and 57 first.)

59. Lucas numbers. The *Lucas sequence* is the Fibonacci-like sequence 1, 3, 4, 7, 11, 18, 29, 47, . . . (first introduced in Exercise 23). The numbers in the Lucas sequence are called the *Lucas numbers*, and we will use L_N to denote the Nth Lucas number. The Lucas numbers satisfy the recursive rule $L_N = L_{N-1} + L_{N-2}$ (just like the Fibonacci numbers), but start with the initial values $L_1 = 1$, $L_2 = 3$.

(a) Show that the Lucas numbers are related to the Fibonacci numbers by the formula $L_N = 2F_{N+1} - F_N$. [*Hint:* Let $K_N = 2F_{N+1} - F_N$, and show that the numbers K_N satisfy exactly the same definition as the Lucas numbers (same initial values and same recursive rule).]

(b) Show that $\left(\frac{L_{N+1}}{L_N}\right) \to \phi$. [Hint: Use (a) combined with the fact that $\left(\frac{F_{N+1}}{F_N}\right) \to \phi$.]

60. (a) Explain what happens to the values of $\left(\frac{1 - \sqrt{5}}{2}\right)^N$ as N gets larger. (*Hint:* Get a calculator and experiment with $N = 6, 7, 8, \ldots$ until you get the picture.)

(b) Explain why $F_N \to \frac{\phi^N}{\sqrt{5}}$. [Hint: Use (a) and the original Binet's formula.]

(c) Using (b), explain why $\left(\frac{F_{N+1}}{F_N}\right) \to \phi$.

61. Explain why the only even Fibonacci numbers are those having a subscript that is a multiple of 3.

62. Show that $F_{N+1}^2 - F_N^2 = (F_{N-1})(F_{N+2})$.

63. Explain why the shaded figure in Fig. 13-34 cannot have a square gnomon.

FIGURE 13-34

64. Find the values of x and y so that in Fig. 13-35 the shaded triangle is a gnomon to the white triangle. (Figure is not drawn to scale.)

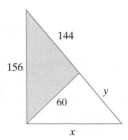

FIGURE 13-35

65. Let $ABCD$ be an arbitrary rectangle as shown in Fig. 13-36. Let AE be perpendicular to the diagonal BD and EF perpendicular to AB as shown. Show that the rectangle $BCEF$ is a gnomon to the rectangle $ADEF$.

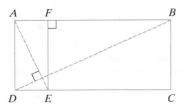

FIGURE 13-36

66. In Fig. 13-37 triangle BCD is a 72-72-36 triangle with base of length 1 and longer side of length x. (Using this choice of values, the ratio of the longer side to the shorter side is $x/1 = x$.)

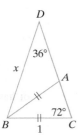

FIGURE 13-37

(a) Show that $x = \phi$. (*Hint*: Triangle ACB is similar to triangle BCD.)

(b) What are the interior angles of triangle DAB?

(c) Show that in the isosceles triangle DAB, the ratio of the longer to the shorter side is also ϕ.

67. Show that each of the diagonals of the regular pentagon shown in Fig. 13-38 has length ϕ.

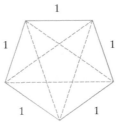

FIGURE 13-38

68. (a) A regular decagon (10 sides) is inscribed in a circle of radius 1. Find the perimeter in terms of ϕ.

(b) Repeat (a) with radius r. Find the perimeter in terms of ϕ and r.

RUNNING

69. Generic Fibonacci-like numbers. A generic Fibonacci-like sequence has the form $a, b, b + a, 2b + a, 3b + 2a, 5b + 3a, \ldots$ (i.e., the sequence starts with two arbitrary numbers a and b and after that each term of the sequence is the sum of the two previous terms). Let G_N denote the Nth term of this sequence.

(a) Show that generic Fibonacci-like numbers are related to the Fibonacci numbers by the formula $G_N = bF_{N-1} + aF_{N-2}$. [*Hint*: Try Exercise 59(a) first.]

(b) Show that $(G_{N+1}/G_N) \rightarrow \phi$. [*Hint*: Try Exercise 59(b) first.]

70. You are designing a straight path 2 ft wide using rectangular paving stones with dimensions 1 ft by 2 ft. How many different designs are possible for a path of length

(a) 4 ft?

(b) 8 ft?

(c) N ft? (*Hint*: Give the answer in terms of Fibonacci numbers.)

71. Show that $F_1 + F_2 + F_3 + \cdots + F_N = F_{N+2} - 1$.

72. Show that $F_1 + F_3 + F_5 + \cdots + F_N = F_{N+1}$. (Note that on the left side of the equation we are adding the Fibonacci numbers with odd subscripts up to N.)

73. Show that every positive integer greater than 2 can be written as the sum of distinct Fibonacci numbers.

74. In Fig. 13-39, $ABCD$ is a square and the three triangles I, II, and III have equal areas. Show that $x/y = \phi$.

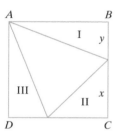

FIGURE 13-39

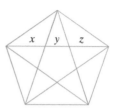

FIGURE 13-40

75. During the time of the Greeks the star pentagram shown in Fig. 13-40 was a symbol of the Brotherhood of Pythagoras. Consider the three segments of lengths x, y, and z shown in the figure.

(a) Show that $x/y = \phi$, $(x+y)/z = \phi$, and $(x+y+z)/(x+y) = \phi$.

(b) Show that if $y = 1$, then $x = \phi$, $(x+y) = \phi^2$, and $x+y+z = \phi^3$.

 PROJECTS AND PAPERS

1 Fibonacci Numbers, the Golden Ratio, and Phyllotaxis

In this chapter we mentioned that Fibonacci numbers and the golden ratio often show up in both the plant and animal worlds. In this project you are asked to expand on this topic.

1. Give several detailed examples of the appearance of Fibonacci numbers and the golden ratio in the plant world. Include examples of branch formation in plants, leaf arrangements around stems, and seed arrangements on circular seedheads (such as sunflower heads).

2. Discuss the concept of *phyllotaxis*. What is it, and what are some of the mathematical theories behind it?

(*Notes:* The literature on Fibonacci numbers, the golden ratio, and phyllotaxis is extensive. A search on the Web should provide plenty of information.)

2 The Golden Ratio in Art, Architecture, and Music

It is often claimed that from the time of the ancient Greeks through the Renaissance to modern times, artists, architects, and musicians have been fascinated by the golden ratio. Choose one of the three fields (art, architecture, or music) and write a paper discussing the history of the golden ratio in that field. Describe famous works of art, architecture, or music in which the golden ratio is alleged to have been used. How? Who were the artists, architects, and composers?

Be forewarned that there are plenty of conjectures, unsubstantiated historical facts, controversies, claims, and counterclaims surrounding some of the alleged uses of the golden ratio and Fibonacci numbers. Whenever appropriate, you should present both sides to a story.

3 The Golden Ratio Hypothesis

A long-held belief among those who study how humans perceive the outside world (mostly psychologists and psychobiologists) is that the *golden ratio* plays a special and prominent role in the human interpretation of "beauty." Shapes and objects whose proportions are close to the golden ratio are believed to be more pleasing to human sensibilities than those that are not. This theory, generally known as *the golden ratio hypothesis*, originated with the experiments of famous psychologist Gustav Fechner in the late 1800s. In a classic experiment, Fechner showed rectangles of various proportions to hundreds of subjects and asked them to choose. His results showed that the rectangles that were close to the proportions of the golden ratio were overwhelmingly preferred over the rest. Since Fechner's original experiment, there has been a lot of controversy about the golden ratio hypothesis, and many modern experiments have cast serious doubts about its validity.

Write a paper describing the history of the golden ratio hypothesis. Start with a description of Fechner's original experiment. Follow up with other experiments duplicating Fechner's results and some of the more recent experiments that seem to disprove the golden ratio hypothesis. Conclude with your own analysis.

ANSWERS TO SELECTED EXERCISES

Chapter 5

WALKING

5.2 An Introduction to Graphs

1. **(a)** $\{A, B, C, X, Y, Z\}$

   (b) $AX, AY, AZ, BB, BC, BX, CX, XY$

   (c) $\deg(A) = 3, \deg(B) = 4, \deg(C) = 2, \deg(X) = 4,$
   $\deg(Y) = 2, \deg(Z) = 1$

   (d)

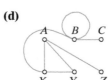

3. (a) $\{A, B, C, D, X, Y, Z\}$

(b) $AX, AX, AY, BX, BY, DZ, XY$

(c) $\deg(A) = 3, \deg(B) = 2, \deg(C) = 0, \deg(D) = 1,$
$\deg(X) = 4, \deg(Y) = 3, \deg(Z) = 1$

(d) 3

5.

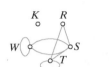

7. (a) A, B, D, E **(b)** AD, BC, DD, DE **(c)** 5   **(d)** 12

9. (a)   **(b)**   **(c)**

11. (a) C, B, A, H, F **(b)** C, B, D, A, H, F **(c)** C, B, A, H, F

(d) C, D, B, A, H, G, G, F **(e)** 4   **(f)** 3   **(g)** 12

13. (a) G, G **(b)** There are none.

(c) $A, B, D, A; B, C, D, B; F, G, H, F$

(d) $A, B, C, D, A; F, G, G, H, F$ **(e)** 6

15. (a) AH, EF **(b)** There are none.   **(c)** AB, BC, BE, CD

17. (a) The clique formed by $A, B, C, D,$ and E.

(b) CI and HJ **(c)** 3

(d) $C, I, H, J.$ The shortest path has length 3.

(e) $C, B, A, E, D, C, A, D, B, E, C, I, G, F, I, H, J.$ Several other answers are possible. Any longest path has length 16.

19.

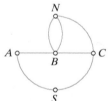

21.

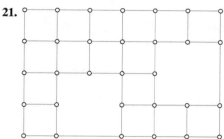

23.

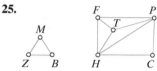

25.

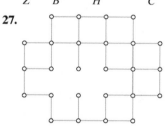

27.

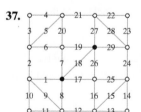

5.3 Euler's Theorems and Fleury's Algorithm

29. (a) (A); all vertices are even.

(b) (C); four vertices are odd.

(c) (D); see Exercises 9(a) and 9(b).

31. (a) (C); four vertices are odd.

(b) (A); all vertices are even.

(c) (C); the graph is disconnected.

33. (a) (B); exactly two vertices are odd.

(b) (A); all vertices are even.

(c) (C); more than two vertices are odd.

35.

Other answers are possible.

37.

Other answers are possible.

39.

41. (a) PD or PB **(b)** BF

5.4 Eulerizing and Semi-Eulerizing Graphs

43.

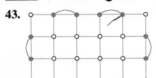

45.

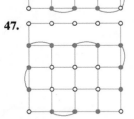

47.

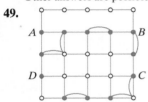

Other answers are possible.

49.

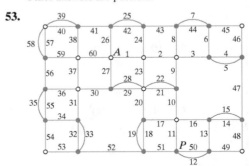

Other answers are possible.

51.

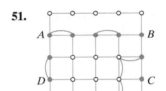

Other answers are possible.

53.

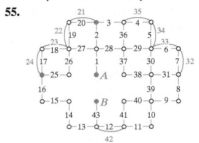

Many other answers are possible.

55.

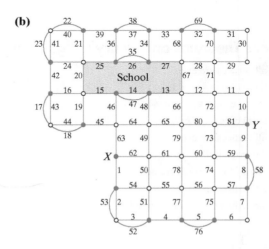

Many other answers are possible.

JOGGING

57. 6; there are 14 odd vertices. Two can be used as the starting and ending vertices. The remaining 12 can be paired so that each pair forces one lifting of the pencil.

59. None. If a vertex had degree 1, then the edge incident to that vertex would be a bridge.

61. **(a)** Both m and n must be even.

   (b) $m = 1$ and $n = 1$, $m = 1$ and $n = 2$, or $m = 2$ and n is odd.

63. **(a)** Make a complete graph with $N - 1$ of the vertices, and leave the other vertex as an isolated vertex.

   (b) $\frac{(N-1)(N-2)}{2}$ dollars

65. **(a)** 12

(b)

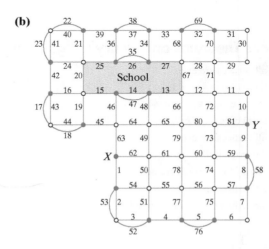

67. $D, L, R, L, C, A, R, B, R, B, D, C, L, D$. Others answers are possible.

69. Yes; one of the many possible journeys is given by crossing the bridges in the following order: $a, b, c, d, e, f, g, h, i, l, m, n, o, p, k$. (*Note:* Euler did not ask that the journey start and end at the same place.)

Chapter 6

WALKING

6.2 Hamilton Paths and Circuits

1. **(a)** 1. A, B, D, C, E, F, G, A;   **(b)** A, G, F, E, C, D, B
       2. A, D, C, E, B, G, F, A;   **(c)** D, A, G, B, C, E, F
       3. A, D, B, E, C, F, G, A

3. $A, B, C, D, E, F, G, A; A, B, E, D, C, F, G, A$ and their mirror images

5. **(a)** A, F, B, C, G, D, E **(b)** A, F, B, C, G, D, E, A
   (c) A, F, B, E, D, G, C **(d)** F, A, B, E, D, C, G

7. **(a)** 8   **(b)** $A, H, C, B, F, D, G, E, A$
   (c) A, H, C, B, F, D, G, E and A, E, G, D, F, B, C, H

9. **(a)** $B, A, D, E, C; A, D, E, C, B; D, E, C, B, A; E, C, B, A, D;$
       C, B, A, D, E
   (b) $A, B, E, D, C; A, D, E, B, C; B, A, E, C, D; B, C, E, A, D; C, B, E,$
       $D, A; C, D, E, B, A; D, C, E, A, B; D, A, E, C, B$

11. **(a)** A, B, C, D, E, F, A and $A, D, C, B E, F, A$ (or their reversals)
    (b) $C, B, A, D, E, F; C, B, E, D, A, F; C, D, A, B, E, F$ and $C, D, E, B,$
       A, F (or their reversals)

13. **(a)** $A, B, E, D, C, I, H, G, K, J, F$
    (b) $K, J, F, G, H, I, C, D, A, B, E$

(c) CI is a bridge of the graph connecting a "left half" and a "right half." If you start at C and go left, there is no way to get to the right half of the graph without going through C again. Conversely, if you start at C and cross over to the right half first, there is no way to get back to the left half without going through C again.

(d) No matter where you start, you would have to cross the bridge CI twice to visit every vertex and get back to where you started.

15. There is no Hamilton circuit since two vertices have degree 1. There is no Hamilton path since any such path must contain edges $AB, BE,$ and BC, which would force vertex B to be visited more than once.

17. **(a)** 6   **(b)** B, D, A, E, C, B; weight $= 27$
    (c) The mirror image B, C, E, A, D, B; weight $= 27$

19. **(a)** A, D, F, E, B, C; weight $= 29$
    (b) A, B, E, D, F, C; weight $= 30$
    (c) A, D, F, E, B, C; weight $= 29$

21. **(a)** ≈ 77 years   **(b)** ≈ 1620 years

23. **(a)** 190   **(b)** 210   **(c)** 50

25. **(a)** $N = 6$ **(b)** $N = 10$ **(c)** $N = 201$

6.3 The Brute-Force Algorithm

27. A, C, B, D, A or its reversal; cost $= 102$

29. A, D, C, B, E, A or its reversal; cost $= 92$ hours

31. B, A, C, D, B or its reversal (44 hours)

33. **(a)** $7! = 5040$ **(b)** 5040   **(c)** $6! = 720$

6.4 The Nearest-Neighbor and Repetitive Nearest-Neighbor Algorithm

35. **(a)** B, C, A, E, D, B; cost $= \$722$
    (b) C, A, E, D, B, C; cost $= \$722$
    (c) D, B, C, A, E, D; cost $= \$722$
    (d) E, C, A, D, B, E; cost $= \$741$

37. **(a)** A, D, E, C, B, A; cost $= \$11,656$
    (b) A, D, B, C, E, A; cost $= \$9,760$

39. **(a)** A, E, B, C, D, A (92 hours)
    (b) A, D, B, C, E, A (93 hours)

41. **(a)** Atlanta, Columbus, Kansas City, Tulsa, Minneapolis, Pierre, Atlanta; cost $= \$2915.25$
    (b) Atlanta, Kansas City, Tulsa, Minneapolis, Pierre, Columbus, Atlanta; cost $= \$2804.25$

43. A, E, B, C, D, A or its reversal (92 hours)

45. Atlanta, Columbus, Minneapolis, Pierre, Kansas City, Tulsa, Atlanta; cost $= \$2439.00$

47. 12.5%

49. A, D, C, B, E, A or its reversal (92 hours)

6.5 The Cheapest-Link Algorithm

51. B, E, C, A, D, B; cost $= \$10,000$

53. Atlanta, Columbus, Pierre, Minneapolis, Kansas City, Tulsa, Atlanta; cost $= \$2598.75$

55. **(a)** A, E, D, B, C, F, A or its reversal (75 days)
    (b) $\varepsilon = 2/73 \approx 2.74\%$

JOGGING

57. $1500

59. **(a)**

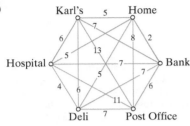

(b) Home, Bank, Post Office, Deli, Hospital, Karl's, Home

61. The graph describing the friendships among the guests does not have a Hamilton circuit. Thus, it is impossible to seat everyone around the table with friends on both sides.

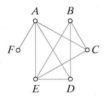

63. **(a)** $I, B_1, C_2, B_2, C_3, B_3, C_4, B_4, C_1$

(b) $C_1, B_1, C_2, B_2, I, B_4, C_4, B_3, C_3$

(c) $C_1, B_4, C_4, B_3, C_3, B_2, C_2, B_1, I$

(d) Suppose that we color the vertices of the grid graph with two colors [say black (B) and white (W)] with adjacent vertices having different colors (see figure). Since there are five black vertices and four white vertices and in any Hamilton path the vertices must alternate color, the only possible Hamilton paths

are of the form $B, W, B, W, B, W, B, W, B$. Since every boundary vertex is white, it is impossible to end a Hamilton path on a boundary vertex.

65. **(a)** $C_1, B_8, B_7, C_4, B_6, I_3, I_1, I_2, I_4, B_5, C_3, B_4, B_3, C_2, B_2, B_1, C_1$

(b) $C_1, B_8, B_7, C_4, B_6, I_3, I_1, B_1, B_2, I_2, I_4, B_5, C_3, B_4, B_3, C_2$

(c) $C_1, B_8, B_7, C_4, B_6, I_3, I_4, B_5, C_3, B_4, B_3, C_2, B_2, B_1, I_1, I_2$

(d) Suppose that X and Y are any two adjacent vertices. If we pick a Hamilton circuit that contains the edge XY and remove that edge, then we get a Hamilton path that has X and Y as its endpoints. (Finding a Hamilton circuit is relatively easy.)

67. Suppose that the cheapest edge in a graph is the edge joining vertices X and Y. Using the nearest-neighbor algorithm, we will eventually visit one of these vertices—suppose that the first one of these vertices we visit is X. Then, since edge XY is the cheapest edge in the graph and since we have not yet visited vertex Y, the nearest-neighbor algorithm will take us to Y.

69. **(a)** Dallas, Houston, Memphis, Louisville, Columbus, Chicago, Kansas City, Denver, Atlanta, Buffalo, Boston, Dallas.

(b) Dallas, Houston, Denver, Boston, Buffalo, Columbus, Louisville, Chicago, Atlanta, Memphis, Kansas City, Dallas.

Chapter 7

WALKING

7.1 Networks and Trees

1. No, the graph is disconnected. A, D, and G are connected to each other but not to the other four.

3. **(a)** 1   **(b)** 3   **(c)** 5

5. **(a)** 3   **(b)** 5   **(c)** 8   **(d)** 8

7. (B) The network violates the $N - 1$ *edges* property of trees.

9. (A) The network satisfies the $N - 1$ *edges* property of trees.

11. (B) A tree must have redundancy $R = 0$.

13. (C) We don't know if other pairs of vertices are connected by single or multiple paths.

15. (B) This network has 5 vertices and 10 edges (the sum of the degrees is 20). It violates the $N - 1$ *edges* property of trees.

17. (A) This network has 5 vertices and 4 edges (the sum of the degrees is 8). It satisfies the $N - 1$ *edges* property of trees.

19. (B) This network has an Euler circuit (see Section 5.3). It can't be a tree.

7.2 Spanning Trees, MSTs, and MaxSTs

21. **(a)**

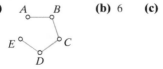

(b) 6   **(c)** 1

(There are many other possible answers.)

23. **(a)** The network is its own spanning tree.   **(b)** 0   **(c)** 6

25. (a)

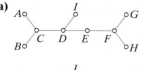

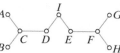

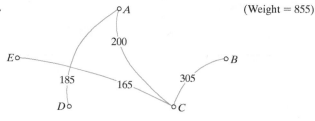

(c) 6

(b)

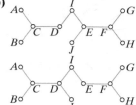

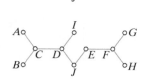

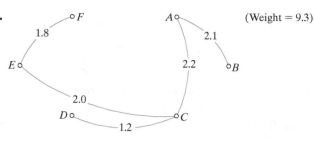

27. (a) 12 **(b)** 54

29. (a) 14 $(6 + 2 \times 4)$ **(b)**

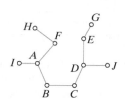

(c)

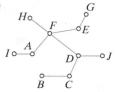

Several other answers are possible.

7.3 Kruskal's Algorithm

31. $380,000; the MST will have 19 edges at a cost of $20,000 each.

33. (Weight = 855)

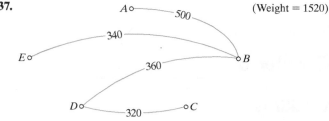

35. (Weight = 9.3)

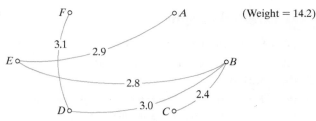

37. (Weight = 1520)

39. (Weight = 14.2)

JOGGING

41. Kansas City–Tulsa, Pierre–Minneapolis, Minneapolis–Kansas City, Atlanta–Columbus, Columbus–Kansas City

43. (a) The MST is shown in the figure below. (When $x > 59$, EG will not replace any edge in the existing MST since it has a larger value.)

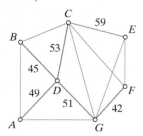

(b) When $x < 59$, EG will replace CE in the MST.

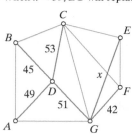

45. (a) $2N - 2$

(b) Let v be the number of vertices in the tree and e the number of edges. Recall that in a tree $v = e + 1$, and in any graph the sum of the degrees of all the vertices is $2e$. Assume that there are exactly

k vertices of degree 1. The remaining $v - k$ vertices must have degree at least 2. Therefore, the sum of the degrees of all the vertices must be at least $k + 2(v - k)$. Putting all this together, we have $2e \geq k + 2(v - k) = k + 2(e + 1 - k) = -k + 2e + 2$, so $k \geq 2$.

(c) By part (b), all vertices would need to be of degree 1. But then the graph would be disconnected.

47. At each step of Kruskal's algorithm we choose (from the available edges that do not close circuits) the edge of least weight. When there is only one choice at each step, there is only one MST possible. The same argument applies to a MaxST.

49. Step 1 of Kruskal's algorithm will always choose XY. There is no other possibility.

51. (a) 3

(b) 4 (Since the graph has no circuits, each component has to be a tree. Thus, in each component the number of edges is one less than the number of vertices. Since $N - M = 4$, there must be 4 components in the graph.)

53. (a)

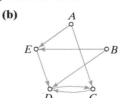

(b) The number of spanning trees is larger than the number of Hamilton circuits. The complete graph with N vertices has $(N - 1)!$ Hamilton circuits and N^{N-2} spanning trees. If we write $(N - 1)! = 2 \times 3 \times 4 \times \cdots \times (N - 1)$ and $N^{N-2} = N \times N \times N \times \cdots \times N$, then we can compare the two factor by factor. Each has $(N - 2)$ factors, and each factor in $(N - 1)!$ is smaller than the corresponding factor in N^{N-2}. Thus, for $N \geq 3$, $(N - 1)! < N^{N-2}$.

Chapter 8

WALKING

8.2 Directed Graphs

1. (a) $\{AB, AC, BD, CA, CD, CE, EA, ED\}$ **(b)** 8 **(c)** 8

3. (a) A, B, D; A, C, D; A, C, E, D; A, C, A, B, D

(b) A, C, A; A, C, E, A

5. (a) C, E **(b)** B, C **(c)** B, C, E **(d)** There are none.

(e) CD, CE, CA **(f)** There are none.

7. (a)

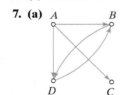

(b)

(c)

9. (a) 2 **(b)** 1 **(c)** 1 **(d)** 0

11. (a) A, B, D, E, F **(b)** A, B, D, E, C, F

(c) B, D, E, B **(d)** $\text{outdeg}(F) = 0$

(e) $\text{indeg}(A) = 0$ **(f)** B, D, E, B is the only cycle.

13.

15. (a) B; that is the only person that everyone respects.

(b) A; that is the only person that no one respects.

(c) The individual corresponding to the vertex having the largest indegree.

17. (a) and **(b)** The band's Web site and the TicketMonster Web site are likely to have large indegree and zero or very small outdegree (the local Smallville Web sites are likely to have hyperlinks to both but are not likely to have hyperlinks coming from either). This makes X and Y the two likely choices. It is much more likely that the rock band's Web site will have a hyperlink to the ticket-selling Web site than the other way around. Given that there is a hyperlink from Y to X but not the other way, the most likely choice is Y for the rock band and X for the TicketMonster Web site.

(c) The radio station is likely to be a major source of information on anything related to the concert (the band, where to buy tickets, where to stay if you are from out of town, etc.), so it should be a vertex with high outdegree. V is the most likely choice.

(d) Z is a vertex linked to only the band's Web site and to the ticket-selling Web site. None of the other Web sites are paying any attention to Z. This is most likely Joe Fan's blog.

(e) The two sister hotels would clearly have links to each other's Web sites, and since they are offering a special package for the concert, they are likely to have a link to the ticket-selling Web site. The logical choices are *U* and *W*.

19.

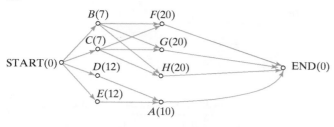

21.

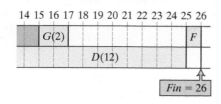

23.

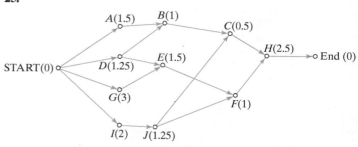

25.

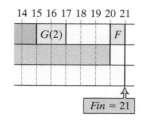

8.3 Priority-List Scheduling

27. (a) 18 hours

(b) There is a total of 75 hours of work to be done. Three processors working without any idle time would take $\frac{75}{3} = 25$ hours to complete the project.

29. There is a total of 75 hours of work to be done. Dividing the work equally between the six processors would require each processor to do $\frac{75}{6} = 12.5$ hours of work. Since there are no $\frac{1}{2}$-hour jobs, the completion time could not be less than 13 hours.

31. $\widehat{AD(8)}$, $\widehat{AW(6)}$, $\widehat{AF(8)}$, $\widehat{IE(5)}$, $\widehat{AP(7)}$, $\widehat{IW(7)}$, $ID(5)$, $IP(4)$, $\widehat{PL(4)}$, $PU(3)$, $HU(4)$, $IC(1)$, $PD(3)$, $EU(2)$, $FW(6)$

33. (a) No. *B* must be completed before *C* can be started.

(b) No. *B* must be completed before *D* can be started.

(c) No. *G* is a ready task and it is ahead of *H* in the priority list.

35. Time: 0 1 2 3 4 5 6 7 8 9 10 11 12 13 ...

P_1	C(9) E(6)
P_2	A(8) B(5)

14 15 16 17 18 19 20 21 22 23 24 25 26

	G(2) F
	D(12)

Fin = 26

37. Time: 0 1 2 3 4 5 6 7 8 9 10 11 12 13 ...

P_1	C(9) E(6)
P_2	A(8) D(12)
P_3	B(5)

14 15 16 17 18 19 20 21

	G(2) F

Fin = 21

39. Both priority lists have all tasks in the top two paths of the digraph listed before any task in the bottom path.

8.4   The Decreasing-Time Algorithm

41.

Time: 0 1 2 3 4 5 6 7 8 9 10 11 12 13...

| P_1 | $C(9)$ | | | | | | | | | $E(6)$ | | | ... |
| P_2 | $A(8)$ | | | | | | | | $B(5)$ | | | |

14 15 16 17 18 19 20 21 22 23 24 25 26

| $G(2)$ | | | | | | | | | | | |
| $D(12)$ | | | | | | | | | | | F |

$Fin = 26$

43.

Time: 0 2 4 6 8 10 12 14 16 18 20 22 24 26 28 30 32...

P_1	$D(15)$						$H(5)$		$J(5)$		...
P_2	$C(10)$					$G(4)$				
P_3	$B(4)$	$F(3)$	A	$E(7)$		$I(15)$				

34 36 38 40 42 44 46 48 50 52

| | | | | | | | | |
| $K(20)$ | | | | | | | | |

$Fin = 51$

45. (a)

Time: 0 1 2 3 4 5 6 7 8 9 10

| P_1 | $E(2)$ | $F(2)$ | A | B | C | D | | | | |
| P_2 | $G(2)$ | $H(2)$ | | | | | | | | |

$Fin = 8$

(b)

Time: 0 1 2 3 4 5 6 7 8

| P_1 | A | B | C | D | $F(2)$ | | | |
| P_2 | $E(2)$ | | $G(2)$ | | $H(2)$ | | | |

$Opt = 6$

(c) $\frac{2}{6} = 33\frac{1}{3}\%$

47. (a)

Time: 0 1 2 3 4 5 6 7 8 9 10 11...

P_1	$E(5)$					$F(5)$				...
P_2	$G(5)$					$H(5)$				
P_3	$I(5)$					$J(5)$				

11 12 13 14 15 16 17 18 19 20 21 22 23 24 25 26

| $A(4)$ | | | | $B(4)$ | | | | $C(4)$ | | | | $D(4)$ | | | |

$Fin = 26$

(b)

Time: 0 1 2 3 4 5 6 7 8 9 10 11 12 13 14 15 16

P_1	$A(4)$			$B(4)$				$C(4)$				$D(4)$			
P_2	$E(5)$				$F(5)$					$H(5)$				
P_3	$G(5)$				$I(5)$					$J(5)$				

$Opt = 16$

(c) $\frac{10}{16} = 62.5\%$

8.5   Critical Paths and the Critical-Path Algorithm

49. (a)

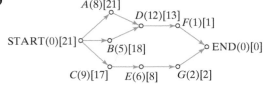

(b) START, $A, D, F,$ END

(c)

Time: 0 1 2 3 4 5 6 7 8 9 10 11...

| P_1 | $A(8)$ | | | | | | | | | | ... |
| P_2 | $B(5)$ | | | | | $C(9)$ | | | | |

11 12 13 14 15 16 17 18 19 20 21 22 23

| $D(12)$ | | | | | | | | | $G(2)$ | |
| | | | $E(6)$ | | | | | F | |

$Fin = 22$

(d) There are a total of 43 work units, so the shortest time the project can be completed by two workers is $\frac{43}{2} = 21.5$ time units. Since there are no tasks taking less than one time unit, the shortest time in which the project can actually be completed is 22 hours.

51. (a) START, $B, E, I, K,$ END

(b)

Time: 0 2 4 6 8 10 12 14 16 18 20 22 24 26...

P_1	B	E		F		I		...
P_2	A	C			G		
P_3	D			H	J	

26 28 30 32 34 36 38 40 42 44 46 48 50

	K										

$Fin = 49$

53. Time: 0 1 2 3 4 5 6 7 8 9 10 11 12 13

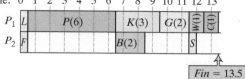

$Fin = 13.5$

55. (a) The critical path is START, F, H, G, D, E, END; critical time $= 20$.

(b) The critical-time priority list is $F, B, H, G, C, A, D, E, J$.

(c) A timeline for the project is shown below. *Fin* $= 25$.

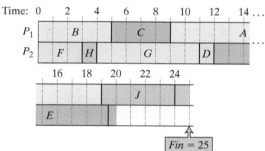

$Fin = 25$

JOGGING

57. Each arc of the graph contributes 1 to the indegree sum and 1 to the outdegree sum.

59. $A, B, C, E, G, H, D, F, I$

61. (a) same as 60(a)

(b) Time: 0 1 2 3 4 5 6 7 8 9 10 11 12 13 14

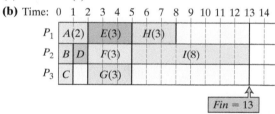

$Fin = 13$

(d) An optimal schedule for $N = 2$ processors with finishing time $Opt = 23$ is shown below. With two processors you can't do any better than $Opt = 23$.

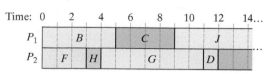

$Opt = 23$

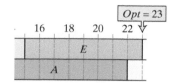

(e) $\varepsilon = \frac{2}{23} = 8.7\%$

(c) When the length of each task was shortened the finishing time increased from 12 to 13 hours.

63. (a) The finishing time of a project is always greater than or equal to the number of hours of work to be done divided by the number of processors doing the work.

(b) The schedule is optimal with no idle time.

(c) The total idle time in the schedule.

Chapter 11

WALKING

11.2 Reflections

1. (a) C   **(b)** F   **(c)** E   **(d)** B

3. (a)

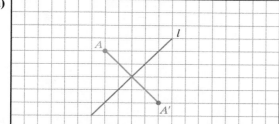

(b) A

5. (a)
(b)

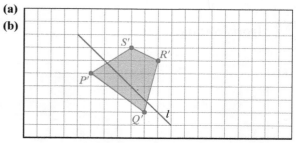

7. (a)
(b)
(c)
(d)

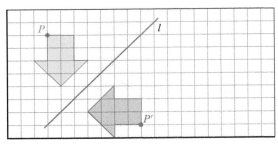

Fixed points on *PQRS*

9. (a)
(b)

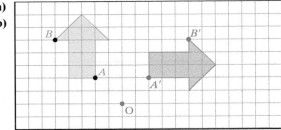

11.3 Rotations

13. (a) *I*   **(b)** *G*   **(c)** *A*   **(d)** *F*   **(e)** *E*
15. (a) 10°   **(b)** 350°   **(c)** 100°   **(d)** 80°
17. (a)
(b)

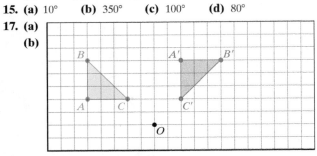

19. (a)
(b)

11.

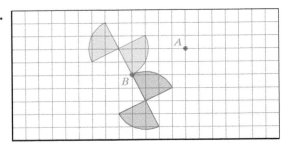

21.

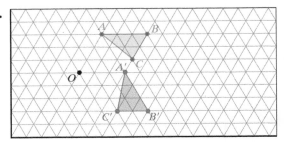

11.4 Translations

23. (a) *C*   **(b)** *C*   **(c)** *A*   **(d)** *D*
25. (a)
(b)
(c)

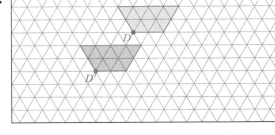

27.

11.5 Glide Reflections

29.

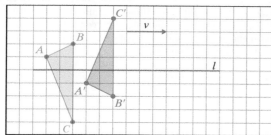

31.

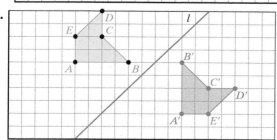

33. (a)
(b)
(c)

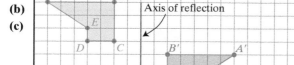

35.

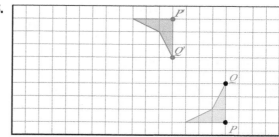

37.

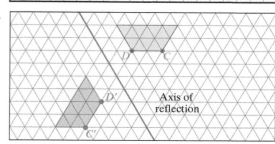

11.6 Symmetries and Symmetry Types

39. (a) reflection with axis going through the midpoints of *AB* and *DC*; reflection with axis going through the midpoints of *AD* and *BC*; identity and half-turn with rotocenter the center of the rectangle

(b) no reflections; identity and half-turn with rotocenter the center of the parallelogram

(c) reflection with axis going through the midpoints of *AB* and *DC*; identity

41. (a) reflections (three of them) with axis going through pairs of opposite vertices; reflections (three of them) with axis going through the midpoints of opposite sides of the hexagon; rota-

tions of 60°, 120°, 180°, 240°, and 300° with rotocenter the center of the hexagon, plus the identify

(b) no reflections; rotations of 72°, 144°, 216°, 288° with rotocenter the center of the star, plus the identity

43. (a) D_2 **(b)** Z_2 **(c)** D_1

45. (a) D_6 **(b)** Z_5

47. (a) D_1 **(b)** D_1 **(c)** Z_1
(d) Z_2 **(e)** D_2 **(f)** Z_2

49. (a) J   **(b)** T   **(c)** Z   **(d)** I

11.7 Patterns

51. (a) $m1$ **(b)** $1m$ **(c)** 12 **(d)** 11
53. (a) $m1$ **(b)** 12 **(c)** $1g$ **(d)** mg

55. 12

57. mm

JOGGING

59. (a) 19 hours   **(b)** 5
61. (a) rotation   **(b)** identity motion
(c) reflection   **(d)** glide reflection
63. (a) *C*   **(b)** *P*   **(c)** *D*   **(d)** *D*

65. The combination of two reflections is a proper rigid motion [see Exercise 64(d)]. Since *C* is a fixed point, the rigid motion must be a rotation with rotocenter *C*.

67. (a) a clockwise rotation with center *C* and angle of rotation 2α
(b) a counterclockwise rotation with center *C* and angle of rotation 2α

69. (a)

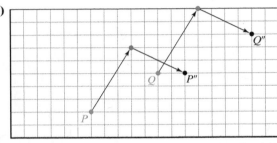

(b)

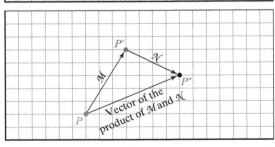

71. Rotations and translations are proper rigid motions. The given motion is an improper rigid motion (it reverses the clockwise-counterclockwise orientation). If the rigid motion were a reflection, then PP', RR', and QQ' would all be perpendicular to the axis of reflection and, hence, would all be parallel. It must be a glide reflection (the only rigid motion left).

Chapter 12

WALKING

12.1 The Koch Snowflake and Self-Similarity

1.

	M	L	P
Step 2	48	9 cm	432 cm
Step 3	192	3 cm	576 cm
Step 4	768	1 cm	768 cm
Step 5	3072	1/3 cm	1024 cm

3.

	R	S	T	Q
Step 3	48	1/9	16/3	376/3
Step 4	192	1/81	64/27	3448/27
Step 5	768	1/729	256/243	31228/243

5.

	M	L	P
Step 2	100	9 cm	900 cm
Step 3	500	3 cm	1500 cm
Step 4	2500	1	2500 cm

7.

	R	S	T	Q
Step 3	100	1/9	100/9	1333/9
Step 4	500	1/81	500/81	12,497/81

9.

	M	L	P
Step 2	48	9 cm	432 cm
Step 3	192	3 cm	576 cm
Step 4	768	1 cm	768 cm
Step 5	3072	1/3 cm	1024 cm

11.

	R	S	T	Q
Step 3	48	1/9	48/9	110/3
Step 4	192	1/81	192/81	926/27
Step 5	768	1/729	768/729	8078/243

13. (a)

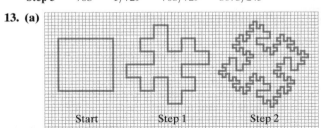

Start   Step 1   Step 2

(b) 128   **(c)** 256

(d) The perimeter doubles at each step of the construction.

15. (a) 256   **(b)** 256

(c) At each step, the area added is the same as the area subtracted.

12.2 The Sierpinski Gasket and the Chaos Game

17.

	R	S	T	Q
Step 3	9	1	9	27
Step 4	27	1/4	27/4	81/4
Step 5	81	1/16	81/16	243/16

19.

	U	V	W
Step 2	9	2 cm	18 cm
Step 3	27	1 cm	27 cm
Step 4	81	1/2 cm	81/2 cm
Step 5	243	1/4 cm	243/4 cm

21. (a) $(3/4)^N A$

(b) The area of the Sierpinski gasket is smaller than the area of the gasket formed at any step of construction. As N gets larger and larger, $(3/4)^N$ gets smaller and smaller (i.e., approaches of 0), and so does $(3/4)^N A$.

23. (a)

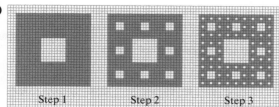

Step 1   Step 2   Step 3

(b) $8/9$ **(c)** $(8/9)^2$ **(d)** $(8/9)^3$ **(e)** $(8/9)^N$

25. (a) $16/3$ **(b)** $80/9$ **(c)** $496/27$

27.

	R	S	T	Q
Step 2	18	$1/81$	$2/9$	$4/9$
Step 3	108	$1/729$	$4/27$	$8/27$
Step 4	648	$1/6561$	$8/81$	$16/81$
Step N	$3 \times 6^{N-1}$	$1/9^N$	$3 \times 6^{N-1}/9^N$	$(2/3)^N$

29.

	U	V	W
Step 2	36	1 cm	36 cm
Step 3	216	$1/3$ cm	72 cm
Step 4	1296	$1/9$ cm	144 cm
Step N	6^N	$1/3^{N-2}$ cm	$9 \cdot 2^N$ cm

31. (a) $5/9$ **(b)** $(5/9)^2$ **(c)** $(5/9)^N$

33.

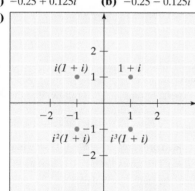

35.

Roll	Point	Coordinates
3	P_1	$(32, 0)$
1	P_2	$(16, 0)$
2	P_3	$(8, 0)$
3	P_4	$(20, 0)$
5	P_5	$(10, 16)$
5	P_6	$(5, 24)$

37. (a)

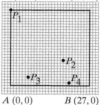

(b)

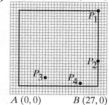

(c)

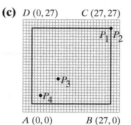

39. (a) $4, 2, 1, 2$ **(b)** $3, 1, 1, 3$ **(c)** $1, 3, 4, 2$

12.4 The Mandelbrot Set

41. (a) $-1 - i$ **(b)** i **(c)** $-1 - i$

43. (a) $-0.25 + 0.125i$ **(b)** $-0.25 - 0.125i$

45. (a)

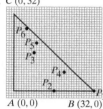

(b)

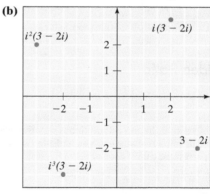

(c) It is a 90-degree counterclockwise rotation.

47. (a) $2, 2, 2, 2$ **(b)** 2

(c) Attracted to 2. Each number in the sequence is 2.

49. (a) $s_1 = -0.25$; $s_2 = -0.4375$; $s_3 \approx -0.3086$; $s_4 \approx -0.4048$; $s_5 \approx -0.3362$

(b) -0.3660

(c) Attracted to -0.3660. From (a) and (b), the sequence gets close to -0.3660 and then $s_N = s_{N+1}$ (approximately).

51. (a) $s_1 = -1 - i$; $s_2 = i$; $s_3 = -1 - i$; $s_4 = i$; $s_5 = -1 - i$

(b) Periodic; the odd terms are $-1 - i$ and the even terms are i.

JOGGING

53. (a)

	H
Step 3	$1 + 3 + 3^2$
Step 4	$1 + 3 + 3^2 + 3^3$
Step 5	$1 + 3 + 3^2 + 3^3 + 3^4$

(b) Using the formula for the sum of the terms in a geometric sequence with $R = 3$ we get $1 + 3 + 3^2 + 3^3 + \cdots + 3^{N-1} = (3^N - 1)/(3 - 1) = (3^N - 1)/2$ holes.

55. (a)

	H
Start	0
Step 1	7
Step 2	$7 + 7 \times 20$
Step 3	$7 + 7 \times 20 + 7 \times 20^2$
Step 4	$7 + 7 \times 20 + 7 \times 20^2 + 7 \times 20^3$
Step 5	$7 + 7 \times 20 + 7 \times 20^2 + 7 \times 20^3 + 7 \times 20^4$

(b) Using the formula for the sum of the terms in a geometric sequence with $P_0 = 7$ and $R = 20$ we get $7/19 \left[20^N - 1 \right]$ holes.

57. (a) reflections with vertical and horizontal lines passing through the center of the carpet; reflections with 45° (clockwise and counterclockwise from horizontal) diagonal axes passing through the center of the carpet

(b) rotations of 90°, 180°, 270°, with rotocenter the center of the carpet, plus the identity

(c) D_4

59. attracted to 1/2

61. escaping

Chapter 13

WALKING

13.1 Fibonacci Numbers

1. (a) 610   **(b)** 608   **(c)** 233   **(d)** 122   **(e)** 2

3. (a) 12   **(b)** 610   **(c)** 6   **(d)** 144

5. (a) one more than three times the Nth Fibonacci number

(b) three times the $(N + 1)$st Fibonacci number

(c) one more than the $(3N)$th Fibonacci number

(d) the $(3N + 1)$st Fibonacci number

7. (a) 39,088,169   **(b)** 63,245,986

9. (a) 9,227,465   **(b)** 5,702,887

11. 6765

13. (a) $1 + 2 + 5 + 13 + 34 + 89 = 144$ **(b)** 22   **(c)** $N + 1$

15. (a) $F_8 \times F_{11} = 21 \times 89 = 1869; F_{10}{}^2 - F_9{}^2 = 55^2 - 34^2 = 1869$

(b) $F_N F_{N+3} = F_{N+2}^2 - F_{N+1}^2$

17. (a) F_{N+3} **(b)** F_{N-1} **(c)** F_{N+6}

19. (a) $\frac{F_{N+1}}{F_{N-1}}$ **(b)** $-\frac{F_{N-2}}{F_N}$

21. (a) 275   **(b)** 375,125   **(c)** $A_N = 5F_N$

23. (a) 322

(b) $2 \times 1 - 1 = 1; 2 \times 2 - 1 = 3; 2 \times 3 - 2 = 4; 2 \times 5 - 3 = 7$;

(c) $L_{20} = 15{,}127$

13.2 The Golden Ratio

25. (a) $x = \frac{1 + \sqrt{5}}{2} \approx 1.61803, x = \frac{1 - \sqrt{5}}{2} \approx -0.61803$

(b) 1

(c) One solution is positive, the second solution is negative, and their sum equals 1. This implies that when you add the two solutions their decimal parts must cancel each other out.

27. (a) $x = \frac{8 + \sqrt{124}}{6} \approx 3.18925, x = \frac{8 - \sqrt{124}}{6} \approx -0.52259$

(b) $\frac{8}{3}$

29. (a) Substituting $x = 1$ into the equation gives $55 = 34 + 21$.

(b) The sum of the two solutions is $\frac{34}{55}$. It follows that the second solution is $x = \frac{34}{55} - 1 = -\frac{21}{55}$.

31. (a) Substituting $x = -1$ into the equation gives $21 = -34 + 55$.

(b) The sum of the two solutions is $\frac{34}{21}$. It follows that the second solution is $x = \frac{34}{21} + 1 = \frac{55}{21}$.

33. (a) Substituting $x = 1$ into the equation gives $F_N = F_{N-1} + F_{N-2}$, true for Fibonacci numbers.

(b) The sum of the two solutions is $\frac{F_{N-1}}{F_N}$. It follows that the second solution is $x = \frac{F_{N-1}}{F_N} - 1 = -\frac{F_{N-2}}{F_N}$.

35. (a) $\frac{1}{\phi} \approx 0.6180339887$

(b) Start with the golden property: $\phi^2 = \phi + 1$. Divide both sides by ϕ and get $\phi = 1 + \frac{1}{\phi}$. This gives $\frac{1}{\phi} = \phi - 1$. It follows that ϕ and $\frac{1}{\phi}$ must have exactly the same decimal part.

37. 1.394×10^{104}

39. (a) 169   **(b)** 2.41429   **(c)** 2.41421   **(d)** 2.41421

13.3 Gnomons

41. (a) 124.5 in.   **(b)** 945 in.^{2}

43. (a) 156 m   **(b)** 2880 m^2

45. $c = 24$

47. $x = 4$

49. 20 by 30

51. (a) $m(\angle ACD) = 72°; m(\angle CAD) = 72°; m(\angle CDA) = 36°$

(b) $AC = 1; CD = \phi; AD = \phi$

53. $x = 12, y = 10$

JOGGING

55. (a) $1, 0.5, 0.666667, 0.6, 0.625, 0.615385, 0.619048, 0.617647, 0.618182,$
$0.61798, 0.618056, 0.618026, 0.618037, 0.618033, \ldots$

(b) We know that $\left(\frac{F_{N+1}}{F_N}\right) \to \phi$. It follows that $\left(\frac{F_N}{F_{N+1}}\right) \to \frac{1}{\phi}$. But $\frac{1}{\phi} = \phi - 1$. [This last assertion follows from taking $\phi^2 = \phi + 1$ and dividing both sides by ϕ. See Exercise 35(b).]

57. (a) $1, 1 + \frac{1}{1} = 2, 1 + \frac{1}{2} = \frac{3}{2}, 1 + \frac{1}{3/2} = \frac{5}{3}, 1 + \frac{1}{5/3} = \frac{8}{5}, 1 + \frac{1}{8/5} = \frac{13}{8}$

(b) $T_N = \frac{F_{N+1}}{F_N}$

59. (a) $K_1 = 2F_2 - F_1 = 2 \times 1 - 1 = 1, K_2 = 2F_3 - F_2 = 2 \times 2 - 1 = 3,$ and $K_{N-1} + K_{N-2} = (2F_N - F_{N-1}) + (2F_{N-1} - F_{N-2}) = 2(F_N + F_{N-1}) - (F_{N-1} + F_{N-2}) = 2F_{N+1} - F_N = K_{N+1}.$ It follows that the $K_N = L_N$.

(b) $\frac{L_{N+1}}{L_N} = \frac{2F_{N+2} - F_{N+1}}{2F_{N+1} - F_N}$. If you divide the numerator and denominator of the right-hand expression by F_{N+1} you get $\frac{2(F_{N+2}/F_{N+1}) - 1}{2 - (F_N/F_{N+1})}$.

As N gets larger and larger, $(F_{N+2}/F_{N+1}) \to \phi$ and $(F_N/F_{N+1}) \to \frac{1}{\phi}$, and it follows that $\frac{2(F_{N+2}/F_{N+1}) - 1}{2 - (F_N/F_{N+1})} \to \frac{2\phi - 1}{2 - 1/\phi} = \phi.$

61. The sum of two odd numbers is always even, and the sum of an odd number and an even number is always odd. Since the seeds in the Fibonacci sequence are both odd, every third number is even and the others are all odd.

63. Attaching a gnomon to the L-shaped figure must result in a new, larger L-shaped figure—it must be higher, wider, and thicker (all by the same proportions). Of all the (five) possible ways of attaching a square to the L-shaped figure, none produces a similar figure.

65. From elementary geometry, $\angle AEF \cong \angle DBA$. So, $\triangle AEF$ is similar to $\triangle DBA$. Thus, $AF/FE = DA/AB$, which shows that rectangle $ADEF$ is similar to rectangle $ABCD$.

67. The result follows from Exercise 66(a) and a dissection of the regular pentagon into three golden triangles using any two nonintersecting diagonals.

PHOTO CREDITS

INDEX OF APPLICATIONS

Pages that follow this page are taken from
Mathematical Ideas, Thirteenth Edition,
by Charles D. Miller, Vern E. Heeren, John Hornsby, and Christopher Heeren.

CONTENTS

NOTE: Trigonometry module and Metrics module available in MyMathLab or online
at www.pearsonhighered.com/mathstatsresources.

After twelve editions and over four decades, *Mathematical Ideas* continues to be one of the most popular textbooks in liberal arts mathematics education. We are proud to present the thirteenth edition of a text that offers non-physical science students a practical coverage that connects mathematics to the world around them. It is a flexible text that has evolved alongside changing trends but remains steadfast to its original objectives.

Mathematical Ideas is written with a variety of students in mind. It is well suited for several courses, including those geared toward the aforementioned liberal arts audience and survey courses in mathematics or finite mathematics. Students taking these courses will pursue careers in nursing and healthcare, the construction trades, communications, hospitality, information technology, criminal justice, retail management and sales, computer programming, political science, school administration, and a myriad of other careers. Accordingly, we have chosen to increase our focus on showcasing how the math in this course will be relevant in this wide array of career options.

- Chapter openers now address how the chapter topics can be applied within the context of work and future careers.

- We made sure to retain the hundreds of examples and exercises from the previous edition that pertain to these interests.

- Every chapter also contains the brand new *When Will I Ever Use This?* features that help students connect mathematics to the workplace.

Interesting and mathematically pertinent movie and television applications and references are still interspersed throughout the chapters.

Ample topics are included for a two-term course, yet the variety of topics and flexibility of sequence makes the text suitable for shorter courses as well. Our main objectives continue to be comprehensive coverage, appropriate organization, clear exposition, an abundance of examples, and well-planned exercise sets with numerous applications.

New to This Edition

- New chapter openers connect the mathematics of the chapter to a particular career area, or in some cases, to an everyday life situation that will be important to people in virtually any career.

- *When Will I Ever Use This*? features in each chapter also connect chapter topics to career or workplace situations and answer that age-old question.

- Career applications have taken on greater prominence.

- Every section of every chapter now begins with a list of clear learning objectives for the student.

- An extensive summary at the end of each chapter includes the following components.

  ◦ A list of *Key Terms* for each section of the chapter

  ◦ *New Symbols,* with definitions, to clarify newly introduced symbols

  ◦ *Test Your Word Power* questions that allow students to test their knowledge of new vocabulary

  ◦ A *Quick Review* that gives a brief summary of concepts covered in the chapter, along with examples illustrating those concepts

- All exercise sets have once again been updated, with over 1000 new or modified exercises, many with a new emphasis on career applications.

- Since Intermediate Algebra is often a prerequisite for the liberal arts course, the algebra chapters have been streamlined to focus in on key concepts, many of which will aid in comprehension of other chapters' content.

- The presentation has been made more uniform whenever clarity for the reader could be served.

- The general style has been freshened, with more pedagogical use of color, new photos and art, and opening of the exposition.

- NEW! An Integrated Review MyMathLab course option provides embedded review of select developmental topics in a Ready to Go format with assignments pre-assigned. This course solution can be used in a co-requisite course model, or simply to help under-prepared students master prerequisite skills and concepts.

- Expanded online resources

  - **NEW! Interactive, conceptual videos** with assignable MML questions walk students through a concept and then ask them to answer a question within the video. If students answer correctly, the concept is summarized. If students select one of the two incorrect answers, the video continues focusing on why students probably selected that answer and works to correct that line of thinking and explain the concept. Then students get another chance to answer a question to prove mastery.

  - **NEW! Learning Catalytics** This student engagement, assessment and classroom intelligence system gives instructors real-time feedback on student learning.

  - **NEW! "When Will I Ever Use This?" videos** bring the ideas in the feature to life in a fun, memorable way.

  - **NEW! An Integrated Review MyMathLab** course option provides an embedded review of selected developmental topics. Assignments are pre-assigned in this course, which includes a Skills Check quiz on skills that students will need in order to learn effectively at the chapter level. Students who demonstrate mastery can move on to the *Mathematical Ideas* content, while students who need additional review can polish up their skills by using the videos supplied and can benefit from the practice they gain from the Integrated Review Worksheets. This course solution can be used either in a co-requisite course model, or simply to help underprepared students master prerequisite skills and concepts.

  - The Trigonometry and Metrics content that was previously in the text is now found in the MyMathLab course, including the assignable MML questions.

  - Extensions previously in the text are now found in the MyMathLab course, along with any assignable MML questions.

Overview of Chapters

- **Chapter 1 (The Art of Problem Solving)** introduces the student to inductive reasoning, pattern recognition, and problem-solving techniques. We continue to provide exercises based on the monthly Calendar from *Mathematics Teacher* and have added new ones throughout this edition. The new chapter opener recounts the solving of the Rubik's cube by a college professor. The *When Will I Ever Use This?* feature (p. 31) shows how estimation techniques may be used by a group home employee charged with holiday grocery shopping.

- **Chapter 2 (The Basic Concepts of Set Theory)** includes updated examples and exercises on surveys. The chapter opener and the *When Will I Ever Use This?* feature (p. 73) address the future job outlook for the nursing profession and the allocation of work crews in the building trade, respectively.

- **Chapter 3 (Introduction to Logic)** introduces the fundamental concepts of inductive and deductive logic. The chapter opener connects logic with fantasy literature, and new exercises further illustrate this relationship. A new *For Further Thought* (p. 99) and new exercises address logic gates in computers. One *When Will I Ever Use This?* feature (p. 108) connects circuit logic to the design and installation of home monitoring systems. Another (p. 128) shows a pediatric nurse applying a logical flowchart and truth tables to a child's vaccination protocol.

- **Chapter 4 (Numeration Systems)** covers historical numeration systems, including Egyptian, Roman, Chinese, Babylonian, Mayan, Greek, and Hindu-Arabic systems. A connection between base conversions in positional numeration systems and computer network design is suggested in the new chapter opener and illustrated in the *When Will I Ever Use This?* feature (p. 168), a new example, and new exercises.

- **Chapter 5 (Number Theory)** presents an introduction to the prime and composite numbers, the Fibonacci sequence, and a cross section of related historical developments, including the fairly new topic of "prime number splicing." The largest currently known prime numbers of various categories are identified, and recent progress on Goldbach's conjecture and the twin prime conjecture are noted. The chapter opener and one *When Will I Ever Use This?* feature (p. 189) apply cryptography and modular arithmetic to criminal justice, relating to cyber security. Another *When Will I Ever Use This?* feature (p. 205) shows how a nurse may use the concept of least common denominator in determining proper drug dosage.

- **Chapter 6 (The Real Numbers and Their Representations)** introduces some of the basic concepts of real numbers, their various forms of representation, and operations of arithmetic with them. The chapter opener and *When Will I Ever Use This?* feature (p. 273) connect percents and basic algebraic procedures to pricing, markup and discount, student grading, and market share analysis, as needed by a retail manager, a teacher, a salesperson, a fashion merchandiser, and a business owner.

- **Chapter 7 (The Basic Concepts of Algebra)** can be used to present the basics of algebra (linear and quadratic equations, applications, exponents, polynomials, and factoring) to students for the first time, or as a review of previous courses. The chapter opener connects proportions to an automobile owner's determination of fuel mileage, and the *When Will I Ever Use This?* feature (p. 330) relates inequalities to a test-taker's computation of the score needed to maintain a certain grade point average.

- **Chapter 8 (Graphs, Functions, and Systems of Equations and Inequalities)** is the second of our two algebra chapters. It continues with graphs, equations, and applications of linear, quadratic, exponential, and logarithmic functions and models, along with systems of equations. The chapter opener shows how an automobile owner can use a linear graph to relate price per gallon, amount purchased, and total cost. The *When Will I Ever Use This?* feature (p. 416) connects logarithms with the interpretation of earthquake reporting in the news.

- **Chapter 9 (Geometry)** covers elementary plane geometry, transformational geometry, basic geometric constructions, non-Euclidean geometry, and chaos and fractals. Section 9.7 now includes projective geometry. At reviewer request, the discussion of networks (the Königsberg Bridge problem) has been moved to Chapter 14 (Graph Theory). The chapter opener and one *When Will I Ever Use This?* feature (p. 497) connect geometric volume formulas to a video game programmer's job of designing the visual field of a game screen. A second *When Will I Ever Use This?* feature (p. 470) relates right triangle geometry to a forester's determining of safe tree-felling parameters.

- **Chapter 10 (Counting Methods)** focuses on elementary counting techniques, in preparation for the probability chapter. The chapter opener relates how a restaurateur used counting methods to help design the sales counter signage in a new restaurant. The *When Will I Ever Use This?* feature (p. 534) describes an entrepreneur's use of probability and sports statistics in designing a game and in building a successful company based on it.

- **Chapter 11 (Probability)** covers the basics of probability, odds, and expected value. The chapter opener relates to the professions of weather forecaster, actuary, baseball manager, and corporate manager, applying probability, statistics, and expected value to interpreting forecasts, determining insurance rates, selecting optimum strategies, and making business decisions. One *When Will I Ever Use This?* feature (p. 586) shows how a tree diagram helps a decision maker provide equal chances of winning to three players in a game of chance. A second such feature (p. 606) shows how knowledge of probability can help a television game show contestant determine the best winning strategy.

- **Chapter 12 (Statistics)** is an introduction to statistics that focuses on the measures of central tendency, dispersion, and position and discusses the normal distribution and its applications. The chapter opener and two *When Will I Ever Use This?* features (pp. 656, 661) connect probability and graph construction and interpretation to how a psychological therapist may motivate and carry out treatment for alcohol and tobacco addiction.

- **Chapter 13 (Personal Financial Management)** provides the student with the basics of the mathematics of finance as applied to inflation, consumer debt, and house buying. We also include a section on investing, with emphasis on stocks, bonds, and mutual funds. Tables, examples, and exercises have been updated to reflect current interest rates and investment returns. New margin notes feature smart apps for financial calculations. Additions in response to reviewer requests include a *When Will I Ever Use This?* feature (p. 741) connecting several topics of the chapter to how a financial planner can provide comparisons between renting and buying a house, and exercises comparing different mortgage options. Another *When Will I Ever Use This?* feature (p. 732) explores the cost-effectiveness of solar energy, using chapter topics essential for a solar energy salesperson. The chapter opener connects the time value of money to how a financial planner can help clients make wise financial decisions.

- **Chapter 14 (Graph Theory)** covers the basic concepts of graph theory and its applications. The chapter opener shows how a writer can apply graph theory to the analysis of poetic rhyme. One *When Will I Ever Use This?* feature (p. 800) connects graph theory to how a postal or delivery service manager could determine the most efficient delivery routes. Another (p. 818) tells of a unique use by an entrepreneur who developed a business based on finding time-efficient ways to navigate theme parks.

- **Chapter 15 (Voting and Apportionment)** deals with issues in voting methods and apportionment of representation, topics that have become increasingly popular in liberal arts mathematics courses. The Adams method of apportionment, as well as the Huntington-Hill method (currently used in United States presidential elections) are now included in the main body of the text. To illustrate the important work of a political consultant, the chapter opener connects different methods of analyzing votes. One *When Will I Ever Use This?* feature (p. 859) relates voting methods to the functioning of governing boards. Another (p. 874) gives an example of how understanding apportionment methods can help in the work of a school administrator.

Course Outline Considerations

Chapters in the text are, in most cases, independent and may be covered in the order chosen by the instructor. The few exceptions are as follows:

- Chapter 6 contains some material dependent on the ideas found in Chapter 5.
- Chapter 6 should be covered before Chapter 7 if student background so dictates.
- Chapters 7 and 8 form an algebraic "package" and should be covered in sequential order.
- A thorough coverage of Chapter 11 depends on knowledge of Chapter 10 material, although probability can be covered without teaching extensive counting methods by avoiding the more difficult exercises.

Features of the Thirteenth Edition

NEW! Chapter Openers In keeping with the career theme, chapter openers address a situation related to a particular career. All are new to this edition. Some openers include a problem that the reader is asked to solve. We hope that you find these chapter openers useful and practical.

ENHANCED! Varied Exercise Sets We continue to present a variety of exercises that integrate drill, conceptual, and applied problems, and there are over 1000 new or modified exercises in this edition. The text contains a wealth of exercises to provide students with opportunities to practice, apply, connect, and extend the mathematical skills they are learning. We have updated the exercises that focus on real-life data and have retained their titles for easy identification. Several chapters are enriched with new applications, particularly Chapters 6, 7, 8, 11, 12, and 13. We continue to use graphs, tables, and charts when appropriate. Many of the graphs use a style similar to that seen by students in today's print and electronic media.

UPDATED! Emphasis on Real Data in the Form of Graphs, Charts, and Tables We continue to use up-to-date information from magazines, newspapers, and the Internet to create real applications that are relevant and meaningful.

Problem-Solving Strategies Special paragraphs labeled "Problem-Solving Strategy" relate the discussion of problem-solving strategies to techniques that have been presented earlier.

For Further Thought These entries encourage students to share their reasoning processes among themselves to gain a deeper understanding of key mathematical concepts.

ENHANCED! Margin Notes This popular feature is a hallmark of this text and has been retained and updated where appropriate. These notes are interspersed throughout the text and are drawn from various sources, such as lives of mathematicians, historical vignettes, anecdotes on mathematics textbooks of the past, newspaper and magazine articles, and current research in mathematics.

Optional Graphing Technology We continue to provide sample graphing calculator screens to show how technology can be used to support results found analytically. It is not essential, however, that a student have a graphing calculator to study from this text. *The technology component is optional.*

NEW! Chapter Summaries Extensive summaries at the end of each chapter include Key Terms, New Symbols with definitions, Test Your Word Power vocabulary checks, and a Quick Review that provides a brief summary of concepts (with examples) covered in the chapter.

Chapter Tests Each chapter concludes with a chapter test so that students can check their mastery of the material.

The Art of Problem Solving

1

Professor Terry Krieger, of Rochester (Minnesota) Community College, shares his thoughts about why he decided to become a mathematics teacher. He is an expert at the Rubik's Cube. Here, he explains how he mastered this classic problem.

From a very young age I always enjoyed solving problems, especially problems involving numbers and patterns. There is something inherently beautiful in the process of discovering mathematical truth. Mathematics may be the only discipline in which different people, using wildly varied but logically sound methods, will arrive at the **same** *correct result—not just once, but every time! It is this aspect of mathematics that led me to my career as an educator. As a mathematics instructor, I get to be part of, and sometimes guide, the discovery process.*

I received a Rubik's Cube as a gift my junior year of high school. I was fascinated by it. I devoted the better part of three months to solving it for the first time, sometimes working 3 or 4 hours per day on it.

1

There was a lot of trial and error involved. I devised a process that allowed me to move only a small number of pieces at a time while keeping other pieces in their places. Most of my moves affect only three or four of the 26 unique pieces of the puzzle. What sets my solution apart from those found in many books is that I hold the cube in a consistent position and work from the top to the bottom. Most book solutions work upward from the bottom.

My first breakthrough came when I realized that getting a single color on one face of the cube was not helpful if the colors along the edges of that face were placed improperly. In other words, it does no good to make the top of the cube all white if one of the edges along the white top shows green, yellow, and blue. It needs to be all green, for example.

I worked on the solution so much that I started seeing cube moves in my sleep. In fact, I figured out the moves for one of my most frustrating sticking points while sleeping. I just woke up knowing how to do it.

The eight corners of the cube represented a particularly difficult challenge for me. Finding a consistent method for placing the corners appropriately took many, many hours. To this day, the amount of time that it takes for me to solve a scrambled cube depends largely on the amount of time that it takes for me to place the corners.

When I first honed my technique, I was able to consistently solve the cube in 2 to 3 minutes. My average time is now about 65 seconds. My fastest time is 42 seconds.

Since figuring out how to solve the cube, I have experimented with other possible color patterns that can be formed. The most complicated one I have created leaves the cube with three different color stripes on all six faces. I have never met another person who can accomplish this arrangement.

1.1   SOLVING PROBLEMS BY INDUCTIVE REASONING

OBJECTIVES

1 Be able to distinguish between inductive and deductive reasoning.

2 Understand that in some cases, inductive reasoning may not lead to valid conclusions.

Characteristics of Inductive and Deductive Reasoning

The development of mathematics can be traced to the Egyptian and Babylonian cultures (3000 B.C.–A.D. 260) as a necessity for counting and problem solving. To solve a problem, a cookbook-like recipe was given, and it was followed repeatedly to solve similar problems. By observing that a specific method worked for a certain type of problem, the Babylonians and the Egyptians concluded that the same method would work for any similar type of problem. Such a conclusion is called a *conjecture*. A **conjecture** is an educated guess based on repeated observations of a particular process or pattern.

The method of reasoning just described is called *inductive reasoning*.

INDUCTIVE REASONING

Inductive reasoning is characterized by drawing a general conclusion (making a conjecture) from repeated observations of specific examples. The conjecture may or may not be true.

In testing a conjecture obtained by inductive reasoning, it takes only one example that does not work to prove the conjecture false. Such an example is called a **counterexample.**

Inductive reasoning provides a powerful method of drawing conclusions, but there is no assurance that the observed conjecture will always be true. For this reason, mathematicians are reluctant to accept a conjecture as an absolute truth until it is formally proved using methods of *deductive reasoning.* Deductive reasoning characterized the development and approach of Greek mathematics, as seen in the works of Euclid, Pythagoras, Archimedes, and others. During the classical Greek period (600 B.C.–A.D. 450), general concepts were applied to specific problems, resulting in a structured, logical development of mathematics.

DEDUCTIVE REASONING

Deductive reasoning is characterized by applying general principles to specific examples.

We now look at examples of these two types of reasoning. In this chapter, we often refer to the **natural,** or **counting, numbers.**

$$1, 2, 3, \ldots \quad \text{Natural (counting) numbers}$$

$$\uparrow$$

Ellipsis points

The three dots (*ellipsis points*) indicate that the numbers continue indefinitely in the pattern that has been established. The most probable rule for continuing this pattern is "Add 1 to the previous number," and this is indeed the rule that we follow.

Now consider the following list of natural numbers:

$$2, 9, 16, 23, 30.$$

What is the next number of this list? What is the pattern? After studying the numbers, we might see that $2 + 7 = 9$, and $9 + 7 = 16$. Do we add 16 and 7 to get 23? Do we add 23 and 7 to get 30? Yes. It seems that any number in the given list can be found by adding 7 to the preceding number, so the next number in the list would be $30 + 7 = 37$.

We set out to find the "next number" by reasoning from observation of the numbers in the list. We may have jumped from these observations to the general statement that any number in the list is 7 more than the preceding number. This is an example of inductive reasoning.

By using inductive reasoning, we concluded that 37 was the next number. Suppose the person making up the list has another answer in mind. The list of numbers

$$2, 9, 16, 23, 30$$

actually gives the dates of Mondays in June if June 1 falls on a Sunday. The next Monday after June 30 is July 7. With this pattern, the list continues as

$$2, 9, 16, 23, 30, 7, 14, 21, 28, \ldots.$$

See the calendar in **Figure 1.** The correct answer would then be 7. The process used to obtain the rule "add 7" in the preceding list reveals a main flaw of inductive reasoning. *We can never be sure that what is true in a specific case will be true in general. Inductive reasoning does not guarantee a true result, but it does provide a means of making a conjecture.*

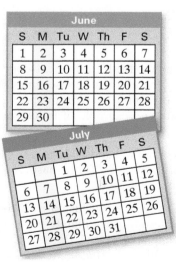

Figure 1

We now review some basic notation. Throughout this book, we use *exponents* to represent repeated multiplication.

$$\text{Base} \rightarrow 4^3 = 4 \cdot 4 \cdot 4 = 64 \qquad \text{4 is used as a factor 3 times.}$$
$$\uparrow$$
$$\text{Exponent}$$

EXPONENTIAL EXPRESSION

If a is a number and n is a counting number $(1, 2, 3, \ldots)$, then the exponential expression a^n is defined as follows.

$$a^n = \underbrace{a \cdot a \cdot a \cdot \ldots \cdot a}_{n \text{ factors of } a}$$

The number a is the **base** and n is the **exponent.**

With deductive reasoning, we use general statements and apply them to specific situations. For example, a basic rule for converting feet to inches is to multiply the number of feet by 12 in order to obtain the equivalent number of inches. This can be expressed as a formula.

$$\text{Number of inches} = 12 \times \text{number of feet}$$

This general rule can be applied to any specific case. For example, the number of inches in 3 feet is $12 \times 3 = 36$ inches.

Reasoning through a problem usually requires certain *premises*. A **premise** can be an assumption, law, rule, widely held idea, or observation. Then reason inductively or deductively from the premises to obtain a **conclusion.** The premises and conclusion make up a **logical argument.**

EXAMPLE 1 Identifying Premises and Conclusions

Identify each premise and the conclusion in each of the following arguments. Then tell whether each argument is an example of inductive or deductive reasoning.

(a) Our house is made of brick. Both of my next-door neighbors have brick houses. Therefore, all houses in our neighborhood are made of brick.

(b) All keyboards have the symbol @. I have a keyboard. My keyboard has the symbol @.

(c) Today is Tuesday. Tomorrow will be Wednesday.

Solution

(a) The premises are "Our house is made of brick" and "Both of my next-door neighbors have brick houses." The conclusion is "Therefore, all houses in our neighborhood are made of brick." Because the reasoning goes from specific examples to a general statement, the argument is an example of inductive reasoning (although it may very well be faulty).

(b) Here the premises are "All keyboards have the symbol @" and "I have a keyboard." The conclusion is "My keyboard has the symbol @." This reasoning goes from general to specific, so deductive reasoning was used.

(c) There is only one premise here, "Today is Tuesday." The conclusion is "Tomorrow will be Wednesday." The fact that Wednesday immediately follows Tuesday is being used, even though this fact is not explicitly stated. Because the conclusion comes from general facts that apply to this special case, deductive reasoning was used. ∎

While inductive reasoning may, at times, lead to false conclusions, in many cases it does provide correct results if we look for the most *probable* answer.

The Fibonacci Sequence

$$1, \ 1, \ 2, \ 3, \ 5, \ 8, \ 13, \ 21, \ \cdots$$

In the 2003 movie *A Wrinkle in Time*, young Charles Wallace, played by David Dorfman, is challenged to identify a particular sequence of numbers. He correctly identifies it as the **Fibonacci sequence.**

EXAMPLE 2 Predicting the Next Number in a Sequence

Use inductive reasoning to determine the *probable* next number in each list below.

(a) 5, 9, 13, 17, 21, 25, 29   **(b)** 1, 1, 2, 3, 5, 8, 13, 21   **(c)** 2, 4, 8, 16, 32

Solution

(a) Each number in the list is obtained by adding 4 to the previous number. The probable next number is $29 + 4 = 33$. (This is an example of an *arithmetic sequence.*)

(b) Beginning with the third number in the list, 2, each number is obtained by adding the two previous numbers in the list. That is,

$$1 + 1 = 2, \quad 1 + 2 = 3, \quad 2 + 3 = 5,$$

and so on. The probable next number in the list is $13 + 21 = 34$. (These are the first few terms of the *Fibonacci sequence.*)

(c) It appears here that to obtain each number after the first, we must double the previous number. Therefore, the probable next number is $32 \times 2 = 64$. (This is an example of a *geometric sequence.*) ∎

EXAMPLE 3 Predicting the Product of Two Numbers

Consider the list of equations. Predict the next multiplication fact in the list.

$$37 \times \ 3 = 111$$
$$37 \times \ 6 = 222$$
$$37 \times \ 9 = 333$$
$$37 \times 12 = 444$$

Solution

The left side of each equation has two factors, the first 37 and the second a multiple of 3, beginning with 3. Each product (answer) consists of three digits, all the same, beginning with 111 for 37×3. Thus, the next multiplication fact would be

$$37 \times 15 = 555, \quad \text{which is indeed true.}$$ ∎

Pitfalls of Inductive Reasoning

There are pitfalls associated with inductive reasoning. A classic example involves the maximum number of regions formed when chords are constructed in a circle. When two points on a circle are joined with a line segment, a *chord* is formed.

Locate a single point on a circle. Because no chords are formed, a single interior region is formed. See **Figure 2(a)** on the next page. Locate two points and draw a chord. Two interior regions are formed, as shown in **Figure 2(b).** Continue this pattern. Locate three points, and draw all possible chords. Four interior regions are formed, as shown in **Figure 2(c).** Four points yield 8 regions and five points yield 16 regions. See **Figures 2(d) and 2(e).**

The results of the preceding observations are summarized in **Table 1.** The pattern formed in the column headed "Number of Regions" is the same one we saw in **Example 2(c),** where we predicted that the next number would be 64. It seems here that for each additional point on the circle, the number of regions doubles.

Table 1

Number of Points	Number of Regions
1	1
2	2
3	4
4	8
5	16

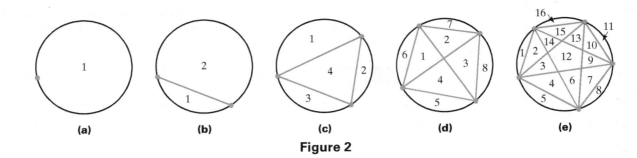

Figure 2

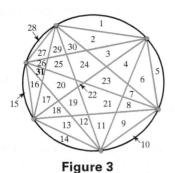

Figure 3

A reasonable inductive conjecture would be that for six points, 32 regions would be formed. But as **Figure 3** indicates, there are *only 31 regions*. The pattern of doubling ends when the sixth point is considered. Adding a seventh point would yield 57 regions. The numbers obtained here are

$$1, 2, 4, 8, 16, 31, 57.$$

For n points on the circle, the number of regions is given by the formula

$$\frac{n^4 - 6n^3 + 23n^2 - 18n + 24}{24}.^*$$

In Exercises 1–16, determine whether the reasoning is an example of deductive or inductive reasoning.

1. The next number in the pattern 2, 4, 6, 8, 10 is 12.

2. My dog barked and woke me up at 1:02 a.m., 2:03 a.m., and 3:04 a.m. So he will bark again and wake me up at 4:05 a.m.

3. To find the perimeter P of a square with side of length s, I can use the formula $P = 4s$. So the perimeter of a square with side of length 7 inches is $4 \times 7 = 28$ inches.

4. A company charges a 10% re-stocking fee for returning an item. So when I return a radio that cost $150, I will only get $135 back.

5. If the mechanic says that it will take seven days to repair your SUV, then it will actually take ten days. The mechanic says, "I figure it'll take exactly one week to fix it, ma'am." Then you can expect it to be ready ten days from now.

6. If you take your medicine, you'll feel a lot better. You take your medicine. Therefore, you'll feel a lot better.

7. It has rained every day for the past six days, and it is raining today as well. So it will also rain tomorrow.

8. Carrie's first five children were boys. If she has another baby, it will be a boy.

9. The 2000 movie *Cast Away* stars Tom Hanks as the only human survivor of a plane crash, stranded on a tropical island. He approximates his distance from where the plane lost radio contact to be 400 miles (a radius), and uses the formula for the area of a circle,

$$\text{Area} = \pi \, (\text{radius})^2$$

to determine that a search party would have to cover an area of over 500,000 square miles to look for him and his "pal" Wilson.

---

*For more information on this and other similar patterns, see "Counting Pizza Pieces and Other Combinatorial Problems," by Eugene Maier, in the January 1988 issue of *Mathematics Teacher,* pp. 22–26.

10. If the same number is subtracted from both sides of a true equation, the new equation is also true. I know that $9 + 18 = 27$. Therefore, $(9 + 18) - 13 = 27 - 13$.

11. If you build it, they will come. You build it. Therefore, they will come.

12. All men are mortal. Socrates is a man. Therefore, Socrates is mortal.

13. It is a fact that every student who ever attended Delgado University was accepted into graduate school. Because I am attending Delgado, I can expect to be accepted to graduate school, too.

14. For the past 126 years, a rare plant has bloomed in Columbia each summer, alternating between yellow and green flowers. Last summer, it bloomed with green flowers, so this summer it will bloom with yellow flowers.

15. In the sequence 5, 10, 15, 20, 25, . . . , the most probable next number is 30.

16. (This anecdote is adapted from a story by Howard Eves in *In Mathematical Circles*.) A scientist had a group of 100 fleas, and one by one he would tell each flea "Jump," and the flea would jump. Then with the same fleas, he yanked off their hind legs and repeated "Jump," but the fleas would not jump. He concluded that when a flea has its hind legs yanked off, it cannot hear.

17. Discuss the differences between inductive and deductive reasoning. Give an example of each.

18. Give an example of faulty inductive reasoning.

Determine the most probable next term in each of the following lists of numbers.

19. 6, 9, 12, 15, 18

20. 13, 18, 23, 28, 33

21. 3, 12, 48, 192, 768

22. 32, 16, 8, 4, 2

23. 3, 6, 9, 15, 24, 39

24. $\dfrac{1}{3}, \dfrac{3}{5}, \dfrac{5}{7}, \dfrac{7}{9}, \dfrac{9}{11}$

25. $\dfrac{1}{2}, \dfrac{3}{4}, \dfrac{5}{6}, \dfrac{7}{8}, \dfrac{9}{10}$

26. 1, 4, 9, 16, 25

27. 1, 8, 27, 64, 125

28. 2, 6, 12, 20, 30, 42

29. 4, 7, 12, 19, 28, 39

30. 27, 21, 16, 12, 9

31. 5, 3, 5, 5, 3, 5, 5, 5, 3, 5, 5, 5, 5, 3, 5, 5, 5, 5

32. 8, 2, 8, 2, 2, 8, 2, 2, 2, 8, 2, 2, 2, 2, 8, 2, 2, 2, 2

33. Construct a list of numbers similar to those in **Exercise 19** such that the most probable next number in the list is 60.

34. Construct a list of numbers similar to those in **Exercise 30** such that the most probable next number in the list is 8.

Use the list of equations and inductive reasoning to predict the next equation, and then verify your conjecture.

35.
$(9 \times 9) + 7 = 88$
$(98 \times 9) + 6 = 888$
$(987 \times 9) + 5 = 8888$
$(9876 \times 9) + 4 = 88{,}888$

36.
$(1 \times 9) + 2 = 11$
$(12 \times 9) + 3 = 111$
$(123 \times 9) + 4 = 1111$
$(1234 \times 9) + 5 = 11{,}111$

37.
$3367 \times 3 = 10{,}101$
$3367 \times 6 = 20{,}202$
$3367 \times 9 = 30{,}303$
$3367 \times 12 = 40{,}404$

38.
$15873 \times 7 = 111{,}111$
$15873 \times 14 = 222{,}222$
$15873 \times 21 = 333{,}333$
$15873 \times 28 = 444{,}444$

39.
$34 \times 34 = 1156$
$334 \times 334 = 111{,}556$
$3334 \times 3334 = 11{,}115{,}556$

40.
$11 \times 11 = 121$
$111 \times 111 = 12{,}321$
$1111 \times 1111 = 1{,}234{,}321$

41.
$$3 = \frac{3(2)}{2}$$
$$3 + 6 = \frac{6(3)}{2}$$
$$3 + 6 + 9 = \frac{9(4)}{2}$$
$$3 + 6 + 9 + 12 = \frac{12(5)}{2}$$

42.
$2 = 4 - 2$
$2 + 4 = 8 - 2$
$2 + 4 + 8 = 16 - 2$
$2 + 4 + 8 + 16 = 32 - 2$

43.
$5(6) = 6(6 - 1)$
$5(6) + 5(36) = 6(36 - 1)$
$5(6) + 5(36) + 5(216) = 6(216 - 1)$
$5(6) + 5(36) + 5(216) + 5(1296) = 6(1296 - 1)$

44.
$$3 = \frac{3(3-1)}{2}$$
$$3 + 9 = \frac{3(9-1)}{2}$$
$$3 + 9 + 27 = \frac{3(27-1)}{2}$$
$$3 + 9 + 27 + 81 = \frac{3(81-1)}{2}$$

45.
$$\frac{1}{2} = 1 - \frac{1}{2}$$
$$\frac{1}{2} + \frac{1}{4} = 1 - \frac{1}{4}$$
$$\frac{1}{2} + \frac{1}{4} + \frac{1}{8} = 1 - \frac{1}{8}$$
$$\frac{1}{2} + \frac{1}{4} + \frac{1}{8} + \frac{1}{16} = 1 - \frac{1}{16}$$

46.
$$\frac{1}{1 \cdot 2} = \frac{1}{2}$$
$$\frac{1}{1 \cdot 2} + \frac{1}{2 \cdot 3} = \frac{2}{3}$$
$$\frac{1}{1 \cdot 2} + \frac{1}{2 \cdot 3} + \frac{1}{3 \cdot 4} = \frac{3}{4}$$
$$\frac{1}{1 \cdot 2} + \frac{1}{2 \cdot 3} + \frac{1}{3 \cdot 4} + \frac{1}{4 \cdot 5} = \frac{4}{5}$$

Legend has it that the great mathematician Carl Friedrich Gauss (1777–1855) at a very young age was told by his teacher to find the sum of the first 100 counting numbers. While his classmates toiled at the problem, Carl simply wrote down a single number and handed the correct answer in to his teacher. The young Carl explained that he observed that there were 50 pairs of numbers that each added up to 101. (See below.) So the sum of all the numbers must be 50 × 101 = 5050.

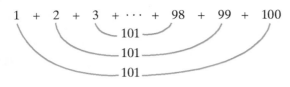

50 sums of 101 = 50 × 101 = 5050

Use the method of Gauss to find each sum.

47. $1 + 2 + 3 + \cdots + 200$ **48.** $1 + 2 + 3 + \cdots + 400$

49. $1 + 2 + 3 + \cdots + 800$ **50.** $1 + 2 + 3 + \cdots + 2000$

51. Modify the procedure of Gauss to find the sum $1 + 2 + 3 + \cdots + 175$.

52. Explain in your own words how the procedure of Gauss can be modified to find the sum $1 + 2 + 3 + \cdots + n$, where n is an odd natural number. (When an odd natural number is divided by 2, it leaves a remainder of 1.)

53. Modify the procedure of Gauss to find the sum $2 + 4 + 6 + \cdots + 100$.

54. Use the result of **Exercise 53** to find the sum $4 + 8 + 12 + \cdots + 200$.

55. What is the most probable next number in this list?

$$12, 1, 1, 1, 2, 1, 3$$

(*Hint:* Think about a clock with chimes.)

56. What is the next term in this list?

$$O, T, T, F, F, S, S, E, N, T$$

(*Hint:* Think about words and their relationship to numbers.)

57. Choose any three-digit number with all different digits, and follow these steps.

(a) Reverse the digits, and subtract the smaller from the larger. Record your result.

(b) Choose another three-digit number and repeat this process. Do this as many times as it takes for you to see a pattern in the different results you obtain. (*Hint:* What is the middle digit? What is the sum of the first and third digits?)

(c) Write an explanation of this pattern.

58. Choose any number, and follow these steps.

(a) Multiply by 2.   **(b)** Add 6.

(c) Divide by 2.   **(d)** Subtract the number you started with.

(e) Record your result.

Repeat the process, except in Step (b), add 8. Record your final result. Repeat the process once more, except in Step (b), add 10. Record your final result.

(f) Observe what you have done. Then use inductive reasoning to explain how to predict the final result.

59. Complete the following.

$142,857 \times 1 = \underline{\hspace{1cm}}$ $142,857 \times 2 = \underline{\hspace{1cm}}$
$142,857 \times 3 = \underline{\hspace{1cm}}$ $142,857 \times 4 = \underline{\hspace{1cm}}$
$142,857 \times 5 = \underline{\hspace{1cm}}$ $142,857 \times 6 = \underline{\hspace{1cm}}$

What pattern exists in the successive answers? Now multiply 142,857 by 7 to obtain an interesting result.

60. Refer to **Figures 2(b)–(e)** and **Figure 3.** Instead of counting interior regions of the circle, count the chords formed. Use inductive reasoning to predict the number of chords that would be formed if seven points were used.

1.2   AN APPLICATION OF INDUCTIVE REASONING: NUMBER PATTERNS

OBJECTIVES

1 Be able to recognize arithmetic and geometric sequences.

2 Be able to apply the method of successive differences to predict the next term in a sequence.

3 Be able to recognize number patterns.

4 Be able to use sum formulas.

5 Be able to recognize triangular, square, and pentagonal numbers.

Number Sequences

An ordered list of numbers such as

$$3, 9, 15, 21, 27, \ldots$$

is called a *sequence*. A **number sequence** is a list of numbers having a first number, a second number, a third number, and so on, called the **terms** of the sequence.

The sequence that begins

$$5, 9, 13, 17, 21, \ldots$$

is an *arithmetic sequence,* or *arithmetic progression*. In an **arithmetic sequence,** each term after the first is obtained by adding the same number, called the **common difference,** to the preceding term. To find the common difference, choose any term after the first and subtract from it the preceding term. If we choose $9 - 5$ (the second term minus the first term), for example, we see that the common difference is 4. To find the term following 21, we add 4 to get $21 + 4 = 25$.

The sequence that begins

$$2, 4, 8, 16, 32, \ldots$$

is a *geometric sequence,* or *geometric progression*. In a **geometric sequence,** each term after the first is obtained by multiplying the preceding term by the same number, called the **common ratio.** To find the common ratio, choose any term after the first and divide it by the preceding term. If we choose $\frac{4}{2}$ (the second term divided by the first term), for example, we see that the common ratio is 2. To find the term following 32, we multiply by 2 to get $32 \cdot 2 = 64$.

EXAMPLE 1   Identifying Arithmetic and Geometric Sequences

For each sequence, determine if it is an *arithmetic sequence,* a *geometric sequence,* or *neither*. If it is either arithmetic or geometric, give the next term in the sequence.

(a) $5, 10, 15, 20, 25, \ldots$ **(b)** $3, 12, 48, 192, 768, \ldots$ **(c)** $1, 4, 9, 16, 25, \ldots$

Solution

(a) If we choose *any* term after the first term, and subtract the preceding term, we find that the common difference is 5.

$$10 - 5 = 5 \qquad 15 - 10 = 5 \qquad 20 - 15 = 5 \qquad 25 - 20 = 5$$

Therefore, this is an arithmetic sequence. The next term in the sequence is

$$25 + 5 = 30.$$

(b) If any term after the first is multiplied by 4, the following term is obtained.

$$\frac{12}{3} = 4 \qquad \frac{48}{12} = 4 \qquad \frac{192}{48} = 4 \qquad \frac{768}{192} = 4$$

Therefore, this is a geometric sequence. The next term in the sequence is

$$768 \cdot 4 = 3072.$$

(c) Although there is a pattern here (the terms are the squares of the first five counting numbers), there is neither a common difference nor a common ratio. This is neither an arithmetic nor a geometric sequence.   ∎

Successive Differences

Some sequences may present more difficulty than our earlier examples when making a conjecture about the next term. Often the **method of successive differences** may be applied in such cases. Consider the sequence

$$2, 6, 22, 56, 114, \ldots.$$

Because the next term is not obvious, subtract the first term from the second term, the second from the third, the third from the fourth, and so on.

$$6 - 2 = 4 \quad 22 - 6 = 16 \quad 56 - 22 = 34 \quad 114 - 56 = 58$$

Now repeat the process with the sequence 4, 16, 34, 58 and continue repeating until the difference is a constant value, as shown in line (4).

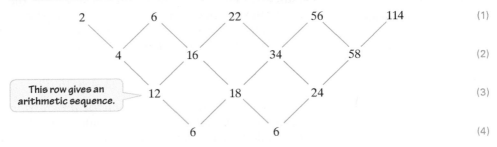

This row gives an arithmetic sequence.

Once a line of constant values is obtained, simply work "backward" by adding until the desired term of the given sequence is obtained. Thus, for this pattern to continue, another 6 should appear in line (4), meaning that the next term in line (3) would have to be $24 + 6 = 30$. The next term in line (2) would be $58 + 30 = 88$. Finally, the next term in the given sequence would be $114 + 88 = \mathbf{202}$.

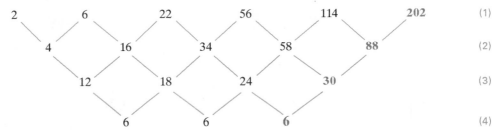

EXAMPLE 2 **Using Successive Differences**

Use successive differences to determine the next number in each sequence.

(a) $14, 22, 32, 44, \ldots$ **(b)** $5, 15, 37, 77, 141, \ldots$

Solution

(a) Subtract a term from the one that follows it, and continue until a pattern is observed.

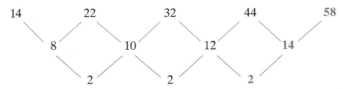

Once the row of 2s was obtained and extended, we were able to obtain

$$12 + 2 = 14, \quad \text{and} \quad 44 + 14 = 58 \quad \text{as shown above.}$$

The next number in the sequence is **58**.

(b) Proceed as before to obtain the following diagram.

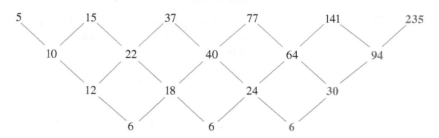

The numbers in the "diagonal" at the far right were obtained by adding: $24 + 6 = 30, 64 + 30 = 94$, and $141 + 94 = 235$. The next number in the sequence is **235**. ∎

The method of successive differences does not always work. For example, try it on the Fibonacci sequence in **Example 2(b)** of **Section 1.1** and see what happens.

Number Patterns and Sum Formulas

Observe the following number pattern.

$$1 = 1^2$$
$$1 + 3 = 2^2$$
$$1 + 3 + 5 = 3^2$$
$$1 + 3 + 5 + 7 = 4^2$$
$$1 + 3 + 5 + 7 + 9 = 5^2$$

In each case, the left side of the equation is the indicated sum of consecutive odd counting numbers beginning with 1, and the right side is the square of the number of terms on the left side. Inductive reasoning would suggest that the next line in this pattern is as follows.

$$1 + 3 + 5 + 7 + 9 + 11 = 6^2$$

Evaluating each side shows that each side simplifies to 36.

We cannot conclude that this pattern will continue indefinitely, because observation of a finite number of examples does *not* guarantee that the pattern will continue. However, mathematicians have proved that this pattern does indeed continue indefinitely, using a method of proof called **mathematical induction.** (See any standard college algebra text.)

Any even counting number may be written in the form $2k$, where k is a counting number. It follows that the kth odd counting number is written $2k - 1$. For example, the **third** odd counting number, 5, can be written

$$2(3) - 1.$$

Using these ideas, we can write the result obtained above as follows.

SUM OF THE FIRST n ODD COUNTING NUMBERS

If n is any counting number, then the following is true.

$$1 + 3 + 5 + \cdots + (2n - 1) = n^2$$

EXAMPLE 3 Predicting the Next Equation in a List

In each of the following, several equations are given illustrating a suspected number pattern. Determine what the next equation would be, and verify that it is indeed a true statement.

(a)
$$1^2 = 1^3$$
$$(1 + 2)^2 = 1^3 + 2^3$$
$$(1 + 2 + 3)^2 = 1^3 + 2^3 + 3^3$$
$$(1 + 2 + 3 + 4)^2 = 1^3 + 2^3 + 3^3 + 4^3$$

(b)
$$1 = 1^3$$
$$3 + 5 = 2^3$$
$$7 + 9 + 11 = 3^3$$
$$13 + 15 + 17 + 19 = 4^3$$

(c)
$$1 = \frac{1 \cdot 2}{2}$$
$$1 + 2 = \frac{2 \cdot 3}{2}$$
$$1 + 2 + 3 = \frac{3 \cdot 4}{2}$$
$$1 + 2 + 3 + 4 = \frac{4 \cdot 5}{2}$$

(d) $12{,}345{,}679 \times 9 = 111{,}111{,}111$
$12{,}345{,}679 \times 18 = 222{,}222{,}222$
$12{,}345{,}679 \times 27 = 333{,}333{,}333$
$12{,}345{,}679 \times 36 = 444{,}444{,}444$
$12{,}345{,}679 \times 45 = 555{,}555{,}555$

> Notice that there is no 8 here.

Solution

(a) The left side of each equation is the square of the sum of the first n counting numbers, and the right side is the sum of their cubes. The next equation in the pattern would be

$$(1 + 2 + 3 + 4 + 5)^2 = 1^3 + 2^3 + 3^3 + 4^3 + 5^3.$$

Each side simplifies to 225, so the pattern is true for this equation.

(b) The left sides of the equations contain the sum of odd counting numbers, starting with the first (1) in the first equation, the second and third (3 and 5) in the second equation, the fourth, fifth, and sixth (7, 9, and 11) in the third equation, and so on. Each right side contains the cube (third power) of the number of terms on the left side. Following this pattern, the next equation would be

$$21 + 23 + 25 + 27 + 29 = 5^3,$$

which can be verified by computation.

(c) The left side of each equation gives the indicated sum of the first n counting numbers, and the right side is always of the form

$$\frac{n(n + 1)}{2}.$$

For the pattern to continue, the next equation would be

$$1 + 2 + 3 + 4 + 5 = \frac{5 \cdot 6}{2}.$$

Because each side simplifies to 15, the pattern is true for this equation.

(d) In each case, the first factor on the left is 12,345,679 and the second factor is a multiple of 9 (that is, 9, 18, 27, 36, 45). The right side consists of a nine-digit number, all digits of which are the same (that is, 1, 2, 3, 4, 5). For the pattern to continue, the next equation would be as follows.

$$12{,}345{,}679 \times 54 = 666{,}666{,}666$$

Verify that this is a true statement.

The patterns established in **Examples 3(a) and 3(c)** can be written as follows.

SPECIAL SUM FORMULAS

For any counting number n, the following are true.

$$(1 + 2 + 3 + \cdots + n)^2 = 1^3 + 2^3 + 3^3 + \cdots + n^3$$

$$1 + 2 + 3 + \cdots + n = \frac{n(n + 1)}{2}$$

We can provide a general deductive argument showing how the second equation is obtained.

Let S represent the sum $1 + 2 + 3 + \cdots + n$. This sum can also be written as $S = n + (n - 1) + (n - 2) + \cdots + 1$. Write these two equations as follows.

$$
\begin{array}{l}
S = 1 \qquad\; + 2 \qquad + 3 \qquad\; + \cdots + n \\
\underline{S = n \qquad\; + (n - 1) + (n - 2) + \cdots + 1} \\
2S = (n + 1) + (n + 1) + (n + 1) + \cdots + (n + 1) \quad \text{Add the corresponding sides.}
\end{array}
$$

$2S = n(n + 1)$ There are n terms of $n + 1$.

$S = \dfrac{n(n + 1)}{2}$ Divide both sides by 2.

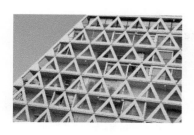

Figurate Numbers

Pythagoras and his Pythagorean brotherhood studied numbers of geometric arrangements of points, such as **triangular numbers, square numbers,** and **pentagonal numbers. Figure 4** illustrates the first few of each of these types of numbers.

The **figurate numbers** possess numerous interesting patterns. For example, every square number greater than 1 is the sum of two consecutive triangular numbers. ($9 = 3 + 6, 25 = 10 + 15$, and so on.)

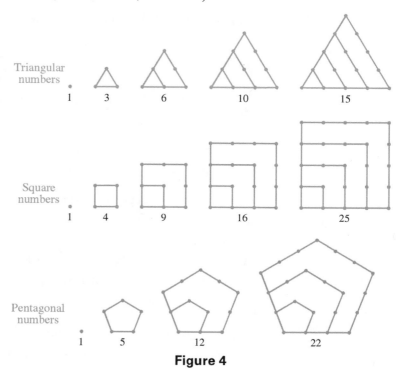

Figure 4

Every pentagonal number can be represented as the sum of a square number and a triangular number. (For example, $5 = 4 + 1$ and $12 = 9 + 3$.) Many other such relationships exist.

In the expression T_n, n is called a **subscript.** T_n is read "**T sub n,**" and it represents the triangular number in the nth position in the sequence. For example,

$$T_1 = 1, \quad T_2 = 3, \quad T_3 = 6, \quad \text{and} \quad T_4 = 10.$$

S_n and P_n represent the nth square and pentagonal numbers, respectively.

FORMULAS FOR TRIANGULAR, SQUARE, AND PENTAGONAL NUMBERS

For any natural number n, the following are true.

The nth triangular number is given by $T_n = \dfrac{n(n + 1)}{2}$.

The nth square number is given by $S_n = n^2$.

The nth pentagonal number is given by $P_n = \dfrac{n(3n - 1)}{2}$.

EXAMPLE 4 Using the Formulas for Figurate Numbers

Use the formulas to find each of the following.

(a) seventh triangular number   **(b)** twelfth square number

(c) sixth pentagonal number

Solution

(a) $T_7 = \dfrac{n(n + 1)}{2} = \dfrac{7(7 + 1)}{2} = \dfrac{7(8)}{2} = \dfrac{56}{2} = 28$ Formula for a triangular number, with $n = 7$

(b) $S_{12} = n^2 = 12^2 = 144$ Formula for a square number, with $n = 12$

$12^2 = 12 \cdot 12$

Inside the brackets, multiply first and then subtract.

(c) $P_6 = \dfrac{n(3n - 1)}{2} = \dfrac{6[3(6) - 1]}{2} = \dfrac{6(18 - 1)}{2} = \dfrac{6(17)}{2} = 51$ ∎

EXAMPLE 5 Illustrating a Figurate Number Relationship

Show that the sixth pentagonal number is equal to the sum of 6 and 3 times the fifth triangular number.

Solution

From **Example 4(c),** $P_6 = 51$. The fifth triangular number is 15. Thus,

$$51 = 6 + 3(15) = 6 + 45 = 51.$$ ∎

The general relationship examined in **Example 5** can be written as follows.

$$P_n = n + 3 \cdot T_{n-1} \quad (n \geq 2)$$

EXAMPLE 6 Predicting the Value of a Pentagonal Number

The first five pentagonal numbers are 1, 5, 12, 22, 35. Use the method of successive differences to predict the sixth pentagonal number.

Solution

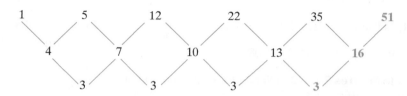

After the second line of successive differences, we work backward to find that the sixth pentagonal number is 51, which was also found in **Example 4(c).** ■

FOR FURTHER THOUGHT

Kaprekar Constants

Take any four-digit number whose digits are all different. Arrange the digits in decreasing order, and then arrange them in increasing order. Now subtract. Repeat the process, called the *Kaprekar routine,* until the same result appears.

For example, suppose that we choose a number whose digits are 1, 5, 7, and 9, such as 1579.

Note that we have obtained the number 6174, and the process will lead to 6174 again. The number 6174 is called a **Kaprekar constant**. This number 6174 will always be generated eventually if this process is applied to such a four-digit number.

For Group or Individual Investigation

1. Apply the process of Kaprekar to a four-digit number of your choice, in which the digits are all different. How many steps did it take for you to arrive at 6174?

2. See **Exercises 77 and 78** in the exercise set that follows.

9751	8721	7443	9963	6642	7641
−1579	−1278	−3447	−3699	−2466	−1467
8172	7443	3996	6264	4176	6174

1.2 EXERCISES

For each sequence, determine if it is an arithmetic *sequence, a* geometric *sequence, or* neither. *If it is either arithmetic or geometric, give the next term in the sequence.*

1. 6, 16, 26, 36, 46, . . .

2. 8, 16, 24, 32, 40, . . .

3. 5, 15, 45, 135, 405, . . .

4. 2, 12, 72, 432, 2592, . . .

5. 1, 8, 27, 81, 243, . . .

6. 2, 8, 18, 32, 50, . . .

7. 256, 128, 64, 32, 16, . . .

8. 4096, 1024, 256, 64, 16, . . .

9. 1, 3, 4, 7, 11, . . .

10. 0, 1, 1, 2, 3, . . .

11. 12, 14, 16, 18, 20, . . .

12. 10, 50, 90, 130, 170, . . .

Use the method of successive differences to determine the next number in each sequence.

13. 1, 4, 11, 22, 37, 56, . . .

14. 3, 14, 31, 54, 83, 118, . . .

15. 6, 20, 50, 102, 182, 296, . . .

16. 1, 11, 35, 79, 149, 251, . . .

17. 0, 12, 72, 240, 600, 1260, 2352, . . .

18. 2, 57, 220, 575, 1230, 2317, . . .

19. 5, 34, 243, 1022, 3121, 7770, 16799, . . .

20. 3, 19, 165, 771, 2503, 6483, 14409, . . .

21. Refer to **Figures 2 and 3** in **Section 1.1.** The method of successive differences can be applied to the sequence of interior regions,

$$1, 2, 4, 8, 16, 31,$$

to find the number of regions determined by seven points on the circle. What is the next term in this sequence? How many regions would be determined by eight points? Verify this using the formula given at the end of that section.

22. The 1952 film *Hans Christian Andersen* stars Danny Kaye as the Danish writer of fairy tales. In a scene outside a schoolhouse window, Kaye sings a song to an inchworm. *Inchworm* was written for the film by the composer Frank Loesser and has been recorded by many artists, including Paul McCartney and Kenny Loggins. It was once featured on an episode of *The Muppets* and sung by Charles Aznavour.

As Kaye sings the song, the children in the school room are heard chanting addition facts: $2 + 2 = 4$, $4 + 4 = 8$, $8 + 8 = 16$, and so on.

(a) Use patterns to state the next addition fact (as heard in the movie).

(b) If the children were to extend their facts to the next four in the pattern, what would those facts be?

In Exercises 23–32, several equations are given illustrating a suspected number pattern. Determine what the next equation would be, and verify that it is indeed a true statement.

23. $(1 \times 9) - 1 = 8$
$(21 \times 9) - 1 = 188$
$(321 \times 9) - 1 = 2888$

24. $(1 \times 8) + 1 = 9$
$(12 \times 8) + 2 = 98$
$(123 \times 8) + 3 = 987$

25. $999,999 \times 2 = 1,999,998$
$999,999 \times 3 = 2,999,997$

26. $101 \times 101 = 10,201$
$10,101 \times 10,101 = 102,030,201$

27. $3^2 - 1^2 = 2^3$
$6^2 - 3^2 = 3^3$
$10^2 - 6^2 = 4^3$
$15^2 - 10^2 = 5^3$

28. $1 = 1^2$
$1 + 2 + 1 = 2^2$
$1 + 2 + 3 + 2 + 1 = 3^2$
$1 + 2 + 3 + 4 + 3 + 2 + 1 = 4^2$

29. $2^2 - 1^2 = 2 + 1$
$3^2 - 2^2 = 3 + 2$
$4^2 - 3^2 = 4 + 3$

30. $1^2 + 1 = 2^2 - 2$
$2^2 + 2 = 3^2 - 3$
$3^2 + 3 = 4^2 - 4$

31. $1 = 1 \times 1$
$1 + 5 = 2 \times 3$
$1 + 5 + 9 = 3 \times 5$

32. $1 + 2 = 3$
$4 + 5 + 6 = 7 + 8$
$9 + 10 + 11 + 12 = 13 + 14 + 15$

Use the formula $S = \dfrac{n(n+1)}{2}$ to find each sum.

33. $1 + 2 + 3 + \cdots + 300$

34. $1 + 2 + 3 + \cdots + 500$

35. $1 + 2 + 3 + \cdots + 675$

36. $1 + 2 + 3 + \cdots + 825$

Use the formula $S = n^2$ to find each sum. (Hint: To find n, add 1 to the last term and divide by 2.)

37. $1 + 3 + 5 + \cdots + 101$

38. $1 + 3 + 5 + \cdots + 49$

39. $1 + 3 + 5 + \cdots + 999$

40. $1 + 3 + 5 + \cdots + 301$

41. Use the formula for finding the sum

$$1 + 2 + 3 + \cdots + n$$

to discover a formula for finding the sum

$$2 + 4 + 6 + \cdots + 2n.$$

42. State in your own words the following formula discussed in this section.

$$(1 + 2 + 3 + \cdots + n)^2 = 1^3 + 2^3 + 3^3 + \cdots + n^3$$

43. Explain how the following diagram geometrically illustrates the formula $1 + 3 + 5 + 7 + 9 = 5^2$.

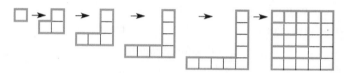

44. Explain how the following diagram geometrically illustrates the formula $1 + 2 + 3 + 4 = \frac{4 \times 5}{2}$.

45. Use patterns to complete the table below.

Figurate Number	1st	2nd	3rd	4th	5th	6th	7th	8th
Triangular	1	3	6	10	15	21		
Square	1	4	9	16	25			
Pentagonal	1	5	12	22				
Hexagonal	1	6	15					
Heptagonal	1	7						
Octagonal	1							

46. The first five triangular, square, and pentagonal numbers can be obtained using sums of terms of sequences as shown below.

Triangular	Square	Pentagonal
$1 = 1$	$1 = 1$	$1 = 1$
$3 = 1 + 2$	$4 = 1 + 3$	$5 = 1 + 4$
$6 = 1 + 2 + 3$	$9 = 1 + 3 + 5$	$12 = 1 + 4 + 7$
$10 = 1 + 2 + 3 + 4$	$16 = 1 + 3 + 5 + 7$	$22 = 1 + 4 + 7 + 10$
$15 = 1 + 2 + 3 + 4 + 5$	$25 = 1 + 3 + 5 + 7 + 9$	$35 = 1 + 4 + 7 + 10 + 13$

Notice the successive differences of the added terms on the right sides of the equations. The next type of figurate number is the **hexagonal** number. (A hexagon has six sides.) Use the patterns above to predict the first five hexagonal numbers.

47. Eight times any triangular number, plus 1, is a square number. Show that this is true for the first four triangular numbers.

48. Divide the first triangular number by 3 and record the remainder. Divide the second triangular number by 3 and record the remainder. Repeat this procedure several more times. Do you notice a pattern?

49. Repeat **Exercise 48,** but instead use square numbers and divide by 4. What pattern is determined?

50. Exercises 48 and 49 are specific cases of the following: When the numbers in the sequence of n-agonal numbers are divided by n, the sequence of remainders obtained is a repeating sequence. Verify this for $n = 5$ and $n = 6$.

51. Every square number can be written as the sum of two triangular numbers. For example, $16 = 6 + 10$. This can be represented geometrically by dividing a square array of dots with a line as shown.

The triangular arrangement above the line represents 6, the one below the line represents 10, and the whole arrangement represents 16. Show how the square numbers 25 and 36 may likewise be geometrically represented as the sum of two triangular numbers.

52. A fraction is in *lowest terms* if the greatest common factor of its numerator and its denominator is 1. For example, $\frac{3}{8}$ is in lowest terms, but $\frac{4}{12}$ is not.

(a) For $n = 2$ to $n = 8$, form the fractions

$$\frac{n\text{th square number}}{(n+1)\text{st square number}}.$$

(b) Repeat part (a) with triangular numbers.

(c) Use inductive reasoning to make a conjecture based on your results from parts (a) and (b), observing whether the fractions are in lowest terms.

In addition to the formulas for T_n, S_n, and P_n, the following formulas are true for **hexagonal** numbers (H), **heptagonal** numbers (Hp), and **octagonal** numbers (O):

$$H_n = \frac{n(4n-2)}{2}, \quad Hp_n = \frac{n(5n-3)}{2}, \quad O_n = \frac{n(6n-4)}{2}.$$

Use these formulas to find each of the following.

53. the sixteenth square number

54. the eleventh triangular number

55. the ninth pentagonal number

56. the seventh hexagonal number

57. the tenth heptagonal number

58. the twelfth octagonal number

59. Observe the formulas given for H_n, Hp_n, and O_n, and use patterns and inductive reasoning to predict the formula for N_n, the nth **nonagonal** number. (A nonagon has nine sides.) Then use the fact that the sixth nonagonal number is 111 to further confirm your conjecture.

60. Use the result of **Exercise 59** to find the tenth nonagonal number.

Use inductive reasoning to answer each question.

61. If you add two consecutive triangular numbers, what kind of figurate number do you get?

62. If you add the squares of two consecutive triangular numbers, what kind of figurate number do you get?

63. Square a triangular number. Square the next triangular number. Subtract the smaller result from the larger. What kind of number do you get?

64. Choose a value of n greater than or equal to 2. Find T_{n-1}, multiply it by 3, and add n. What kind of figurate number do you get?

In an arithmetic sequence, the nth term a_n is given by the formula

$$a_n = a_1 + (n-1)d,$$

where a_1 is the first term and d is the common difference. Similarly, in a geometric sequence, the nth term is given by

$$a_n = a_1 \cdot r^{n-1}.$$

Here r is the common ratio. In Exercises 65–76, use these formulas to determine the indicated term in the given sequence.

65. The eleventh term of $2, 6, 10, 14, \ldots$

66. The sixteenth term of $5, 15, 25, 35, \ldots$

67. The 21st term of $19, 39, 59, 79, \ldots$

68. The 36th term of $8, 38, 68, 98, \ldots$

69. The 101st term of $\frac{1}{2}, 1, \frac{3}{2}, 2, \ldots$

70. The 151st term of $0.75, 1.50, 2.25, 3.00, \ldots$

71. The eleventh term of $2, 4, 8, 16, \ldots$

72. The ninth term of $1, 4, 16, 64, \ldots$

73. The 12th term of $1, \frac{1}{2}, \frac{1}{4}, \frac{1}{8}, \ldots$

74. The 10th term of $1, \frac{1}{3}, \frac{1}{9}, \frac{1}{27}, \ldots$

75. The 8th term of $40, 10, \frac{5}{2}, \frac{5}{8}, \ldots$

76. The 9th term of $10, 2, \frac{2}{5}, \frac{2}{25}, \ldots$

77. In the *For Further Thought* investigation of this section, we saw that the number 6174 is a Kaprekar constant. Use the procedure described there, starting with a three-digit number of your choice whose digits are all different. You should arrive at a particular three-digit number that has the same property described for 6174. What is this three-digit number?

78. Applying the Kaprekar routine to a five-digit number does not reach a single repeating result but instead reaches one of the following ten numbers and then cycles repeatedly through a subset of these ten numbers.

53955, 59994, 61974, 62964, 63954,

71973, 74943, 75933, 82962, 83952

(a) Start with the number 45986 and determine which one of the ten numbers above is reached first.

(b) Start with a five-digit number of your own, and determine which one of the ten numbers is eventually reached first.

*The mathematical array of numbers known as **Pascal's triangle** consists of rows of numbers, each of which contains one more entry than the previous row. The first six rows are shown here.*

Refer to this array to answer Exercises 79–82.

79. Each row begins and ends with a 1. Discover a method whereby the other entries in a row can be determined from the entries in the row immediately above it. (*Hint:* See the entries in color above.) Find the next three rows of the triangle, and prepare a copy of the first nine rows for later reference.

80. Find the sum of the entries in each of the first eight rows. What is the pattern that emerges? Predict the sum of the entries in the ninth row, and confirm your prediction.

81. The first six rows of the triangle are arranged "flush left" here.

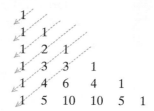

Add along the blue diagonal lines. Write these sums in order from left to right. What sequence is this?

82. Find the values of the first four powers of the number 11, starting with 11^0, which by definition is equal to 1. Predict what the next power of 11 will equal by observing the rows of Pascal's triangle. Confirm your prediction by actual computation.

1.3	**STRATEGIES FOR PROBLEM SOLVING**

OBJECTIVES

1 Know George Polya's four-step method of problem solving.

2 Be able to apply various strategies for solving problems.

A General Problem-Solving Method

In the first two sections of this chapter we stressed the importance of pattern recognition and the use of inductive reasoning in solving problems. Probably the most famous study of problem-solving techniques was developed by George Polya (1888–1985), among whose many publications was the modern classic *How to Solve It*. In this book, Polya proposed a four-step method for problem solving.

POLYA'S FOUR-STEP METHOD FOR PROBLEM SOLVING

Step 1 **Understand the problem.** You cannot solve a problem if you do not understand what you are asked to find. The problem must be read and analyzed carefully. You may need to read it several times. After you have done so, ask yourself, *"What must I find?"*

Step 2 **Devise a plan.** There are many ways to attack a problem. Decide what plan is appropriate for the particular problem you are solving.

Step 3 **Carry out the plan.** Once you know how to approach the problem, carry out your plan. You may run into "dead ends" and unforeseen roadblocks, but be persistent.

Step 4 **Look back and check.** Check your answer to see that it is reasonable. *Does it satisfy the conditions of the problem? Have you answered all the questions the problem asks? Can you solve the problem a different way and come up with the same answer?*

In Step 2 of Polya's problem-solving method, we are told to devise a plan. Here are some strategies that may prove useful.

George Polya, author of the classic *How to Solve It*, died at the age of 97 on September 7, 1985. A native of Budapest, Hungary, he was once asked why there were so many good mathematicians to come out of Hungary at the turn of the century. He theorized that it was because mathematics is the cheapest science. It does not require any expensive equipment, only pencil and paper.

Polya authored or coauthored more than 250 papers in many languages, wrote a number of books, and was a brilliant lecturer and teacher. Yet, interestingly enough, he never learned to drive a car.

Problem-Solving Strategies

- Make a table or a chart.
- Look for a pattern.
- Solve a similar, simpler problem.
- Draw a sketch.
- Use inductive reasoning.
- Write an equation and solve it.

- If a formula applies, use it.
- Work backward.
- Guess and check.
- Use trial and error.
- Use common sense.
- Look for a "catch" if an answer seems too obvious or impossible.

Using a Table or Chart

EXAMPLE 1 **Solving Fibonacci's Rabbit Problem**

A man put a pair of rabbits in a cage. During the first month the rabbits produced no offspring but each month thereafter produced one new pair of rabbits. If each new pair thus produced reproduces in the same manner, how many pairs of rabbits will there be at the end of 1 year? (This problem is a famous one in the history of mathematics and first appeared in *Liber Abaci*, a book written by the Italian mathematician Leonardo Pisano (also known as Fibonacci) in the year 1202.)

Solution

Step 1 **Understand the problem.** We can reword the problem as follows:

> *How many pairs of rabbits will the man have at the end of one year if he starts with one pair, and they reproduce this way: During the first month of life, each pair produces no new rabbits, but each month thereafter each pair produces one new pair?*

Step 2 **Devise a plan.** Because there is a definite pattern to how the rabbits will reproduce, we can construct **Table 2.**

Table 2

Month	Number of Pairs at Start	Number of New Pairs Produced	Number of Pairs at End of Month
1st			
2nd			
3rd			
4th			
5th			
6th			
7th			
8th			
9th			
10th			
11th			
12th			

The answer will go here.

Fibonacci (1170–1250) discovered the sequence named after him in a problem on rabbits. Fibonacci ("son of Bonaccio") is one of several names for Leonardo of Pisa. His father managed a warehouse in present-day Bougie (or Bejaia), in Algeria. Thus it was that Leonardo Pisano studied with a Moorish teacher and learned the "Indian" numbers that the Moors and other Moslems brought with them in their westward drive.

Fibonacci wrote books on algebra, geometry, and trigonometry.

On January 23, 2005, the CBS television network presented the first episode of *NUMB3RS*, a show focusing on how mathematics is used in solving crimes. David Krumholtz plays Charlie Eppes, a brilliant mathematician who assists his FBI agent brother (Rob Morrow).

In the first-season episode "Sabotage" (2/25/2005), one of the agents admits that she was not a good math student, and Charlie uses the **Fibonacci sequence** and its relationship to nature to enlighten her.

The sequence shown in color in **Table 3** is the Fibonacci sequence, mentioned in **Example 2(b)** of **Section 1.1.**

Step 3 **Carry out the plan.** At the start of the first month, there is only one pair of rabbits. No new pairs are produced during the first month, so there is $1 + 0 = 1$ pair present at the end of the first month. This pattern continues. In **Table 3,** we add the number in the first column of numbers to the number in the second column to get the number in the third.

Table 3

Month	Number of Pairs at Start	+	Number of New Pairs Produced	=	Number of Pairs at End of Month	
1st	1		0		1	$1 + 0 = 1$
2nd	1		1		2	$1 + 1 = 2$
3rd	2		1		3	$2 + 1 = 3$
4th	3		2		5	•
5th	5		3		8	•
6th	8		5		13	•
7th	13		8		21	•
8th	21		13		34	•
9th	34		21		55	•
10th	55		34		89	•
11th	89		55		144	•
12th	144		89		233	$144 + 89 = 233$

The answer is the final entry.

There will be 233 pairs of rabbits at the end of one year.

Step 4 **Look back and check.** Go back and make sure that we have interpreted the problem correctly. Double-check the arithmetic. We have answered the question posed by the problem, so the problem is solved. ■

Working Backward

EXAMPLE 2 **Determining a Wager at the Track**

Ronnie goes to the racetrack with his buddies on a weekly basis. One week he tripled his money, but then lost $12. He took his money back the next week, doubled it, but then lost $40. The following week he tried again, taking his money back with him. He quadrupled it, and then played well enough to take that much home, a total of $224. How much did he start with the first week?

Solution

This problem asks us to find Ronnie's starting amount. Since we know his final amount, the method of working backward can be applied.

Because his final amount was $224 and this represents four times the amount he started with on the third week, we *divide* $224 by 4 to find that he started the third week with $56. Before he lost $40 the second week, he had this $56 plus the $40 he lost, giving him $96.

Augustus De Morgan was an English mathematician and philosopher, who served as professor at the University of London. He wrote numerous books, one of which was *A Budget of Paradoxes*. His work in set theory and logic led to laws that bear his name and are covered in other chapters.

The $96 represented double what he started with, so he started with $96 *divided by* 2, or $48, the second week. Repeating this process once more for the first week, before his $12 loss he had

$$\$48 + \$12 = \$60,$$

which represents triple what he started with. Therefore, he started with

$$\$60 \div 3 = \$20. \quad \text{Answer}$$

To check, observe the following equations that depict winnings and losses.

> ***First week:*** $(3 \times \$20) - \$12 = \$60 - \$12 = \$48$
> ***Second week:*** $(2 \times \$48) - \$40 = \$96 - \$40 = \$56$
> ***Third week:*** $(4 \times \$56) = \$224$ His final amount ∎

Using Trial and Error

Recall that $5^2 = 5 \cdot 5 = 25$. That is, 5 squared is 25. Thus, 25 is called a **perfect square,** a term that we use in **Example 3.**

$$1, \quad 4, \quad 9, \quad 16, \quad 25, \quad 36, \quad \text{and so on} \quad \text{Perfect squares}$$

EXAMPLE 3 **Finding Augustus De Morgan's Birth Year**

The mathematician Augustus De Morgan lived in the nineteenth century. He made the following statement: "I was x years old in the year x^2." In what year was he born?

Solution

We must find the year of De Morgan's birth. The problem tells us that he lived in the nineteenth century, which is another way of saying that he lived during the 1800s. One year of his life was a perfect square, so we must find a number between 1800 and 1900 that is a perfect square. Use trial and error.

$$42^2 = 42 \cdot 42 = 1764$$
$$43^2 = 43 \cdot 43 = 1849 \quad \boxed{\text{1849 is between 1800 and 1900.}}$$
$$44^2 = 44 \cdot 44 = 1936$$

The only natural number whose square is between 1800 and 1900 is 43, because $43^2 = 1849$. Therefore, De Morgan was 43 years old in 1849. The final step in solving the problem is to subtract 43 from 1849 to find the year of his birth.

$$1849 - 43 = 1806 \quad \boxed{\text{He was born in 1806.}}$$

To check this answer, look up De Morgan's birth date in a book dealing with mathematics history, such as *An Introduction to the History of Mathematics*, Sixth Edition, by Howard W. Eves. ∎

Guessing and Checking

As mentioned above, $5^2 = 25$. The inverse procedure for squaring a number is called taking the **square root.** We indicate the positive square root using a **radical symbol** $\sqrt{}$. Thus, $\sqrt{25} = 5$. Also,

$$\sqrt{4} = 2, \quad \sqrt{9} = 3, \quad \sqrt{16} = 4, \quad \text{and so on.} \quad \text{Square roots}$$

The next problem deals with a square root and dates back to Hindu mathematics, circa 850.

EXAMPLE 4 Finding the Number of Camels

One-fourth of a herd of camels was seen in the forest. Twice the square root of that herd had gone to the mountain slopes, and 3 times 5 camels remained on the riverbank. What is the numerical measure of that herd of camels?

Solution

The numerical measure of a herd of camels must be a counting number. Because the problem mentions "one-fourth of a herd" and "the square root of that herd," the number of camels must be both a multiple of 4 and a perfect square, so that only whole numbers are used. The least counting number that satisfies both conditions is 4.

We write an equation where x represents the numerical measure of the herd, and then substitute 4 for x to see if it is a solution.

One-fourth of the herd	+	Twice the square root of that herd	+	3 times 5 camels	=	The numerical measure of the herd.
$\frac{1}{4}x$	+	$2\sqrt{x}$	+	$3 \cdot 5$	=	x

$$\frac{1}{4}(4) + 2\sqrt{4} + 3 \cdot 5 \stackrel{?}{=} 4 \qquad \text{Let } x = 4.$$

$$1 + 4 + 15 \stackrel{?}{=} 4 \qquad \sqrt{4} = 2$$

$$20 \neq 4$$

Because 4 is not the solution, try **16**, the next perfect square that is a multiple of 4.

$$\frac{1}{4}(16) + 2\sqrt{16} + 3 \cdot 5 \stackrel{?}{=} 16 \qquad \text{Let } x = 16.$$

$$4 + 8 + 15 \stackrel{?}{=} 16 \qquad \sqrt{16} = 4$$

$$27 \neq 16$$

Because 16 is not a solution, try **36**.

$$\frac{1}{4}(36) + 2\sqrt{36} + 3 \cdot 5 \stackrel{?}{=} 36 \qquad \text{Let } x = 36.$$

$$9 + 12 + 15 \stackrel{?}{=} 36 \qquad \sqrt{36} = 6$$

$$36 = 36$$

Thus, 36 is the numerical measure of the herd.

Check: "One-fourth of 36, plus twice the square root of 36, plus 3 times 5" gives 9 plus 12 plus 15, which equals 36. ∎

Considering a Similar, Simpler Problem

EXAMPLE 5 Finding the Units Digit of a Power

The digit farthest to the right in a counting number is called the *ones* or *units* digit, because it tells how many ones are contained in the number when grouping by tens is considered. What is the ones (or units) digit in 2^{4000}?

Solution

Recall that 2^{4000} means that 2 is used as a factor 4000 times.

$$2^{4000} = \underbrace{2 \times 2 \times 2 \times \cdots \times 2}_{\text{4000 factors}}$$

Solution to the Jugs-of-Water Riddle
This is one way to do it: With both jugs empty, fill the 3-gallon jug and pour its contents into the 5-gallon jug. Then fill the 3-gallon jug again, and pour it into the 5-gallon jug until the latter is filled. There is now $(3 + 3) - 5 = 1$ gallon in the 3-gallon jug. Empty the 5-gallon jug, and pour the 1 gallon of water from the 3-gallon jug into the 5-gallon jug. Finally, fill the 3-gallon jug and pour all of it into the 5-gallon jug, resulting in $1 + 3 = 4$ gallons in the 5-gallon jug.

(*Note:* There is another way to solve this problem. See if you can discover the alternative solution.)

To answer the question, we examine some smaller powers of 2 and then look for a pattern. We start with the exponent 1 and look at the first twelve powers of 2.

$$2^1 = 2 \qquad 2^5 = 32 \qquad 2^9 = 512$$
$$2^2 = 4 \qquad 2^6 = 64 \qquad 2^{10} = 1024$$
$$2^3 = 8 \qquad 2^7 = 128 \qquad 2^{11} = 2048$$
$$2^4 = 16 \qquad 2^8 = 256 \qquad 2^{12} = 4096$$

Notice that in any one of the four rows above, the ones digit is the same all the way across the row. The final row, which contains the exponents 4, 8, and 12, has the ones digit 6. Each of these exponents is divisible by 4, and because 4000 is divisible by 4, we can use inductive reasoning to predict that the units digit in 2^{4000} is 6.

(*Note:* The units digit for any other power can be found if we divide the exponent by 4 and consider the remainder. Then compare the result to the list of powers above. For example, to find the units digit of 2^{543}, divide 543 by 4 to get a quotient of 135 and a remainder of 3. The units digit is the same as that of 2^3, which is 8.) ■

Drawing a Sketch

EXAMPLE 6 **Connecting the Dots**

An array of nine dots is arranged in a 3×3 square, as shown in **Figure 5.** Is it possible to join the dots with exactly four straight line segments if you are not allowed to pick up your pencil from the paper and may not trace over a segment that has already been drawn? If so, show how.

Solution

Figure 6 shows three attempts. In each case, something is wrong. In the first sketch, one dot is not joined. In the second, the figure cannot be drawn without picking up your pencil from the paper or tracing over a line that has already been drawn. In the third figure, all dots have been joined, but you have used five line segments as well as retraced over the figure.

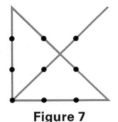

Figure 5

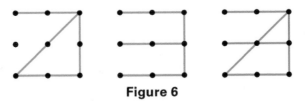

Figure 6

The conditions of the problem can be satisfied, as shown in **Figure 7.** We "went outside of the box," which was not prohibited by the conditions of the problem. This is an example of creative thinking—we used a strategy that often is not considered at first. ■

Figure 7

Using Common Sense

Problem-Solving Strategies

Some problems involve a "catch." They seem too easy or perhaps impossible at first because we tend to overlook an obvious situation. Look carefully at the use of language in such problems. And, of course, never forget to use common sense.

EXAMPLE 7 Determining Coin Denominations

Two currently minted United States coins together have a total value of $1.05. One is not a dollar. What are the two coins?

Solution

Our initial reaction might be, "The only way to have two such coins with a total of $1.05 is to have a nickel and a dollar, but the problem says that one of them is not a dollar." This statement is indeed true. What we must realize here is that the one that is not a dollar is the nickel, and the *other* coin is a dollar! So the two coins are a dollar and a nickel.

1.3 EXERCISES

One of the most popular features in the journal Mathematics Teacher, *published by the National Council of Teachers of Mathematics, is the monthly calendar. It provides an interesting, unusual, or challenging problem for each day of the month. Some of these exercises, and others later in this text, are chosen from these calendars (the day, month, and year of publication of each problem are indicated). The authors want to thank the many contributors for permission to use these problems.*

Use the various problem-solving strategies to solve each problem. In many cases there is more than one possible approach, so be creative.

1. **Broken Elevator** A man enters a building on the first floor and runs up to the third floor in 20 seconds. At this rate, how many seconds would it take for the man to run from the first floor up to the sixth floor? (October 3, 2010)

2. **Saving Her Dollars** Every day Sally saved a penny, a dime, and a quarter. What is the least number of days required for her to save an amount equal to an integral (counting) number of dollars? (January 11, 2012)

3. **Do You Have a Match?** Move 4 of the matches in the figure to create exactly 3 equilateral triangles. (An *equilateral triangle* has all three sides the same length.) (February 20, 2011)

4. **Sudoku** Sudoku is an $n \times n$ puzzle that requires the solver to fill in all the squares using the integers 1 through n. Each row, column, and subrectangle contains exactly one of each number. Complete the $n \times n$ puzzle. (June 25, 2012)

			4
2			
	1		
		1	

5. **Break This Code** Each letter of the alphabet is assigned an integer, starting with A = 0, B = 1, and so on. The numbers repeat after every seven letters, so that G = 6, H = 0, and I = 1, continuing on to Z. What two-letter word is represented by the digits 16? (October 3, 2011)

6. **A Real Problem** We are given the following sequence:

PROBLEMSOLVINGPROBLEMSOLVINGPROB ...

If the pattern continues, what letter will be in the 2012th position? (November 1, 2012)

7. **How Old Is Mommy?** A mother has two children whose ages differ by 5 years. The sum of the squares of their ages is 97. The square of the mother's age can be found by writing the squares of the children's ages one after the other as a four-digit number. How old is the mother? (March 9, 2012)

8. **An Alarming Situation** You have three alarms in your room. Your cell phone alarm is set to ring every 30 minutes, your computer alarm is set to ring every 20 minutes, and your clock alarm is set to ring every 45 minutes. If all three alarms go off simultaneously at 12:34 p.m., when is the next time that they will go off simultaneously? (November 2, 2012)

9. Laundry Day Every Monday evening, a mathematics teacher stops by the dry cleaners, drops off the shirts that he wore for the week, and picks up his previous week's load. If he wears a clean shirt every day, including Saturday and Sunday, what is the minimum number of shirts that he can own? (April 1, 2012)

10. Pick an Envelope Three envelopes contain a total of six bills. One envelope contains two $10 bills, one contains two $20 bills, and the third contains one $10 and one $20 bill. A label on each envelope indicates the sum of money in one of the other envelopes. It is possible to select one envelope, see one bill in that envelope, and then state the contents of all of the envelopes. Which envelope should you choose? (May 1, 2012)

11. Class Members A classroom contains an equal number of boys and girls. If 8 girls leave, twice as many boys as girls remain. What was the original number of students present? (May 24, 2008)

12. Give Me a Digit Given a two-digit number, make a three-digit number by putting a 6 as the rightmost digit. Then add 6 to the resulting three-digit number and remove the rightmost digit to obtain another two-digit number. If the result is 76, what is the original two-digit number? (October 18, 2009)

13. Missing Digit Look for a pattern and find the missing digit x.

$$
\begin{array}{cccc}
3 & 2 & 4 & 8 \\
7 & 2 & 1 & 3 \\
8 & 4 & x & 5 \\
4 & 3 & 6 & 9
\end{array}
$$

(February 14, 2009)

14. Abundancy An integer $n > 1$ is **abundant** if the sum of its proper divisors (positive integer divisors smaller than n) is greater than n. Find the smallest abundant integer. (November 27, 2009)

15. Cross-Country Competition The schools in an athletic conference compete in a cross-country meet to which each school sends three participants. Erin, Katelyn, and Iliana are the three representatives from one school. Erin finished the race in the middle position; Katelyn finished after Erin, in the 19th position; and Iliana finished 28th. How many schools took part in the race? (May 27, 2008)

16. Gone Fishing Four friends go fishing one day and bring home a total of 11 fish. If each person caught at least 1 fish, then which of the following *must* be true?

A. One person caught exactly 2 fish.

B. One person caught exactly 3 fish.

C. One person caught fewer than 3 fish.

D. One person caught more than 3 fish.

E. Two people each caught more than 1 fish.

(May 24, 2008)

17. Cutting a Square in Half In how many ways can a single straight line cut a square in half? (October 2, 2008)

18. You Lie! Max, Sam, and Brett were playing basketball. One of them broke a window, and the other two saw him break it. Max said, "I am innocent." Sam said, "Max and I are both innocent." Brett said, "Max and Sam are both innocent." If only one of them is telling the truth, who broke the window? (September 21, 2008)

19. Bookworm Snack A 26-volume encyclopedia (one for each letter) is placed on a bookshelf in alphabetical order from left to right. Each volume is 2 inches thick, including the front and back covers. Each cover is $\frac{1}{4}$ inch thick. A bookworm eats straight through the encyclopedia, beginning inside the front cover of volume A and ending after eating through the back cover of volume Z. How many inches of book did the bookworm eat? (November 12, 2008)

20. Pick a Card, Any Card Three face cards from an ordinary deck of playing cards lie facedown in a horizontal row and are arranged such that immediately to the right of a king is a queen or two queens, immediately to the left of a queen is a queen or two queens, immediately to the left of a heart is a spade or two spades, and immediately to the right of a spade is a spade or two spades. Name the three cards in order. (April 23, 2008)

21. Catwoman's Cats If you ask Batman's nemesis, Catwoman, how many cats she has, she answers with a riddle: "Five-sixths of my cats plus seven." How many cats does Catwoman have? (April 20, 2003)

22. *Pencil Collection*   Bob gave four-fifths of his pencils to Barbara, then he gave two-thirds of the remaining pencils to Bonnie. If he ended up with ten pencils for himself, with how many did he start? (October 12, 2003)

23. *Adding Gasoline*   The gasoline gauge on a van initially read $\frac{1}{8}$ full. When 15 gallons were added to the tank, the gauge read $\frac{3}{4}$ full. How many more gallons are needed to fill the tank? (November 25, 2004)

24. *Gasoline Tank Capacity*   When 6 gallons of gasoline are put into a car's tank, the indicator goes from $\frac{1}{4}$ of a tank to $\frac{5}{8}$. What is the total capacity of the gasoline tank? (February 21, 2004)

25. *Number Pattern*   What is the relationship between the rows of numbers?

$$18, \quad 38, \quad 24, \quad 46, \quad 42$$
$$8, \quad 24, \quad 8, \quad 24, \quad 8$$

(May 26, 2005)

26. *Locking Boxes*   You and I each have one lock and a corresponding key. I want to mail you a box with a ring in it, but any box that is not locked will be emptied before it reaches its recipient. How can I safely send you the ring? (Note that you and I each have keys to our own lock but not to the other lock.) (May 4, 2004)

27. *Number in a Sequence*   In the sequence 16, 80, 48, 64, A, B, C, D, each term beyond the second term is the arithmetic mean (average) of the two previous terms. What is the value of D? (April 26, 2004)

28. *Unknown Number*   Cindy was asked by her teacher to subtract 3 from a certain number and then divide the result by 9. Instead, she subtracted 9 and then divided the result by 3, giving an answer of 43. What would her answer have been if she had worked the problem correctly? (September 3, 2004)

29. *Unfolding and Folding a Box*   An unfolded box is shown below.

	2		
1	3	5	6
	4		

Which figure shows the box folded up? (November 7, 2001)

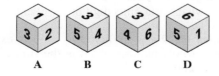

30. *Vertical Symmetry in States' Names*   (If a vertical line is drawn through the center of a figure, and the left and right sides are reflections of each other across this line, the figure is said to have vertical symmetry.) When spelled with all capital letters, each letter in HAWAII has vertical symmetry. Find the name of a state whose letters all have vertical and horizontal symmetry. (September 11, 2001)

31. *Labeling Boxes*   You are working in a store that has been very careless with the stock. Three boxes of socks are each incorrectly labeled. The labels say *red socks, green socks,* and *red and green socks.* How can you relabel the boxes correctly by taking only one sock out of one box, without looking inside the boxes? (October 22, 2001)

32. *Mr. Green's Age*   At his birthday party, Mr. Green would not directly tell how old he was. He said, "If you add the year of my birth to this year, subtract the year of my tenth birthday and the year of my fiftieth birthday, and then add my present age, the result is eighty." How old was Mr. Green? (December 14, 1997)

33. *Sum of Hidden Dots on Dice*   Three dice with faces numbered 1 through 6 are stacked as shown. Seven of the eighteen faces are visible, leaving eleven faces hidden on the back, on the bottom, and between dice. The total number of dots not visible in this view is _____ .

A. 21
B. 22
C. 31
D. 41
E. 53

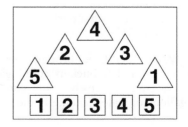

(September 17, 2001)

34. *Age of the Bus Driver*   Today is your first day driving a city bus. When you leave downtown, you have twenty-three passengers. At the first stop, three people exit and five people get on the bus. At the second stop, eleven people exit and eight people get on the bus. At the third stop, five people exit and ten people get on. How old is the bus driver? (April 1, 2002)

35. *Matching Triangles and Squares*   How can you connect each square with the triangle that has the same number? Lines cannot cross, enter a square or triangle, or go outside the diagram. (October 15, 1999)

36. *Forming Perfect Square Sums* How must one place the integers from 1 to 15 in each of the spaces below in such a way that no number is repeated and the sum of the numbers in any two consecutive spaces is a perfect square? (November 11, 2001)

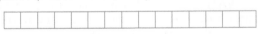

37. *Difference Triangle* Balls numbered 1 through 6 are arranged in a **difference triangle.** Note that in any row, the difference between the larger and the smaller of two successive balls is the number of the ball that appears below them. Arrange balls numbered 1 through 10 in a difference triangle. (May 6, 1998)

38. *Clock Face* By drawing two straight lines, divide the face of a clock into three regions such that the numbers in the regions have the same total. (October 28, 1998)

39. *Alphametric* If *a, b,* and *c* are digits for which

$$\begin{array}{r} 7\ a\ 2 \\ -4\ 8\ b \\ \hline c\ 7\ 3, \end{array}$$

then $a + b + c =$ _____.

A. 14 **B.** 15 **C.** 16 **D.** 17 **E.** 18

(September 22, 1999)

40. *Perfect Square* Only one of these numbers is a perfect square. Which one is it? (October 8, 1997)

    329476   389372   964328
        326047   724203

41. *Sleeping on the Way to Grandma's House* While traveling to his grandmother's for Christmas, George fell asleep halfway through the journey. When he awoke, he still had to travel half the distance that he had traveled while sleeping. For what part of the entire journey had he been asleep? (December 25, 1998)

42. *Buckets of Water* You have brought two unmarked buckets to a stream. The buckets hold 7 gallons and 3 gallons of water, respectively. How can you obtain exactly 5 gallons of water to take home? (October 19, 1997)

43. *Counting Puzzle (Rectangles)* How many rectangles are in the figure? (March 27, 1997)

44. *Digit Puzzle* Place each of the digits 1, 2, 3, 4, 5, 6, 7, and 8 in separate boxes so that boxes that share common corners do not contain successive digits. (November 29, 1997)

45. *Palindromic Number* (*Note*: A **palindromic number** is a number whose digits read the same left to right as right to left. For example, 383, 12321, and 9876789 are palindromic.) The odometer of the family car read 15951 when the driver noticed that the number was palindromic. "Curious," said the driver to herself. "It will be a long time before that happens again." But 2 hours later, the odometer showed a new palindromic number. (*Author's note:* Assume it was the next possible one.) How fast was the car driving in those 2 hours? (December 26, 1998)

46. *How Much Is That Doggie in the Window?* A man wishes to sell a puppy for $11. A customer who wants to buy it has only foreign currency. The exchange rate for the foreign currency is as follows: 11 round coins = $15, 11 square coins = $16, 11 triangular coins = $17. How many of each coin should the customer pay? (April 20, 2008)

47. *Final Digits of a Power of 7* What are the final two digits of 7^{1997}? (November 29, 1997)

48. *Units Digit of a Power of 3* If you raise 3 to the 324th power, what is the units digit of the result?

49. *Summing the Digits* When $10^{50} - 50$ is expressed as a single whole number, what is the sum of its digits? (April 7, 2008)

50. *Frog Climbing up a Well* A frog is at the bottom of a 20-foot well. Each day it crawls up 4 feet, but each night it slips back 3 feet. After how many days will the frog reach the top of the well?

51. *Units Digit of a Power of 7* What is the units digit in 7^{491}?

52. *Money Spent at a Bazaar* Christine bought a book for $10 and then spent half her remaining money on a train ticket. She then bought lunch for $4 and spent half her remaining money at a bazaar. She left the bazaar with $8. How much money did she start with?

53. *Going Postal* Joanie wants to mail a package that requires $1.53 in postage. If she has only 5-cent and 8-cent stamps, what is the smallest number of stamps she could use that would total exactly $1.53? (August 20, 2008)

54. *Counting Puzzle (Squares)* How many squares are in the figure?

55. *Matching Socks* A drawer contains 20 black socks and 20 white socks. If the light is off and you reach into the drawer to get your socks, what is the minimum number of socks you must pull out in order to be sure that you have a matching pair?

56. *Counting Puzzle (Triangles)* How many triangles are in the figure?

57. *Perfect Number* A **perfect number** is a counting number that is equal to the sum of all its counting number divisors except itself. For example, 28 is a perfect number because its divisors other than itself are 1, 2, 4, 7, and 14, and $1 + 2 + 4 + 7 + 14 = 28$. What is the least perfect number?

58. *Naming Children* Becky's mother has three daughters. She named her first daughter Penny and her second daughter Nichole. What did she name her third daughter?

59. *Growth of a Lily Pad* A lily pad grows so that each day it doubles its size. On the twentieth day of its life, it completely covers a pond. On what day was the pond half covered?

60. *Interesting Property of a Sentence* Comment on an interesting property of this sentence: "A man, a plan, a canal, Panama." (*Hint:* See **Exercise 45.**)

61. *High School Graduation Year of Author* One of the authors of this book graduated from high school in the year that satisfies these conditions: (1) The sum of the digits is 23; (2) The hundreds digit is 3 more than the tens digit; (3) No digit is an 8. In what year did he graduate?

62. *Where in the World Is Matt Lauer?* Matt Lauer is one of the hosts of the *Today* show on the NBC television network. From time to time he travels the world and is in a new location each day of the week, which is unknown even to his co-hosts back in the studio in New York. On one day, he decided to give them a riddle as a hint to where he would be on the following day. Here's the riddle:

This country is an ANAGRAM of a SYNONYM of a HOMOPHONE of an EVEN PRIME NUMBER.

In what country was Matt going to be the following day? (If you are unfamiliar with some of the terms in capital letters, look up their definitions.)

63. *Adam and Eve's Assets* Eve said to Adam, "If you give me one dollar, then we will have the same amount of money." Adam then replied, "Eve, if you give me one dollar, I will have double the amount of money you are left with." How much does each have?

64. *Missing Digits Puzzle* In the addition problem below, some digits are missing, as indicated by the blanks. If the problem is done correctly, what is the sum of the missing digits?

$$
\begin{array}{r}
\_\ 3\ 5 \\
8\ \_\ 6 \\
+\ 1\ 4\ \_ \\
\hline
\_\ 4\ 0\ 8
\end{array}
$$

65. *Missing Digits Puzzle* Fill in the blanks so that the multiplication problem below uses all digits $0, 1, 2, 3, \ldots, 9$ exactly once and is worked correctly.

$$
\begin{array}{r}
\_\ 0\ 2 \\
\times\ \ \ \ \ 3\ \_ \\
\hline
\_\ 5,\ \_\ \_\ \_
\end{array}
$$

66. *Magic Square*   A **magic square** is a square array of numbers that has the property that the sum of the numbers in any row, column, or diagonal is the same. Fill in the square below so that it becomes a magic square, and all digits 1, 2, 3, . . . , 9 are used exactly once.

6		8
	5	
		4

67. *Magic Square*   Refer to **Exercise 66.** Complete the magic square below so that all counting numbers 1, 2, 3, . . . , 16 are used exactly once, and the sum in each row, column, or diagonal is 34.

6			9
	15		14
11		10	
16		13	

68. *Decimal Digit*   What is the 100th digit in the decimal representation for $\frac{1}{7}$?

69. *Pitches in a Baseball Game*   What is the minimum number of pitches that a baseball player who pitches a complete game can make in a regulation 9-inning baseball game?

70. *Weighing Coins*   You have eight coins. Seven are genuine and one is a fake, which weighs a little less than the other seven. You have a balance scale, which you may use only three times. Tell how to locate the bad coin in three weighings. (Then show how to detect the bad coin in only *two* weighings.)

71. *Geometry Puzzle*   When the diagram shown is folded to form a cube, what letter is opposite the face marked Z?

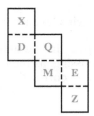

72. *Geometry Puzzle*   Draw the following figure without picking up your pencil from the paper and without tracing over a line you have already drawn.

73. *Geometry Puzzle*   Repeat **Exercise 72** for this figure.

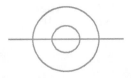

74. *Books on a Shelf*   Volumes 1 and 2 of *The Complete Works of Wally Smart* are standing in numerical order from left to right on your bookshelf. Volume 1 has 450 pages and Volume 2 has 475 pages. Excluding the covers, how many pages are between page 1 of Volume 1 and page 475 of Volume 2?

75. *Paying for a Mint*   Brian has an unlimited number of cents (pennies), nickels, and dimes. In how many different ways can he pay 15¢ for a chocolate mint? (For example, one way is 1 dime and 5 pennies.)

76. *Teenager's Age*   A teenager's age increased by 2 gives a perfect square. Her age decreased by 10 gives the square root of that perfect square. She is 5 years older than her brother. How old is her brother?

77. *Area and Perimeter*   Triangle ABC has sides 10, 24, and 26 cm long. A rectangle that has an area equal to that of the triangle is 3 cm wide. Find the perimeter of the rectangle. (November 13, 2008)

78. *Making Change*   In how many different ways can you make change for a half dollar using currently minted U.S. coins, if cents (pennies) are not allowed?

79. *Ages*   James, Dan, Jessica, and Cathy form a pair of married couples. Their ages are 36, 31, 30, and 29. Jessica is married to the oldest person in the group. James is older than Jessica but younger than Cathy. Who is married to whom, and what are their ages?

80. *Final Digit*   What is the last digit of $49{,}327^{1783}$? (April 11, 2009)

81. *Geometry Puzzle*   What is the maximum number of small squares in which we may place crosses ($\times$) and not have any row, column, or diagonal completely filled with crosses? Illustrate your answer.

82. *Making Change*   Webster has some pennies, dimes, and quarters in his pocket. When Josefa asks him for change for a dollar, Webster discovers that he cannot make the change exactly. What is the largest possible total value of the coins in his pocket? (October 5, 2009)

WHEN Will I Ever USE This ?

Suppose that you are an employee of a group home, and you have been assigned to provide the necessary items for a Thanksgiving meal for ten of the residents of the home, who will be preparing the meal for themselves. You decide that the dinner will be a traditional one: turkey, stuffing, cranberry sauce, yams, green bean casserole, rolls, and iced tea. You must go to the supermarket for these items and have decided to use cash to pay for them. Of course, you do not want to approach the checkout counter and not have enough for the purchase. You also know that a sales tax of 8.75% will be added to the total. You take your allotment of $80 in cash with you.

In a situation like this, it is not difficult to get a fairly accurate idea of what the total will be by mentally rounding each item (up or down) to the nearest dollar and keeping a running total along the way as you place items in the shopping cart. Here is an example of this procedure.

Item	Actual Cost	Estimate
18-lb turkey	$26.82	$30
12-pack of dinner rolls	2.29	2
15-oz container of margarine	2.79	3
40-oz can of yams	3.34	3
28-oz can of cranberry sauce	3.97	4
26-oz can of cream of mushroom soup	2.99	3
14-oz bag of herb stuffing	3.59	4
1-lb bag of pecans	8.79	9
50-oz can of green beans	2.59	3
28-oz can of onion flakes	2.19	2
22-bag pack of tea bags	4.29	4

Before reaching the checkout counter, look at the items in the basket (move from the top to the bottom in the third column) and add them, rounding off whenever doing so helps to simplify the computation. Here is one of many ways this can be done. (Remember, this is not an *exact* computation, so thought processes will vary.)

"30 plus 2 gives 32; I notice that the next three items total 10, so 32 plus 10 equals 42, which I will round down to 40; plus 3 gives 43; plus 4 gives 47, which I will round up to 50; I will round 9 to 10 and add 50 to 10 to give 60; the final three items total 9, which I will round down to 8 (because I rounded up just before) and add to 60 to get 68; 68 is about 70."

Before tax is added, the items total about $70. The sales tax is 8.75%, so round this to 10%. Taking 10% of a number is simple: Just move the decimal point one unit to the left. In this case, the tax will be about $7. So add 7 to 70 to get an approximate total of $77. It looks like $80 will cover the total cost.

Now, as the cashier rings up the purchase, the screen shows that the actual total cost is $63.65, the sales tax is $5.57, and the grand total is $69.22. The estimate is a bit high in this example (because most of the roundoffs were "upward"), but this is what "being in the ballpark" means: The estimate is close enough for our purpose.

Happy Thanksgiving.

1.4 NUMERACY IN TODAY'S WORLD

The familiar term *literacy* applies to language in the same way that the term **numeracy** applies to mathematics. It is virtually impossible to function in the world today without understanding fundamental number concepts. The basic ideas of calculating, estimating, interpreting data from graphs, and conveying mathematics via language and writing are among the skills required to be "numerate."

Calculation

The search for easier ways to calculate and compute has culminated in the development of hand-held calculators and computers. For the general population, a calculator that performs the operations of arithmetic and a few other functions is sufficient. These are known as **four-function calculators.** Students who take higher mathematics courses (engineers, for example) usually need the added power of **scientific calculators. Graphing calculators,** which actually plot graphs on small screens, are also available. *Always refer to your owner's manual if you need assistance in performing an operation with your calculator. If you need further help, ask your instructor or another student who is using the same model.*

Today's smartphones routinely include a calculator application (app). For example, Apple's iPhone has an app that serves as a four-function calculator when the phone is held vertically, but it becomes a scientific calculator when held horizontally. Furthermore, graphing calculator apps are available at little or no cost. Although it is not necessary to have a graphing calculator to study the material presented in this text, we occasionally include graphing calculator screens to support results obtained or to provide supplemental information.*

The screens that follow illustrate some common entries and operations.

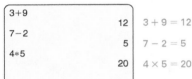

3+9	12
7−2	5
4*5	20

$3 + 9 = 12$
$7 − 2 = 5$
$4 \times 5 = 20$

A

24/20	1.2
Ans▶Frac	$\frac{6}{5}$
5−(8−7)	4

$\frac{24}{20} = 1.2$
$1.2 = \frac{6}{5}$
$5 − (8 − 7) = 4$

B

7^2	49
5^3	125
$\sqrt{81}$	9

$7^2 = 49$
$5^3 = 125$
$\sqrt{81} = 9$

C

Shown here is an example of a **calculator app** from a smartphone. Since the introduction of hand-held calculators in the early 1970s, the methods of everyday arithmetic have been drastically altered. One of the first consumer models available was the Texas Instruments SR-10, which sold for nearly $150 in 1973. It could perform the four operations of arithmetic and take square roots, but it could do very little more.

Screen A illustrates how two numbers can be added, subtracted, or multiplied. Screen B shows how two numbers can be divided, how the decimal quotient (stored in the memory cell Ans) can be converted into a fraction, and how parentheses can be used in a computation. Screen C shows how a number can be squared, how it can be cubed, and how its square root can be taken.

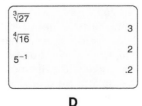

$\sqrt[3]{27}$	3
$\sqrt[4]{16}$	2
5^{-1}	.2

$\sqrt[3]{27} = 3$
$\sqrt[4]{16} = 2$
$5^{-1} \left(\text{or } \frac{1}{5} \right) = .2$

D

π	3.141592654
5!	120
6265804*8980591	5.627062301ᴇ13

E

$\pi \approx 3.141592654$
$5! \,(\text{or } 1 \times 2 \times 3 \times 4 \times 5) = 120$
$6,265,804 \times 8,980,591 \approx 5.627062301 \times 10^{13}$
$\approx$ indicates "is approximately equal to"

*Because it is one of the most popular graphing calculators, we include screens similar to those generated by the TI-83 Plus and TI-84 Plus from Texas Instruments.

The popular **TI-84 Plus** graphing calculator is shown here.

Screen D shows how other roots (cube root and fourth root) can be found, and how the reciprocal of a number can be found using -1 as an exponent. Screen E shows how π can be accessed with its own special key, how a *factorial* (as indicated by !) can be found, and how a result might be displayed in *scientific notation*. (The "E13" following 5.627062301 means that this number is multiplied by 10^{13}. This answer is still only an approximation, because the product $6{,}265{,}804 \times 8{,}980{,}591$ contains more digits than the calculator can display.)

In **Section 1.3** we presented a list of problem-solving strategies. As Terry Krieger points out in the chapter opener, "mathematics may be the only discipline in which different people, using wildly varied but logically sound methods, will arrive at the same correct result" with respect to solving problems. Sometimes more than one strategy can be used in a particular situation. In **Example 1,** we present a type of problem that has been around for thousands of years in various forms, and is solved by observing a pattern within a table. One ancient form of this problem deals with doubling a kernel of corn for each square on a checkerbord. (See http://mathforum.org/sanders/geometry/GP11Fable.html.) It illustrates an example of exponential growth, covered in more detail in a later chapter.

EXAMPLE 1 Calculating a Sum That Involves a Pattern

Following her success in *I Love Lucy,* Lucille Ball starred in *The Lucy Show,* which aired for six seasons on CBS in the 1960s. She worked for Mr. Mooney (Gale Gordon), who was very careful with his money.

In the September 26, 1966, show "Lucy, the Bean Queen," Lucy learned a lesson about saving money. Mr. Mooney had refused to lend her $1500 to buy furniture, because he claimed she did not know the value of money. He explained to her that if she were to save so that she would have one penny on Day 1, two pennies on Day 2, four pennies on Day 3, and so on, she would have more than enough money to buy her furniture after only nineteen days. Use a calculator to verify this fact.

Solution

A calculator will help in constructing **Table 4.**

Table 4

Day Number	Accumulated Savings on That Day	Day Number	Accumulated Savings on That Day
1	$0.01	11	$10.24
2	0.02	12	20.48
3	0.04	13	40.96
4	0.08	14	81.92
5	0.16	15	163.84
6	0.32	16	327.68
7	0.64	17	655.36
8	1.28	18	1310.72
9	2.56	19	2621.44
10	5.12		

So, indeed, Lucy will have accumulated $2621.44 on day 19, which is enough to buy the furniture.) ∎

Estimation

Although calculators can make life easier when it comes to computations, many times we need only estimate an answer to a problem, and in these cases, using a calculator may not be necessary or appropriate.

EXAMPLE 2 Estimating an Appropriate Number of Birdhouses

A birdhouse for swallows can accommodate up to 8 nests. How many birdhouses would be necessary to accommodate 58 nests?

Solution

If we divide 58 by 8 either by hand or with a calculator, we get 7.25. Can this possibly be the desired number? Of course not, because we cannot consider fractions of birdhouses. Do we need 7 or 8 birdhouses?

To provide nesting space for the nests left over after the 7 birdhouses (as indicated by the decimal fraction), we should plan to use 8 birdhouses. In this problem, we must round our answer *up* to the next counting number. ∎

EXAMPLE 3 Approximating Average Number of Yards per Carry

In 2013, Fred Jackson of the Buffalo Bills carried the football a total of 206 times for 890 yards (*Source:* www.nfl.com). Approximate his average number of yards per carry that year.

Solution

Because we are told only to find Jackson's approximate average, we can say that he carried about 200 times for about 900 yards, and his average was therefore about $\frac{900}{200} = 4.5$ yards per carry. (A calculator shows that his average to the nearest tenth was 4.3 yards per carry. Verify this.) ∎

Interpretation of Graphs

In the introduction to his book *Innumeracy: Mathematical Illiteracy and Its Consequences,* Temple University professor **John Allen Paulos** writes

> ***Innumeracy,*** *an inability to deal comfortably with the fundamental notions of number and chance, plagues far too many otherwise knowledgeable citizens.*
>
> *. . .*
>
> *(W)e were watching the news and the TV weathercaster announced that there was a 50 percent chance of rain for Saturday and a 50 percent chance for Sunday, and concluded that there was therefore a 100 percent chance of rain that weekend. . . . (U)nlike other failings which are hidden, mathematical illiteracy is often flaunted. "I can't even balance my checkbook." "I'm a people person, not a numbers person." Or "I always hated math."*

In a **circle graph,** or **pie chart,** a circle is used to indicate the total of all the data categories represented. The circle is divided into sectors, or wedges (like pieces of a pie), whose sizes show the relative magnitudes of the categories. The sum of all the fractional parts must be 1 (for one whole circle).

EXAMPLE 4 Interpreting Information in a Circle Graph

In a recent month there were about 2100 million (2.1 billion) Internet users worldwide. The circle graph in **Figure 8** shows the approximate shares of these users living in various regions of the world.

(a) Which region had the largest share of Internet users? What was that share?

(b) Estimate the number of Internet users in North America.

(c) How many actual Internet users were there in North America?

Worldwide Internet Users by Region

- North America 13%
- Asia 44%
- Other 20.5%
- Europe 22.5%

Source: www.internetworldstats.com

Figure 8

Solution

(a) In the circle graph, the sector for Asia is the largest, so Asia had the largest share of Internet users, 44%.

(b) A share of 13% can be rounded down to 10%. Then find 10% of 2100 million by finding $\frac{1}{10}$ of 2100, or 210. There were *about* 210 million users in North America. (This estimate is low, because we rounded *down*.)

(c) To find the actual number of users, find 13% of 2100 million. We do this by multiplying 0.13×2100 million.

$$\underbrace{0.13}_{13\%} \quad \times \quad \underbrace{2100 \text{ million}}_{\substack{\text{of} \\ \text{total}}} \quad = \quad \underbrace{273 \text{ million}}_{\substack{\text{Actual number} \\ \text{of users in} \\ \text{North America}}}$$

A **bar graph** is used to show comparisons. It consists of a series of bars (or simulations of bars) arranged either vertically or horizontally. In a bar graph, values from two categories are paired with each other (for example, years with dollar amounts).

EXAMPLE 5 Interpreting Information in a Bar Graph

The bar graph in **Figure 9** shows annual per-capita spending on health care in the United States for the years 2004 through 2009.

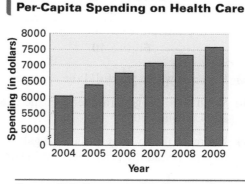

Per-Capita Spending on Health Care

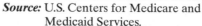

Source: U.S. Centers for Medicare and Medicaid Services.

Figure 9

(a) In what years was per-capita health care spending greater than $7000?

(b) Estimate per-capita health care spending in 2004 and 2008.

(c) Describe the change in per-capita spending as the years progressed.

Solution

(a) Locate 7000 on the vertical axis and follow the line across to the right. Three years—2007, 2008, and 2009—have bars that extend above the line for 7000, so per-capita health care spending was greater than $7000 in those years.

(b) Locate the top of the bar for 2004 and move horizontally across to the vertical scale to see that it is about 6000. Per-capita health care spending for 2004 was about $6000.

Similarly, follow the top of the bar for 2008 across to the vertical scale to see that it lies a little more than halfway between 7000 and 7500, so per-capita health care spending in 2008 was about $7300.

(c) As the years progressed, per-capita spending on health care increased steadily, from about $6000 in 2004 to about $7500 in 2009. ∎

A **line graph** is used to show changes or trends in data over time. To form a line graph, we connect a series of points representing data with line segments.

EXAMPLE 6 Interpreting Information in a Line Graph

The line graph in **Figure 10** shows average prices of a gallon of regular unleaded gasoline in the United States for the years 2004 through 2011.

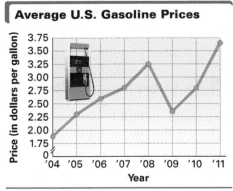

Source: U.S. Department of Energy.

Figure 10

(a) Between which years did the average price of a gallon of gasoline decrease?

(b) What was the general trend in the average price of a gallon of gasoline from 2004 through 2008?

(c) Estimate the average price of a gallon of gasoline in 2004 and in 2008. About how much did the price increase between 2004 and 2008?

Solution

(a) The line between 2008 and 2009 falls, so the average price of a gallon of gasoline decreased from 2008 to 2009.

(b) The line graph rises from 2004 to 2008, so the average price of a gallon of gasoline increased over those years.

(c) Move up from 2004 on the horizontal scale to the point plotted for 2004. This point is about halfway between the lines on the vertical scale for $1.75 and $2.00. Halfway between $1.75 and $2.00 would be about $1.88. Therefore, a gallon of gasoline cost about $1.88 in 2004.

Similarly, locate the point plotted for 2008. Moving across to the vertical scale, the graph indicates that the price for a gallon of gasoline in 2008 was about $3.25.

Between 2004 and 2008, the average price of a gallon of gasoline increased by about

$$\$3.25 - \$1.88 = \$1.37.$$
∎

Communicating Mathematics through Language Skills

Research has indicated that the ability to express mathematical observations in writing can serve as a positive force in one's continued development as a mathematics student. The implementation of writing in the mathematics class can use several approaches.

One way of using writing in mathematics is to keep a **journal** in which you spend a few minutes explaining what happened in class that day. The journal entries may be general or specific, depending on the topic covered, the degree to which you understand the topic, your interest level at the time, and so on. Journal entries are usually written in informal language.

Although journal entries are for the most part informal writings in which the student's thoughts are allowed to roam freely, entries in **learning logs** are typically more formal. An instructor may pose a specific question for a student to answer in a learning log. In this text, we intersperse in each exercise set exercises that require written answers that are appropriate for answering in a learning log.

Mathematical writing takes many forms. One of the most famous author/mathematicians was **Charles Dodgson** (1832–1898), who used the pen name **Lewis Carroll.**

Dodgson was a mathematics lecturer at Oxford University in England. Queen Victoria told Dodgson how much she enjoyed *Alice's Adventures in Wonderland* and how much she wanted to read his next book; he is said to have sent her *Symbolic Logic,* his most famous mathematical work.

The *Alice* books made Carroll famous. Late in life, however, Dodgson shunned attention and denied that he and Carroll were the same person, even though he gave away hundreds of signed copies to children and children's hospitals.

EXAMPLE 7 Writing an Answer to a Conceptual Exercise

Exercise 17 of **Section 1.1** reads as follows.

> ***Discuss the differences between inductive and deductive reasoning. Give an example of each.***

Write a short paragraph to answer this exercise.

Solution
Here is one possible response.

> Deductive reasoning occurs when you go from general ideas to specific ones. For example, I know that I can multiply both sides of $\frac{1}{2}x = 6$ by 2 to get $x = 12$, because I can multiply both sides of any equation by whatever I want (except 0). Inductive reasoning goes the other way. If I have a general conclusion from specific observations, that's inductive reasoning. Example – in the numbers 4, 8, 12, 16, and so on, I can conclude that the next number is 20, since I always add 4 to get the next number.

The motto "Publish or perish" has long been around, implying that a scholar in pursuit of an academic position must publish in a journal in his or her field. There are numerous such journals in mathematics research and/or mathematics education. The National Council of Teachers of Mathematics publishes *Teaching Children Mathematics, Mathematics Teaching in the Middle School, Mathematics Teacher, Journal for Research in Mathematics Education, Mathematics Teacher Educator,* and *Student Explorations in Mathematics.* Refer to the Web site www.nctm.org to access these journals, or refer to print copies in your local library.

Writing a report on a journal article can help you understand what mathematicians do and what ideas mathematics teachers use to convey concepts to their students. Many professors in mathematics survey courses require short term papers of their students. In doing such research, students can become aware of the plethora of books and articles on mathematics and mathematicians, many written specifically for the layperson.

A list of important mathematicians, philosophers, and scientists follows.

Abel, N.	Cardano, G.	Gauss, C.	Noether, E.
Agnesi, M. G.	Copernicus, N.	Hilbert, D.	Pascal, B.
Agnesi, M. T.	De Morgan, A.	Kepler, J.	Plato
Al-Khowârizmi	Descartes, R.	Kronecker, L.	Polya, G.
Apollonius	Euler, L.	Lagrange, J.	Pythagoras
Archimedes	Fermat, P.	Leibniz, G.	Ramanujan, S.
Aristotle	Fibonacci	L'Hôspital, G.	Riemann, G.
Babbage, C.	(Leonardo	Lobachevsky, N.	Russell, B.
Bernoulli, Jakob	of Pisa)	Mandelbrot, B.	Somerville, M.
Bernoulli,	Galileo (Galileo	Napier, J.	Tartaglia, N.
Johann	Galilei)	Nash, J.	Whitehead, A.
Cantor, G.	Galois, E.	Newton, I.	Wiles, A.

The following topics in the history and development of mathematics can also be used for term papers.

Babylonian mathematics	Pascal's triangle
Egyptian mathematics	The origins of probability theory
The origin of zero	Women in mathematics
Plimpton 322	Mathematical paradoxes
The Rhind papyrus	Unsolved problems in mathematics
Origins of the Pythagorean theorem	The four-color theorem
The regular (Platonic) solids	The proof of Fermat's Last Theorem
The Pythagorean brotherhood	The search for large primes
The Golden Ratio (Golden Section)	Fractal geometry
The three famous construction problems of the Greeks	The co-inventors of calculus
The history of the approximations of π	The role of the computer in the study of mathematics
Euclid and his *Elements*	Mathematics and music
Early Chinese mathematics	Police mathematics
Early Hindu mathematics	The origins of complex numbers
Origin of the word *algebra*	Goldbach's conjecture
Magic squares	The use of the Internet in mathematics education
Figurate numbers	The development of graphing calculators
The Fibonacci sequence	Mathematics education reform movement
The Cardano/Tartaglia controversy	Multicultural mathematics
Historical methods of computation (logarithms, the abacus, Napier's rods, the slide rule, etc.)	The Riemann Hypothesis

1.4 EXERCISES

Perform the indicated operations, and give as many digits in your answer as shown on your calculator display. (The number of displayed digits may vary depending on the model used.)

1. $39.7 + (8.2 - 4.1)$

2. $2.8 \times (3.2 - 1.1)$

3. $\sqrt{5.56440921}$

4. $\sqrt{37.38711025}$

5. $\sqrt[3]{418.508992}$

6. $\sqrt[3]{700.227072}$

7. 2.67^2

8. 3.49^3

9. 5.76^5

10. 1.48^6

11. $\dfrac{14.32 - 8.1}{2 \times 3.11}$

12. $\dfrac{12.3 + 18.276}{3 \times 1.04}$

13. $\sqrt[5]{1.35}$

14. $\sqrt[6]{3.21}$

15. $\dfrac{\pi}{\sqrt{2}}$

16. $\dfrac{2\pi}{\sqrt{3}}$

17. $\sqrt[4]{\dfrac{2143}{22}}$

18. $\dfrac{12{,}345{,}679 \times 72}{\sqrt[3]{27}}$

19. $\dfrac{\sqrt{2}}{\sqrt[3]{6}}$

20. $\dfrac{\sqrt[3]{12}}{\sqrt{3}}$

21. Choose any number consisting of five digits. Multiply it by 9 on your calculator. Now add the digits in the answer. If the sum is more than 9, add the digits of this sum, and repeat until the sum is less than 10. Your answer will always be 9. Repeat the exercise with a number consisting of six digits. Does the same result hold?

22. Use your calculator to *square* the following two-digit numbers ending in 5: 15, 25, 35, 45, 55, 65, 75, 85. Write down your results, and examine the pattern that develops. Then use inductive reasoning to predict the value of 95^2. Write an explanation of how you can mentally square a two-digit number ending in 5.

Perform each calculation and observe the answers. Then fill in the blank with the appropriate response.

23. $\boxed{\dfrac{-3}{-8}}$; $\boxed{\dfrac{-5}{-4}}$; $\boxed{\dfrac{-2.7}{-4.3}}$

Dividing a negative number by another negative number gives a _____ product.
(negative/positive)

24. $\boxed{5 * -4}$; $\boxed{-3 * 8}$; $\boxed{2.7 * -4.3}$

Multiplying a negative number by a positive number gives a _____ product.
(negative/positive)

25. $\boxed{5.6^0}$; $\boxed{\pi^0}$; $\boxed{2^0}$; $\boxed{120^0}$

Raising a nonzero number to the power 0 gives a result of _____.

26. $\boxed{1^2}$; $\boxed{1^3}$; $\boxed{1^{-3}}$; $\boxed{1^0}$

Raising 1 to any power gives a result of _____.

27. $\boxed{\dfrac{1}{7}}$; $\boxed{\dfrac{1}{-9}}$; $\boxed{\dfrac{1}{3}}$; $\boxed{\dfrac{1}{-8}}$

The sign of the reciprocal of a number is _____ the sign of the number.
(the same as/different from)

28. $\boxed{5 \div 0}$; $\boxed{9 \div 0}$; $\boxed{0 \div 0}$

Dividing a number by 0 gives a(n) _____ on a calculator.

29. $\boxed{0 \div 8}$; $\boxed{0 \div -2}$; $\boxed{0 \div \pi}$

Zero divided by a nonzero number gives a quotient of _____.

30. $\boxed{\sqrt{-3}}$; $\boxed{\sqrt{-4}}$; $\boxed{\sqrt{-10}}$

Taking the square root of a negative number gives a(n) _____ on a calculator.

31. $\boxed{-3 * -4 * -5}$; $\boxed{-3 * -4 * -5 * -6 * -7}$; $\boxed{-3 * -4 * -5 * -6 * -7 * -8 * -9}$

Multiplying an *odd* number of negative numbers gives a _____ product.
(positive/negative)

32. $\boxed{-3 * -4}$; $\boxed{-3 * -4 * -5 * -6}$; $\boxed{-3 * -4 * -5 * -6 * -7 * -8}$

Multiplying an *even* number of negative numbers gives a _____ product.
(positive/negative)

33. Find the decimal representation of $\frac{1}{6}$ on your calculator. Following the decimal point will be a 1 and a string of 6s. The final digit will be a 7 if your calculator *rounds off* or a 6 if it *truncates*. Which kind of calculator do you have?

34. Choose any three-digit number and enter the digits into a calculator. Then enter them again to get a six-digit number. Divide this six-digit number by 7. Divide the result by 13. Divide the result by 11. What is interesting about your answer? Explain why this happens.

35. Choose any digit except 0. Multiply it by 429. Now multiply the result by 259. What is interesting about your answer? Explain why this happens.

36. Refer to **Example 1.** If Lucy continues to double her savings amount each day, on what day will she become a millionaire?

Give an appropriate counting number answer to each question in Exercises 37–40. (Find the least counting number that will work.)

37. *Pages to Store Trading Cards* A plastic page designed to hold trading cards will hold up to 9 cards. How many pages will be needed to store 563 cards?

38. *Drawers for DVDs* A sliding drawer designed to hold DVD cases has 20 compartments. If Chris wants to house his collection of 408 Disney DVDs, how many such drawers will he need?

39. *Containers for African Violets* A gardener wants to fertilize 800 African violets. Each container of fertilizer will supply up to 60 plants. How many containers will she need to do the job?

40. *Fifth-Grade Teachers Needed* False River Academy has 155 fifth-grade students. The principal has decided that each fifth-grade teacher should have a maximum of 24 students. How many fifth-grade teachers does he need?

In Exercises 41–46, use estimation to determine the choice closest to the correct answer.

41. *Price per Acre of Land* To build a "millennium clock" on Mount Washington in Nevada that would tick once each year, chime once each century, and last at least 10,000 years, the nonprofit Long Now Foundation purchased 80 acres of land for $140,000. Which one of the following is the closest estimate to the price per acre?

A. $1000   **B.** $2000   **C.** $4000   **D.** $11,200

42. *Time of a Round Trip* The distance from Seattle, Washington, to Springfield, Missouri, is 2009 miles. About how many hours would a round trip from Seattle to Springfield and back take a bus that averages 50 miles per hour for the entire trip?

A. 60   **B.** 70   **C.** 80   **D.** 90

43. *People per Square Mile* Baton Rouge, LA has a population of 230,058 and covers 76.9 square miles. About how many people per square mile live in Baton Rouge?

A. 3000   **B.** 300   **C.** 30   **D.** 30,000

44. *Revolutions of Mercury* The planet Mercury takes 88.0 Earth days to revolve around the sun once. Pluto takes 90,824.2 days to do the same. When Pluto has revolved around the sun once, about how many times will Mercury have revolved around the sun?

A. 100,000   **B.** 10,000   **C.** 1000   **D.** 100

45. *Reception Average* In 2013, A. J. Green of the Cincinnati Bengals caught 98 passes for 1426 yards. His approximate number of yards gained per catch was _____.

A. $\frac{1}{14}$ **B.** 0.07   **C.** 139,748   **D.** 14

46. *Area of the Sistine Chapel* The Sistine Chapel in Vatican City measures 40.5 meters by 13.5 meters.

Which is the closest approximation to its area?

A. 110 meters   **B.** 55 meters
C. 110 square meters   **D.** 600 square meters

Foreign-Born Americans Approximately 37.5 million people living in the United States in a recent year were born in other countries. The circle graph gives the share from each region of birth for these people. Use the graph to answer each question in Exercises 47–50.

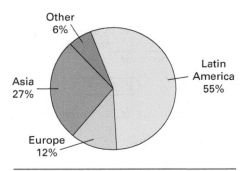

U.S. Foreign-Born Population by Region of Birth

Other 6%
Latin America 55%
Asia 27%
Europe 12%

47. What share was from other regions?

48. What share was from Latin America or Asia?

49. How many people (in millions) were born in Europe?

50. How many more people (in millions) were born in Latin America than in Asia?

Milk Production *The bar graph shows total U.S. milk production (in billions of pounds) for the years 2004 through 2010. Use the bar graph to work Exercises 51–54.*

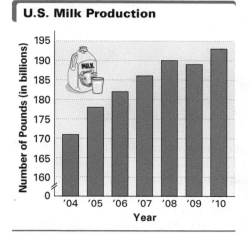

U.S. Milk Production

Source: U.S. Department of Agriculture.

51. In what years was U.S. milk production greater than 185 billion pounds?

52. In what years was U.S. milk production about the same?

53. Estimate U.S. milk production in 2004 and 2010.

54. Describe the change from 2004 to 2010.

U.S. Car Imports *The line graph shows the number of new and used passenger cars (in millions) imported into the United States over the years 2005 through 2010. Use the line graph to work Exercises 55–58.*

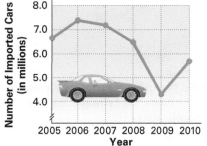

Passenger Cars Imported into the U.S.

Source: U.S. Census Bureau.

55. Over which two consecutive years did the number of imported cars increase the most? About how much was this increase?

56. Estimate the number of cars imported during 2007, 2008, and 2009.

57. Describe the trend in car imports from 2006 to 2009.

58. During which year(s) were fewer than 6 millions cars imported into the United States?

Use effective writing skills to address the following.

59. ***Mathematics Web Sites*** The following Web sites provide a fascinating list of mathematics-related topics. Investigate, choose a topic that interests you, and report on it according to the guidelines provided by your instructor.

www.mathworld.wolfram.com

world.std.com/~reinhold/mathmovies.html

www.maths.surrey.ac.uk/hosted-sites/R.Knott/

http://dir.yahoo.com/Science/Mathematics/

www.cut-the-knot.org

www.ics.uci.edu/~eppstein/recmath.html

www.coolmathguy.com

ptri1.tripod.com

mathforum.org

rosettacode.org

plus.maths.org

60. ***The Simpsons*** The longest-running animated television series is *The Simpsons,* having begun in 1989. The Web site www.simpsonsmath.com explores the occurrence of mathematics in the episodes on a season-by-season basis. Watch several episodes and elaborate on the mathematics found in them.

61. ***Donald in Mathmagic Land*** One of the most popular mathematical films of all time is *Donald in Mathmagic Land,* a 1959 Disney short that is available on DVD. Spend an entertaining half-hour watching this film, and write a report on it according to the guidelines provided by your instructor.

62. ***Mathematics in Hollywood*** A theme of mathematics-related scenes in movies and television is found throughout this text. Prepare a report on one or more such scenes, and determine whether the mathematics involved is correct or incorrect. If correct, show why. If incorrect, find the correct answer.

KEY TERMS

1.1

conjecture
inductive reasoning
counterexample
deductive reasoning
natural (counting) numbers
base
exponent
premise
conclusion
logical argument

1.2

number sequence
terms of a sequence
arithmetic sequence
common difference
geometric sequence
common ratio
method of successive
  differences
mathematical
  induction

triangular, square, and
  pentagonal numbers
figurate number
subscript
Kaprekar constant

1.3

perfect square
square root
radical symbol

1.4

numeracy
four-function calculator
scientific calculator
graphing calculator
circle graph (pie chart)
bar graph
line graph
journal
learning log

TEST YOUR WORD POWER

See how well you have learned the vocabulary in this chapter.

1. A **conjecture** is
  A. a statement that has been proved to be true.
  B. an educated guess based on repeated observations.
  C. an example that shows that a general statement is false.
  D. an example of deductive reasoning.

2. An example of a **natural number** is
  A. 0.   **B.** $\frac{1}{2}$.   **C.** -1.   **D.** 1.

3. An **arithmetic sequence** is
  A. a sequence that has a common difference between any two successive terms.
  B. a sequence that has a common sum of any two successive terms.
  C. a sequence that has a common ratio between any two successive terms.
  D. a sequence that can begin 1, 1, 2, 3, 5. . . .

4. A **geometric sequence** is
  A. a sequence that has a common difference between any two successive terms.
  B. a sequence that has a common sum of any two successive terms.
  C. a sequence that has a common ratio between any two successive terms.
  D. A sequence that can begin 1, 1, 2, 3, 5, ...

5. The symbol T_n, which uses the **subscript** n, is read
  A. "T to the nth power."   **B.** "T times n."
  C. "T of n."   **D.** "T sub n."

ANSWERS
1. B   **2.** D   **3.** A   **4.** C   **5.** D

QUICK REVIEW

Concepts	*Examples*
1.1 **Solving Problems by Inductive Reasoning**	
Inductive Reasoning Inductive reasoning is characterized by drawing a general conclusion (making a conjecture) from repeated observations of specific examples. The conjecture may or may not be true.	Consider the following: *When I square the first twenty numbers ending in 5, the result always ends in 25. Therefore, I make the conjecture that this happens in the twenty-first case.*
A general conclusion from inductive reasoning can be shown to be false by providing a single counterexample.	This is an example of inductive reasoning because a general conclusion follows from repeated observations.

Concepts	**Examples**
Deductive Reasoning Deductive reasoning is characterized by applying general principles to specific examples.	Consider the following: *The formula for finding the perimeter P of a rectangle with length L and width W is P = 2L + 2W. Therefore, the perimeter P is* $$2(5) + 2(3) = 16.$$ 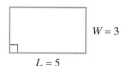 This is an example of deductive reasoning because a specific conclusion follows from a mathematical formula that is true in general.

1.2 An Application of Inductive Reasoning: Number Patterns

Sequences
A number sequence is a list of numbers having a first number, a second number, a third number, and so on, which are called the terms of the sequence.

Arithmetic Sequence
In an arithmetic sequence, each term after the first is obtained by adding the same number, called the common difference.

The arithmetic sequence that begins
$$2, 4, 6, 8$$
has common difference $4 - 2 = 2$, and the next term in the sequence is $8 + 2 = 10$.

Geometric Sequence
In a geometric sequence, each term after the first is obtained by multiplying by the same number, called the common ratio.

The geometric sequence that begins
$$4, 20, 100, 500$$
has common ratio $\frac{20}{4} = 5$, and the next term in the sequence is $500 \times 5 = 2500$.

Method of Successive Differences
The next term in a sequence can sometimes be found by computing successive differences between terms until a pattern can be established.

The sequence that begins
$$7, 15, 25, 37$$
has the following successive differences.

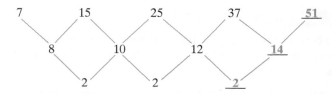

The next term in the sequence is $37 + 14 = 51$.

Figurate Numbers
Figurate numbers, such as triangular, square, and pentagonal numbers, can be represented by geometric arrangements of points.

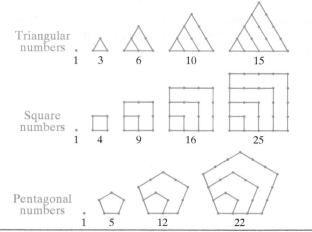

Concepts	Examples

1.3 **Strategies for Problem Solving**

Polya's Four-Step Method for Problem Solving

Step 1 Understand the problem.

Step 2 Devise a plan.

Step 3 Carry out the plan.

Step 4 Look back and check.

Problem-Solving Strategies

- Make a table or a chart.
- Look for a pattern.
- Solve a similar, simpler problem.
- Draw a sketch.
- Use inductive reasoning.
- Write an equation and solve it.
- If a formula applies, use it.
- Work backward.
- Guess and check.
- Use trial and error.
- Use common sense.
- Look for a "catch" if an answer seems too obvious or impossible.

What is the ones, or units, digit in 7^{350}?

Solution

We can observe a pattern in the table of simpler powers of 7. (Use a calculator.)

$7^1 = 7$	$7^5 = 16,807$	$7^9 = 40,353,607$
$7^2 = 49$	$7^6 = 117,649$	$\ldots$
$7^3 = 343$	$7^7 = 823,543$	$\ldots$
$7^4 = 2401$	$7^8 = 5,764,801$	$\ldots$

The ones digit appears in a pattern of four digits over and over: 7, 9, 3, 1, 7, 9, 3, 1, ... If the exponent is divided by 4, the remainder helps predict the ones digit. If we divide the exponent 350 by 4, the quotient is 87 and the remainder is 2, just as it is in the second row above for 7^2 and 7^6, where the units digit is 9. So the units digit in 7^{350} is 9.

How many ways are there to make change equivalent to one dollar using only nickels, dimes, and quarters? You do not need at least one coin of each denomination. (December 26, 2013)

Solution   (Verify each of the following by trial and error.)

If we start with 4 quarters, there is 1 way to make change for a dollar.

If we start with 3 quarters, there are 3 ways.

If we start with 2 quarters, there are 6 ways.

If we start with 1 quarter, there are 8 ways.

If we start with 0 quarters, there are 11 ways.

Thus, there are $1 + 3 + 6 + 8 + 11 = 29$ ways in all.

1.4 **Numeracy in Today's World**

There are a variety of types of calculators available; four-function, scientific, and graphing calculators are some of them.

In practical applications, it is often convenient to simply approximate to get an idea of an answer to a problem.

Circle graphs (pie charts), bar graphs, and line graphs are used in today's media to illustrate data in a compact way.

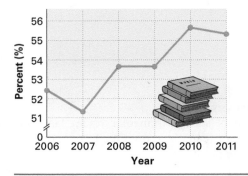

Percents of Students Who Return for Second Year (2-Year Public Institutions)

Source: ACT.

Over which two consecutive years did the percent stay the same? Estimate this percent.

Solution

The graph is horizontal between 2008 and 2009, at about 53.7%.

CHAPTER 1 / TEST

In Exercises 1 and 2, decide whether the reasoning involved is an example of inductive or deductive reasoning.

1. Michelle is a sales representative for a publishing company. For the past 16 years, she has exceeded her annual sales goal, primarily by selling mathematics textbooks. Therefore, she will also exceed her annual sales goal this year.

2. For all natural numbers n, n^2 is also a natural number. 176 is a natural number. Therefore, 176^2 is a natural number.

3. ***Counting Puzzle (Rectangles)*** How many rectangles of any size are in the figure shown? (September 10, 2001)

4. Use the list of equations and inductive reasoning to predict the next equation, and then verify your conjecture.

   $65,359,477,124,183 \times 17 = 1,111,111,111,111,111$
   $65,359,477,124,183 \times 34 = 2,222,222,222,222,222$
   $65,359,477,124,183 \times 51 = 3,333,333,333,333,333$

5. Use the method of successive differences to find the next term in the sequence

   $$3, 11, 31, 69, 131, 223, \ldots .$$

6. Find the sum $1 + 2 + 3 + \cdots + 250$.

7. Consider the following equations, where the left side of each is an octagonal number.

   $$1 = 1$$
   $$8 = 1 + 7$$
   $$21 = 1 + 7 + 13$$
   $$40 = 1 + 7 + 13 + 19$$

   Use the pattern established on the right sides to predict the next octagonal number. What is the next equation in the list?

8. Use the result of **Exercise 7** and the method of successive differences to find the first eight octagonal numbers. Then divide each by 4 and record the remainder. What is the pattern obtained?

9. Describe the pattern used to obtain the terms of the Fibonacci sequence below. What is the next term?

   $$1, 1, 2, 3, 5, 8, 13, 21, \ldots .$$

Use problem-solving strategies to solve each problem, taken from the date indicated in the monthly calendar of Mathematics Teacher.

10. ***Building a Fraction*** Each of the four digits 2, 4, 6, and 9 is placed in one of the boxes to form a fraction. The numerator and the denominator are both two-digit whole numbers. What is the smallest value of all the common fractions that can be formed? Express your answer as a common fraction. (November 17, 2004)

11. ***Units Digit of a Power of 9*** What is the units digit (ones digit) in the decimal representation of 9^{1997}? (January 27, 1997)

12. ***Counting Puzzle (Triangles)*** How many triangles are in this figure? (January 6, 2000)

13. ***Make Them Equal*** Consider the following:

    $$1\ 2\ 3\ 4\ 5\ 6\ 7\ 8\ 9\ 0 = 100.$$

    Leaving all the numerals in the order given, insert addition and subtraction signs into the expression to make the equation true. (March 23, 2008)

14. ***Shrinkage*** Dr. Small is 36 inches tall, and Ms. Tall is 96 inches tall. If Dr. Small shrinks 2 inches per year and Ms. Tall grows $\frac{2}{3}$ of an inch per year, how tall will Ms. Tall be when Dr. Small disappears altogether? (November 2, 2007)

15. ***Units Digit of a Sum*** Find the units digit (ones digit) of the decimal numeral representing the number

    $$11^{11} + 14^{14} + 16^{16}. \text{ (February 14, 1994)}$$

16. Based on your knowledge of elementary arithmetic, describe the pattern that can be observed when the following operations are performed.

    $$9 \times 1, \quad 9 \times 2, \quad 9 \times 3, \ldots, \quad 9 \times 9$$

    (*Hint:* Add the digits in the answers. What do you notice?)

Use your calculator to evaluate each of the following. Give as many decimal places as the calculator displays.

17. $\sqrt{98.16}$

18. 3.25^3

19. *Basketball Scoring Results* During the 2012–13 NCAA women's basketball season, Brittney Griner of Baylor made 148 of her 208 free throw attempts. This means that for every 20 attempts, she made approximately _____ of them.

A. 10 **B.** 14 **C.** 8 **D.** 11

20. *Unemployment Rate* *The line graph shows the overall unemployment rate in the U.S. civilian labor force for the years 2003 through 2010.*

  (a) Between which pairs of consecutive years did the unemployment rate decrease?

  (b) What was the general trend in the unemployment rate between 2007 and 2010?

  (c) Estimate the overall unemployment rate in 2008 and 2009. About how much did the unemployment rate increase between 2008 and 2009?

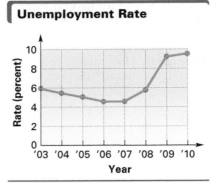

Unemployment Rate

Source: Bureau of Labor Statistics.

The Basic Concepts of Set Theory

2

For many reasons, the job outlook in the United States is good—and improving—for all types of nursing careers, as well as other health-related categories. Students may be considering groups of different training programs; lists of certificate or degree objectives; an array of employment opportunities; the pros and cons of different opportunities relative to upward mobility, stress level, and flexibility; and many others. The properties of these arrays, groups, and collections can be better understood by treating them all as *sets* (the mathematical term) and applying the methods presented in this chapter. (See, for example, the opening discussion of **Section 2.4** on page 71.)

Refer to the table on the next page. To the nearest tenth of a percent, what percentage increase is predicted for number of jobs over the decade 2012–2022 for RNs? For LPNs? (See page 50 for the answer.)

	2012 Median Salary	Number of Jobs in 2012	Predicted Increase in Number of Jobs, 2012–2022
Registered Nurses, RNs	$65,470	2,711,500	526,800
Licensed Practical (or Vocational) Nurses, LPNs (or LVNs)	$41,540	738,400	182,900

Source of data: www.bls.gov

| 2.1 | **SYMBOLS AND TERMINOLOGY** |

OBJECTIVES

1 Use three methods to designate sets.

2 Understand important categories of numbers, and determine cardinal numbers of sets.

3 Distinguish between finite and infinite sets.

4 Determine whether two sets are equal.

The basic ideas of set theory were developed by the German mathematician **Georg Cantor** (1845–1918) in about 1875. Cantor created a new field of theory and at the same time continued the long debate over infinity that began in ancient times. He developed counting by one-to-one correspondence to determine how many objects are contained in a set. Infinite sets differ from finite sets by not obeying the familiar law that the whole is greater than any of its parts.

Designating Sets

A **set** is a collection of objects. The objects belonging to the set are called the **elements,** or **members,** of the set. Sets are designated using the following three methods: (1) *word description,* (2) the *listing method,* and (3) *set-builder notation.*

The set of even counting numbers less than 10	Word description
$\{2, 4, 6, 8\}$	Listing method
$\{x \mid x$ is an even counting number less than 10$\}$	Set-builder notation

The set-builder notation above is read "the set of all x such that x is an even counting number less than 10." Set-builder notation uses the algebraic idea of a *variable.* (Any symbol would do, but just as in other algebraic applications, the letter x is a common choice.)

Variable representing an
element in general
↓

$$\{x \mid x \text{ is an even counting number less than 10}\}$$

↑
Criteria by which an element
qualifies for membership in the set

Sets are commonly given names (usually capital letters), such as E for the set of all letters of the English alphabet.

$$E = \{a, b, c, d, e, f, g, h, i, j, k, l, m, n, o, p, q, r, s, t, u, v, w, x, y, z\}$$

The listing notation can often be shortened by establishing the pattern of elements included and using ellipsis points to indicate a continuation of the pattern.

$$E = \{a, b, c, d, \ldots, x, y, z\}, \quad \text{or} \quad E = \{a, b, c, d, e, \ldots, z\}$$

The set containing no elements is called the **empty set,** or **null set.** The symbol $\varnothing$ is used to denote the empty set, so $\varnothing$ and $\{\ \}$ have the same meaning. We do *not* denote the empty set with the symbol $\{\varnothing\}$ because this notation represents a set with one element (that element being the empty set).

EXAMPLE 1 Listing Elements of Sets

Give a complete listing of all the elements of each set.

(a) the set of counting numbers between eight and thirteen

(b) $\{5, 6, 7, \ldots, 13\}$

(c) $\{x \mid x \text{ is a counting number between 4 and 5}\}$

Solution

(a) This set can be denoted $\{9, 10, 11, 12\}$. (Notice that the word *between* excludes the endpoint values.)

(b) This set begins with the element 5, then 6, then 7, and so on, with each element obtained by adding 1 to the previous element in the list. This pattern stops at 13, so a complete listing is

$$\{5, 6, 7, 8, 9, 10, 11, 12, 13\}.$$

(c) There are no counting numbers between 4 and 5, so this is the empty set: $\{\ \}$, or $\varnothing$. ■

For a set to be useful, it must be *well defined*. For example, the preceding set E of the letters of the English alphabet is well defined. Given the letter q, we know that q is an element of E. Given the Greek letter θ (theta), we know that it is not an element of set E.

However, given the set C of all good singers, and a particular singer, Adilah, it may not be possible to say whether

Adilah is an element of C or   Adilah is *not* an element of C.

The problem is the word "good"; how good is good? Because we cannot necessarily decide whether a given singer belongs to set C, set C is not well defined.

The fact that the letter q is an element of set E is denoted by using the symbol $\in$.

$$q \in E \qquad \text{This is read "q is an element of set } E\text{."}$$

The letter θ is not an element of E. To show this, $\in$ with a slash mark is used.

$$\theta \notin E \qquad \text{This is read "}\theta\text{ is not an element of set } E\text{."}$$

Many other mathematical symbols also have their meanings negated by use of a **slash mark.** The most common example, $\neq$, means "does not equal" or "is not equal to."

EXAMPLE 2 Applying the Symbol $\in$

Decide whether each statement is *true* or *false*.

(a) $4 \in \{1, 2, 5, 8, 13\}$ **(b)** $0 \in \{0, 1, 2, 3\}$ **(c)** $\dfrac{1}{5} \notin \left\{\dfrac{1}{3}, \dfrac{1}{4}, \dfrac{1}{6}\right\}$

Solution

(a) Because 4 is *not* an element of the set $\{1, 2, 5, 8, 13\}$, the statement is *false*.

(b) Because 0 is indeed an element of the set $\{0, 1, 2, 3\}$, the statement is *true*.

(c) This statement says that $\frac{1}{5}$ is not an element of the set $\left\{\frac{1}{3}, \frac{1}{4}, \frac{1}{6}\right\}$, which is *true*. ■

Sets of Numbers and Cardinality

Important categories of numbers are summarized below.

Most concepts in this chapter will be illustrated using the **sets of numbers** shown here, not only to solidify understanding of these sets of numbers but also because all these sets are precisely, or "well," defined and therefore provide clear illustrations.

SETS OF NUMBERS

Natural numbers (or counting numbers) $\{1, 2, 3, 4, \dots\}$

Whole numbers $\{0, 1, 2, 3, 4, \dots\}$

Integers $\{\dots, -3, -2, -1, 0, 1, 2, 3, \dots\}$

Rational numbers $\left\{\frac{p}{q} \mid p \text{ and } q \text{ are integers, and } q \neq 0\right\}$

(*Examples:* $\frac{3}{5}$, $-\frac{7}{9}$, 5, 0. Any rational number may be written as a terminating decimal number, such as 0.25, or a repeating decimal number, such as $0.666\dots$.)

Real numbers $\{x \mid x \text{ is a number that can be expressed as a decimal}\}$

Irrational numbers $\{x \mid x \text{ is a real number and } x \text{ cannot be expressed as a quotient of integers}\}$

(*Examples:* $\sqrt{2}$, $\sqrt[3]{4}$, π. Decimal representations of irrational numbers are neither terminating nor repeating.)

The number of elements in a set is called the **cardinal number,** or **cardinality,** of the set. The symbol

$$n(A), \quad \text{which is read "}n \text{ of } A\text{,"}$$

represents the cardinal number of set A. If elements are repeated in a set listing, they should not be counted more than once when determining the cardinal number of the set.

EXAMPLE 3 Finding Cardinal Numbers

Find the cardinal number of each set.

(a) $K = \{3, 9, 27, 81\}$ **(b)** $M = \{0\}$ **(c)** $B = \{1, 1, 2, 3, 2\}$

(d) $R = \{7, 8, \dots, 15, 16\}$ **(e)** $\varnothing$

Solution

(a) Set K contains four elements, so the cardinal number of set K is 4, and $n(K) = 4$.

(b) Set M contains only one element, 0, so $n(M) = 1$.

(c) Do not count repeated elements more than once. Set B has only three *distinct* elements, so $n(B) = 3$.

(d) Although only four elements are listed, the ellipsis points indicate that there are other elements in the set. Counting them all, we find that there are ten elements, so $n(R) = 10$.

(e) The empty set, $\varnothing$, contains no elements, so $n(\varnothing) = 0$. ■

Finite and Infinite Sets

If the cardinal number of a set is a particular whole number (0 or a counting number), as in all parts of **Example 3,** we call that set a **finite set.** Given enough time, we could finish counting all the elements of any finite set and arrive at its cardinal number.

Some sets, however, are so large that we could never finish the counting process. The counting numbers themselves are such a set. Whenever a set is so large that its cardinal number is not found among the whole numbers, we call that set an **infinite set.**

Answers to the Chapter Opener questions
RNs: 19.4%
LPNs: 24.8%

A close-up of a camera lens shows the **infinity symbol,** ∞, defined in this case as any distance greater than 1000 times the focal length of a lens.

The sign was invented by the mathematician John Wallis in 1655. Wallis used $1/\infty$ to represent an infinitely small quantity.

EXAMPLE 4 Designating an Infinite Set

Designate all odd counting numbers by the three common methods of set notation.

Solution

The set of all odd counting numbers	Word description
$\{1, 3, 5, 7, 9, \dots\}$	Listing method
$\{x \mid x \text{ is an odd counting number}\}$	Set-builder notation

Equality of Sets

SET EQUALITY

Set A is **equal** to set B provided the following two conditions are met:

1. Every element of A is an element of B, and
2. Every element of B is an element of A.

Two sets are equal if they contain exactly the same elements, regardless of order.

$$\{a, b, c, d\} = \{a, c, d, b\} \quad \text{Both sets contain exactly the same elements.}$$

Repetition of elements in a set listing does not add new elements.

$$\{1, 0, 1, 5, 3, 3\} = \{0, 1, 3, 5\} \quad \text{Both sets contain exactly the same elements.}$$

EXAMPLE 5 Determining Whether Two Sets Are Equal

Are $\{-4, 3, 2, 5\}$ and $\{-4, 0, 3, 2, 5\}$ equal sets?

Solution

Every element of the first set is an element of the second. However, 0 is an element of the second and not of the first. The sets do not contain exactly the same elements.

$$\{-4, 3, 2, 5\} \neq \{-4, 0, 3, 2, 5\} \quad \text{The sets are not equal.}$$

Two sets are **equivalent** if they have the *same number* of elements. (See **Exercises 87–90.**) Georg Cantor extended the idea of equivalence to infinite sets, used one-to-one correspondence to establish equivalence, and showed that, surprisingly, the natural numbers, the whole numbers, the integers, and the rational numbers are all equivalent. The elements of any one of these sets will match up, one-to-one, with those of any other, with no elements left over in either set. All these sets have cardinal number $\aleph_0$ (which is read **aleph null**).

However, the irrational numbers and the real numbers, though equivalent to one another, are of a higher infinite order than the sets mentioned above. Their cardinal number is denoted **c** (representing the **continuum** of points on a line).

EXAMPLE 6 Determining Whether Two Sets Are Equal

Decide whether each statement is *true* or *false*.

(a) $\{3\} = \{x \mid x \text{ is a counting number between 1 and 5}\}$

(b) $\{x \mid x \text{ is a negative whole number}\} = \{y \mid y \text{ is a number that is both rational and irrational}\}$

(c) $\{(0, 0), (1, 1), (2, 4)\} = \{(x, y) \mid x \text{ is a natural number less than 3, and } y = x^2\}$

Solution

(a) The set on the right contains *all* counting numbers between 1 and 5, namely 2, 3, and 4, while the set on the left contains *only* the number 3. Because the sets do not contain exactly the same elements, they are not equal. The statement is *false*.

(b) No whole numbers are negative, so the set on the left is $\varnothing$. By definition, if a number is rational, it cannot be irrational, so the set on the right is also $\varnothing$. Because each set is the empty set, the sets are equal. The statement is *true*.

(c) The first listed ordered pair in the set on the left has x-value 0, which is not a natural number. Therefore, the ordered pair $(0, 0)$ is not an element of the set on the right, even though the relationship $y = x^2$ is true for $(0, 0)$. Thus the sets are not equal. The statement is *false*.

2.1 EXERCISES

Match each set in Group I with the appropriate description in Group II.

I

1. $\{1, 3, 5, 7, 9\}$

2. $\{x \mid x$ is an even integer greater than 4 and less than 6$\}$

3. $\{\ldots, -4, -3, -2, -1\}$

4. $\{\ldots, -5, -3, -1, 1, 3, 5, \ldots\}$

5. $\{2, 4, 8, 16, 32\}$

6. $\{\ldots, -4, -2, 0, 2, 4, \ldots\}$

7. $\{2, 4, 6, 8, 10\}$

8. $\{2, 4, 6, 8\}$

II

A. the set of all even integers

B. the set of the five least positive integer powers of 2

C. the set of even positive integers less than 10

D. the set of all odd integers

E. the set of all negative integers

F. the set of odd positive integers less than 10

G. $\varnothing$

H. the set of the five least positive integer multiples of 2

List all the elements of each set. Use set notation and the listing method to describe the set.

9. the set of all counting numbers less than or equal to 6

10. the set of all whole numbers greater than 8 and less than 18

11. the set of all whole numbers not greater than 4

12. the set of all natural numbers between 4 and 14

13. $\{6, 7, 8, \ldots, 14\}$

14. $\{3, 6, 9, 12, \ldots, 30\}$

15. $\{2, 4, 8, \ldots, 256\}$

16. $\{90, 87, 84, \ldots, 69\}$

17. $\{x \mid x$ is an even whole number less than 11$\}$

18. $\{x \mid x$ is an odd integer between -8 and 7$\}$

Denote each set by the listing method. There may be more than one correct answer.

19. the set of all multiples of 20 that are greater than 200

20. $\{x \mid x$ is a negative multiple of 6$\}$

21. the set of U.S. Great Lakes

22. the set of U.S. presidents who served after Richard Nixon and before Barack Obama

23. $\{x \mid x$ is the reciprocal of a natural number$\}$

24. $\{x \mid x$ is a positive integer power of 4$\}$

25. $\{(x, y) \mid x$ and y are whole numbers and $x^2 + y^2 = 25\}$

26. $\{(x, y) \mid x$ and y are integers, and $x^2 = 9y^2 + 16\}$

Denote each set by set-builder notation, using x as the variable. There may be more than one correct answer.

27. the set of all rational numbers

28. the set of all even natural numbers

29. $\{1, 3, 5, \ldots, 75\}$

30. $\{35, 40, 45, \ldots, 95\}$

Give a word description for each set. There may be more than one correct answer.

31. $\{-9, -8, -7, \ldots, 7, 8, 9\}$

32. $\left\{\dfrac{1}{2}, \dfrac{2}{3}, \dfrac{3}{4}, \ldots\right\}$

33. $\{$Alabama, Alaska, Arizona, $\ldots$, Wisconsin, Wyoming$\}$

34. $\{$Alaska, California, Hawaii, Oregon, Washington$\}$

Identify each set as finite *or* infinite.

35. $\{2, 4, 6, \ldots, 932\}$

36. $\{6, 12, 18\}$

37. $\left\{1, \dfrac{1}{2}, \dfrac{1}{3}, \dfrac{1}{4}, \ldots\right\}$

38. $\{3, 6, 9, \ldots\}$

39. $\{x \mid x$ is a natural number greater than 50$\}$

40. $\{x \mid x$ is a natural number less than 50$\}$

41. $\{x \mid x$ is a rational number$\}$

42. $\{x \mid x$ is a rational number between 0 and 1$\}$

Find n(A) for each set.

43. $A = \{0, 1, 2, 3, 4, 5, 6, 7\}$

44. $A = \{-3, -1, 1, 3, 5, 7, 9\}$

45. $A = \{2, 4, 6, \ldots, 1000\}$

46. $A = \{0, 1, 2, 3, \ldots, 2000\}$

47. $A = \{a, b, c, \ldots, z\}$

48. $A = \{x \mid x$ is a vowel in the English alphabet$\}$

49. $A =$ the set of integers between -20 and 20

50. $A =$ the set of sanctioned U.S. senate seats

51. $A = \left\{ \dfrac{1}{3}, \dfrac{2}{4}, \dfrac{3}{5}, \dfrac{4}{6}, \ldots, \dfrac{27}{29}, \dfrac{28}{30} \right\}$

52. $A = \left\{ \dfrac{1}{2}, -\dfrac{1}{2}, \dfrac{1}{3}, -\dfrac{1}{3}, \ldots, \dfrac{1}{10}, -\dfrac{1}{10} \right\}$

53. Although x is a consonant, why can we write

"x is a vowel in the English alphabet"

in **Exercise 48?**

54. Explain how **Exercise 51** can be answered without actually listing and then counting all the elements.

Identify each set as well defined *or* not well defined.

55. $\{x \mid x$ is a real number$\}$

56. $\{x \mid x$ is a good athlete$\}$

57. $\{x \mid x$ is a difficult course$\}$

58. $\{x \mid x$ is a counting number less than 2$\}$

Fill each blank with either $\in$ or $\notin$ to make each statement true.

59. 3 ___ $\{2, 4, 5, 7\}$

60. -4 ___ $\{4, 7, 8, 12\}$

61. 8 ___ $\{3, 8, 12, 18\}$

62. 0 ___ $\{-2, 0, 5, 9\}$

63. 8 ___ $\{10 - 2, 10\}$

64. $\{6\}$ ___ $\{5 + 1, 6 + 1\}$

65. Is the statement $\{0\} = \varnothing$ true, or is it false?

66. The statement

$$3 \in \{9 - 6, 8 - 6, 7 - 6\}$$

is true even though the *symbol* 3 does not appear in the set. Explain.

Write true *or* false *for each statement.*

67. $3 \in \{2, 5, 6, 8\}$

68. $m \in \{l, m, n, o, p\}$

69. $c \in \{c, d, a, b\}$

70. $2 \in \{-2, 5, 8, 9\}$

71. $\{k, c, r, a\} = \{k, c, a, r\}$

72. $\{e, h, a, n\} = \{a, h, e, n\}$

73. $\{5, 8, 9\} = \{5, 8, 9, 0\}$

74. $\{3, 7\} = \{3, 7, 0\}$

75. $\{4\} \in \{\{3\}, \{4\}, \{5\}\}$

76. $4 \in \{\{3\}, \{4\}, \{5\}\}$

77. $\{x \mid x$ is a natural number less than 3$\} = \{1, 2\}$

78. $\{x \mid x$ is a natural number greater than 10$\}$
$= \{11, 12, 13, \ldots\}$

Write true *or* false *for each statement in Exercises 79–84.*

Let $A = \{2, 4, 6, 8, 10, 12\}$, $B = \{2, 4, 8, 10\}$,
and $C = \{4, 10, 12\}$.

79. $4 \in A$

80. $10 \in B$

81. $4 \notin C$

82. $10 \notin A$

83. Every element of C is also an element of A.

84. Every element of C is also an element of B.

85. The human mind likes to create collections. Why do you suppose this is so? In your explanation, use one or more particular "collections," mathematical or otherwise.

86. Explain the difference between a well-defined set and a set that is not well defined. Give examples, and use terms introduced in this section.

*Two sets are **equal** if they contain identical elements. Two sets are **equivalent** if they contain the same number of elements (but not necessarily the same elements). For each condition, give an example or explain why it is impossible.*

87. two sets that are neither equal nor equivalent

88. two sets that are equal but not equivalent

89. two sets that are equivalent but not equal

90. two sets that are both equal and equivalent

91. *Hiring Nurses* A medical organization plans to hire three nurses from the pool of applicants shown.

Name	Certification
Bernice	RN
Heather	RN
Marcy	LVN
Natalie	LVN
Susan	RN

Show all possible sets of hires that would include

(a) two RNs and one LVN.

(b) one RN and two LVNs.

(c) no LVNs.

92. *Burning Calories* Candice Cotton likes cotton candy, each serving of which contains 220 calories. To burn off unwanted calories, Candice participates in her favorite activities, shown in the next column, in increments of 1 hour and never repeats a given activity on a given day.

Activity	Symbol	Calories Burned per Hour
Volleyball	v	160
Golf	g	260
Canoeing	c	340
Swimming	s	410
Running	r	680

(a) On Monday, Candice has time for no more than two hours of activities. List all possible sets of activities that would burn off at least the number of calories obtained from three cotton candies.

(b) Assume that Candice can afford up to three hours of time for activities on Wednesday. List all sets of activities that would burn off at least the number of calories in five cotton candies.

(c) Candice can spend up to four hours in activities on Saturday. List all sets of activities that would burn off at least the number of calories in seven cotton candies.

2.2   VENN DIAGRAMS AND SUBSETS

OBJECTIVES

1 Use Venn diagrams to depict set relationships.

2 Determine the complement of a set within a universal set.

3 Determine whether one set is a subset of another.

4 Understand the distinction between a subset and a proper subset.

5 Determine the number of subsets of a given set.

Venn Diagrams

In most discussions, there is either a stated or an implied **universe of discourse.** The universe of discourse includes all things under discussion at a given time. For example, if the topic of interest is what courses to offer at a vocational school, the universe of discourse might be all students at the school, or the board of trustees of the school, or the members of a local overseer board, or the members of a state regulatory agency, or perhaps all these groups of people.

In set theory, the universe of discourse is called the **universal set,** typically designated by the letter **U.** The universal set might change from one discussion to another.

Also in set theory, we commonly use **Venn diagrams,** developed by the logician John Venn (1834–1923). In these diagrams, the universal set is represented by a rectangle, and other sets of interest within the universal set are depicted by circular regions (sometimes ovals or other shapes). See **Figure 1.**

Complement of a Set

The colored region inside U and outside the circle in **Figure 1** is labeled **A′** (read "**A** prime"). This set, called the *complement* of A, contains all elements that are contained in U but are not contained in A.

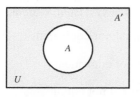

The entire region bounded by the rectangle represents the universal set U, and the portion bounded by the circle represents set A.

Figure 1

> **THE COMPLEMENT OF A SET**
>
> For any set A within a universal set U, the **complement** of A, written A', is the set of elements of U that are not elements of A. That is,
>
> $$A' = \{x \mid x \in U \text{ and } x \notin A\}.$$

EXAMPLE 1 Finding Complements

Find each set.

Let $U = \{a, b, c, d, e, f, g, h\}$, $M = \{a, b, e, f\}$, and $N = \{b, d, e, g, h\}$.

(a) M' **(b)** N'

Solution

(a) Set M' contains all the elements of set U that are *not* in set M. Because set M contains a, b, e, and f, these elements will be disqualified from belonging to set M'.

$$M' = \{c, d, g, h\}$$

(b) Set N' contains all the elements of U that are not in set N, so $N' = \{a, c, f\}$. ∎

Consider the complement of the universal set, U'. The set U' is found by selecting all the elements of U that do not belong to U. There are no such elements, so there can be no elements in set U'. This means that for any universal set U,

$$U' = \varnothing.$$

Now consider the complement of the empty set, $\varnothing'$. The set $\varnothing'$ includes all elements of U that do *not* belong to $\varnothing$. All elements of U qualify, because none of them belongs to $\varnothing$. Therefore, for any universal set U,

$$\varnothing' = U.$$

Subsets of a Set

Suppose that we are given the universal set $U = \{1, 2, 3, 4, 5\}$, while $A = \{1, 2, 3\}$. Every element of set A is also an element of set U. Because of this, set A is called a *subset* of set U, written

$$A \subseteq U.$$

("A is not a subset of set U" would be written $A \nsubseteq U$.)

A Venn diagram showing that set M is a subset of set N is shown in **Figure 2**.

Figure 2

SUBSET OF A SET

Set A is a **subset** of set B if every element of A is also an element of B. This is written $A \subseteq B.$

EXAMPLE 2 Determining If One Set Is a Subset of Another

Write $\subseteq$ or $\nsubseteq$ in each blank to make a true statement.

(a) $\{3, 4, 5, 6\}$ _____ $\{3, 4, 5, 6, 8\}$ **(b)** $\{1, 2, 6\}$ _____ $\{2, 4, 6, 8\}$

(c) $\{5, 6, 7, 8\}$ _____ $\{6, 5, 8, 7\}$

Solution

(a) Because every element of $\{3, 4, 5, 6\}$ is also an element of $\{3, 4, 5, 6, 8\}$, the first set is a subset of the second, so $\subseteq$ goes in the blank.

$$\{3, 4, 5, 6\} \subseteq \{3, 4, 5, 6, 8\}$$

(b) $\{1, 2, 6\} \nsubseteq \{2, 4, 6, 8\}$ 1 does not belong to $\{2, 4, 6, 8\}$.

(c) $\{5, 6, 7, 8\} \subseteq \{6, 5, 8, 7\}$ ∎

As **Example 2(c)** suggests, every set is a subset of itself.

$$B \subseteq B, \quad \text{for any set } B.$$

SET EQUALITY (ALTERNATIVE DEFINITION)

Suppose A and B are sets. Then $A = B$ if $A \subseteq B$ and $B \subseteq A$ are both true.

Proper Subsets

Suppose that we are given the following sets.

$$B = \{5, 6, 7, 8\} \quad \text{and} \quad A = \{6, 7\}$$

A is a subset of B, but A is not all of B. There is at least one element in B that is not in A. (Actually, in this case there are two such elements, 5 and 8.) In this situation, A is called a *proper subset* of B, written $A \subset B$.

Notice the similarity of the subset symbols, $\subset$ and $\subseteq$, to the inequality symbols from algebra, $<$ and $\leq$.

PROPER SUBSET OF A SET

Set A is a **proper subset** of set B if $A \subseteq B$ and $A \neq B$. This is written $\boldsymbol{A \subset B}$.

EXAMPLE 3 **Determining Subsets and Proper Subsets**

Decide whether $\subset$, $\subseteq$, or both could be placed in each blank to make a true statement.

(a) $\{5, 6, 7\}$ _____ $\{5, 6, 7, 8\}$ **(b)** $\{a, b, c\}$ _____ $\{a, b, c\}$

Solution

(a) Every element of $\{5, 6, 7\}$ is contained in $\{5, 6, 7, 8\}$, so $\subseteq$ could be placed in the blank. Also, the element 8 belongs to $\{5, 6, 7, 8\}$ but not to $\{5, 6, 7\}$, making $\{5, 6, 7\}$ a proper subset of $\{5, 6, 7, 8\}$. Thus $\subset$ could also be placed in the blank.

(b) The set $\{a, b, c\}$ is a subset of $\{a, b, c\}$. Because the two sets are equal, $\{a, b, c\}$ is not a proper subset of $\{a, b, c\}$. Only $\subseteq$ may be placed in the blank. ∎

Set A is a subset of set B if every element of set A is also an element of set B. Alternatively, we say that set A is a subset of set B if there are no elements of A that are not also elements of B. Thus, the empty set is a subset of any set.

$$\varnothing \subseteq B, \quad \text{for any set } B.$$

One-to-one correspondence was employed by Georg Cantor to establish many controversial facts about infinite sets. For example, the correspondence

$$\{1, 2, 3, 4, \ldots, n, \ldots\}$$
$$\updownarrow \updownarrow \updownarrow \updownarrow \quad \updownarrow$$
$$\{2, 4, 6, 8, \ldots, 2n, \ldots\},$$

which can be continued indefinitely without leaving any elements in either set unpaired, shows that the counting numbers and the even counting numbers are equivalent (have the same number of elements), even though logic may seem to say that the first set has twice as many elements as the second.

This is true because it is not possible to find any element of $\varnothing$ that is not also in B. (There are no elements in $\varnothing$.) The empty set $\varnothing$ is a proper subset of every set except itself.

$$\varnothing \subset B \quad \text{if } B \text{ is any set other than } \varnothing.$$

Every set (except $\varnothing$) has at least two subsets, $\varnothing$ and the set itself.

EXAMPLE 4 **Listing All Subsets of a Set**

Find all possible subsets of each set.

(a) $\{7, 8\}$ **(b)** $\{a, b, c\}$

Solution

(a) By trial and error, the set $\{7, 8\}$ has four subsets: $\varnothing, \{7\}, \{8\}, \{7, 8\}$.

(b) Here, trial and error leads to eight subsets for $\{a, b, c\}$:

$$\varnothing, \{a\}, \{b\}, \{c\}, \{a, b\}, \{a, c\}, \{b, c\}, \{a, b, c\}. \quad \blacksquare$$

35. The Venn diagram below correctly represents the relationship among sets *A*, *D*, and *U*.

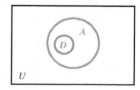

36. The Venn diagram below correctly represents the relationship among sets *B*, *C*, and *U*.

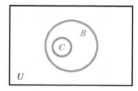

For Exercises 37–40, find **(a)** *the number of subsets and* **(b)** *the number of proper subsets of each set.*

37. {a, b, c, d, e, f }

38. the set of days of the week

39. {*x* | *x* is an odd integer between −4 and 6}

40. {*x* | *x* is an even whole number less than 4}

For Exercises 41–44, let $U = \{1, 2, 3, 4, 5, 6, 7, 8, 9, 10\}$ *and find the complement of each set.*

41. *U*   **42.** ∅

43. {1, 2, 3, 4, 6, 8}   **44.** {2, 5, 9, 10}

Vacationing in California   *Terry is planning a trip with her two sons to California. In weighing her options concerning whether to fly or drive from their home in Iowa, she has listed the following considerations.*

Fly to California	Drive to California
Higher cost	Lower cost
Educational	Educational
More time to see the sights in California	Less time to see the sights in California
Cannot visit friends along the way	Can visit friends along the way

Refer to the table for Exercises 45–50.

45. Find the smallest universal set *U* that contains all listed considerations of both options.

Let F represent the set of considerations of the flying option and let D represent the set of considerations of the driving option. Use the universal set from ***Exercise 45.***

46. Give the set *F* ′.   **47.** Give the set *D* ′.

Find the set of elements common to both sets in Exercises 48–50.

48. *F* and *D*   **49.** *F* ′ and *D* ′

50. *F* and *D* ′

Meeting in the Conference Room   *Amie, Bruce, Corey, Dwayne, and Eric, members of an architectural firm, plan to meet in the company conference room to discuss the project coordinator's plans for their next project. Denoting these five people by A, B, C, D, and E, list all the possible sets of this group in which the given number of them can gather.*

51. five people   **52.** four people

53. three people   **54.** two people

55. one person   **56.** no people

57. Find the total number of ways that members of this group can gather. (*Hint:* Find the total number of sets in your answers to **Exercises 51–56.**)

58. How does your answer in **Exercise 57** compare with the number of subsets of a set of five elements? Interpret the answer to **Exercise 57** in terms of subsets.

59. **Selecting a Club Delegation**   The twenty-five members of the mathematics club must send a delegation to a meeting for student groups at their school. The delegation can include as many members of the club as desired, but at least one member must attend. How many different delegations are possible? (*Mathematics Teacher* calendar problem)

60. In **Exercise 59,** suppose ten of the club members say they do not want to be part of the delegation. Now how many delegations are possible?

61. **Selecting Bills**   Suppose you have the bills shown here.

(a) How many sums of money can you make using nonempty subsets of these bills?

(b) Repeat part (a) without the condition "nonempty."

62. *Selecting Coins* The photo shows a group of obsolete U.S. coins, consisting of one each of the penny, nickel, dime, quarter, and half dollar. Repeat **Exercise 61,** replacing "bill(s)" with "coin(s)."

63. In discovering the expression (2^n) for finding the number of subsets of a set with n elements, we observed that for the first few values of n, increasing the number of elements by one doubles the number of subsets.

Here, you can prove the formula in general by showing that the same is true for any value of n. Assume set A has n elements and s subsets. Now add one additional element, say e, to the set A. (We now have a new set, say B, with $n + 1$ elements.) Divide the subsets of B into those that do not contain e and those that do.

(a) How many subsets of B do not contain e? (*Hint:* Each of these is a subset of the original set A.)

(b) How many subsets of B do contain e? (*Hint:* Each of these would be a subset of the original set A, with the additional element e included.)

(c) What is the total number of subsets of B?

(d) What do you conclude?

64. Explain why $\varnothing$ is both a subset and an element of $\{\varnothing\}$.

2.3   SET OPERATIONS

OBJECTIVES

1 Determine intersections of sets.

2 Determine unions of sets.

3 Determine the difference of two sets.

4 Understand ordered pairs and their uses.

5 Determine Cartesian products of sets.

6 Analyze sets and set operations with Venn diagrams.

7 Apply De Morgan's laws for sets.

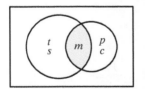

Figure 4

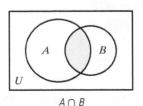

$A \cap B$
Figure 5

Intersection of Sets

Two candidates, Aimee and Darien, are running for a seat on the city council. A voter deciding for whom she should vote recalled the campaign promises, each given a code letter, made by the candidates.

Honest Aimee	Determined Darien
Spend less money, m	Spend less money, m
Emphasize traffic law enforcement, t	Crack down on crooked politicians, p
Increase service to suburban areas, s	Increase service to the city, c

The only promise common to both candidates is promise m, to spend less money. Suppose we take each candidate's promises to be a set. The promises of Aimee give the set $\{m, t, s\}$, while the promises of Darien give $\{m, p, c\}$. The common element m belongs to the *intersection* of the two sets, as shown in color in the Venn diagram in **Figure 4.**

$$\{m, t, s\} \cap \{m, p, c\} = \{m\} \quad \cap \text{ represents set intersection.}$$

The intersection of two sets is itself a set.

INTERSECTION OF SETS

The **intersection** of sets A and B, written $A \cap B$, is the set of elements common to both A and B.

$$A \cap B = \{x \mid x \in A \text{ and } x \in B\}$$

Form the intersection of sets A and B by taking all the elements included in both sets, as shown in color in **Figure 5.**

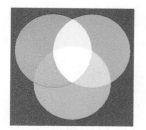

White light can be viewed as the intersection of the three primary colors.

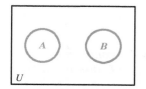

Disjoint sets

Figure 6

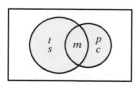

Figure 7

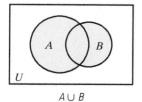

$A \cup B$

Figure 8

EXAMPLE 1   Finding Intersections

Find each intersection.

(a) $\{3, 4, 5, 6, 7\} \cap \{4, 6, 8, 10\}$ **(b)** $\{9, 14, 25, 30\} \cap \{10, 17, 19, 38, 52\}$

(c) $\{5, 9, 11\} \cap \varnothing$

Solution

(a) The elements common to both sets are 4 and 6.

$$\{3, 4, 5, 6, 7\} \cap \{4, 6, 8, 10\} = \{4, 6\}$$

(b) These two sets have no elements in common.

$$\{9, 14, 25, 30\} \cap \{10, 17, 19, 38, 52\} = \varnothing$$

(c) There are no elements in $\varnothing$, so there can be no elements belonging to both $\{5, 9, 11\}$ and $\varnothing$.

$$\{5, 9, 11\} \cap \varnothing = \varnothing$$ ∎

Examples 1(b) and 1(c) show two sets that have no elements in common. Sets with no elements in common are called **disjoint sets.** (See **Figure 6.**) A set of dogs and a set of cats would be disjoint sets.

Sets A and B are disjoint if $A \cap B = \varnothing$.

Union of Sets

Referring again to the lists of campaign promises, suppose a pollster wants to summarize the types of promises made by the candidates. The pollster would need to study *all* the promises made by *either* candidate, or the set

$$\{m, t, s, p, c\}.$$

This set is the *union* of the sets of promises, as shown in color in the Venn diagram in **Figure 7.**

> Be careful not to confuse this symbol with the universal set U.

$$\{m, t, s\} \cup \{m, p, c\} = \{m, t, s, p, c\}$$ $\cup$ denotes set union.

Again, the union of two sets is a set.

> **UNION OF SETS**
>
> The **union** of sets A and B, written $A \cup B$, is the set of all elements belonging to either A or B.
>
> $$A \cup B = \{x \mid x \in A \text{ or } x \in B\}$$

Form the union of sets A and B by first taking every element of set A and then also including every element of set B that is not already listed. See Figure 8.

EXAMPLE 2 Finding Unions

Find each union.

(a) $\{2, 4, 6\} \cup \{4, 6, 8, 10, 12\}$ **(b)** $\{a, b, d, f, g, h\} \cup \{c, f, g, h, k\}$

(c) $\{3, 4, 5\} \cup \varnothing$

Solution

(a) Start by listing all the elements from the first set, 2, 4, and 6. Then list all the elements from the second set that are not in the first set, 8, 10, and 12. The union is made up of *all* these elements.

$$\{2, 4, 6\} \cup \{4, 6, 8, 10, 12\} = \{2, 4, 6, 8, 10, 12\}$$

(b) $\{a, b, d, f, g, h\} \cup \{c, f, g, h, k\} = \{a, b, c, d, f, g, h, k\}$

(c) Because there are no elements in $\varnothing$, the union of $\{3, 4, 5\}$ and $\varnothing$ contains only the elements 3, 4, and 5.

$$\{3, 4, 5\} \cup \varnothing = \{3, 4, 5\}$$ ■

Recall from the previous section that A' represents the *complement* of set A. *Set A' is formed by taking every element of the universal set U that is not in set A.*

EXAMPLE 3 Finding Intersections and Unions of Complements

Find each set. Let

$$U = \{1, 2, 3, 4, 5, 6, 9\}, \quad A = \{1, 2, 3, 4\}, \quad B = \{2, 4, 6\}, \quad \text{and} \quad C = \{1, 3, 6, 9\}.$$

(a) $A' \cap B$ **(b)** $B' \cup C'$ **(c)** $A \cap (B \cup C')$ **(d)** $(B \cup C)'$

Solution

(a) First identify the elements of set A', the elements of U that are not in set A.

$$A' = \{5, 6, 9\}$$

Now, find $A' \cap B$, the set of elements belonging both to A' and to B.

$$A' \cap B = \{5, 6, 9\} \cap \{2, 4, 6\} = \{6\}$$

(b) $B' \cup C' = \{1, 3, 5, 9\} \cup \{2, 4, 5\} = \{1, 2, 3, 4, 5, 9\}$

(c) First find the set inside the parentheses.

$$B \cup C' = \{2, 4, 6\} \cup \{2, 4, 5\} = \{2, 4, 5, 6\}$$

Now, find the intersection of this set with A.

$$A \cap (B \cup C') = A \cap \{2, 4, 5, 6\}$$
$$= \{1, 2, 3, 4\} \cap \{2, 4, 5, 6\}$$
$$= \{2, 4\}$$

(d) $B \cup C = \{2, 4, 6\} \cup \{1, 3, 6, 9\} = \{1, 2, 3, 4, 6, 9\}$,   so

$$(B \cup C)' = \{5\}.$$ ■

Comparing **Examples 3(b)** and **3(d)**, we see that, interestingly, $(B \cup C)'$ is not the same as $B' \cup C'$. This fact will be investigated further later in this section.

FOR FURTHER THOUGHT

Comparing Properties

The arithmetic operations of addition and multiplication, when applied to numbers, have some familiar properties. If a, b, and c are *real numbers*, then the **commutative property of addition** says that the order of the numbers being added makes no difference:

$$a + b = b + a.$$

(Is there a **commutative property of multiplication?**) The **associative property of addition** says that when three numbers are added, the grouping used makes no difference:

$$(a + b) + c = a + (b + c).$$

(Is there an **associative property of multiplication?**) The number 0 is called the **identity element for addition** since adding it to any number does not change that number:

$$a + 0 = a.$$

(What is the **identity element for multiplication?**) Finally, the **distributive property of multiplication over addition** says that

$$a(b + c) = ab + ac.$$

(Is there a distributive property of addition over multiplication?)

For Group or Individual Investigation

Now consider the operations of union and intersection, applied to sets. By recalling definitions, trying examples, or using Venn diagrams, answer the following questions.

1. Is set union commutative?   Set intersection?
2. Is set union associative?   Set intersection?
3. Is there an identity element for set union? If so, what is it? How about set intersection?
4. Is set intersection distributive over set union? Is set union distributive over set intersection?

EXAMPLE 4 Describing Sets in Words

Describe each set in words.

(a) $A \cap (B \cup C')$ **(b)** $(A' \cup C') \cap B'$

Solution

(a) This set might be described as "the set of all elements that are in A, and also are in B or not in C."

(b) One possibility is "the set of all elements that are not in A or not in C, and also are not in B." ∎

Difference of Sets

Suppose that $A = \{1, 2, 3, \ldots, 10\}$ and $B = \{2, 4, 6, 8, 10\}$. If the elements of B are excluded (or taken away) from A, the set $C = \{1, 3, 5, 7, 9\}$ is obtained. C is called the *difference* of sets A and B.

DIFFERENCE OF SETS

The **difference** of sets A and B, written $A - B$, is the set of all elements belonging to set A and not to set B.

$$A - B = \{x \mid x \in A \text{ and } x \notin B\}$$

Assume a universal set U containing both A and B. Then because $x \notin B$ has the same meaning as $x \in B'$, the set difference $A - B$ can also be described as

$$\{x \mid x \in A \text{ and } x \in B'\}, \quad \text{or} \quad A \cap B'.$$

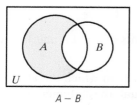

$A - B$

Figure 9

Figure 9 illustrates the idea of set difference. The region in color represents $A - B$.

EXAMPLE 5 Finding Set Differences

Find each set.

$$\text{Let} \quad U = \{1, 2, 3, 4, 5, 6, 7\}, \quad A = \{1, 2, 3, 4, 5, 6\},$$
$$B = \{2, 3, 6\}, \quad \text{and} \quad C = \{3, 5, 7\}.$$

(a) $A - B$ **(b)** $B - A$ **(c)** $(A - B) \cup C'$

Solution

(a) Begin with set A and exclude any elements found also in set B.

$$A - B = \{1, 2, 3, 4, 5, 6\} - \{2, 3, 6\} = \{1, 4, 5\}$$

(b) To be in $B - A$, an element must be in set B and not in set A. But all elements of B are also in A. Thus, $B - A = \varnothing$.

(c) From part (a), $A - B = \{1, 4, 5\}$. Also, $C' = \{1, 2, 4, 6\}$.

$$(A - B) \cup C' = \{1, 2, 4, 5, 6\} \qquad \blacksquare$$

The results in **Examples 5(a) and 5(b)** illustrate that, in general,

$$\boldsymbol{A - B \neq B - A.}$$

Ordered Pairs

When writing a set that contains several elements, the order in which the elements appear is not relevant. For example,

$$\{1, 5\} = \{5, 1\}.$$

However, there are many instances in mathematics where, when two objects are paired, the order in which the objects are written is important. This leads to the idea of *ordered pair*. When writing ordered pairs, use parentheses rather than braces, which are reserved for writing sets.

ORDERED PAIRS

In the **ordered pair** (a, b), a is called the **first component** and b is called the **second component**. In general, $(a, b) \neq (b, a)$.

Two ordered pairs (a, b) and (c, d) are **equal** provided that their first components are equal and their second components are equal.

$$\boldsymbol{(a, b) = (c, d) \quad \text{if and only if} \quad a = c \quad \text{and} \quad b = d.}$$

EXAMPLE 6 Determining Equality of Sets and of Ordered Pairs

Decide whether each statement is *true* or *false*.

(a) $(3, 4) = (5 - 2, 1 + 3)$ **(b)** $\{3, 4\} \neq \{4, 3\}$ **(c)** $(7, 4) = (4, 7)$

Solution

(a) Because $3 = 5 - 2$ and $4 = 1 + 3$, the first components are equal and the second components are equal. The statement is *true*.

(b) Because these are sets and not ordered pairs, the order in which the elements are listed is not important. Because these sets are equal, the statement is *false*.

(c) The ordered pairs $(7, 4)$ and $(4, 7)$ are not equal because their corresponding components are not equal. The statement is *false*. $\qquad \blacksquare$

Cartesian Product of Sets

A set may contain ordered pairs as elements. If A and B are sets, then each element of A can be paired with each element of B, and the results can be written as ordered pairs. The set of all such ordered pairs is called the *Cartesian product* of A and B, which is written $A \times B$ and read **"A cross B."** The name comes from that of the French mathematician René Descartes, profiled in **Chapter 8.**

CARTESIAN PRODUCT OF SETS

The **Cartesian product** of sets A and B is defined as follows.

$$A \times B = \{(a, b) \mid a \in A \text{ and } b \in B\}$$

EXAMPLE 7 **Finding Cartesian Products**

Let $A = \{1, 5, 9\}$ and $B = \{6, 7\}$. Find each set.

(a) $A \times B$ **(b)** $B \times A$

Solution

(a) Pair each element of A with each element of B. Write the results as ordered pairs, with the element of A written first and the element of B written second. Write as a set.

$$A \times B = \{(1, 6), (1, 7), (5, 6), (5, 7), (9, 6), (9, 7)\}$$

(b) Because B is listed first, this set will consist of ordered pairs that have their components interchanged when compared to those in part (a).

$$B \times A = \{(6, 1), (7, 1), (6, 5), (7, 5), (6, 9), (7, 9)\}$$ ■

The order in which the ordered pairs themselves are listed is not important. For example, another way to write $B \times A$ in **Example 7(b)** would be

$$\{(6, 1), (6, 5), (6, 9), (7, 1), (7, 5), (7, 9)\}.$$

From **Example 7** it can be seen that, in general,

$$A \times B \neq B \times A,$$

because they do not contain exactly the same ordered pairs. However, each set contains the same *number* of elements, six. Furthermore, $n(A) = 3$, $n(B) = 2$, and $n(A \times B) = n(B \times A) \doteq 6$. Because $3 \cdot 2 = 6$, one might conclude that the cardinal number of the Cartesian product of two sets is equal to the product of the cardinal numbers of the sets. In general, this conclusion is correct.

CARDINAL NUMBER OF A CARTESIAN PRODUCT

If $n(A) = a$ and $n(B) = b$, then the following is true.

$$n(A \times B) = n(B \times A) = n(A) \cdot n(B) = n(B) \cdot n(A) = ab = ba$$

EXAMPLE 8 **Finding Cardinal Numbers of Cartesian Products**

Find $n(A \times B)$ and $n(B \times A)$ from the given information.

(a) $A = \{a, b, c, d, e, f, g\}$ and $B = \{2, 4, 6\}$ **(b)** $n(A) = 24$ and $n(B) = 5$

Solution

(a) Because $n(A) = 7$ and $n(B) = 3$, $n(A \times B)$ and $n(B \times A)$ both equal $7 \cdot 3$, or 21.

(b) $n(A \times B) = n(B \times A) = 24 \cdot 5 = 5 \cdot 24 = 120$ ■

An **operation** is a rule or procedure by which one or more objects are used to obtain another object. The most common operations on sets are summarized in the following box.

SET OPERATIONS

Let A and B be any sets within a universal set U.

The **complement** of A, written A', is

$$A' = \{x \mid x \in U \text{ and } x \notin A\}.$$

The **intersection** of A and B is

$$A \cap B = \{x \mid x \in A \text{ and } x \in B\}.$$

The **union** of A and B is

$$A \cup B = \{x \mid x \in A \text{ or } x \in B\}.$$

The **difference** of A and B is

$$A - B = \{x \mid x \in A \text{ and } x \notin B\}.$$

The **Cartesian product** of A and B is

$$A \times B = \{(x, y) \mid x \in A \text{ and } y \in B\}.$$

More on Venn Diagrams

It is often helpful to use numbers in Venn diagrams, as in **Figures 10, 11, and 12,** depending on whether the discussion involves one, two, or three (distinct) sets, respectively. In each case, the numbers are neither elements nor cardinal numbers, but simply arbitrary labels for the various regions within the diagram.

In **Figure 11,** region 3 includes the elements belonging to both A and B, while region 4 includes those elements (if any) belonging to B but not to A. How would you describe region 7 in **Figure 12?**

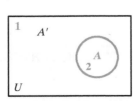

Figure 10

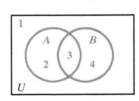

Figure 11

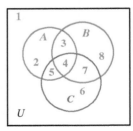

Figure 12

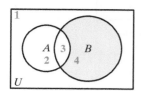

Figure 13

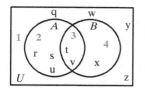

Figure 14

 Shading Venn Diagrams to Represent Sets

Draw a Venn diagram similar to **Figure 11,** and shade the region or regions representing each set.

(a) $A' \cap B$ **(b)** $A' \cup B'$

Solution

(a) See **Figure 11.** Set A' contains all the elements outside of set A—in other words, the elements in regions 1 and 4. Set B contains the elements in regions 3 and 4. The intersection of sets A' and B is made up of the elements in the region common to (1 and 4) and (3 and 4), which is region 4. Thus, $A' \cap B$ is represented by region 4, shown in color in **Figure 13.** This region can also be described as $B - A$.

(b) Again, set A' is represented by regions 1 and 4, and B' is made up of regions 1 and 2. The union of A' and B', the set $A' \cup B'$, is made up of the elements belonging to the union of (1 and 4) with (1 and 2)—that is, regions 1, 2, and 4, shown in color in **Figure 14.** ■

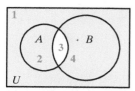

Figure 15

 Locating Elements in a Venn Diagram

Place the elements of the sets in their proper locations in a Venn diagram.

Let $U = \{q, r, s, t, u, v, w, x, y, z\}$, $A = \{r, s, t, u, v\}$,   and $B = \{t, v, x\}$.

Solution

Because $A \cap B = \{t, v\}$, elements t and v are placed in region 3 in **Figure 15.** The remaining elements of A, that is, r, s, and u, go in region 2. The figure shows the proper placement of all other elements. ■

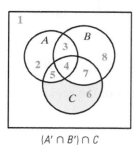

Figure 16

EXAMPLE 11 Shading a Set in a Venn Diagram

Shade the set $(A' \cap B') \cap C$ in a Venn diagram similar to the one in **Figure 12.**

Solution

Work first inside the parentheses. Set A' is made up of the regions outside set A, or regions 1, 6, 7, and 8. Set B' is made up of regions 1, 2, 5, and 6. The intersection of these sets is given by the overlap of regions 1, 6, 7, 8 and 1, 2, 5, 6, or regions 1 and 6.

For the final Venn diagram, find the intersection of regions 1 and 6 with set C. Set C is made up of regions 4, 5, 6, and 7. The overlap of regions 1, 6 and 4, 5, 6, 7 is region 6, the region shown in color in **Figure 16.** ■

EXAMPLE 12 Verifying a Statement Using a Venn Diagram

Suppose $A, B \subseteq U$. Is the statement $(A \cap B)' = A' \cup B'$ true for every choice of sets A and B?

Solution

Use the regions labeled in **Figure 11.** Set $A \cap B$ is made up of region 3, so $(A \cap B)'$ is made up of regions 1, 2, and 4. These regions are shown in color in **Figure 17(a)** on the next page.

To identify set $A' \cup B'$, proceed as in **Example 9(b).** The result, shown in **Figure 14,** is repeated in **Figure 17(b)** on the next page.

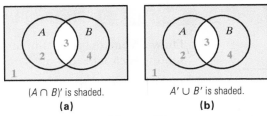

(A ∩ B)' is shaded.   A' ∪ B' is shaded.
   (a)   **(b)**

Figure 17

The fact that the same regions are in color in both Venn diagrams suggests that

$$(A \cap B)' = A' \cup B'. \qquad \blacksquare$$

De Morgan's Laws

The result of **Example 12** can be stated in words.

> *The complement of the intersection of two sets is equal to the union of the complements of the two sets.*

Interchanging the words "intersection" and "union" produces another true statement.

> *The complement of the union of two sets is equal to the intersection of the complements of the two sets.*

Both of these "laws" were established by the British logician Augustus De Morgan (1806–1871), profiled on **page 22.** They are stated in set symbols as follows.

DE MORGAN'S LAWS FOR SETS

For any sets A and B, where $A, B \subseteq U$,

$$(A \cap B)' = A' \cup B' \quad \text{and} \quad (A \cup B)' = A' \cap B'.$$

The Venn diagrams in **Figure 17** strongly suggest the truth of the first of De Morgan's laws. They provide a *conjecture*. Actual proofs of De Morgan's laws would require methods used in more advanced courses in set theory.

EXAMPLE 13 **Describing Venn Diagram Regions Using Symbols**

For the Venn diagrams, write several symbolic descriptions of the region in color, using $A, B, C, \cap, \cup, -$, and $'$ as necessary.

(a) 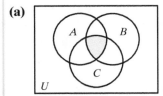   **(b)**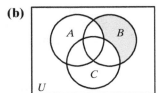

Solution

(a) The region in color can be described as belonging to all three sets, A and B and C. Therefore, the region corresponds to

$$(A \cap B) \cap C, \quad \text{or} \quad A \cap (B \cap C), \quad \text{or} \quad A \cap B \cap C.$$

(b) The region in color is in set B and is not in A and is not in C. Because it is not in A, it is in A', and similarly it is in C'. The region can be described as

$$B \cap A' \cap C', \quad \text{or} \quad B - (A \cup C), \quad \text{or} \quad B \cap (A \cup C)'. \qquad \blacksquare$$

2.3 EXERCISES

Match each term in Group I with the appropriate description from A–F in Group II. Assume that A and B are sets.

I

1. the intersection of A and B

2. the union of A and B

3. the difference of A and B

4. the complement of A

5. the Cartesian product of A and B

6. the difference of B and A

II

A. the set of elements in A that are not in B

B. the set of elements common to both A and B

C. the set of elements in the universal set that are not in A

D. the set of elements in B that are not in A

E. the set of ordered pairs such that each first element is from A and each second element is from B, with every element of A paired with every element of B

F. the set of elements that are in A or in B or in both A and B

Perform the indicated operations, and designate each answer using the listing method.

Let $U = \{a, b, c, d, e, f, g\}$, $X = \{a, c, e, g\}$,
$Y = \{a, b, c\}$, and $Z = \{b, c, d, e, f\}$.

7. $X \cap Y$

8. $X \cup Y$

9. $Y \cup Z$

10. $Y \cap Z$

11. X'

12. Y'

13. $X' \cap Y'$

14. $X' \cap Z$

15. $X \cup (Y \cap Z)$

16. $Y \cap (X \cup Z)$

17. $X - Y$

18. $Y - X$

19. $(Z \cup X')' \cap Y$

20. $(Y \cap X')' \cup Z'$

21. $X \cap (X - Y)$

22. $Y \cup (Y - X)$

23. $X' - Y$

24. $Y' - (X \cap Z)$

Describe each set in words.

25. $A \cup (B' \cap C')$

26. $(A \cap B') \cup (B \cap A')$

27. $(C - B) \cup A$

28. $(A' \cap B') \cup C'$

Adverse Effects of Tobacco and Alcohol *The table lists some common adverse effects of prolonged tobacco and alcohol use.*

Tobacco	Alcohol
Emphysema, e	Liver damage, l
Heart damage, h	Brain damage, b
Cancer, c	Heart damage, h

In Exercises 29–32, let T be the set of listed effects of tobacco and A be the set of listed effects of alcohol. Find each set.

29. the smallest possible universal set U that includes all the effects listed

30. $T \cap A$

31. $T \cup A$

32. $T \cap A'$

An accountant is sorting tax returns in her files that require attention in the next week.

Describe in words each set in Exercises 33–36.

Let U = the set of all tax returns in the file,
A = the set of all tax returns with itemized deductions,
B = the set of all tax returns showing business income,
C = the set of all tax returns filed in 2014,
D = the set of all tax returns selected for audit.

33. $C - A$

34. $D \cup A'$

35. $(A \cup B) - D$

36. $(C \cap A) \cap B'$

For Exercises 37–40, assume that A and B represent any two sets. Identify each statement as either always true *or* not always true.

37. $(A \cap B) \subseteq A$

38. $A \subseteq (A \cap B)$

39. $n(A \cup B) = n(A) + n(B)$

40. $n(A \cup B) = n(A) + n(B) - n(A \cap B)$

For Exercises 41–44, use your results in parts (a) and (b) to answer part (c).

Let $U = \{1, 2, 3, 4, 5\}$, $X = \{1, 3, 5\}$, $Y = \{1, 2, 3\}$, and $Z = \{3, 4, 5\}$.

41. (a) Find $X \cup Y$. **(b)** Find $Y \cup X$.

   (c) State a conjecture.

42. (a) Find $X \cap Y$. **(b)** Find $Y \cap X$.

   (c) State a conjecture.

43. (a) Find $X \cup (Y \cup Z)$. **(b)** Find $(X \cup Y) \cup Z$.

   (c) State a conjecture.

44. (a) Find $X \cap (Y \cap Z)$. **(b)** Find $(X \cap Y) \cap Z$.

   (c) State a conjecture.

Decide whether each statement is true *or* false.

45. $(3, 2) = (5 - 2, 1 + 1)$

46. $(2, 13) = (13, 2)$

47. $\{6, 3\} = \{3, 6\}$

48. $\{(5, 9), (4, 8), (4, 2)\} = \{(4, 8), (5, 9), (2, 4)\}$

Find $A \times B$ and $B \times A$, for A and B defined as follows.

49. $A = \{d, o, g\}$, $B = \{p, i, g\}$

50. $A = \{3, 6, 9, 12\}$, $B = \{6, 8\}$

Use the given information to find $n(A \times B)$ and $n(B \times A)$.

51. $n(A) = 35$ and $n(B) = 6$

52. $n(A) = 13$ and $n(B) = 5$

Find the cardinal number specified.

53. If $n(A \times B) = 72$ and $n(A) = 12$, find $n(B)$.

54. If $n(A \times B) = 300$ and $n(B) = 30$, find $n(A)$.

Place the elements of these sets in the proper locations in the given Venn diagram.

55. Let $U = \{a, b, c, d, e, f, g\}$,

    $A = \{b, d, f, g\}$,

    $B = \{a, b, d, e, g\}$.

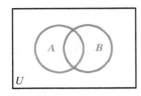

56. Let $U = \{5, 6, 7, 8, 9, 10, 11, 12, 13\}$,

    $M = \{5, 8, 10, 11\}$,

    $N = \{5, 6, 7, 9, 10\}$.

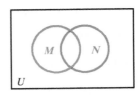

Use a Venn diagram similar to the one shown below to shade each set.

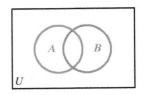

57. $A' \cup B$ **58.** $A' \cap B'$

59. $B \cap A'$ **60.** $A \cup B$

61. $B' \cap B$ **62.** $A' \cup A$

63. $B' \cup (A' \cap B')$ **64.** $(A - B) \cup (B - A)$

In Exercises 65 and 66, place the elements of the sets in the proper locations in a Venn diagram similar to the one shown below.

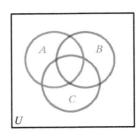

65. Let $U = \{m, n, o, p, q, r, s, t, u, v, w\}$,

    $A = \{m, n, p, q, r, t\}$,

    $B = \{m, o, p, q, s, u\}$,

    $C = \{m, o, p, r, s, t, u, v\}$.

66. Let $U = \{1, 2, 3, 4, 5, 6, 7, 8, 9\}$,

    $A = \{1, 3, 5, 7\}$,

    $B = \{1, 3, 4, 6, 8\}$,

    $C = \{1, 4, 5, 6, 7, 9\}$.

Use a Venn diagram to shade each set.

67. $(A \cap B) \cap C$ **68.** $(A' \cap B) \cap C$

69. $(A' \cap B') \cap C$ **70.** $(A \cap C') \cap B$

71. $(A \cap B') \cap C'$ **72.** $(A \cap B)' \cup C$

Write a description of each shaded area. Use the symbols A,
B, C, ∩, ∪, −, and '. Different answers are possible.

73.
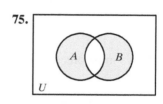

74.
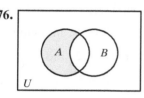

75.
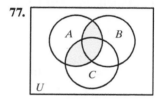

76.
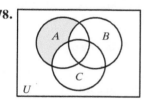

77.

78.

Suppose A and B are sets. Describe the conditions under
which each statement would be true.

79. $A = A − B$ **80.** $A = B − A$

81. $A = A − \varnothing$ **82.** $A \cap \varnothing = \varnothing$

83. $A \cup B = A$ **84.** $A \cap B = B$

For Exercises 85–88, draw two Venn diagrams to decide
whether the statement is always true *or* not always true.

85. $(A \cap B) \subseteq A$ **86.** $(A \cup B) \subseteq A$

87. If $A \subseteq B$, then $A \cup B = A$.

88. If $A \subseteq B$, then $A \cap B = A$.

89. Explain why, if A and B are sets, it is not necessarily true
that $n(A − B) = n(A) − n(B)$. Give a counterexample.

90. The five set operations listed on **page 66** are applied to
subsets of U (that is, to A and/or B). Is the result always
a subset of U also? Explain why or why not.

2.4   SURVEYS AND CARDINAL NUMBERS

OBJECTIVES

1 Analyze survey results.

2 Apply the cardinal
number formula.

3 Interpret information
from tables.

Surveys

As suggested in the chapter opener, the techniques of set theory can be applied to
many different groups of people (or objects). The problems addressed sometimes
require analyzing known information about certain subsets to obtain cardinal
numbers of other subsets. In this section, we apply three problem-solving strategies
to such problems:

> Venn diagrams,   cardinal number formulas,   and   tables.

The "known information" is quite often (although not always) obtained by conduct-
ing a survey.

Suppose a group of attendees at an educational seminar, all of whom desire to
become registered nurses (RNs), are asked their preferences among the three traditional ways to become an RN, and the following information is produced.

23 would consider pursuing the Bachelor of Science in Nursing (BSN).

16 would consider pursuing the Associate Degree in Nursing (ADN).

7 would consider a Diploma program (Diploma).

10 would consider both the BSN and the ADN.

5 would consider both the BSN and the Diploma.

3 would consider both the ADN and the Diploma.

2 would consider all three options.

4 are looking for an option other than these three.

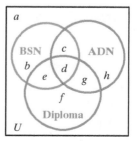

Figure 18

To determine the total number of attendees surveyed, we cannot just add the eight numbers above because there is some overlap. For example, in **Figure 18,** the 23 who like
the BSN option should not be positioned in region b but, rather, should be distributed
among regions b, c, d, and e in a way that is consistent with all of the data. (Region b
actually contains those who like the BSN but neither of the other two options.)

Because, at the start, we do not know how to distribute the 23 who like the BSN, we look first for some more manageable data. The smallest total listed, the 2 who like all three options, can be placed in region d (the intersection of the three sets). The 4 who like none of the three must go into region a. Then, the 10 who like the BSN and the ADN must go into regions c and d. Because region d already contains 2 attendees, we must place

$$10 - 2 = 8 \quad \text{in region } c.$$

Because 5 like BSN and Diploma (regions d and e), we place

$$5 - 2 = 3 \quad \text{in region } e.$$

Now that regions c, d, and e contain 8, 2, and 3, respectively, we must place

$$23 - 8 - 2 - 3 = 10 \quad \text{in region } b.$$

By similar reasoning, all regions are assigned their correct numbers. See **Figure 19.**

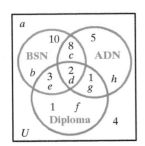

Figure 19

EXAMPLE 1 Analyzing a Survey

Using the survey data on personal preferences for nursing preparation, as summarized in **Figure 19,** answer each question.

(a) How many persons like the BSN option only?

(b) How many persons like exactly two of these three options?

(c) How many persons were surveyed?

Solution

(a) A person who likes BSN only does not like ADN and does not like Diploma. These persons are inside the regions for BSN and outside the regions for ADN and Diploma. Region b is the appropriate region in **Figure 19,** and we see that ten persons like BSN only.

(b) The persons in regions c, e, and g like exactly two of the three options. The total number of such persons is

$$8 + 3 + 1 = 12.$$

(c) Each person surveyed has been placed in exactly one region of **Figure 19,** so the total number surveyed is the sum of the numbers in all eight regions:

$$4 + 10 + 8 + 2 + 3 + 1 + 1 + 5 = 34. \qquad \blacksquare$$

Cardinal Number Formula

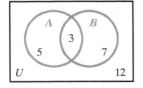

Figure 20

If the numbers shown in **Figure 20** are the cardinal numbers of the individual regions, then

$$n(A) = 5 + 3 = 8, \quad n(B) = 3 + 7 = 10, \quad n(A \cap B) = 3,$$

and

$$n(A \cup B) = 5 + 3 + 7 = 15.$$

Notice that $n(A \cup B) = n(A) + n(B) - n(A \cap B)$ because $15 = 8 + 10 - 3$. This relationship is true for any two sets A and B.

CARDINAL NUMBER FORMULA

For any two sets A and B, the following is true.

$$n(A \cup B) = n(A) + n(B) - n(A \cap B)$$

The cardinal number formula can be rearranged to find any one of its four terms when the others are known.

EXAMPLE 2   Applying the Cardinal Number Formula

Find $n(A)$ if $n(A \cup B) = 22$, $n(A \cap B) = 8$, and $n(B) = 12$.

Solution

We solve the cardinal number formula for $n(A)$.

$$n(A) = n(A \cup B) - n(B) + n(A \cap B)$$
$$= 22 - 12 + 8$$
$$= 18$$

Sometimes, even when information is presented as in **Example 2,** it is more convenient to fit that information into a Venn diagram as in **Example 1.**

WHEN Will I Ever USE This ?

Suppose you run a small construction company, building a few "spec" homes at a time. This week's work will require the following jobs:

Hanging drywall (D),   Installing roofing (R),   Doing electrical work (E).

You will assign 9 workers, with job skills as described here.

6 of the 9 can do D	5 can do both D and E
4 can do R	4 can do both R and E
7 can do E	4 can do all three

1. Construct a Venn diagram to decide how many of your workers have

   (a) exactly two of the three skills

   (b) none of the three skills

   (c) no more than one of the three skills.

2. Which skill is common to the greatest number of workers, and how many possess that skill?

Answers: 1. (a) 1 (b) 1 (c) 4 2. Electrical work; 7

EXAMPLE 3 **Analyzing Data in a Report**

Scott, who leads a group of software engineers who investigate illegal activities on social networking sites, reported the following information.

T = the set of group members following patterns on Twitter

F = the set of group members following patterns on Facebook

L = the set of group members following patterns on LinkedIn

$$n(T) = 13 \quad n(T \cap F) = 9 \quad n(T \cap F \cap L) = 5$$
$$n(F) = 16 \quad n(F \cap L) = 10 \quad n(T' \cap F' \cap L') = 3$$
$$n(L) = 13 \quad n(T \cap L) = 6$$

How many engineers are in Scott's group?

Solution

The data supplied by Scott are reflected in **Figure 21.** The sum of the numbers in the diagram gives the total number of engineers in the group.

$$3 + 3 + 1 + 2 + 5 + 5 + 4 + 2 = 25 \qquad \blacksquare$$

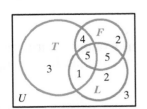

Figure 21

Tables

Sometimes information appears in a table rather than a Venn diagram, but the basic ideas of union and intersection still apply.

EXAMPLE 4 **Analyzing Data in a Table**

Melanie, the officer in charge of the cafeteria on a military base, wanted to know if the beverage that enlisted men and women preferred with lunch depended on their ages. On a given day, Melanie categorized her lunch patrons according to age and preferred beverage, recording the results in a table.

| | | Beverage | | | |
		Cola (C)	Iced Tea (I)	Sweet Tea (S)	Totals
	18–25 (Y)	45	10	35	90
Age	**26–33 (M)**	20	25	30	75
	Over 33 (O)	5	30	20	55
	Totals	70	65	85	220

Using the letters in the table, find the number of people in each set.

(a) $Y \cap C$ **(b)** $O' \cup I$

Solution

(a) The set Y includes all personnel represented across the top row of the table (90 in all), while C includes the 70 down the left column. The intersection of these two sets is just the upper left entry, 45 people.

(b) The set O' excludes the bottom row, so it includes the first and second rows. The set I includes the middle column only. The union of the two sets represents

$$45 + 10 + 35 + 20 + 25 + 30 + 30 = 195 \text{ people.} \qquad \blacksquare$$

2.4 EXERCISES

Use the numerals representing cardinalities in the Venn diagrams to give the cardinality of each set specified.

1.
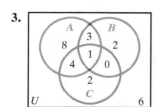

  (a) $A \cap B$ (b) $A \cup B$
  (c) $A \cap B'$ (d) $A' \cap B$
  (e) $A' \cap B'$

2.
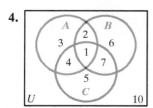

  (a) $A \cap B$ (b) $A \cup B$
  (c) $A \cap B'$ (d) $A' \cap B$
  (e) $A' \cap B'$

3.

  (a) $A \cap B \cap C$ (b) $A \cap B \cap C'$
  (c) $A \cap B' \cap C$ (d) $A' \cap B \cap C$
  (e) $A' \cap B' \cap C$ (f) $A \cap B' \cap C'$
  (g) $A' \cap B \cap C'$ (h) $A' \cap B' \cap C'$

4.

  (a) $A \cap B \cap C$ (b) $A \cap B \cap C'$
  (c) $A \cap B' \cap C$ (d) $A' \cap B \cap C$
  (e) $A' \cap B' \cap C$ (f) $A \cap B' \cap C'$
  (g) $A' \cap B \cap C'$ (h) $A' \cap B' \cap C'$

In Exercises 5–10, make use of an appropriate formula.

5. Find the value of $n(A \cup B)$ if $n(A) = 12, n(B) = 14$, and $n(A \cap B) = 5$.

6. Find the value of $n(A \cup B)$ if $n(A) = 16, n(B) = 28$, and $n(A \cap B) = 5$.

7. Find the value of $n(A \cap B)$ if $n(A) = 20, n(B) = 12$, and $n(A \cup B) = 25$.

8. Find the value of $n(A \cap B)$ if $n(A) = 20, n(B) = 24$, and $n(A \cup B) = 30$.

9. Find the value of $n(A)$ if $n(B) = 35, n(A \cap B) = 15$, and $n(A \cup B) = 55$.

10. Find the value of $n(B)$ if $n(A) = 20, n(A \cap B) = 6$, and $n(A \cup B) = 30$.

Draw a Venn diagram and use the given information to fill in the number of elements in each region.

11. $n(A) = 19$, $n(B) = 13$, $n(A \cup B) = 25$, $n(A') = 11$

12. $n(U) = 43$, $n(A) = 25$, $n(A \cap B) = 5$, $n(B') = 30$

13. $n(A') = 25$, $n(B) = 28$, $n(A' \cup B') = 40$, $n(A \cap B) = 10$

14. $n(A \cup B) = 15$, $n(A \cap B) = 8$, $n(A) = 13$, $n(A' \cup B') = 11$

15. $n(A) = 57$, $n(A \cap B) = 35$, $n(A \cup B) = 81$, $n(A \cap B \cap C) = 15$, $n(A \cap C) = 21, n(B \cap C) = 25$, $n(C) = 49$, $n(B') = 52$

16. $n(A) = 24$, $n(B) = 24$, $n(C) = 26$, $n(A \cap B) = 10$, $n(B \cap C) = 8$, $n(A \cap C) = 15$, $n(A \cap B \cap C) = 6$, $n(U) = 50$

17. $n(A) = 15$, $n(A \cap B \cap C) = 5$, $n(A \cap C) = 13$, $n(A \cap B') = 9, n(B \cap C) = 8, n(A' \cap B' \cap C') = 21$, $n(B \cap C') = 3$, $n(B \cup C) = 32$

18. $n(A \cap B) = 21$, $n(A \cap B \cap C) = 6$, $n(A \cap C) = 26$, $n(B \cap C) = 7$, $n(A \cap C') = 20$, $n(B \cap C') = 25$, $n(C) = 40$, $n(A' \cap B' \cap C') = 2$

Use Venn diagrams to work each problem.

19. ***Writing and Producing Music*** Joe Long worked on 9 music projects last year.

Joe Long, Bob Gaudio, Tommy DeVito, and Frankie Valli
The Four Seasons

He wrote and produced 3 projects.

He wrote a total of 5 projects.

He produced a total of 7 projects.

  (a) How many projects did he write but not produce?

  (b) How many projects did he produce but not write?

20. *Compact Disc Collection* Gitti is a fan of the music of Paul Simon and Art Garfunkel. In her collection of 25 compact discs, she has the following:

>   5 on which both Simon and Garfunkel sing
>
>   7 on which Simon sings
>
>   8 on which Garfunkel sings
>
>   15 on which neither Simon nor Garfunkel sings.

(a) How many of her compact discs feature only Paul Simon?

(b) How many of her compact discs feature only Art Garfunkel?

(c) How many feature at least one of these two artists?

(d) How many feature at most one of these two artists?

21. *Student Response to Classical Composers* The 65 students in a classical music lecture class were polled, with the following results:

>   37 like Wolfgang Amadeus Mozart
>
>   36 like Ludwig van Beethoven
>
>   31 like Franz Joseph Haydn
>
>   14 like Mozart and Beethoven
>
>   21 like Mozart and Haydn
>
>   14 like Beethoven and Haydn
>
>   8 like all three composers.

How many of these students like:

(a) exactly two of these composers?

(b) exactly one of these composers?

(c) none of these composers?

(d) Mozart, but neither Beethoven nor Haydn?

(e) Haydn and exactly one of the other two?

(f) no more than two of these composers?

22. *Financial Aid for Students* At a southern university, half of the 48 mathematics majors were receiving federal financial aid.

>   5 had Pell Grants
>
>   14 participated in the College Work Study Program
>
>   4 had TOPS scholarships
>
>   2 had TOPS scholarships and participated in Work Study.
>
>   Those with Pell Grants had no other federal aid.

How many of the 48 math majors had:

(a) no federal aid?

(b) more than one of these three forms of aid?

(c) federal aid other than these three forms?

(d) a TOPS scholarship or Work Study?

(e) exactly one of these three forms of aid?

(f) no more than one of these three forms of aid?

23. *Animated Movies* A middle school counselor, attempting to correlate school performance with leisure interests, found the following information for a group of students:

>   34 had seen *Despicable Me*
>
>   29 had seen *Epic*
>
>   26 had seen *Turbo*
>
>   16 had seen *Despicable Me* and *Epic*
>
>   12 had seen *Despicable Me* and *Turbo*
>
>   10 had seen *Epic* and *Turbo*
>
>   4 had seen all three of these films
>
>   5 had seen none of the three films.

(a) How many students had seen *Turbo* only?

(b) How many had seen exactly two of the films?

(c) How many students were surveyed?

24. *Non-Mainline Religious Beliefs* 140 U.S. adults were surveyed.

Let *A* = the set of respondents who believe in astrology,

>   *R* = the set of respondents who believe in reincarnation,
>
>   *Y* = the set of respondents who believe in the spirituality of yoga.

The survey revealed the following information:

$$n(A) = 35 \qquad n(R \cap Y) = 8$$
$$n(R) = 36 \qquad n(A \cap Y) = 10$$
$$n(Y) = 32 \qquad n(A \cap R \cap Y) = 6$$
$$n(A \cap R) = 19$$

How many of the respondents believe in:

(a) astrology but not reincarnation?

(b) at least one of these three things?

(c) reincarnation but neither of the others?

(d) exactly two of these three things?

(e) none of the three?

25. *Survey on Attitudes toward Religion* Researchers interviewed a number of people and recorded the following data. Of all the respondents:

> 240 think Hollywood is unfriendly toward religion
>
> 160 think the media are unfriendly toward religion
>
> 181 think scientists are unfriendly toward religion
>
> 145 think both Hollywood and the media are unfriendly toward religion
>
> 122 think both scientists and the media are unfriendly toward religion
>
> 80 think exactly two of these groups are unfriendly toward religion
>
> 110 think all three groups are unfriendly toward religion
>
> 219 think none of these three groups is unfriendly toward religion.

How many respondents:

(a) were surveyed?

(b) think exactly one of these three groups is unfriendly toward religion?

26. *Student Goals* Sofia, who sells college textbooks, interviewed first-year students on a community college campus to find out the main goals of today's students.

Let W = the set of those who want to be wealthy,

  F = the set of those who want to raise a family,

  E = the set of those who want to become experts in their fields.

Sofia's findings are summarized here.

$$n(W) = 160 \qquad n(E \cap F) = 90$$
$$n(F) = 140 \qquad n(W \cap F \cap E) = 80$$
$$n(E) = 130 \qquad n(E') = 95$$
$$n(W \cap F) = 95 \qquad n[(W \cup F \cup E)'] = 10$$

Find the total number of students interviewed.

27. *Hospital Patient Symptoms* A survey was conducted among 75 patients admitted to a hospital cardiac unit during a two-week period.

Let B = the set of patients with high blood pressure,

  C = the set of patients with high cholesterol levels,

  S = the set of patients who smoke cigarettes.

The survey produced the following data.

$$n(B) = 47 \qquad n(B \cap S) = 33$$
$$n(C) = 46 \qquad n(B \cap C) = 31$$
$$n(S) = 52 \qquad n(B \cap C \cap S) = 21$$
$$n[(B \cap C) \cup (B \cap S) \cup (C \cap S)] = 51$$

Find the number of these patients who:

(a) had either high blood pressure or high cholesterol levels, but not both

(b) had fewer than two of the indications listed

(c) were smokers but had neither high blood pressure nor high cholesterol levels

(d) did not have exactly two of the indications listed.

28. *Song Themes* It was once said that country-western songs emphasize three basic themes: love, prison, and trucks. A survey of the local country-western radio station produced the following data.

> 12 songs about a truck driver who is in love while in prison
>
> 13 about a prisoner in love
>
> 28 about a person in love
>
> 18 about a truck driver in love
>
> 3 about a truck driver in prison who is not in love
>
> 2 about people in prison who are not in love and do not drive trucks
>
> 8 about people who are out of prison, are not in love, and do not drive trucks
>
> 16 about truck drivers who are not in prison

(a) How many songs were surveyed?

Find the number of songs about:

(b) truck drivers

(c) prisoners

(d) truck drivers in prison

(e) people not in prison

(f) people not in love.

29. Use the figure to find the numbers of the regions belonging to each set.

(a) $A \cap B \cap C \cap D$

(b) $A \cup B \cup C \cup D$

(c) $(A \cap B) \cup (C \cap D)$

(d) $(A' \cap B') \cap (C \cup D)$

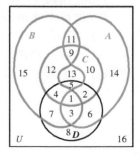

30. Sports Viewing A survey of 130 TV viewers was taken.

> 52 watch football
>
> 56 watch basketball
>
> 62 watch tennis
>
> 60 watch golf
>
> 21 watch football and basketball
>
> 19 watch football and tennis
>
> 22 watch basketball and tennis
>
> 27 watch football and golf
>
> 30 watch basketball and golf
>
> 21 watch tennis and golf
>
> 3 watch football, basketball, and tennis
>
> 15 watch football, basketball, and golf
>
> 10 watch football, tennis, and golf
>
> 10 watch basketball, tennis, and golf
>
> 3 watch all four of these sports
>
> 5 don't watch any of these four sports

Use a Venn diagram to answer these questions.

(a) How many of these viewers watch football, basketball, and tennis, but not golf?

(b) How many watch exactly one of these four sports?

(c) How many watch exactly two of these four sports?

Solve each problem.

31. Basketball Positions Sakda runs a basketball program in California. On the first day of the season, 60 young women showed up and were categorized by age level and by preferred basketball position, as shown in the following table.

	Position			
	Guard (G)	Forward (F)	Center (N)	Totals
Junior High (J)	9	6	4	19
Age Senior High (S)	12	5	9	26
College (C)	5	8	2	15
Totals	26	19	15	60

Using the set labels (letters) in the table, find the number of players in each of the following sets.

(a) $J \cap G$ **(b)** $S \cap N$

(c) $N \cup (S \cap F)$ **(d)** $S' \cap (G \cup N)$

(e) $(S \cap N') \cup (C \cap G')$ **(f)** $N' \cap (S' \cap C')$

32. Army Housing A study of U.S. Army housing trends categorized personnel as commissioned officers (C), warrant officers (W), or enlisted (E), and categorized their living facilities as on-base (B), rented off-base (R), or owned off-base (O). One survey yielded the following data.

		Facilities			
		B	R	O	Totals
	C	12	29	54	95
Personnel	W	4	5	6	15
	E	374	71	285	730
	Totals	390	105	345	840

Find the number of personnel in each of the following sets.

(a) $W \cap O$

(b) $C \cup B$

(c) $R' \cup W'$

(d) $(C \cup W) \cap (B \cup R)$

(e) $(C \cap B) \cup (E \cap O)$

(f) $B \cap (W \cup R)'$

33. Could the information of **Example 4** have been presented in a Venn diagram similar to those in **Examples 1 and 3?** If so, construct such a diagram. Otherwise, explain the essential difference of **Example 4.**

34. Explain how a cardinal number formula can be derived for the case where *three* sets occur. Specifically, give a formula relating $n(A \cup B \cup C)$ to

$$n(A), \ n(B), \ n(C), \ n(A \cap B), \ n(A \cap C),$$
$$n(B \cap C), \ \text{and} \ n(A \cap B \cap C).$$

Illustrate with a Venn diagram.

CHAPTER 2	SUMMARY

KEY TERMS

2.1
set
elements
members
empty (null) set
natural (counting) numbers
whole numbers
integers
rational numbers
real numbers
irrational numbers
cardinal number
  (cardinality)
finite set
infinite set

2.2
universal set
Venn diagram
complement (of a set)
subset (of a set)
proper subset (of a set)
tree diagram

2.3
intersection (of sets)
disjoint sets
union (of sets)
difference (of sets)
ordered pairs
Cartesian product (of sets)
operation (on sets)

NEW SYMBOLS

$\varnothing$	empty set (or null set)	$\not\subseteq$	is not a subset of
$\in$	is an element of	$\subset$	is a proper subset of
$\notin$	is not an element of	$\cap$	intersection (of sets)
$n(A)$	cardinal number of set A	$\cup$	union (of sets)
$\aleph_0$	aleph null	$-$	difference (of sets)
U	universal set	(a, b)	ordered pair
A'	complement of set A	$\times$	Cartesian product
$\subseteq$	is a subset of		

TEST YOUR WORD POWER

See how well you have learned the vocabulary in this chapter.

1. In an **ordered pair,**
  A. the components are always numbers of the same type.
  B. the first component must be less than the second.
  C. the components can be any kinds of objects.
  D. the first component is a subset of the second component.

2. The **complement** of a set
  A. contains only some, but not all, of that set's elements.
  B. contains the same number of elements as the given set.
  C. always contains fewer elements than the given set.
  D. cannot be determined until a universal set is given.

3. Any **subset** of set A
  A. must have fewer elements than A.
  B. has fewer elements than A only if it is a proper subset.
  C. is an element of A.
  D. contains all the elements of A, plus at least one additional element.

4. Examples of **operations on sets** are
  A. union, intersection, and subset.
  B. Cartesian product, difference, and proper subset.
  C. complement, supplement, and intersection.
  D. complement, union, and Cartesian product.

5. The **set difference $A - B$** must have cardinality
  A. $n(A) - n(B)$.
  B. less than or equal to $n(A)$.
  C. greater than or equal to $n(B)$.
  D. less than $n(A)$.

6. The **cardinal number formula** says that
  A. $n(A \cup B) = n(A) + n(B) - n(A \cap B)$.
  B. $n(A \cup B) = n(A) + n(B) + n(A \cap B)$.
  C. $n(A \cup B) = n(A) + n(B)$.
  D. $n(A \cup B) = n(A) \cdot n(B)$.

ANSWERS
1. C **2.** D **3.** B **4.** D **5.** B **6.** A

QUICK REVIEW

Concepts	Examples

2.1 Symbols and Terminology

Designating Sets

Sets are designated using the following methods:

(1) word descriptions,

(2) the listing method,

(3) set-builder notation.

The **cardinal number** of a set is the number of elements it contains.

Equal sets have exactly the same elements.

The set of odd counting numbers less than 7

$\{1, 3, 5\}$

$\{x \mid x$ is an odd counting number and $x < 7\}$

⎫ All are equal. ⎭

If $A = \{10, 20, 30, \ldots, 80\}$, then $n(A) = 8$.

$\{a, e, i, o, u\} = \{i, o, u, a, e\}$, $\{q, r, s, t\} \neq \{q, p, s, t\}$

2.2 Venn Diagrams and Subsets

Sets are normally discussed within the context of a designated **universal set, U.**

The **complement** of a set A contains all elements in U that are not in A.

Set B is a **subset** of set A if every element of B is also an element of A.

Set B is a **proper subset** of A if $B \subseteq A$ and $B \neq A$

If a set has cardinal number n, it has 2^n subsets and $2^n - 1$ proper subsets.

Let $U = \{x \mid x$ is a whole number$\}$

and

$\qquad A = \{x \mid x$ is an even whole number$\}$.

Then $A' = \{x \mid x$ is an odd whole number$\}$.

Let $U = \{2, 3, 5, 7\}$, $A = \{3, 5, 7\}$, and $B = \{5\}$.
Then $A' = \{2\}$ and $B \subseteq A$.

For the sets A and B given above, $B \subset A$.

If $D = \{x, y, z\}$, then $n(D) = 3$.
D has $2^3 = 8$ subsets and $2^3 - 1 = 8 - 1 = 7$ proper subsets.

2.3 Set Operations

Intersection of sets

$\qquad A \cap B = \{x \mid x \in A \text{ and } x \in B\}$

Union of sets

$\qquad A \cup B = \{x \mid x \in A \text{ or } x \in B\}$

Difference of sets

$\qquad A - B = \{x \mid x \in A \text{ and } x \notin B\}$

Cartesian product of sets

$\qquad A \times B = \{(a, b) \mid a \in A \text{ and } b \in B\}$

Cardinal number of a Cartesian product

If $n(A) = a$ and $n(B) = b$, then

$\qquad n(A \times B) = n(A) \cdot n(B) = ab.$

$\{1, 2, 7\} \cap \{5, 7, 9, 11\} = \{7\}$

$\{20, 40, 60\} \cup \{40, 60, 80\} = \{20, 40, 60, 80\}$

$\{5, 6, 7, 8\} - \{1, 3, 5, 7\} = \{6, 8\}$

$\{1, 2\} \times \{30, 40, 50\}$
$\quad = \{(1, 30), (1, 40), (1, 50), (2, 30), (2, 40), (2, 50)\}$

If $A = \{2, 4, 6, 8\}$ and $B = \{3, 7\}$, then

$\qquad n(A \times B) = n(A) \cdot n(B) = 4 \cdot 2 = 8.$

Verify by listing the elements of $A \times B$.

$\quad \{(2, 3), (2, 7), (4, 3), (4, 7), (6, 3), (6, 7), (8, 3), (8, 7)\}$

It, indeed, has 8 elements.

Concepts	Examples
Numbering the regions in a Venn diagram facilitates identification of various sets and relationships among them.	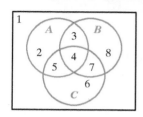

A consists of regions 2, 3, 4, and 5.

$A \cap B$ consists of regions 3 and 4.

$B \cup C$ consists of regions 3, 4, 5, 6, 7, and 8.

$(A \cup B) \cap C'$ consists of regions 2, 3, and 8.

$A \cap B \cap C$ consists of region 4.

$(A \cup B \cup C)'$ consists of region 1.

$A - C$ consists of regions 2 and 3.

De Morgan's Laws

For any sets A and B, where $A, B \subseteq U$, the following are true.

$$(A \cap B)' = A' \cup B'$$

Let $U = \{1, 2, 3, 4, \ldots, 9\}$, $A = \{2, 4, 6, 8\}$, and $B = \{4, 5, 6, 7\}$.

Then $A \cap B = \{4, 6\}$,

so $(A \cap B)' = \{1, 2, 3, 5, 7, 8, 9\}$.

Also $A' = \{1, 3, 5, 7, 9\}$ and $B' = \{1, 2, 3, 8, 9\}$,   Same

so $A' \cup B' = \{1, 2, 3, 5, 7, 8, 9\}$.

Using the same sets A and B as above,

$$A \cup B = \{2, 4, 5, 6, 7, 8\},$$

$$(A \cup B)' = A' \cap B'$$

so $(A \cup B)' = \{1, 3, 9\}$.

Also, $A' = \{1, 3, 5, 7, 9\}$ and $B' = \{1, 2, 3, 8, 9\}$,   Same

so $A' \cap B' = \{1, 3, 9\}$.

2.4 Surveys and Cardinal Numbers

Cardinal Number Formula

For any two sets A and B, the following is true.

$$n(A \cup B) = n(A) + n(B) - n(A \cap B)$$

Suppose $n(A) = 5$, $n(B) = 12$, and $n(A \cup B) = 10$. Then, to find $n(A \cap B)$, first solve the formula for that term.

$$n(A \cap B) = n(A) + n(B) - n(A \cup B)$$

$$= 5 + 12 - 10 = 7$$

Enter known facts in a Venn diagram to find desired facts.

Given $n(A) = 12$, $n(B) = 27$, $n(A \cup B) = 32$, and $n(U) = 50$, find $n(A - B)$ and $n[(A \cap B)']$.

$$n(A \cap B) = n(A) + n(B) - n(A \cup B)$$

$$= 12 + 27 - 32$$

$$= 7$$

Then the cardinalities of all regions can be entered in the diagram, starting with 7 in the center.

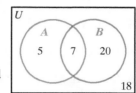

Now observe that $n(A - B) = 5$ and $n[(A \cap B)'] = 18 + 5 + 20 = 43$.

CHAPTER 2 | TEST

In Exercises 1–14, let

$$U = \{a, b, c, d, e, f, g, h\}, \quad A = \{a, b, c, d\},$$
$$B = \{b, e, a, d\}, \quad and \quad C = \{e, a\}.$$

Find each set.

1. $A \cup C$

2. $B \cap A$

3. B'

4. $A - (B \cap C')$

Identify each statement as true *or* false.

5. $e \in A$

6. $C \subseteq B$

7. $B \subset (A \cup C)$

8. $c \notin C$

9. $n[(A \cup B) - C] = 4$

10. $\emptyset \not\subset C$

11. $A \cap B'$ is equivalent to $B \cap A'$

12. $(A \cup B)' = A' \cap B'$

Find each of the following.

13. $n(B \times A)$

14. the number of proper subsets of B

Give a word description for each set.

15. $\{-3, -1, 1, 3, 5, 7, 9\}$

16. $\{\text{Sun, Mon, Tue}, \ldots, \text{Sat}\}$

Express each set in set-builder notation.

17. $\{-1, -2, -3, -4, \ldots\}$

18. $\{24, 32, 40, 48, \ldots, 88\}$

Place $\subset$, $\subseteq$, *both, or* neither *in each blank to make a true statement.*

19. $\emptyset$ _____ $\{x \mid x \text{ is a counting number between 20 and 21}\}$

20. $\{3, 5, 7\}$ _____ $\{4, 5, 6, 7, 8, 9, 10\}$

Shade each set in an appropriate Venn diagram.

21. $X \cup Y'$

22. $X' \cap Y'$

23. $(X \cup Y) - Z$

24. $[(X \cap Y) \cup (X \cap Z)] - (Y \cap Z)$

25. State De Morgan's laws for sets in words rather than symbols.

Facts about Inventions The table lists ten inventions, together with other pertinent data.

Invention	Date	Inventor	Nation
Adding machine	1642	Pascal	France
Baking powder	1843	Bird	England
Electric razor	1917	Schick	U.S.
Fiber optics	1955	Kapany	England
Geiger counter	1913	Geiger	Germany
Pendulum clock	1657	Huygens	Holland
Radar	1940	Watson-Watt	Scotland
Telegraph	1837	Morse	U.S.
Thermometer	1593	Galileo	Italy
Zipper	1891	Judson	U.S.

Let $U =$ the set of all ten inventions,

$\quad A =$ the set of items invented in the United States,

and $T =$ the set of items invented in the twentieth century.

List the elements of each set.

26. $A \cap T$ **27.** $(A \cup T)'$ **28.** $T' - A'$

29. The numerals in the Venn diagram indicate the number of elements in each particular subset. Determine the number of elements in each set.

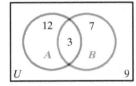

(a) $A \cup B$ **(b)** $A \cap B'$

(c) $(A \cap B)'$

30. *Financial Aid to College Students* Three sources of financial aid are government grants, private scholarships, and the colleges themselves. Susan, a financial aid director of a private college, surveyed the records of 100 sophomores and found the following:

49 receive government grants

55 receive private scholarships

43 receive aid from the college

23 receive government grants and private scholarships

18 receive government grants and aid from the college

28 receive private scholarships and aid from the college

8 receive help from all three sources.

How many of the students in the survey:

(a) have government grants only?

(b) have scholarships but not government grants?

(c) receive financial aid from only one of these sources?

(d) receive aid from exactly two of these sources?

(e) receive no financial aid from any of these sources?

(f) receive no aid from the college or the government?

Introduction to Logic

3

To capture the imagination of their readers, authors of fantasy literature (such as J. R. R. Tolkien, J. K. Rowling, and Lewis Carroll) have long used magical imagery, including riddles. Such a riddle confronts a hero named Humphrey, who finds himself trapped in a magical maze with only two exits.

> *One door to freedom opens wide,*
> *The other naught but dungeon hides.*
> *Twin watchers, one by truth is bound,*
> *The other never truth will sound.*
>
> *The watcher here shall speak when he*
> *Spies a man who would be free.*
> *Name him Lying Troll or Truthful,*
> *Rightly named he shall be useful.*
>
> *If he moves, then be not late,*
> *Choose a door and seal thy fate.*

As Humphrey approaches the troll, it speaks:

> *"If truly Truthful Troll I be,*
> *then go thou east, and be thou free."*

Logic, the topic of this chapter, is useful to authors in the creation of such puzzles—and also to readers in solving them.

3.1 STATEMENTS AND QUANTIFIERS

OBJECTIVES

1 Distinguish between statements and non-statements.

2 Compose negations of statements.

3 Translate between words and symbols.

4 Interpret statements with quantifiers and form their negations.

5 Find truth values of statements involving quantifiers and number sets.

Statements

This section introduces the study of **symbolic logic,** which uses letters to represent statements, and symbols for words such as *and, or, not.* Logic is used to determine the **truth value** (that is, the truth or falsity) of statements with multiple parts. The truth value of such statements depends on their components.

Many kinds of sentences occur in ordinary language, including factual statements, opinions, commands, and questions. Symbolic logic discusses only statements that involve facts. A **statement** is a declarative sentence that is either true or false, but not both simultaneously.

Electronic mail provides a means of communication. } Statements
$12 + 6 = 13$ } Each is either true or false.

Access the file.
Did the Seahawks win the Super Bowl? } Not statements
Dustin Pedroia is a better baseball player than Miguel Cabrera. } Each cannot be identified as being
This sentence is false. } either true or false.

Of the sentences that are not statements, the first is a command, and the second is a question. The third is an opinion. "This sentence is false" is a paradox: If we assume it is true, then it is false, and if we assume it is false, then it is true.

A **compound statement** may be formed by combining two or more statements. The statements making up a compound statement are called **component statements.** Various **logical connectives,** or simply **connectives,** such as *and, or, not,* and *if . . . then,* can be used in forming compound statements. (Although a statement such as "Today is not Tuesday" does not consist of two component statements, for convenience it is considered compound, because its truth value is determined by noting the truth value of a different statement, "Today is Tuesday.")

EXAMPLE 1 Deciding Whether a Statement Is Compound

Decide whether each statement is compound. If so, identify the connective.

(a) Lord Byron wrote sonnets, and the poem exhibits iambic pentameter.

(b) You can pay me now, or you can pay me later.

(c) If it's on the Internet, then it must be true.

(d) My pistol was made by Smith and Wesson.

Solution

(a) This statement is compound, because it is made up of the component statements "Lord Byron wrote sonnets" and "the poem exhibits iambic pentameter." The connective is *and.*

(b) The connective here is *or.* The statement is compound.

(c) The connective here is *if . . . then,* discussed in more detail in **Section 3.3.** The statement is compound.

(d) Although the word "and" is used in this statement, it is not used as a *logical* connective. It is part of the name of the manufacturer. The statement is not compound. ◼

Negations

The sentence "Anthony Mansella has a red truck" is a statement. The **negation** of this statement is "Anthony Mansella does not have a red truck." ***The negation of a true statement is false, and the negation of a false statement is true.***

Gottfried Leibniz (1646–1716) was a wide-ranging philosopher and a universalist who tried to patch up Catholic–Protestant conflicts. He promoted cultural exchange between Europe and the East. Chinese ideograms led him to search for a universal symbolism. He was an early inventor of **symbolic logic.**

EXAMPLE 2 Forming Negations

Form the negation of each statement.

(a) That city has a mayor.   **(b)** The moon is not a planet.

Solution

(a) To negate this statement, we introduce *not* into the sentence: "That city does not have a mayor."

(b) The negation is "The moon is a planet." ◼

One way to detect incorrect negations is to check truth values. ***A negation must have the opposite truth value from the original statement.***

The next example uses some of the inequality symbols in **Table 1.** In the case of an inequality involving a variable, the negation must have the opposite truth value for *any* replacement of the variable.

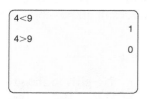

TEST LOGIC
1: =
2: ≠
3: >
4: ≥
5: <
6: ≤

The TEST menu of the TI-83/84 Plus calculator allows the user to test the truth value of statements involving =, ≠, >, ≥, <, and ≤. If a statement is true, it returns a 1. If a statement is false, it returns a 0.

Table 1

Symbolism	Meaning	Examples	
$a < b$	a is less than b	$4 < 9$	$\frac{1}{2} < \frac{3}{4}$
$a > b$	a is greater than b	$6 > 2$	$-5 > -11$
$a \le b$	a is less than or equal to b	$8 \le 10$	$3 \le 3$
$a \ge b$	a is greater than or equal to b	$-2 \ge -3$	$-5 \ge -5$

```
4<9
                    1
4>9
                    0
```

$4 < 9$ is true, as indicated by the 1.
$4 > 9$ is false, as indicated by the 0.

EXAMPLE 3 Negating Inequalities

Give a negation of each inequality. Do *not* use a slash symbol.

(a) $x < 9$ **(b)** $7x + 11y \ge 77$

Solution

(a) The negation of "x is less than 9" is "x is *not* less than 9." Because we cannot use "not," which would require writing $x \not< 9$, phrase the negation as "x is greater than or equal to 9," or

$$x \ge 9.$$

(b) The negation, with no slash, is

$$7x + 11y < 77.$$ ◼

Symbols

The study of logic uses symbols. Statements are represented with letters, such as *p*, *q*, or *r*. Several symbols for connectives are shown in **Table 2**.

Table 2

Connective	Symbol	Type of Statement
and	$\wedge$	Conjunction
or	$\vee$	Disjunction
not	$\sim$	Negation

The symbol $\sim$ represents the connective *not*. If *p* represents the statement "Barack Obama was president in 2014," then $\sim p$ represents "Barack Obama was *not* president in 2014."

EXAMPLE 4 Translating from Symbols to Words

Let *p* represent the statement "Nursing informatics is a growing field," and let *q* represent "Critical care will always be in demand." Translate each statement from symbols to words.

(a) $p \vee q$ **(b)** $\sim p \wedge q$ **(c)** $\sim (p \vee q)$ **(d)** $\sim (p \wedge q)$

Solution

(a) From the table, $\vee$ symbolizes *or*. Thus, $p \vee q$ represents

Nursing informatics is a growing field, or critical care will always be in demand.

(b) Nursing informatics is not a growing field and critical care will always be in demand.

(c) It is not the case that nursing informatics is a growing field or critical care will always be in demand. (This is usually translated as **"Neither *p* nor *q*."**)

(d) It is not the case that nursing informatics is a growing field and critical care will always be in demand. ∎

Quantifiers

Quantifiers are used to indicate *how many* cases of a particular situation exist. The words *all, each, every,* and *no(ne)* are **universal quantifiers,** while words and phrases such as *some, there exists,* and *(for) at least one* are **existential quantifiers.**

    Be careful when forming the negation of a statement involving quantifiers. A statement and its negation must have opposite truth values in all possible cases. Consider this statement.

All girls in the group are named Mary.

Many people would write the negation of this statement as "No girls in the group are named Mary" or "All girls in the group are not named Mary." But neither of these is correct. To see why, look at the three groups below.

Group I: Mary Jane Payne, Mary Meyer, Mary O'Hara

Group II: Mary Johnson, Lisa Pollak, Margaret Watson

Group III: Donna Garbarino, Paula Story, Rhonda Alessi, Kim Falgout

These groups contain all possibilities that need to be considered. In Group I, *all* girls are named Mary. In Group II, *some* girls are named Mary (and some are not). In Group III, *no* girls are named Mary.

Aristotle, the first to systematize the logic we use in everyday life, appears above in a detail from the painting *The School of Athens,* by Raphael. He is shown debating a point with his teacher **Plato.**

Consider **Table 3**. Keep in mind that "some" means "at least one (and possibly all)."

Table 3 Truth Value as Applied to:

	Group I	Group II	Group III
(1) All girls in the group are named Mary. (Given)	T	F	F
(2) No girls in the group are named Mary. (Possible negation)	F	F	T
(3) All girls in the group are not named Mary. (Possible negation)	F	F	T
(4) Some girls in the group are not named Mary. (Possible negation)	F	T	T

Negation

The negation of the given statement (1) must have opposite truth values in *all* cases. It can be seen that statements (2) and (3) do not satisfy this condition (for Group II), but statement (4) does. It may be concluded that the correct negation for "All girls in the group are named Mary" is "Some girls in the group are not named Mary." Other ways of stating the negation include the following.

Not all girls in the group are named Mary.

It is not the case that all girls in the group are named Mary.

At least one girl in the group is not named Mary.

Table 4 shows how to find the negation of a statement involving quantifiers.

Table 4 Negations of Quantified Statements

Statement	Negation
All do.	Some do not. (Equivalently: Not all do.)
Some do.	None do. (Equivalently: All do not.)

The negation of the negation of a statement is simply the statement itself. For instance, the negations of the statements in the Negation column are simply the corresponding original statements in the Statement column.

EXAMPLE 5 Forming Negations of Quantified Statements

Form the negation of each statement.

(a) Some cats have fleas.   **(b)** Some cats do not have fleas.

(c) No cats have fleas.

Solution

(a) Because *some* means "at least one," the statement "Some cats have fleas" is really the same as "At least one cat has fleas." The negation of this is

"No cat has fleas."

(b) The statement "Some cats do not have fleas" claims that at least one cat, somewhere, does not have fleas. The negation of this is

"All cats have fleas."

(c) The negation is "Some cats have fleas." ——— Avoid the incorrect answer "All cats have fleas."

Quantifiers and Number Sets

Earlier we introduced sets of numbers.

SETS OF NUMBERS

Natural numbers (or counting numbers) $\{1, 2, 3, 4, \dots\}$

Whole numbers $\{0, 1, 2, 3, 4, \dots\}$

Integers $\{\dots, -3, -2, -1, 0, 1, 2, 3, \dots\}$

Rational numbers $\left\{\frac{p}{q} \,\middle|\, p \text{ and } q \text{ are integers, and } q \neq 0\right\}$

Real numbers $\{x \mid x \text{ is a number that can be written as a decimal}\}$

Irrational numbers $\{x \mid x \text{ is a real number and } x \text{ cannot be written as a quotient of integers}\}$

EXAMPLE 6 **Deciding Whether Quantified Statements Are True or False**

Decide whether each statement involving a quantifier is *true* or *false*.

(a) There exists a whole number that is not a natural number.

(b) Every integer is a natural number.

(c) Every natural number is a rational number.

(d) There exists an irrational number that is not real.

Solution

(a) Because there is such a whole number (it is 0), this statement is true.

(b) This statement is false, because we can find at least one integer that is not a natural number. For example, -1 is an integer but is not a natural number.

(c) Because every natural number can be written as a fraction with denominator 1, this statement is true.

(d) In order to be an irrational number, a number must first be real. Because we cannot give an irrational number that is not real, this statement is false. (Had we been able to find at least one, the statement would have been true.) ∎

3.1 EXERCISES

Decide whether each is a statement or is not a statement.

1. February 2, 2009, was a Monday.

2. The ZIP code for Oscar, Louisiana, is 70762.

3. Listen, my children, and you shall hear of the midnight ride of Paul Revere.

4. Did you yield to oncoming traffic?

5. $5 + 9 \neq 14$ and $4 - 1 = 12$

6. $5 + 9 \neq 12$ or $4 - 2 = 5$

7. Some numbers are positive.

8. Grover Cleveland was president of the United States in 1885 and 1897.

9. Accidents are the main cause of deaths of children under the age of 7.

10. It is projected that in the United States between 2010 and 2020, there will be over 500,000 job openings per year for elementary school teachers, with median annual salaries of about $51,000.

11. Where are you going tomorrow?

12. Behave yourself and sit down.

13. Kevin "Catfish" McCarthy once took a prolonged continuous shower for 340 hours, 40 minutes.

14. One gallon of milk weighs more than 3 pounds.

Decide whether each statement is compound.

15. I read the *Detroit Free Press,* and I read the *Sacramento Bee.*

16. My brother got married in Copenhagen.

17. Tomorrow is Saturday.

18. Jing is younger than 18 years of age, and so is her friend Shu-fen.

19. Jay's wife loves Ben and Jerry's ice cream.

20. The sign on the back of the car read "Canada or bust!"

21. If Lorri sells her quota, then Michelle will be happy.

22. If Bobby is a politician, then Mitch is a crook.

Write a negation for each statement.

23. Her aunt's name is Hermione.

24. No rain fell in southern California today.

25. Some books are longer than this book.

26. All students present will get another chance.

27. No computer repairman can play blackjack.

28. Some people have all the luck.

29. Everybody loves somebody sometime.

30. Everyone needs a friend.

31. The trash needs to be collected.

32. Every architect who wants a job can find one.

Give a negation of each inequality. Do not use a slash symbol.

33. $x > 12$

34. $x < -6$

35. $x \geq 5$

36. $x \leq 19$

37. Try to negate the sentence "The exact number of words in this sentence is ten" and see what happens. Explain the problem that arises.

38. Explain why the negation of "$x > 5$" is not "$x < 5$."

Let p represent the statement "She has green eyes" *and let q represent the statement* "He is 60 years old." *Translate each symbolic compound statement into words.*

39. $\sim p$

40. $\sim q$

41. $p \wedge q$

42. $p \vee q$

43. $\sim p \vee q$

44. $p \wedge \sim q$

45. $\sim p \vee \sim q$

46. $\sim p \wedge \sim q$

47. $\sim (\sim p \wedge q)$

48. $\sim (p \vee \sim q)$

Let p represent the statement "Tyler collects DVDs" *and let q represent the statement* "Josh is an art major." *Convert each compound statement into symbols.*

49. Tyler collects DVDs and Josh is not an art major.

50. Tyler does not collect DVDs or Josh is not an art major.

51. Tyler does not collect DVDs or Josh is an art major.

52. Josh is an art major and Tyler does not collect DVDs.

53. Neither Tyler collects DVDs nor Josh is an art major.

54. Either Josh is an art major or Tyler collects DVDs, and it is not the case that both Josh is an art major and Tyler collects DVDs.

55. Incorrect use of quantifiers often is heard in everyday language. Suppose you hear that a local electronics chain is having a 40% off sale, and the radio advertisement states "All items are not available in all stores." Do you think that, literally translated, the ad really means what it says? What do you think is really meant? Explain your answer.

56. Repeat **Exercise 55** for the following: "All people don't have the time to devote to maintaining their vehicles properly."

Refer to the groups of art labeled A, B, and C, and identify by letter the group or groups that satisfy the given statements involving quantifiers in Exercises 57–64.

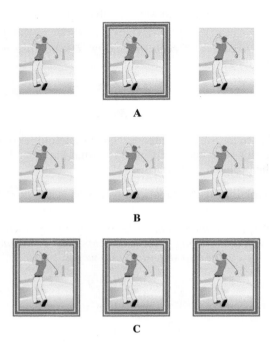

A

B

C

57. All pictures have frames.

58. No picture has a frame.

59. At least one picture does not have a frame.

60. Not every picture has a frame.

61. At least one picture has a frame.

62. No picture does not have a frame.

63. All pictures do not have frames.

64. Not every picture does not have a frame.

Decide whether each statement in Exercises 65–74 involving a quantifier is true *or* false.

65. Every whole number is an integer.

66. Every integer is a whole number.

67. There exists a natural number that is not an integer.

68. There exists an integer that is not a natural number.

69. All rational numbers are real numbers.

70. All irrational numbers are real numbers.

71. Some rational numbers are not integers.

72. Some whole numbers are not rational numbers.

73. Each whole number is a positive number.

74. Each rational number is a positive number.

75. Explain the difference between the statements "All students did not pass the test" and "Not all students passed the test."

76. The statement "For some real number x, $x^2 \geq 0$" is true. However, your friend does not understand why, because he claims that $x^2 \geq 0$ is true for *all* real numbers x (and not *some*). How would you explain his misconception to him?

77. Write the following statement using "every": There is no one here who has not made mistakes before.

78. Only one of these statements is true. Which one is it?

A. For some real number x, $x \not< 0$.

B. For all real numbers x, $x^3 > 0$.

C. For all real numbers x less than 0, x^2 is also less than 0.

D. For some real number x, $x^2 < 0$.

Symbolic logic also uses symbols for quantifiers. The symbol for the existential quantifier is

$$\exists \quad (a\ rotated\ \mathrm{E}),$$

and the symbol for the universal quantifier is

$$\forall \quad (an\ inverted\ \mathrm{A}).$$

The statement "For some x, p is true" can be symbolized

$$(\exists x)(p).$$

The statement "For all x, p is true" can be symbolized

$$(\forall x)(p).$$

The negation of $(\exists x)(p)$ is

$$(\forall x)(\sim p),$$

and the negation of $(\forall x)(p)$ is

$$(\exists x)(\sim p).$$

79. Refer to **Example 5.** If we let c represent "cat" and f represent "The cat has fleas," then the statement "Some cats have fleas" can be represented by $(\exists c)(f)$. Use symbols to express the negation of this statement.

80. Use symbols to express the statements for parts (b) and (c) of **Example 5** and their negations. Verify that the symbolic expressions translate to the negations found in the text.

3.2 TRUTH TABLES AND EQUIVALENT STATEMENTS

OBJECTIVES

1 Find the truth value of a conjunction.

2 Find the truth value of a disjunction.

3 Find the truth values for compound mathematical statements.

4 Construct truth tables for compound statements.

5 Understand and determine equivalence of statements.

6 Use De Morgan's laws to find negations of compound statements.

Conjunctions

Truth values of component statements are used to find truth values of compound statements. To begin, we must decide on truth values of the **conjunction *p and q,*** symbolized *p* ∧ *q.* Here, the connective *and* implies the idea of "both." The following statement is true, because each component statement is true.

Monday immediately follows Sunday, and March immediately follows February.

True

On the other hand, the following statement is false, even though part of the statement (Monday immediately follows Sunday) is true.

Monday immediately follows Sunday, and March immediately follows January.

False

For the conjunction p ∧ q to be true, both p and q must be true. This result is summarized by a table, called a **truth table,** which shows truth values of *p* ∧ *q* for all four possible combinations of truth values for the component statements *p* and *q*.

TRUTH TABLE FOR THE CONJUNCTION   *p* and *q*

p and *q*

p	*q*	*p* ∧ *q*
T	T	T
T	F	F
F	T	F
F	F	F

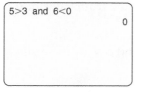

The calculator returns a 0 for

5 > 3 *and* 6 < 0,

indicating that the statement is false.

EXAMPLE 1 Finding the Truth Value of a Conjunction

Let *p* represent "5 > 3" and let *q* represent "6 < 0." Find the truth value of *p* ∧ *q*.

Solution

Here *p* is true and *q* is false. The second row of the conjunction truth table shows that *p* ∧ *q* is false in this case. ■

In some cases, the logical connective *but* is used in compound statements.

He wants to go to the mountains but she wants to go to the beach.

Here, *but* is used in place of *and* to give a different emphasis to the statement. We consider this statement as we would consider the conjunction using the word *and.* The truth table for the conjunction, given above, would apply.

Disjunctions

In ordinary language, the word *or* can be ambiguous. The expression "this or that" can mean either "this or that or both," or "this or that but not both." For example, consider the following statement.

I will paint the wall or I will paint the ceiling.

This statement probably means: "I will paint the wall or I will paint the ceiling or I will paint both."

On the other hand, consider the following statement.

I will wear my glasses or my contact lenses.

It probably means "I will wear my glasses, or I will wear my contacts, but I will not wear both."

The symbol ∨ represents the first *or* described. That is,

$p \vee q$ **means** **"*p* or *q* or both."**   Disjunction

With this meaning of *or*, $p \vee q$ is called the **inclusive disjunction,** or just the **disjunction** of *p* and *q*. In everyday language, the disjunction implies the idea of "either." For example, consider the following disjunction.

I have a quarter or I have a dime.

It is true whenever I have either a quarter, a dime, or both. The only way this disjunction could be false would be if I had neither coin. ***The disjunction $p \vee q$ is false only if both component statements are false.***

TRUTH TABLE FOR THE DISJUNCTION *p* or *q*		
	p or *q*	
p	*q*	$p \vee q$
T	T	T
T	F	T
F	T	T
F	F	F

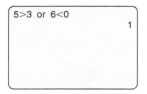

The calculator returns a 1 for

$5 > 3 \ or \ 6 < 0,$

indicating that the statement is true.

EXAMPLE 2 Finding the Truth Value of a Disjunction

Let *p* represent "5 > 3" and let *q* represent "6 < 0." Find the truth value of $p \vee q$.

Solution

Here, as in **Example 1,** *p* is true and *q* is false. The second row of the disjunction truth table shows that $p \vee q$ is true. ∎

The symbol ≥ is read **"is greater than or equal to,"** while ≤ is read **"is less than or equal to."** If *a* and *b* are real numbers, then $a \leq b$ is true if $a < b$ or $a = b$. See **Table 5.**

Table 5

Statement	Reason It Is True
$8 \geq 8$	$8 = 8$
$3 \geq 1$	$3 > 1$
$-5 \leq -3$	$-5 < -3$
$-4 \leq -4$	$-4 = -4$

Negations

The **negation** of a statement *p*, symbolized **~*p*,** must have the opposite truth value from the statement *p* itself. This leads to the truth table for the negation.

TRUTH TABLE FOR THE NEGATION not *p*	
not *p*	
p	~*p*
T	F
F	T

EXAMPLE 3 Finding the Truth Value of a Compound Statement

Suppose p is false, q is true, and r is false. What is the truth value of the compound statement $\sim p \wedge (q \vee \sim r)$?

Solution

Here parentheses are used to group q and $\sim r$ together. Work first inside the parentheses. Because r is false, $\sim r$ will be true. Because $\sim r$ is true and q is true, the truth value of $q \vee \sim r$ is T, as shown in the first row of the *or* truth table.

Because p is false, $\sim p$ is true, and the truth value of $\sim p \wedge (q \vee \sim r)$ is found in the top row of the *and* truth table. The statement

$$\sim p \wedge (q \vee \sim r) \quad \text{is true.}$$

We can use a shortcut symbolic method that involves replacing the statements with their truth values, letting T represent a true statement and F represent a false statement.

$$\sim p \wedge (q \vee \sim r)$$
$$\sim F \wedge (T \vee \sim F) \quad \boxed{\text{Work within parentheses first.}}$$
$$T \wedge (T \vee T) \quad \sim F \text{ gives T.}$$
$$T \wedge T \quad T \vee T \text{ gives T.}$$

The compound statement is true. $\longrightarrow$ **T** $\quad$ T $\wedge$ T gives T. ∎

Mathematical Statements

We can use truth tables to determine the truth values of compound mathematical statements.

EXAMPLE 4 Deciding Whether Compound Mathematical Statements Are True or False

Let p represent the statement $3 > 2$, q represent $5 < 4$, and r represent $3 < 8$. Decide whether each statement is *true* or *false*.

(a) $\sim p \wedge \sim q$ **(b)** $\sim (p \wedge q)$ **(c)** $(\sim p \wedge r) \vee (\sim q \wedge \sim p)$

Solution

(a) Because p is true, $\sim p$ is false. By the *and* truth table, if one part of an "and" statement is false, the entire statement is false.

$$\sim p \wedge \sim q \quad \text{is false.}$$

(b) For $\sim (p \wedge q)$, first work within the parentheses. Because p is true and q is false, $p \wedge q$ is false by the *and* truth table. Next, apply the negation. The negation of a false statement is true.

$$\sim (p \wedge q) \quad \text{is true.}$$

(c) Here p is true, q is false, and r is true. This makes $\sim p$ false and $\sim q$ true. By the *and* truth table, $\sim p \wedge r$ is false, and $\sim q \wedge \sim p$ is also false. By the *or* truth table,

$$(\sim p \wedge r) \vee (\sim q \wedge \sim p) \quad \text{is false.}$$
$$\qquad\qquad \downarrow \qquad\qquad\qquad \downarrow \qquad\qquad \text{(Alternatively, see } \textbf{Example 8(b)}.)$$
$$\qquad\qquad F \qquad \vee \qquad F$$

∎

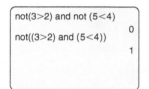

not(3>2) and not (5<4)
0
not((3>2) and (5<4))
1

Example 4(a) explains why

$$\sim (3 > 2) \wedge \sim (5 < 4)$$

is false. The calculator returns a 0. For a true statement such as

$$\sim[(3 > 2) \wedge (5 < 4)]$$

from **Example 4(b)**, it returns a 1.

When a quantifier is used with a conjunction or a disjunction, we must be careful in determining the truth value, as shown in the following example.

George Boole (1815–1864) grew up in poverty. His father, a London tradesman, gave him his first mathematics lessons and taught him to make optical instruments. Boole was largely self-educated. At 16 he worked in an elementary school and by age 20 had opened his own school. He studied mathematics in his spare time. He died of lung disease at age 49.

   Boole's ideas have been used in the design of computers, telephone systems, and search engines.

EXAMPLE 5 **Deciding Whether Quantified Mathematical Statements Are True or False**

Decide whether each statement is *true* or *false*.

(a) For some real number x, $x < 5$ and $x > 2$.

(b) For every real number x, $x > 0$ or $x < 1$.

(c) For all real numbers x, $x^2 > 0$.

Solution

(a) Because "some" is an *existential* quantifier, we need only find one real number x that makes both component statements true, and $x = 3$ is such a number. The statement is true by the *and* truth table.

(b) No matter which real number might be tried as a replacement for x, at least one of the two statements

$$x > 0, \quad x < 1$$

will be true. Because an "or" statement is true if one or both component statements are true, the entire statement as given is true.

(c) Because "for all" is a *universal* quantifier, we need only find one case in which the inequality is false to make the entire statement false. Can we find a real number whose square is not positive (that is, not greater than 0)? Yes, we can— 0 is such a number. In fact 0 is the *only* real number whose square is not positive. This statement is false. ■

FOR FURTHER THOUGHT

Whose Picture Am I Looking At?

Raymond Smullyan is one of today's foremost writers of logic puzzles. This professor of mathematics and philosophy is now retired from Indiana University and has written several books on recreational logic, including *What Is the Name of This Book?*, *The Lady or the Tiger?*, and *The Gödelian Puzzle Book.* The first of these includes the following puzzle, which has been around for many years.

For Group or Individual Investigation

A man was looking at a portrait. Someone asked him, "Whose picture are you looking at?" He replied: "Brothers and sisters, I have none, but this man's father is my father's son." ("This man's father" means, of course, the father of the man in the picture.)

Whose picture was the man looking at? (The answer is on **page 96.**)

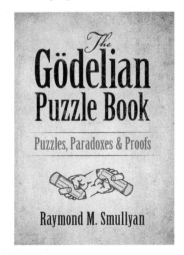

Truth Tables

In the preceding examples, the truth value for a given statement was found by going back to the basic truth tables. It is generally easier to first create a complete truth table for the given statement itself. Then final truth values can be read directly from this table.

   In this book we use the standard format shown in the margin for listing the possible truth values in compound statements involving two component statements.

p	q	Compound Statement
T	T	
T	F	
F	T	
F	F	

EXAMPLE 6   Constructing a Truth Table

Consider the statement $(\sim p \wedge q) \vee \sim q$.

(a) Construct a truth table.

(b) Suppose both p and q are true. Find the truth value of the compound statement.

Solution

(a) As shown below, begin by listing all possible combinations of truth values for p and q. Then list the truth values of $\sim p$, which are the opposite of those of p.

Use the "$\sim p$" and "q" columns, along with the *and* truth table, to find the truth values of $\sim p \wedge q$. List them in a separate column.

Next include a column for $\sim q$.

p	q	$\sim p$	$\sim p \wedge q$	$\sim q$
T	T	F	F	F
T	F	F	F	T
F	T	T	T	F
F	F	T	F	T

Finally, make a column for the entire compound statement. To find the truth values, use *or* to combine $\sim p \wedge q$ with $\sim q$ and refer to the *or* truth table.

p	q	$\sim p$	$\sim p \wedge q$	$\sim q$	$(\sim p \wedge q) \vee \sim q$
T	T	F	F	F	F
T	F	F	F	T	T
F	T	T	T	F	T
F	F	T	F	T	T

(b) Look in the first row of the final truth table above, where both p and q have truth value T. Read across the row to find that the compound statement is false. ■

EXAMPLE 7   Constructing a Truth Table

Construct the truth table for $p \wedge (\sim p \vee \sim q)$.

Solution

p	q	$\sim p$	$\sim q$	$\sim p \vee \sim q$	$p \wedge (\sim p \vee \sim q)$
T	T	F	F	F	F
T	F	F	T	T	T
F	T	T	F	T	F
F	F	T	T	T	F

■

If a compound statement involves three component statements p, q, and r, we will use the following standard format in setting up the truth table.

p	q	r	**Compound Statement**
T	T	T	
T	T	F	
T	F	T	
T	F	F	
F	T	T	
F	T	F	
F	F	T	
F	F	F	

Emilie, Marquise du Châtelet
(1706–1749) participated in the scientific activity of the generation after Newton and Leibniz. Educated in science, music, and literature, she was studying mathematics at the time (1733) she began a long intellectual relationship with the philosopher **François Voltaire** (1694–1778). She and Voltaire competed independently in 1738 for a prize offered by the French Academy on the subject of fire. Although du Châtelet did not win, her dissertation was published by the academy in 1744.

EXAMPLE 8 **Constructing a Truth Table**

Consider the statement $(\sim p \wedge r) \vee (\sim q \wedge \sim p)$.

(a) Construct a truth table.

(b) Suppose p is true, q is false, and r is true. Find the truth value of this statement.

Solution

(a) There are three component statements: p, q, and r. The truth table thus requires eight rows to list all possible combinations of truth values of p, q, and r. The final truth table can be found in much the same way as the ones earlier.

p	q	r	$\sim p$	$\sim p \wedge r$	$\sim q$	$\sim q \wedge \sim p$	$(\sim p \wedge r) \vee (\sim q \wedge \sim p)$
T	T	T	F	F	F	F	F
T	T	F	F	F	F	F	F
T	F	T	F	F	T	F	F
T	F	F	F	F	T	F	F
F	T	T	T	T	F	F	T
F	T	F	T	F	F	F	F
F	F	T	T	T	T	T	T
F	F	F	T	F	T	T	T

(b) By the third row of the truth table in part (a), the compound statement is false. (This is an alternative method for working part (c) of **Example 4**.) ■

Problem-Solving Strategy

One strategy for problem solving is to notice a pattern and then use inductive reasoning. This strategy is applied in the next example.

EXAMPLE 9 **Using Inductive Reasoning**

Suppose that n is a counting number, and a logical statement is composed of n component statements. How many rows will appear in the truth table for the compound statement?

Solution

We examine some of the earlier truth tables in this section. The truth table for the negation has one statement and two rows. The truth tables for the conjunction and the disjunction have two component statements, and each has four rows. The truth table in **Example 8(a)** has three component statements and eight rows.

Summarizing these in **Table 6** (seen in the margin) reveals a pattern encountered earlier. Inductive reasoning leads us to the conjecture that if a logical statement is composed of n component statements, it will have 2^n rows. This can be proved using more advanced concepts. ■

Table 6

Number of Statements	Number of Rows
1	$2 = 2^1$
2	$4 = 2^2$
3	$8 = 2^3$

The result of **Example 9** is reminiscent of the formula for the number of subsets of a set having n elements.

NUMBER OF ROWS IN A TRUTH TABLE

A logical statement having n component statements will have 2^n rows in its truth table.

Alternative Method for Constructing Truth Tables

After making a reasonable number of truth tables, some people prefer the shortcut method shown in **Example 10,** which repeats **Examples 6 and 8.**

Ada Lovelace (1815–1852) was born Augusta Ada Byron. Her talents as a mathematician and logician led to her work with **Charles Babbage** (1791–1871) on his Analytical Engine, the first programmable mechanical computer. Lovelace's notes on this machine include what is regarded by many as the first computer program and reveal her visionary belief that computing machines would have applications beyond numerical calculations.

EXAMPLE 10 Constructing Truth Tables

Construct the truth table for each compound statement.

(a) $(\sim p \wedge q) \vee \sim q$ **(b)** $(\sim p \wedge r) \vee (\sim q \wedge \sim p)$

Solution

(a) Start by inserting truth values for $\sim p$ and for q. Then use the *and* truth table to obtain the truth values for $\sim p \wedge q$.

p	q	(~p	∧	q)	∨	~q
T	T	F			T	
T	F	F			F	
F	T	T			T	
F	F	T			F	

p	q	(~p	∧	q)	∨	~q
T	T	F	F	T		
T	F	F	F	F		
F	T	T	T	T		
F	F	T	F	F		

Now disregard the two preliminary columns of truth values for $\sim p$ and for q, and insert truth values for $\sim q$. Finally, use the *or* truth table.

p	q	(~p ∧ q)	∨	~q
T	T	F		F
T	F	F		T
F	T	T		F
F	F	F		T

p	q	(~p ∧ q)	∨	~q
T	T	F	F	F
T	F	F	T	T
F	T	T	T	F
F	F	F	T	T

These steps can be summarized as follows.

p	q	(~p	∧	q)	∨	~q
T	T	F	F	T	F	F
T	F	F	F	F	T	T
F	T	T	T	T	T	F
F	F	T	F	F	T	T
		①	②	①	④	③

> The circled numbers indicate the order in which the various columns of the truth table were found.

(b) Work as follows.

p	q	r	(~p	∧	r)	∨	(~q	∧	~p)
T	T	T	F	F	T	F	F	F	F
T	T	F	F	F	F	F	F	F	F
T	F	T	F	F	T	F	T	F	F
T	F	F	F	F	F	F	T	F	F
F	T	T	T	T	T	T	F	F	T
F	T	F	T	F	F	F	F	F	T
F	F	T	T	T	T	T	T	T	T
F	F	F	T	F	F	T	T	T	T
			①	②	①	⑤	③	④	③

> The circled numbers indicate the order.

Equivalent Statements and De Morgan's Laws

Two statements are **equivalent** if they have the same truth value in *every* possible situation. The columns of the two truth tables that were the last to be completed will be the same for equivalent statements.

EXAMPLE 11 Deciding Whether Two Statements Are Equivalent

Are the following two statements equivalent?

$$\sim p \wedge \sim q \quad \text{and} \quad \sim (p \vee q)$$

Solution

Construct a truth table for each statement.

p	q	$\sim p \wedge \sim q$	p	q	$\sim (p \vee q)$
T	T	F	T	T	F
T	F	F	T	F	F
F	T	F	F	T	F
F	F	T	F	F	T

Because the truth values are the same in all cases, as shown in the columns in color, the statements $\sim p \wedge \sim q$ and $\sim (p \vee q)$ are equivalent.

$$\sim p \wedge \sim q \equiv \sim (p \vee q) \qquad \text{The symbol} \equiv \text{denotes equivalence.} \qquad \blacksquare$$

In the same way, the statements $\sim p \vee \sim q$ and $\sim (p \wedge q)$ are equivalent. We call these equivalences *De Morgan's laws*.

DE MORGAN'S LAWS FOR LOGICAL STATEMENTS

Compare **De Morgan's Laws** for logical statements with the set theoretical version on **page 68.**

For any statements p and q, the following equivalences are valid.

$$\sim (p \vee q) \equiv \sim p \wedge \sim q \quad \text{and} \quad \sim (p \wedge q) \equiv \sim p \vee \sim q$$

EXAMPLE 12 Applying De Morgan's Laws

Find a negation of each statement by applying De Morgan's laws.

(a) I got an A or I got a B.   **(b)** She won't try and he will succeed.

(c) $\sim p \vee (q \wedge \sim p)$

Solution

(a) If p represents "I got an A" and q represents "I got a B," then the compound statement is symbolized $p \vee q$. The negation of $p \vee q$ is $\sim (p \vee q)$. By one of De Morgan's laws, this is equivalent to $\sim p \wedge \sim q$, or, in words,

> **I didn't get an A and I didn't get a B.**

This negation is reasonable—the original statement says that I got either an A or a B. The negation says that I didn't get *either* grade.

(b) From De Morgan's laws, $\sim (p \wedge q) \equiv \sim p \vee \sim q$, so the negation becomes

> **She will try or he won't succeed.**

(c) Negate both component statements and change $\vee$ to $\wedge$.

$$\sim [\sim p \vee (q \wedge \sim p)] \equiv p \wedge \sim (q \wedge \sim p)$$
$$\equiv p \wedge (\sim q \vee \sim (\sim p)) \qquad \text{Apply De Morgan's law again.}$$
$$\equiv p \wedge (\sim q \vee p)$$

A truth table will show that the statements

$$\sim p \vee (q \wedge \sim p) \quad \text{and} \quad p \wedge (\sim q \vee p) \quad \text{are negations of each other.} \qquad \blacksquare$$

FOR FURTHER THOUGHT

The Logic Behind Computers

Computer designers use *logic gates* at the foundation of digital circuits. Logic gates treat the binary digits 0 and 1 as logical values, and give a single output of 1 or 0 based on the input value(s), which also have a value of 1 or 0. Since 1 and 0 are the only digits in the binary number system, that system is the perfect bridge between logic and numerical computation (as Leibniz realized).

There are three basic logic gates: the AND gate, the OR gate, and the NOT gate, whose symbols and truth tables follow.

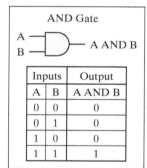

Inputs		Output
A	B	A AND B
0	0	0
0	1	0
1	0	0
1	1	1

Inputs		Output
A	B	A OR B
0	0	0
0	1	1
1	0	1
1	1	1

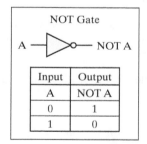

Input	Output
A	NOT A
0	1
1	0

Other logic gates include NAND, NOR (the negations of AND and OR, respectively), XOR (exclusive OR—see **Exercise 77** in this section), and XNOR (the negation of XOR). Their symbols are shown below.

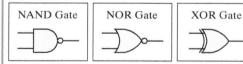

Early logic gates were constructed with electrical relays and vacuum tubes, but the development of semiconductors and the transistor have made possible the placement of millions of logic gates in integrated circuits, microchips that perform billions of logical calculations per second. More recently, logic gates have even been fashioned from biological organisms and DNA.

There are some excellent Android Apps (such as Logic Simulator, free in the Android Play Store) for simulating logic circuits. The simulator shown allows the user to add logic gates, switches (connected to inputs), and light bulbs (connected to outputs). Red highlighting indicates where current is flowing. These four screenshots show the truth values for the XOR logic gate.

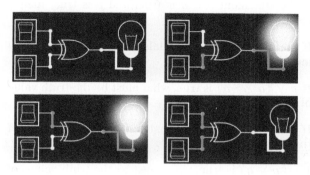

For Group or Individual Investigation

1. Create the truth table for A XOR B using the accompanying screenshots. (Remember that the red nodes are "hot," which is indicated by a 1 or a T in the truth table.)

2. Charles Peirce (1839–1914) showed that all of the logic gates we have mentioned could be constructed using only NAND gates. Construct a truth table for the logic circuit below to show that it is equivalent to the XOR gate. *Hint:* The output of the circuit shown is

   [A NAND (A NAND B)] NAND [(A NAND B) NAND B],

   which is equivalent to

   $\sim(\sim(A \wedge \sim(A \wedge B)) \wedge \sim(\sim(A \wedge B) \wedge B))$.

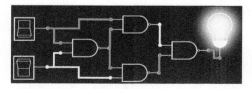

3. Download and install an app to simulate logic gates, and use it to verify your truth table from **Exercise 2**. One image of the simulated circuit is shown below.

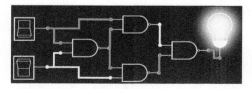

4. Use the simulator to build circuits to verify De Morgan's laws for logic.

3.2 EXERCISES

Use the concepts introduced in this section to answer Exercises 1–8.

1. If q is false, what must be the truth value of the statement $(p \wedge \sim q) \wedge q$?

2. If q is true, what must be the truth value of the statement $q \vee (q \wedge \sim p)$?

3. If the statement $p \wedge q$ is true, and p is true, then q must be _____.

4. If the statement $p \vee q$ is false, and p is false, then q must be _____.

5. If $p \vee (q \wedge \sim q)$ is true, what must be the truth value of p?

6. If $p \wedge \sim (q \vee r)$ is true, what must be the truth value of the component statements?

7. If $\sim (p \vee q)$ is true, what must be the truth values of the component statements?

8. If $\sim (p \wedge q)$ is false, what must be the truth values of the component statements?

Let p represent a false statement and let q represent a true statement. Find the truth value of the given compound statement.

9. $\sim p$

10. $\sim q$

11. $p \vee q$

12. $p \wedge q$

13. $p \vee \sim q$

14. $\sim p \wedge q$

15. $\sim p \vee \sim q$

16. $p \wedge \sim q$

17. $\sim (p \wedge \sim q)$

18. $\sim (\sim p \vee \sim q)$

19. $\sim [\sim p \wedge (\sim q \vee p)]$

20. $\sim [(\sim p \wedge \sim q) \vee \sim q]$

21. Is the statement $6 \geq 2$ a conjunction or a disjunction? Why?

22. Why is the statement $8 \geq 3$ true? Why is $5 \geq 5$ true?

Let p represent a true statement, and let q and r represent false statements. Find the truth value of the given compound statement.

23. $(p \wedge r) \vee \sim q$

24. $(q \vee \sim r) \wedge p$

25. $p \wedge (q \vee r)$

26. $(\sim p \wedge q) \vee \sim r$

27. $\sim (p \wedge q) \wedge (r \vee \sim q)$

28. $(\sim r \wedge \sim q) \vee (\sim r \wedge q)$

29. $\sim [(\sim p \wedge q) \vee r]$

30. $\sim [r \vee (\sim q \wedge \sim p)]$

31. $\sim [\sim q \vee (r \wedge \sim p)]$

32. $\sim (p \vee q) \wedge \sim (p \wedge q)$

Let p represent the statement $16 < 8$, let q represent the statement $5 \not> 4$, and let r represent the statement $17 \leq 17$. Find the truth value of the given compound statement.

33. $p \wedge r$

34. $p \vee \sim q$

35. $\sim q \vee \sim r$

36. $\sim p \wedge \sim r$

37. $(p \wedge q) \vee r$

38. $\sim p \vee (\sim r \vee \sim q)$

39. $(\sim r \wedge q) \vee \sim p$

40. $\sim (p \vee \sim q) \vee \sim r$

Give the number of rows in the truth table for each compound statement.

41. $p \vee \sim r$

42. $p \wedge (r \wedge \sim s)$

43. $(\sim p \wedge q) \vee (\sim r \vee \sim s) \wedge r$

44. $[(p \vee q) \wedge (r \wedge s)] \wedge (t \vee \sim p)$

45. $[(\sim p \wedge \sim q) \wedge (\sim r \wedge s \wedge \sim t)] \wedge (\sim u \vee \sim v)$

46. $[(\sim p \wedge \sim q) \vee (\sim r \vee \sim s)]$
$\vee [(\sim m \wedge \sim n) \wedge (u \wedge \sim v)]$

47. If the truth table for a certain compound statement has 64 rows, how many distinct component statements does it have?

48. Is it possible for the truth table of a compound statement to have exactly 54 rows? Why or why not?

Construct a truth table for each compound statement.

49. $\sim p \wedge q$

50. $\sim p \vee \sim q$

51. $\sim (p \wedge q)$

52. $p \vee \sim q$

53. $(q \vee \sim p) \vee \sim q$

54. $(p \wedge \sim q) \wedge p$

55. $(p \vee \sim q) \wedge (p \wedge q)$

56. $(\sim p \wedge \sim q) \vee (\sim p \vee q)$

57. $(\sim p \wedge q) \wedge r$

58. $r \vee (p \wedge \sim q)$

59. $(\sim p \wedge \sim q) \vee (\sim r \vee \sim p)$

60. $(\sim r \vee \sim p) \wedge (\sim p \vee \sim q)$

61. $\sim (\sim p \wedge \sim q) \vee (\sim r \vee \sim s)$

62. $(\sim r \vee s) \wedge (\sim p \wedge q)$

Use one of De Morgan's laws to write the negation of each statement.

63. You can pay me now or you can pay me later.

64. I am not going or she is going.

65. It is summer and there is no snow.

66. $\frac{1}{2}$ is a positive number and −9 is less than zero.

67. I said yes but she said no.

68. Dan tried to sell the software, but he was unable to do so.

69. $6 - 1 = 5$ and $9 + 13 \neq 7$

70. $8 < 10$ or $5 \neq 2$

71. Prancer or Vixen will lead Santa's reindeer sleigh next Christmas.

72. The lawyer and the client appeared in court.

Identify each statement as true *or* false.

73. For every real number x, $x < 14$ or $x > 6$.

74. For every real number x, $x > 9$ or $x < 9$.

75. There exists an integer n such that $n > 0$ and $n < 0$.

76. For some integer n, $n \geq 3$ and $n \leq 3$.

77. Complete the truth table for *exclusive disjunction*. The symbol $\veebar$ represents "one or the other is true, but not both."

p	q	$p \veebar q$
T	T	
T	F	
F	T	
F	F	

Exclusive disjunction

78. Attorneys sometimes use the phrase "and/or." This phrase corresponds to which usage of the word *or:* inclusive or exclusive disjunction?

Decide whether each compound statement is true *or* false. Remember that $\veebar$ is the exclusive disjunction of* **Exercise 77.**

79. $3 + 1 = 4 \veebar 2 + 5 = 7$

80. $3 + 1 = 4 \veebar 2 + 5 = 10$

81. $3 + 1 = 6 \veebar 2 + 5 = 7$

82. $3 + 1 = 12 \veebar 2 + 5 = 10$

83. In his book *The Lady or the Tiger and Other Logic Puzzles,* Raymond Smullyan proposes the following problem. It is taken from the classic Frank Stockton short story, in which a prisoner must make a choice between two doors: behind one is a beautiful lady, and behind the other is a hungry tiger.

What if each door has a sign, and the man knows that only one sign is true?

The sign on Door 1 reads:

IN THIS ROOM THERE IS A LADY AND IN THE OTHER ROOM THERE IS A TIGER.

The sign on Door 2 reads:

IN ONE OF THESE ROOMS THERE IS A LADY AND IN ONE OF THESE ROOMS THERE IS A TIGER.

With this information, the man is able to choose the correct door. Can you?

84. (a) Build truth tables for

$$p \vee (q \wedge r) \quad \text{and} \quad (p \vee q) \wedge (p \vee r).$$

Decide whether it can be said that "OR distributes over AND." Explain.

(b) Build truth tables for

$$p \wedge (q \vee r) \quad \text{and} \quad (p \wedge q) \vee (p \wedge r).$$

Decide whether it can be said that "AND distributes over OR." Explain.

(c) Describe how the logical equivalences developed in parts (a) and (b) are related to the set-theoretical equations

$$X \cup (Y \cap Z) = (X \cup Y) \cap (X \cup Z)$$

and

$$X \cap (Y \cup Z) = (X \cap Y) \cup (X \cap Z).$$

85. De Morgan's law

$$\sim(p \vee q) \equiv \sim p \wedge \sim q$$

can be stated verbally, "The negation of a disjunction is equivalent to the conjunction of the negations." Give a similar verbal statement of

$$\sim(p \wedge q) \equiv \sim p \vee \sim q.$$

3.3   THE CONDITIONAL AND CIRCUITS

Conditionals

"If truly Truthful Troll I be,
then go thou east, and be thou free."

This of course is the statement uttered by the troll on the second page of this chapter. A more modern paraphrase would be, "*If* I am the troll who always tells the truth, *then* the door to the east is the one that leads to freedom."

The troll's utterance is an example of a conditional statement. A **conditional** statement is a compound statement that uses the connective *if . . . then.*

If I read for too long, *then* I get tired.

If looks could kill, *then* I would be dead.

If he doesn't get back soon, *then* you should go look for him.

} Conditional statements

In each of these conditional statements, the component coming after the word *if* gives a condition (but not necessarily the only condition) under which the statement coming after *then* will be true. For example, "If it is over 90°, then I'll go to the mountains" tells one possible condition under which I will go to the mountains—if the temperature is over 90°.

The conditional is written with an arrow and symbolized as follows.

$$p \rightarrow q \qquad \text{If } p, \text{ then } q.$$

We read $p \rightarrow q$ as "*p* **implies** *q*" or "**If *p*, then *q*.**" In the conditional $p \rightarrow q$, the statement *p* is the **antecedent**, while *q* is the **consequent.**

The conditional connective may not always be explicitly stated. That is, it may be "hidden" in an everyday expression. For example, consider the following statement.

Quitters never win.

It can be written in *if . . . then* form as

If you're a quitter, *then* you will never win.

As another example, consider this statement.

It is difficult to study when you are distracted.

It can be written

If you are distracted, *then* it is difficult to study.

In the quotation "If you aim at nothing, you will hit it every time," the word "then" is not stated but understood from the context of the statement. "You aim at nothing" is the antecedent, and "you will hit it every time" is the consequent.

The conditional truth table is more difficult to define than the tables in the previous section. To see how to define the conditional truth table, imagine you have bought a used car (with financing from the car dealer), and the used-car salesman says,

If you fail to make your payment on time, *then* your car will be taken.

Let *p* represent "You fail to make your payment on time," and let *q* represent "Your car will be taken." There are four combinations of truth values for the two component statements.

In his April 21, 1989, five-star review of **Field of Dreams,** the *Chicago Sun-Times* movie critic Roger Ebert gave an explanation of why the movie has become an American classic.

There is a speech in this movie about baseball that is so simple and true that it is heartbreaking. And the whole attitude toward the players reflects that attitude. Why do they come back from the great beyond and play in this cornfield? Not to make any kind of vast, earthshattering statement, but simply to hit a few and field a few, and remind us of a good and innocent time.

The photo above was taken in 2007 in Dyersville, Iowa, at the actual scene of the filming. The carving "Ray Loves Annie" in the bleacher seats can be seen in a quick shot during the movie. It has weathered over time.

What famous **conditional statement** inspired Ray to build a baseball field in his cornfield?

As we consider these four possibilities, it is helpful to ask,

"Did the salesman lie?"

If so, then the conditional statement is considered false. Otherwise, the conditional statement is considered true.

Possibility	Failed to Pay on Time?	Car Taken?	
1	Yes	Yes	p is T, q is T.
2	Yes	No	p is T, q is F.
3	No	Yes	p is F, q is T.
4	No	No	p is F, q is F.

The four possibilities are as follows.

1. In the first case, assume you failed to make your payment on time, and your car *was* taken (*p* is T, *q* is T). The salesman told the truth, so place T in the first row of the truth table. (We do not claim that your car was taken *because* you failed to pay on time. It may be gone for a completely different reason.)

2. In the second case, assume that you failed to make your payment on time, and your car was *not* taken (*p* is T, *q* is F). The salesman lied (gave a false statement), so place an F in the second row of the truth table.

3. In the third case, assume that you paid on time, but your car was taken anyway (*p* is F, *q* is T). The salesman did *not* lie. He only said what would happen if you were late on payments, not what would happen if you paid on time. (The crime here is stealing, not lying.) Since we cannot say that the salesman lied, place a T in the third row of the truth table.

4. Finally, assume that you made timely payment, and your car was not taken (*p* is F, *q* is F). This certainly does not contradict the salesman's statement, so place a T in the last row of the truth table.

The completed truth table for the conditional is defined as follows.

TRUTH TABLE FOR THE CONDITIONAL   If *p*, then *q*

If *p*, then *q*

p	*q*	$p \rightarrow q$
T	T	T
T	F	F
F	T	T
F	F	T

The use of the conditional connective in no way implies a cause-and-effect relationship. Any two statements may have an arrow placed between them to create a compound statement. Consider this example.

If I pass mathematics, then the sun will rise the next day.

It is true, because the consequent is true. (See the special characteristics following **Example 1** on the next page.) There is, however, no cause-and-effect connection between my passing mathematics and the rising of the sun. The sun will rise no matter what grade I get.

```
PROGRAM:PARITY
: Prompt N
: If N/2 = int (N/2)
:Then
: Disp "EVEN"
:
:
```

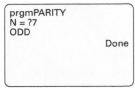

```
PROGRAM:PARITY
:
: Else
: Disp "ODD"
: End
:
```

```
prgmPARITY
N = ?7
ODD
                    Done
```

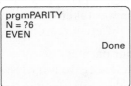

```
prgmPARITY
N = ?6
EVEN
                    Done
```

Conditional statements are useful in writing programs. The short program in the first two screens determines whether an integer is even. Notice the lines that begin with *If* and *Then*.

EXAMPLE 1 Finding the Truth Value of a Conditional

Given that p, q, and r are all false, find the truth value of the following statement.

$$(p \rightarrow \sim q) \rightarrow (\sim r \rightarrow q)$$

Solution

Using the shortcut method explained in **Example 3** of the previous section, we can replace p, q, and r with F (since each is false) and proceed as before, using the negation and conditional truth tables as necessary.

$$
\begin{array}{ccl}
(p \rightarrow \sim q) & \rightarrow & (\sim r \rightarrow q) \\
(F \rightarrow \sim F) & \rightarrow & (\sim F \rightarrow F) \\
(F \rightarrow T) & \rightarrow & (T \rightarrow F) \quad \text{Use the negation truth table.} \\
T & \rightarrow & F \quad\quad\quad \text{Use the conditional truth table.} \\
& \mathbb{F} &
\end{array}
$$

The statement $(p \rightarrow \sim q) \rightarrow (\sim r \rightarrow q)$ is false when p, q, and r are all false. ■

SPECIAL CHARACTERISTICS OF CONDITIONAL STATEMENTS

1. $p \rightarrow q$ is false only when the antecedent is *true* and the consequent is *false*.

2. If the antecedent is *false*, then $p \rightarrow q$ is automatically *true*.

3. If the consequent is *true*, then $p \rightarrow q$ is automatically *true*.

EXAMPLE 2 Determining Whether Conditionals Are True or False

Write *true* or *false* for each statement. Here T represents a true statement, and F represents a false statement.

(a) $T \rightarrow (7 = 3)$ **(b)** $(8 < 2) \rightarrow F$ **(c)** $(4 \neq 3 + 1) \rightarrow T$

Solution

(a) Because the antecedent is true, while the consequent, $7 = 3$, is false, the given statement is false by the first point mentioned above.

(b) The antecedent is false, so the given statement is true by the second observation.

(c) The consequent is true, making the statement true by the third characteristic of conditional statements. ■

EXAMPLE 3 Constructing Truth Tables

Construct a truth table for each statement.

(a) $(\sim p \rightarrow \sim q) \rightarrow (\sim p \wedge q)$ **(b)** $(p \rightarrow q) \rightarrow (\sim p \vee q)$

Solution

(a) Insert the truth values of $\sim p$ and $\sim q$. Find the truth values of $\sim p \rightarrow \sim q$.

p	q	$\sim p$	$\sim q$	$\sim p \rightarrow \sim q$
T	T	F	F	T
T	F	F	T	T
F	T	T	F	F
F	F	T	T	T

Next use $\sim p$ and q to find the truth values of $\sim p \wedge q$.

p	q	$\sim p$	$\sim q$	$\sim p \rightarrow \sim q$	$\sim p \wedge q$
T	T	F	F	T	F
T	F	F	T	T	F
F	T	T	F	F	T
F	F	T	T	T	F

Now find the truth values of $(\sim p \rightarrow \sim q) \rightarrow (\sim p \wedge q)$.

p	q	$\sim p$	$\sim q$	$\sim p \rightarrow \sim q$	$\sim p \wedge q$	$(\sim p \rightarrow \sim q) \rightarrow (\sim p \wedge q)$
T	T	F	F	T	F	F
T	F	F	T	T	F	F
F	T	T	F	F	T	T
F	F	T	T	T	F	F

(b) For $(p \rightarrow q) \rightarrow (\sim p \vee q)$, go through steps similar to the ones above.

p	q	$p \rightarrow q$	$\sim p$	$\sim p \vee q$	$(p \rightarrow q) \rightarrow (\sim p \vee q)$
T	T	T	F	T	T
T	F	F	F	F	T
F	T	T	T	T	T
F	F	T	T	T	T

As the truth table in **Example 3(b)** shows, the statement

$$(p \rightarrow q) \rightarrow (\sim p \vee q)$$

is always true, no matter what the truth values of the components. Such a statement is called a **tautology.** Several other examples of tautologies (as can be checked by forming truth tables) are

$$p \vee \sim p, \quad p \rightarrow p, \quad \text{and} \quad (\sim p \vee \sim q) \rightarrow \sim (p \wedge q). \quad \text{Tautologies}$$

The truth tables in **Example 3** also could have been found by the alternative method shown in **Section 3.2.**

Writing a Conditional as a Disjunction

p	q	$p \rightarrow q$
T	T	T
T	F	F
F	T	T
F	F	T

Recall that the truth table for the conditional (repeated in the margin) shows that $p \rightarrow q$ is false only when p is true and q is false. But we also know that the disjunction is false for only one combination of component truth values, and it is easy to see that $\sim p \vee q$ will be false only when p is true and q is false, as the following truth table indicates.

p	q	$\sim p$	$\vee$	q
T	T	F	T	T
T	F	F	F	F
F	T	T	T	T
F	F	T	T	F

Thus we see that the disjunction $\sim p \vee q$ is equivalent to the conditional $p \rightarrow q$.

WRITING A CONDITIONAL AS A DISJUNCTION

$p \rightarrow q$ is equivalent to $\sim p \vee q.$

We now know that

$$p \to q \equiv \sim p \lor q,$$

so the negation of the conditional is

$$\sim(p \to q) \equiv \sim(\sim p \lor q).$$

Applying De Morgan's law to the right side of the above equivalence gives the negation as a conjunction.

NEGATION OF $p \to q$

The negation of $p \to q$ is $p \land \sim q.$

EXAMPLE 4 **Determining Negations**

Determine the negation of each statement.

(a) If I'm hungry, I will eat.   **(b)** All dogs have fleas.

Solution

(a) If p represents "I'm hungry" and q represents "I will eat," then the given statement can be symbolized by $p \to q$. The negation of $p \to q$, as shown earlier, is $p \land \sim q$, so the negation of the statement is

> I'm hungry and I will not eat.

> Do not try to negate a conditional with another conditional.

(b) First, we must restate the given statement in *if . . . then* form.

> If it is a dog, then it has fleas.

Based on our earlier discussion, the negation is

> It is a dog and it does not have fleas. ∎

As seen in **Example 4,** the negation of a conditional statement is written as a conjunction.

EXAMPLE 5 **Determining Statements Equivalent to Conditionals**

Write each conditional as an equivalent statement without using *if . . . then*.

(a) If the Indians win the pennant, then Johnny will go to the World Series.

(b) If it's Borden's, it's got to be good.

Solution

(a) Because the conditional $p \to q$ is equivalent to $\sim p \lor q$, let p represent "The Indians win the pennant" and q represent "Johnny will go to the World Series." Restate the conditional as

> The Indians do not win the pennant or Johnny will go to the World Series.

(b) If p represents "it's Borden's" and if q represents "it's got to be good," the conditional may be restated as

> It's not Borden's or it's got to be good. ∎

Figure 1

Series circuit

Figure 2

Parallel circuit

Figure 3

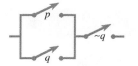

Figure 4

Switch Position	Current	Truth Value
Closed	flows	T
Open	stops	F

Circuits

One of the first nonmathematical applications of symbolic logic was seen in the master's thesis of Claude Shannon in 1937. Shannon showed how logic could be used to design electrical circuits. His work was immediately used by computer designers. Then in the developmental stage, computers could be simplified and built for less money using the ideas of Shannon.

To see how Shannon's ideas work, look at the electrical switch shown in **Figure 1.** We assume that current will flow through this switch when it is closed and not when it is open.

Figure 2 shows two switches connected in *series.* In such a circuit, current will flow only when both switches are closed. Note how closely a series circuit corresponds to the conjunction $p \wedge q$. We know that $p \wedge q$ is true only when both p and q are true.

A circuit corresponding to the disjunction $p \vee q$ can be found by drawing a *parallel* circuit, as in **Figure 3.** Here, current flows if either p or q is closed or if both p and q are closed.

The circuit in **Figure 4** corresponds to the statement $(p \vee q) \wedge \sim q$, which is a compound statement involving both a conjunction and a disjunction.

Simplifying an electrical circuit depends on the idea of equivalent statements from **Section 3.2.** Recall that two statements are equivalent if they have the same truth table final column. The symbol $\equiv$ is used to indicate that the two statements are equivalent. Some equivalent statements are shown in the following box.

EQUIVALENT STATEMENTS USED TO SIMPLIFY CIRCUITS

$$p \vee (q \wedge r) \equiv (p \vee q) \wedge (p \vee r) \qquad p \vee p \equiv p$$

$$p \wedge (q \vee r) \equiv (p \wedge q) \vee (p \wedge r) \qquad p \wedge p \equiv p$$

$$p \rightarrow q \equiv \sim q \rightarrow \sim p \qquad \sim(p \wedge q) \equiv \sim p \vee \sim q$$

$$p \rightarrow q \equiv \sim p \vee q \qquad \sim(p \vee q) \equiv \sim p \wedge \sim q$$

If T represents any true statement and F represents any false statement, then

$$p \vee T \equiv T \qquad p \vee \sim p \equiv T$$

$$p \wedge F \equiv F \qquad p \wedge \sim p \equiv F.$$

Circuits can be used as models of compound statements, with a closed switch corresponding to T (current flowing) and an open switch corresponding to F (current not flowing).

Figure 5

EXAMPLE 6 Simplifying a Circuit

Simplify the circuit of **Figure 5.**

Solution

At the top of **Figure 5,** p and q are connected in series, and at the bottom, p and r are connected in series. These are interpreted as the compound statements $p \wedge q$ and $p \wedge r$, respectively. These two conjunctions are connected in parallel, as indicated by the figure treated as a whole.

Write the disjunction of the two conjunctions.

$$(p \wedge q) \vee (p \wedge r)$$

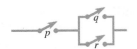

Figure 6

(Think of the two switches labeled "p" as being controlled by the same lever.) By one of the pairs of equivalent statements in the preceding box,

$$(p \wedge q) \vee (p \wedge r) \equiv p \wedge (q \vee r),$$

which has the circuit of **Figure 6.** This circuit is logically equivalent to the one in **Figure 5,** and yet it contains only three switches instead of four—which might well lead to a large savings in manufacturing costs. ∎

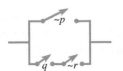

Figure 7

EXAMPLE 7 Drawing a Circuit for a Conditional Statement

Draw a circuit for $p \rightarrow (q \wedge \sim r)$.

Solution

From the list of equivalent statements in the box, $p \rightarrow q$ is equivalent to $\sim p \vee q$. This equivalence gives $p \rightarrow (q \wedge \sim r) \equiv \sim p \vee (q \wedge \sim r)$, which has the circuit diagram in **Figure 7.** ∎

WHEN Will I Ever USE This ?

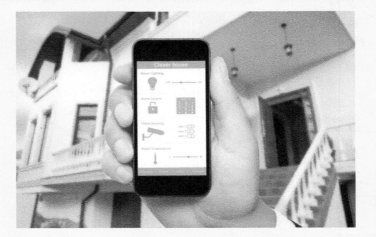

Suppose you are a home-monitoring and control system designer. A home-owner wants the capability of turning his air-conditioning system on or off at home via his smartphone (in case he forgets before leaving for vacation). You will need to install a control module for the AC unit that receives signals from your customer's smartphone.

Draw a circuit that will allow the AC unit to turn on when both a master switch and the control module are activated, and when either (or both) of two thermostats is (or are) triggered. Then write a logical statement for the circuit.

Since the master switch (m) and the control module (c) both need to be activated, they must be connected in series, followed by two thermostats T_1 and T_2 in parallel (because only one needs to be triggered). The circuit is shown below, and the corresponding logical statement is $m \wedge c \wedge (T_1 \vee T_2)$.

Rewrite each statement using the if . . . then *connective. Rearrange the wording or add words as necessary.*

1. You can do it if you just believe.

2. It must be bad for you if it's sweet.

3. Every even integer divisible by 5 is divisible by 10.

4. No perfect square integers have units digit 2, 3, 7, or 8.

5. No grizzly bears live in California.

6. No guinea pigs get lonely.

7. Surfers can't stay away from the beach.

8. Running Bear loves Little White Dove.

Decide whether each statement is true *or* false.

9. If the antecedent of a conditional statement is false, the conditional statement is true.

10. If the consequent of a conditional statement is true, the conditional statement is true.

11. If q is true, then $(p \land (q \to r)) \to q$ is true.

12. If p is true, then $\sim p \to (q \lor r)$ is true.

13. The negation of "If pigs fly, I'll believe it" is "If pigs don't fly, I won't believe it."

14. The statements "If it flies, then it's a bird" and "It does not fly or it's a bird" are logically equivalent.

15. Given that $\sim p$ is true and q is false, the conditional $p \to q$ is true.

16. Given that $\sim p$ is false and q is false, the conditional $p \to q$ is true.

17. Explain why the statement "If $3 > 5$, then $4 < 6$" is true.

18. In a few sentences, explain how to determine the truth value of a conditional statement.

Tell whether each conditional is true (T) *or* false (F).

19. $\text{T} \to (7 < 3)$ **20.** $\text{F} \to (4 \neq 8)$

21. $\text{F} \to (5 \neq 5)$ **22.** $(8 \geq 8) \to \text{F}$

23. $(5^2 \neq 25) \to (8 - 8 = 16)$

24. $(5 = 12 - 7) \to (9 > 0)$

Let s represent "She sings for a living," *let p represent* "he fixes cars," *and let m represent* "they collect classics." *Express each compound statement in words.*

25. $\sim m \to p$ **26.** $p \to \sim m$

27. $s \to (m \land p)$ **28.** $(s \land p) \to m$

29. $\sim p \to (\sim m \lor s)$ **30.** $(\sim s \lor \sim m) \to \sim p$

Let b represent "I take my ball," *let s represent* "it is sunny," *and let p represent* "the park is open." *Write each compound statement in symbols.*

31. If I take my ball, then the park is open.

32. If I do not take my ball, then it is not sunny.

33. The park is open, and if it is sunny then I do not take my ball.

34. I take my ball, or if the park is open then it is sunny.

35. It is sunny if the park is open.

36. I'll take my ball if it is not sunny.

Find the truth value of each statement. Assume that p and r are false, and q is true.

37. $\sim r \rightarrow q$ **38.** $q \rightarrow p$

39. $p \rightarrow q$ **40.** $\sim r \rightarrow p$

41. $\sim p \rightarrow (q \wedge r)$ **42.** $(\sim r \vee p) \rightarrow p$

43. $\sim q \rightarrow (p \wedge r)$

44. $(\sim p \wedge \sim q) \rightarrow (p \wedge \sim r)$

45. $(p \rightarrow \sim q) \rightarrow (\sim p \wedge \sim r)$

46. $[(p \rightarrow \sim q) \wedge (p \rightarrow r)] \rightarrow r$

47. Explain why we know that

$$[r \vee (p \vee s)] \rightarrow [(p \vee q) \vee \sim p]$$

is true, even if we are not given the truth values of p, q, r, and s.

48. Construct a true statement involving a conditional, a conjunction, a disjunction, and a negation (not necessarily in that order) that consists of component statements p, q, and r, with all of these component statements false.

Construct a truth table for each statement. Identify any tautologies.

49. $\sim q \rightarrow p$

50. $(\sim q \rightarrow \sim p) \rightarrow \sim q$

51. $(\sim p \rightarrow q) \rightarrow p$

52. $(p \wedge q) \rightarrow (p \vee q)$

53. $(p \vee q) \rightarrow (q \vee p)$

54. $(\sim p \rightarrow \sim q) \rightarrow (p \wedge q)$

55. $[(r \vee p) \wedge \sim q] \rightarrow p$

56. $[(r \wedge p) \wedge (p \wedge q)] \rightarrow p$

57. $(\sim r \rightarrow s) \vee (p \rightarrow \sim q)$

58. $(\sim p \wedge \sim q) \rightarrow (s \rightarrow r)$

59. What is the minimum number of Fs that must appear in the final column of a truth table for us to be assured that the statement is not a tautology?

60. If all truth values in the final column of a truth table are F, how can we easily transform the statement into a tautology?

Write the negation of each statement. Remember that the negation of $p \rightarrow q$ is $p \wedge \sim q$.

61. If that is an authentic Coach bag, I'll be surprised.

62. If Muley Jones hits that note, he will shatter glass.

63. If the bullfighter doesn't get going, he's going to get gored.

64. If you don't say "I do," then you'll regret it for the rest of your life.

65. "If you want to be happy for the rest of your life, never make a pretty woman your wife." *Jimmy Soul*

66. "If I had a hammer, I'd hammer in the morning." *Lee Hayes and Pete Seeger*

Write each statement as an equivalent statement that does not use the if . . . then connective. Remember that

$$p \rightarrow q \quad is\ equivalent\ to \quad \sim p \vee q.$$

67. If you give your plants tender, loving care, they flourish.

68. If you scratch my back, I'll scratch yours.

69. If she doesn't, he will.

70. If I say "black," she says "white."

71. All residents of Pensacola are residents of Florida.

72. All women were once girls.

Use truth tables to decide which of the pairs of statements are equivalent.

73. $p \rightarrow q$; $\sim p \vee q$ **74.** $\sim (p \rightarrow q)$; $p \wedge \sim q$

75. $p \rightarrow q$; $\sim q \rightarrow \sim p$ **76.** $p \rightarrow q$; $q \rightarrow p$

77. $p \rightarrow \sim q$; $\sim p \vee \sim q$ **78.** $\sim p \wedge q$; $\sim p \rightarrow q$

79. $q \rightarrow \sim p$; $p \rightarrow \sim q$

80. $\sim(p \lor q) \rightarrow r$; $(p \lor q) \lor r$

Write a logical statement representing each of the following circuits. Simplify each circuit when possible.

81.

82.
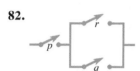

83.
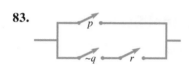

84.
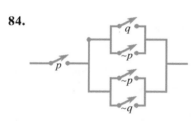

85.
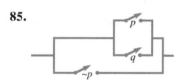

86.
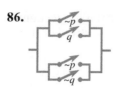

Draw circuits representing the following statements as they are given. Simplify if possible.

87. $p \land (q \lor \sim p)$ **88.** $(\sim p \land \sim q) \land \sim r$

89. $(p \lor q) \land (\sim p \land \sim q)$

90. $(\sim q \land \sim p) \lor (\sim p \lor q)$

91. $[(p \lor q) \land r] \land \sim p$

92. $[(\sim p \land \sim r) \lor \sim q] \land (\sim p \land r)$

93. $\sim q \rightarrow (\sim p \rightarrow q)$ **94.** $\sim p \rightarrow (\sim p \lor \sim q)$

95. Refer to **Figures 5 and 6** in **Example 6.** Suppose the cost of the use of one switch for an hour is $0.06. By using the circuit in **Figure 6** rather than the circuit in **Figure 5,** what is the savings for a year of 365 days, assuming that the circuit is in continuous use?

96. Explain why the circuit shown will always have exactly one open switch. What does this circuit simplify to?

97. Refer to the "For Further Thought" at the end of **Section 3.2.** Verify that the logic circuit shown below is equivalent to the conditional statement $A \rightarrow B$.

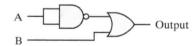

THE CONDITIONAL AND RELATED STATEMENTS

OBJECTIVES

1 Determine the converse, inverse, and contrapositive of a conditional statement.

2 Translate conditional statements into alternative forms.

3 Understand the structure of the biconditional.

4 Summarize the truth tables of compound statements.

Converse, Inverse, and Contrapositive

Many mathematical properties and theorems are stated in *if . . . then* form. Any conditional statement $p \rightarrow q$ is made up of an antecedent p and a consequent q. If they are interchanged, negated, or both, a new conditional statement is formed. Suppose that we begin with a conditional statement.

> If you stay, then I go.   Conditional statement

By interchanging the antecedent ("you stay") and the consequent ("I go"), we obtain a new conditional statement.

> If I go, then you stay.   Converse

This new conditional is called the **converse** of the given conditional statement.

By negating both the antecedent and the consequent, we obtain the **inverse** of the given conditional statement.

> If you do not stay, then I do not go.   Inverse

Alfred North Whitehead (1861–1947) and Bertrand Russell worked together on *Principia Mathematica*. During that time, Whitehead was teaching mathematics at Cambridge University and had written *Universal Algebra*. In 1910 he went to the University of London, exploring not only the philosophical basis of science but also the "aims of education" (as he called one of his books). It was as a philosopher that he was invited to Harvard University in 1924. Whitehead died at the age of 86 in Cambridge, Massachusetts.

If the antecedent and the consequent are both interchanged *and* negated, the **contrapositive** of the given conditional statement is formed.

If I do not go, then you do not stay.   Contrapositive

These three related statements for the conditional $p \rightarrow q$ are summarized below.

RELATED CONDITIONAL STATEMENTS

Conditional Statement	$p \rightarrow q$	(If p, then q.)
Converse	$q \rightarrow p$	(If q, then p.)
Inverse	$\sim p \rightarrow \sim q$	(If not p, then not q.)
Contrapositive	$\sim q \rightarrow \sim p$	(If not q, then not p.)

Notice that the inverse is the contrapositive of the converse.

EXAMPLE 1 **Determining Related Conditional Statements**

Determine each of the following, given the conditional statement

If I am running, then I am moving.

(a) the converse   **(b)** the inverse   **(c)** the contrapositive

Solution

(a) Let p represent "I am running" and q represent "I am moving." Then the given statement may be written $p \rightarrow q$. The converse, $q \rightarrow p$, is

If I am moving, then I am running.

The converse is not necessarily true, even though the given statement is true.

(b) The inverse of $p \rightarrow q$ is $\sim p \rightarrow \sim q$. Thus the inverse is

If I am not running, then I am not moving.

Again, this is not necessarily true.

(c) The contrapositive, $\sim q \rightarrow \sim p$, is

If I am not moving, then I am not running.

The contrapositive, like the given conditional statement, is true.   ■

Example 1 shows that the converse and inverse of a true statement need not be true. They *can* be true, but they need not be. The relationships between the related conditionals are shown in the truth table that follows.

		Conditional	Converse	Inverse	Contrapositive
		Equivalent			
			Equivalent		
p	q	$p \rightarrow q$	$q \rightarrow p$	$\sim p \rightarrow \sim q$	$\sim q \rightarrow \sim p$
T	T	T	T	T	T
T	F	F	T	T	F
F	T	T	F	F	T
F	F	T	T	T	T

Bertrand Russell (1872–1970) was a student of Whitehead's before they wrote the *Principia.* Like his teacher, Russell turned toward philosophy. His works include a critique of Leibniz, analyses of mind and of matter, and a history of Western thought.

Russell became a public figure because of his involvement in social issues. Deeply aware of human loneliness, he was "passionately desirous of finding ways of diminishing this tragic isolation." During World War I he was an antiwar crusader, and he was imprisoned briefly. Again in the 1960s he championed peace. He wrote many books on social issues, winning the Nobel Prize for Literature in 1950.

As this truth table shows,

1. *A conditional statement and its contrapositive always have the same truth value,* making it possible to replace any statement with its contrapositive without affecting the logical meaning.

2. *The converse and inverse always have the same truth value.*

EQUIVALENCES

A conditional statement and its contrapositive are equivalent. Also, the converse and the inverse are equivalent.

EXAMPLE 2 Determining Related Conditional Statements

For the conditional statement $\sim p \rightarrow q$, write each of the following.

(a) the converse   **(b)** the inverse   **(c)** the contrapositive

Solution

(a) The converse of $\sim p \rightarrow q$ is $q \rightarrow \sim p$.

(b) The inverse is $\sim(\sim p) \rightarrow \sim q$, which simplifies to $p \rightarrow \sim q$.

(c) The contrapositive is $\sim q \rightarrow \sim(\sim p)$, which simplifies to $\sim q \rightarrow p$.   ■

Alternative Forms of "If p, then q"

The conditional statement "If p, then q" can be stated in several other ways in English. Consider this statement.

> If you take Tylenol, then you will find relief from your symptoms.

It can also be written as follows.

> Taking Tylenol is *sufficient* for relieving your symptoms.

According to this statement, taking Tylenol is enough to relieve your symptoms. Taking other medications or using other treatment techniques *might* also result in symptom relief, but at least we *know* that taking Tylenol will. Thus $p \rightarrow q$ can be written "p is sufficient for q." Knowing that p has occurred is sufficient to guarantee that q will also occur.

On the other hand, consider this statement, which has a different structure.

> Fresh ingredients are necessary for making a good pizza.   (*)

This statement claims that fresh ingredients are one condition for making a good pizza. But there may be other conditions (such as a working oven, for example). The statement labeled (*) could be written as

> If you want good pizza, then you need fresh ingredients.

As this example suggests, $p \rightarrow q$ is the same as "q is necessary for p." In other words, if q doesn't happen, then neither will p. Notice how this idea is closely related to the idea of equivalence between a conditional statement and its contrapositive.

Kurt Gödel (1906–1978) is widely regarded as the most influential mathematical logician of the twentieth century. He proved by his Incompleteness Theorem that the search for a set of axioms from which all mathematical truths could be proved was futile. In particular, "the vast structure of the *Principia Mathematica* of Whitehead and Russell was inadequate for deciding all mathematical questions."

After the death of his friend **Albert Einstein** (1879–1955), Gödel developed paranoia, and his life ended tragically when, convinced he was being poisoned, he refused to eat, essentially starving himself to death.

COMMON TRANSLATIONS OF $p \rightarrow q$

The conditional $p \rightarrow q$ can be translated in any of the following ways, none of which depends on the truth or falsity of $p \rightarrow q$.

If p, then q.	p is sufficient for q.
If p, q.	q is necessary for p.
p implies q.	All p are q.
p only if q.	q if p.

Example: If you live in Alamogordo, then you live in New Mexico. Statement

You live in New Mexico if you live in Alamogordo.
You live in Alamogordo only if you live in New Mexico.
Living in New Mexico is necessary for living in Alamogordo. Common translations
Living in Alamogordo is sufficient for living in New Mexico.
All residents of Alamogordo are residents of New Mexico.
Being a resident of Alamogordo implies residency in New Mexico.

EXAMPLE 3 Rewording Conditional Statements

Rewrite each statement in the form "If p, then q."

(a) You'll get sick if you eat that.

(b) Go to the doctor only if your temperature exceeds 101°F.

(c) Everyone at the game had a great time.

Solution

(a) If you eat that, then you'll get sick.

(b) If you go to the doctor, then your temperature exceeds 101°F.

(c) If you were at the game, then you had a great time. ■

EXAMPLE 4 Translating from Words to Symbols

Let p represent "A triangle is equilateral," and let q represent "A triangle has three sides of equal length." Write each of the following in symbols.

(a) A triangle is equilateral if it has three sides of equal length.

(b) A triangle is equilateral only if it has three sides of equal length.

Solution

(a) $q \rightarrow p$ **(b)** $p \rightarrow q$ ■

Biconditionals

The compound statement **p if and only if q** (often abbreviated **p iff q**) is called a **biconditional.** It is symbolized $p \leftrightarrow q$ and is interpreted as the conjunction of the two conditionals $p \rightarrow q$ and $q \rightarrow p$.

Principia Mathematica, the title chosen by Whitehead and Russell, was a deliberate reference to *Philosophiae naturalis principia mathematica,* or "mathematical principles of the philosophy of nature," Isaac Newton's epochal work of 1687. Newton's *Principia* pictured a kind of "clockwork universe" that ran via his Law of Gravitation. Newton independently invented the calculus, unaware that Leibniz had published his own formulation of it earlier.

Using symbols, the conjunction of the conditionals $p \rightarrow q$ and $q \rightarrow p$ is written $(q \rightarrow p) \wedge (p \rightarrow q)$ so that, by definition,

$$p \leftrightarrow q \equiv (q \rightarrow p) \wedge (p \rightarrow q).$$ Biconditional

The truth table for the biconditional $p \leftrightarrow q$ can be determined using this definition.

TRUTH TABLE FOR THE BICONDITIONAL p if and only if q

p if and only if *q*

p	q	$p \leftrightarrow q$
T	T	T
T	F	F
F	T	F
F	F	T

A biconditional is true when both component statements have the same truth value. It is false when they have different truth values.

EXAMPLE 5 Determining Whether Biconditionals Are True or False

Determine whether each biconditional statement is *true* or *false.*

(a) $6 + 8 = 14$ if and only if $11 + 5 = 16$

(b) $6 = 5$ if and only if $12 \neq 12$

(c) Mars is a moon if and only if Jupiter is a planet.

Solution

(a) Both $6 + 8 = 14$ and $11 + 5 = 16$ are true. By the truth table for the biconditional, this biconditional is true.

(b) Both component statements are false, so by the last line of the truth table for the biconditional, this biconditional statement is true.

(c) Because the first component Mars is a moon is false, and the second is true, this biconditional statement is false. ■

Summary of Truth Tables

Truth tables have been derived for several important types of compound statements.

SUMMARY OF BASIC TRUTH TABLES

1. $\sim p$, the **negation** of p, has truth value opposite that of p.

2. $p \wedge q$, the **conjunction,** is true only when both p and q are true.

3. $p \vee q$, the **disjunction,** is false only when both p and q are false.

4. $p \rightarrow q$, the **conditional,** is false only when p is true and q is false.

5. $p \leftrightarrow q$, the **biconditional,** is true only when both p and q have the same truth value.

3.4 EXERCISES

*For each given conditional statement (or statement that can be written as a conditional), write (**a**) the converse, (**b**) the inverse, and (**c**) the contrapositive in if . . . then form. In some of the exercises, it may be helpful to first restate the given statement in if . . . then form.*

1. If beauty were a minute, then you would be an hour.

2. If you lead, then I will follow.

3. If it ain't broke, don't fix it.

4. If I had a nickel for each time that happened, I would be rich.

5. Walking in front of a moving car is dangerous to your health.

6. Milk contains calcium.

7. Birds of a feather flock together.

8. A rolling stone gathers no moss.

9. If you build it, he will come.

10. Where there's smoke, there's fire.

11. $p \rightarrow \sim q$

12. $\sim p \rightarrow q$

13. $\sim p \rightarrow \sim q$

14. $\sim q \rightarrow \sim p$

15. $p \rightarrow (q \vee r)$ (*Hint:* Use one of De Morgan's laws as necessary.)

16. $(r \vee \sim q) \rightarrow p$ (*Hint:* Use one of De Morgan's laws as necessary.)

17. Discuss the equivalences that exist among a given conditional statement, its converse, its inverse, and its contrapositive.

18. State the contrapositive of "If the square of a natural number is odd, then the natural number is odd." The two statements must have the same truth value. Use several examples and inductive reasoning to decide whether both are true or both are false.

Write each statement in the form "if p, then q."

19. If the Kings go to the playoffs, pigs will fly.

20. If I score 90% or higher on my test, I'll go to a movie.

21. Legs of 3 and 4 imply a hypotenuse of 5.

22. "This is a leap year" implies that next year is not.

23. All whole numbers are rational numbers.

24. No irrational numbers are rational.

25. Doing logic puzzles is sufficient for driving me crazy.

26. Being in Kalamazoo is sufficient for being in Michigan.

27. Two coats of paint are necessary to cover the graffiti.

28. Being an environmentalist is necessary for being elected.

29. Employment will improve only if the economy recovers.

30. The economy will recover only if employment improves.

31. No whole numbers are not integers.

32. No integers are irrational numbers.

33. The Phillies will win the pennant when their pitching improves.

34. The grass will be greener when we're on the other side.

35. A rectangle is a parallelogram with perpendicular adjacent sides.

36. A square is a rectangle with two adjacent sides equal.

37. A triangle with two perpendicular sides is a right triangle.

38. A parallelogram is a four-sided figure with opposite sides parallel.

39. The square of a three-digit number whose units digit is 5 will end in 25.

40. An integer whose units digit is 0 or 5 is divisible by 5.

41. One of the following statements is not equivalent to all the others. Which one is it?

    A. r only if s.   **B.** r implies s.

    C. If r, then s.   **D.** r is necessary for s.

42. Many students have difficulty interpreting *necessary* and *sufficient*. Use the statement "Being in Vancouver is sufficient for being in North America" to explain why "p is sufficient for q" translates as "if p, then q."

43. Use the statement "To be an integer, it is necessary that a number be rational" to explain why "p is necessary for q" translates as "if q, then p."

44. Explain why the statement "A week has eight days if and only if October has forty days" is true.

Identify each statement as true *or* false.

45. $6 = 9 - 3$ if and only if $8 + 2 = 10$.

46. $3 + 1 \neq 7$ if and only if $8 \neq 8$.

47. $8 + 7 \neq 15$ if and only if $3 \times 5 \neq 8$.

48. $6 \times 2 = 18$ if and only if $9 + 7 \neq 16$.

49. George H. W. Bush was president if and only if George W. Bush was not president.

50. McDonald's sells Whoppers if and only if Apple manufactures Ipods.

*Two statements that can both be true about the same object are **consistent**. For example, "It is green" and "It weighs 60 pounds" are consistent statements. Statements that cannot both be true about the same object are called **contrary**. "It is a Nissan" and "It is a Mazda" are contrary. In Exercises 51–55, label each pair of statements as either* contrary *or* consistent.

51. Michael Jackson is alive. Michael Jackson is dead.

52. That book is nonfiction. That same book costs more than $150.

53. This number is a whole number. This same number is irrational.

54. This number is positive. This same number is a natural number.

55. This number is an integer. This same number is a rational number.

56. Refer to the "For Further Thought" on **page 99** at the end of **Section 3.2.** Verify that the logic circuit at the top of the next column (consisting of only NOR gates) is equivalent to the biconditional $A \leftrightarrow B$. Build a truth table for the statement $\sim(p \veebar q)$ (the negation of the Exclusive OR statement). What is the relationship between this and the biconditional?

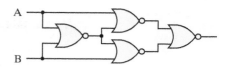

Exercises 57 and 58 refer to the Chapter Opener on **page 83.** *Humphrey the hero deduced from the riddle that there are twin trolls who take shifts guarding the magical doors. One of them tells only truths, the other only lies. When the troll standing guard sees Humphrey, he says,*

"If truly Truthful Troll I be, then go thou east and be thou free."

Humphrey needs to decide which troll he is addressing, call him by name, and tell him which door he would like opened.

There are two things Humphrey must get right: the name of the troll and the proper door. If he misidentifies the troll, no door will be opened. If he correctly names the troll and picks the wrong door, he will be confined to the dungeon behind it.

57. Because the troll either always lies or always tells the truth, Humphrey knows that

(1) if the troll is Truthful Troll, then the conditional statement he uttered is true, and

(2) if the conditional statement he uttered is true, then he is Truthful Troll.

Let p represent "the troll is Truthful Troll" and let q represent "the door to the east leads to freedom." Express the statements in (1) and (2) in symbolic form.

58. The conjunction of the answers from **Exercise 57** is a biconditional that must be true.

(a) Build a truth table for this biconditional.

(b) Use the fact that it *must* be true to solve Humphrey's riddle.

3.5   ANALYZING ARGUMENTS WITH EULER DIAGRAMS

OBJECTIVES

1 Define logical arguments.

2 Use Euler diagrams to analyze arguments with universal quantifiers.

3 Use Euler diagrams to analyze arguments with existential quantifiers.

Logical Arguments

With inductive reasoning we observe patterns to solve problems. Now we study how deductive reasoning may be used to determine whether logical arguments are valid or invalid.

A logical argument is made up of **premises** (assumptions, laws, rules, widely held ideas, or observations) and a **conclusion.** Recall that *deductive* reasoning involves drawing specific conclusions from given general premises. When reasoning from the premises of an argument to obtain a conclusion, we want the argument to be valid.

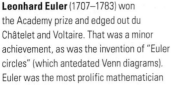

Leonhard Euler (1707–1783) won the Academy prize and edged out du Châtelet and Voltaire. That was a minor achievement, as was the invention of "Euler circles" (which antedated Venn diagrams). Euler was the most prolific mathematician of his generation despite blindness that forced him to dictate from memory.

VALID AND INVALID ARGUMENTS

An argument is **valid** if the fact that all the premises are true forces the conclusion to be true. An argument that is not valid is **invalid.** It is called a **fallacy.**

"Valid" and "true" do not have the same meaning—an argument can be valid even though the conclusion is false (see Example 4), *or invalid even though the conclusion is true* (see Example 6).

Arguments with Universal Quantifiers

Several techniques can be used to check whether an argument is valid. One such technique is based on **Euler diagrams.**

Leonhard Euler (pronounced "Oiler") was one of the greatest mathematicians who ever lived. He is immortalized in mathematics history with the important irrational number *e*, named in his honor. This number appears throughout mathematics and is discussed in **Chapters 6 and 8.**

EXAMPLE 1 Using an Euler Diagram to Determine Validity

Is the following argument valid?

> No accidents happen on purpose.
> Spilling the beans was an accident.
> _____
> The beans were not spilled on purpose.

Solution

To begin, draw regions to represent the first premise. Because no accidents happen on purpose, the region for "accidents" goes outside the region for "things that happen on purpose," as shown in **Figure 8.**

The second premise, "Spilling the beans was an accident," suggests that "spilling the beans" belongs in the region representing "accidents." Let *x* represent "spilling the beans." **Figure 9** shows that "spilling the beans" is not in the region for "things that happen on purpose." If both premises are true, the conclusion that the beans were not spilled on purpose is also true. The argument is valid. ■

Figure 8

Figure 9

EXAMPLE 2 Using an Euler Diagram to Determine Validity

Is the following argument valid?

> All rainy days are cloudy.
> Today is not cloudy.
> _____
> Today is not rainy.

Solution

In **Figure 10,** the region for "rainy days" is drawn entirely inside the region for "cloudy days." Since "Today is *not* cloudy," place an *x* for "today" *outside* the region for "cloudy days." See **Figure 11.** Placing the *x* outside the region for "cloudy days" forces it also to be outside the region for "rainy days." Thus, if the two premises are true, then it is also true that today is not rainy. The argument is valid. ■

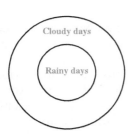

Figure 10

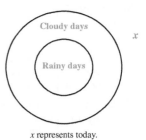

x represents today.

Figure 11 ■

▊EXAMPLE 3▊ Using an Euler Diagram to Determine Validity

Is the following argument valid?

> All magnolia trees have green leaves.
> That plant has green leaves.
> _____
> That plant is a magnolia tree.

Solution

Figure 12

The region for "magnolia trees" goes entirely inside the region for "things that have green leaves." See **Figure 12.** The x that represents "that plant" must go inside the region for "things that have green leaves," but it can go either inside or outside the region for "magnolia trees." Even if the premises are true, we are not forced to accept the conclusion as true. This argument is invalid. It is a fallacy. ∎

▊EXAMPLE 4▊ Using an Euler Diagram to Determine Validity

Is the following argument valid?

> All expensive things are desirable.
> All desirable things make you feel good.
> All things that make you feel good make you live longer.
> _____
> All expensive things make you live longer.

Solution

A diagram for the argument is given in **Figure 13.** If each premise is true, then the conclusion must be true because the region for "expensive things" lies completely within the region for "things that make you live longer." Thus, the argument is valid. (This argument is an example of the fact that a *valid* argument need *not* have a true conclusion.)

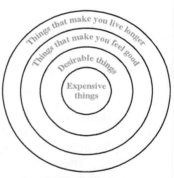

Figure 13 ∎

Arguments with Existential Quantifiers

▊EXAMPLE 5▊ Using an Euler Diagram to Determine Validity

Is the following argument valid?

> Many students drive Hondas.
> I am a student.
> _____
> I drive a Honda.

Solution

Figure 14

Figure 15

The first premise is sketched in **Figure 14,** where many (but not necessarily *all*) students drive Hondas. There are two possibilities for *I*, as shown in **Figure 15.** One possibility is that *I* drive a Honda. The other is that *I* don't. Since the truth of the premises does not force the conclusion to be true, the argument is invalid. ∎

EXAMPLE 6 Using an Euler Diagram to Determine Validity

Is the following argument valid?

> All fish swim.
> All whales swim.
> _____
> A whale is not a fish.

Solution

The premises lead to two possibilities. **Figure 16** shows the set of fish and the set of whales as intersecting, while **Figure 17** does not. Both diagrams are valid interpretations of the given premises, but only one supports the conclusion.

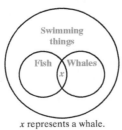

x represents a whale.   *x* represents a whale.

Figure 16   **Figure 17**

Because the truth of the premises does not force the conclusion to be true, the argument is invalid. Even though we know the conclusion to be true, this knowledge is not deduced from the premises. ■

FOR FURTHER THOUGHT

Common Fallacies

Discussions in everyday conversation, politics, and advertising provide a nearly endless stream of examples of **fallacies**—arguments exhibiting illogical reasoning. There are many general forms of fallacies, and we now present descriptions and examples of some of the more common ones. (Much of this list is adapted from the document Reader Mission Critical, located on the San Jose State University Web site, www.sjsu.edu)

1. **Circular Reasoning** (also called *Begging the Question*) The person making the argument assumes to be true what he is trying to prove.

   Husband: What makes you say that this dress makes you look fat?

   Wife: Because it does.

   Here the wife makes her case by stating what she wants to prove.

2. **False Dilemma** (also called the *Either-Or Fallacy*, or the *Black and White Fallacy*) Presenting two options with the assumption that they are contradictions (that is, the truth of one implies the falsity of the other) when in fact they are not, is the basis of a common fallacy.

   Politician: America: Love it or leave it.

   This argument implies only two choices. It is possible that someone may love America and yet leave, while someone else may not love America and yet stay.

3. **Loaded Question and Complex Claims** This fallacy involves one person asking a question or making a statement that is constructed in such a way as to obtain an answer in which the responder agrees to something with which he does not actually agree.

   Teenager Beth to her father: I hope you enjoyed embarrassing me in front of my friends.

   If Beth gets the expected response "No, I didn't enjoy it," the answer allows Beth to interpret that while her father didn't enjoy it, he did indeed embarrass her.

4. **Post Hoc Reasoning** An argument that is based on the false belief that if event A preceded event B, then A must have caused B is called *post hoc reasoning*.

   Johnny: I wore my Hawaiian shirt while watching all three playoff games, and my team won all three games. So I am going to wear that shirt every time I watch them.

The fact that Johnny put the same shirt on before each game has nothing to do with the outcomes of the games.

5. **Red Herring** (also called *Smoke Screen,* or *Wild Goose Chase*) This fallacy involves introducing an irrelevant topic to divert attention away from the original topic, allowing the person making the argument to seemingly prevail.

(The following script is from a political advertisement during the 2008 presidential campaign, intended to establish that John McCain lacked understanding of the economy.)

Maybe you're struggling just to pay the mortgage on your home. But recently, John McCain said, "The fundamentals of our economy are strong." Hmm. Then again, that same day, when asked how many houses he owns, McCain lost track. He couldn't remember. Well, it's seven. Seven houses. And here's one house America can't afford to let John McCain move into (showing a picture of the White House).

The advertisement shifted the focus to the number of houses McCain owned, which had nothing to do with the state of the economy, or the ability of "average" citizens to make their mortgage payments.

6. **Shifting the Burden of Proof** A person making a claim usually is required to support that claim. In this fallacy, if the claim is difficult to support, that person turns the burden of proof of that claim over to someone else.

Employee: You accuse me of embezzling money? That's ridiculous.

Employer: Well, until you can prove otherwise, you will just have to accept it as true.

If money has been disappearing, it is up to the employer to prove that this employee is guilty. The burden of proof is on the employer, but he is insinuating that the employee must prove that he is not the one taking the money.

7. **Straw Man** This fallacy involves creating a false image (like a scarecrow, or straw man) of someone else's position in an argument.

Dan Quayle: I have as much experience in the Congress as Jack Kennedy did when he sought the presidency.

Lloyd Bentsen: Senator, I served with Jack Kennedy. I knew Jack Kennedy. Jack Kennedy was a friend of mine. And Senator, you're no Jack Kennedy.

Dan Quayle: That was really uncalled for, Senator.

Lloyd Bentsen: You're the one that was making the comparison, Senator.

While this was the defining moment of the 1988 vice-presidential debate, Bentsen expertly used the straw man fallacy. Quayle did not compare himself or his accomplishments to those of Kennedy, but merely stated that he had spent as much time in Congress as Kennedy had when the latter ran for president.

For Group or Individual Investigation

Use the Internet to investigate the following additional logical fallacies.

Appeal to Authority	Appeal to Common	Common Practice
Two Wrongs	Belief	Wishful
Appeal to Fear	Indirect Consequences	Thinking
Appeal to Prejudice	Appeal to Loyalty	Appeal to Pity
Guilt by Association	Appeal to Spite	Appeal to Vanity
	Slippery Slope	Hasty Generalization

3.5 EXERCISES

Decide whether each argument is valid or invalid.

1. All amusement parks have thrill rides.
   Universal Orlando is an amusement park.
   Universal Orlando has thrill rides.

2. All disc jockeys play music.
   Calvin is a disc jockey.
   Calvin plays music.

3. All celebrities have problems.
That man has problems.

That man is a celebrity.

4. All Southerners speak with an accent.
Nick speaks with an accent.

Nick is a Southerner.

5. All dogs love to bury bones.
Puddles does not love to bury bones.

Puddles is not a dog.

6. All vice presidents use cell phones.
Bob does not use a cell phone.

Bob is not a vice president.

7. All residents of Colorado know how to breathe thin air.
Julie knows how to breathe thin air.

Julie lives in Colorado.

8. All drivers must have a photo I.D.
Kay has a photo I.D.

Kay is a driver.

9. Some dinosaurs were plant eaters.
Danny was a plant eater.

Danny was a dinosaur.

10. Some philosophers are absent minded.
Nicole is a philosopher.

Nicole is absent minded.

11. Many nurses belong to unions.
Heather is a nurse.

Heather belongs to a union.

12. Some trucks have sound systems.
Some trucks have gun racks.

Some trucks with sound systems have gun racks.

13. Refer to **Example 3.** If the second premise and the conclusion were interchanged, would the argument then be valid?

14. Refer to **Example 4.** Give a different conclusion from the one given there so that the argument is still valid.

Construct a valid argument based on the Euler diagram shown.

15.

x represents Erin.

16.

x represents vaccinations.

As mentioned in the text, an argument can have a true conclusion yet be invalid. In these exercises, each argument has a true conclusion. Identify each argument as valid *or* invalid.

17. All birds fly.
All planes fly.

A bird is not a plane.

18. All actors have cars.
All cars use gas.

All actors have gas.

19. All chickens have beaks.
All hens are chickens.

All hens have beaks.

20. All chickens have beaks.
All birds have beaks.

All chickens are birds.

21. Amarillo is northeast of El Paso.
Amarillo is northeast of Deming.

El Paso is northeast of Deming.

22. Beaverton is north of Salem.
Salem is north of Lebanon.

Beaverton is north of Lebanon.

23. No whole numbers are negative.
−3 is negative.

−3 is not a whole number.

24. A scalene triangle has a longest side.
A scalene triangle has a largest angle.

The largest angle in a scalene triangle is opposite the longest side.

In Exercises 25–30, the premises marked A, B, *and* C *are followed by several possible conclusions. Take each conclusion in turn, and check whether the resulting argument is* valid *or* invalid.

A. *All people who drive contribute to air pollution.*

B. *All people who contribute to air pollution make life a little worse.*

C. *Some people who live in a suburb make life a little worse.*

25. Some people who live in a suburb contribute to air pollution.

26. Some people who live in a suburb drive.

27. Suburban residents never drive.

28. Some people who contribute to air pollution live in a suburb.

29. Some people who make life a little worse live in a suburb.

30. All people who drive make life a little worse.

3.6 ANALYZING ARGUMENTS WITH TRUTH TABLES

Using Truth Tables to Determine Validity

In **Section 3.5** we used Euler diagrams to test the validity of arguments. While Euler diagrams often work well for simple arguments, difficulties can develop with more complex ones, because Euler diagrams must show every possible case. In complex arguments, it is hard to be sure that all cases have been considered.

In deciding whether to use Euler diagrams to test the validity of an argument, look for quantifiers such as "all," "some," or "no." These words often indicate arguments best tested by Euler diagrams. If these words are absent, it may be better to use truth tables to test the validity of an argument.

EXAMPLE 1 Using a Truth Table to Determine Validity

Determine whether the argument is *valid* or *invalid*.

> If there is a problem, then I must fix it.
> There is a problem.
> _____
> I must fix it.

Solution

To test the validity of this argument, we begin by assigning the letters p and q to represent these statements.

p represents "There is a problem."

q represents "I must fix it."

Now we write the two premises and the conclusion in symbols.

$$\text{Premise 1: } p \rightarrow q$$
$$\text{Premise 2: } p$$
$$\text{Conclusion: } q$$

To decide if this argument is valid, we must determine whether the conjunction of both premises implies the conclusion for all possible combinations of truth values for p and q. Therefore, write the conjunction of the premises as the antecedent of a conditional statement, and write the conclusion as the consequent.

$$[(p \rightarrow q) \quad \wedge \quad p] \quad \rightarrow \quad q$$

premise   and   premise   implies   conclusion

Finally, construct the truth table for this conditional statement, as shown below.

p	q	$p \rightarrow q$	$(p \rightarrow q) \wedge p$	$[(p \rightarrow q) \wedge p] \rightarrow q$
T	T	T	T	T
T	F	F	F	T
F	T	T	F	T
F	F	T	F	T

Because the final column, shown in color, indicates that the conditional statement that represents the argument is true for all possible truth values of p and q, the statement is a tautology. Thus, the argument is valid. ∎

In the 2007 Spanish film *La Habitacion de Fermat (Fermat's Room)*, four mathematicians are invited to dinner, only to discover that the room in which they are meeting is designed to eventually crush them as walls creep in closer and closer. The only way for them to delay the inevitable is to answer enigmas, questions, puzzles, problems, and riddles that they are receiving on a cell phone.

One of the enigmas deals with a hermetically sealed room that contains a single light bulb. There are three switches outside the room, all of them are off, and only one of these switches controls the bulb. You are allowed to flip any or all of the switches as many times as you wish before you enter the room, but once you enter, you cannot return to the switches outside. How can you determine which one controls the bulb? (The answer is on **page 124.**)

Answer to the Light Bulb question on page 123.
    Label the switches 1, 2, and 3. Turn switch 1 on and leave it on for several minutes. Then turn switch 1 off, turn switch 2 on, and then immediately enter the room. If the bulb is on, then you know that switch 2 controls it. If the bulb is off, touch it to see if it is still warm. If it is, then switch 1 controls it. If the bulb is not warm, then switch 3 controls it.

The pattern of the argument in **Example 1**

$$\begin{array}{l} p \rightarrow q \\ \underline{p} \\ q \end{array}$$

is called **modus ponens,** or the *law of detachment.*

To test the validity of an argument using a truth table, follow the steps in the box.

TESTING THE VALIDITY OF AN ARGUMENT WITH A TRUTH TABLE

Step 1 Assign a letter to represent each component statement in the argument.

Step 2 Express each premise and the conclusion symbolically.

Step 3 Form the symbolic statement of the entire argument by writing the *conjunction* of *all* the premises as the antecedent of a conditional statement, and the conclusion of the argument as the consequent.

Step 4 Complete the truth table for the conditional statement formed in Step 3. If it is a tautology, then the argument is valid; otherwise, it is invalid.

EXAMPLE 2 Using a Truth Table to Determine Validity

Determine whether the argument is *valid* or *invalid.*

> If my check arrives in time, I'll register for fall semester.
> I've registered for fall semester.
> _____
> My check arrived in time.

Solution

Let p represent "My check arrives (arrived) in time." Let q represent "I'll register (I've registered) for fall semester." The argument can be written as follows.

$$\begin{array}{l} p \rightarrow q \\ \underline{q} \\ p \end{array}$$

To test for validity, construct a truth table for the statement $[(p \rightarrow q) \wedge q] \rightarrow p$.

p	q	$p \rightarrow q$	$(p \rightarrow q) \wedge q$	$[(p \rightarrow q) \wedge q] \rightarrow p$
T	T	T	T	T
T	F	F	F	T
F	T	T	T	F
F	F	T	F	T

The final column of the truth table contains an F. The argument is invalid. ∎

If a conditional and its converse were logically equivalent, then an argument of the type found in **Example 2** would be valid. Because a conditional and its converse are *not* equivalent, the argument is an example of what is sometimes called the **fallacy of the converse.**

EXAMPLE 3 Using a Truth Table to Determine Validity

Determine whether the argument is *valid* or *invalid.*

> If I can avoid sweets, I can avoid the dentist.
> I can't avoid the dentist.
> _____
> I can't avoid sweets.

Solution

If p represents "I can avoid sweets" and q represents "I can avoid the dentist," the argument is written as follows.

$$\begin{array}{c} p \rightarrow q \\ \sim q \\ \hline \sim p \end{array}$$

The symbolic statement of the entire argument is as follows.

$$[(p \rightarrow q) \wedge \sim q] \rightarrow \sim p$$

The truth table for this argument indicates a tautology, and the argument is valid.

p	q	$p \rightarrow q$	$\sim q$	$(p \rightarrow q) \wedge \sim q$	$\sim p$	$[(p \rightarrow q) \wedge \sim q] \rightarrow \sim p$
T	T	T	F	F	F	T
T	F	F	T	F	F	T
F	T	T	F	F	T	T
F	F	T	T	T	T	T

The pattern of reasoning of this example is called **modus tollens,** or the *law of contraposition*, or *indirect reasoning*.   ∎

With reasoning similar to that used to name the fallacy of the converse, the fallacy

$$\begin{array}{c} p \rightarrow q \\ \sim p \\ \hline \sim q \end{array}$$

Concluding $\sim q$ from $\sim p$ wrongly assumes $\sim p \rightarrow \sim q$, the *inverse* of the given premise $p \rightarrow q$.

---

is called the **fallacy of the inverse.** An example of such a fallacy is "If it rains, I get wet. It doesn't rain. Therefore, I don't get wet."

EXAMPLE 4   Using a Truth Table to Determine Validity

Determine whether the argument is *valid* or *invalid*.

> I'll buy a car or I'll take a vacation.
> I won't buy a car.
> _____
> I'll take a vacation.

Solution

If p represents "I'll buy a car" and q represents "I'll take a vacation," the argument is symbolized as follows.

$$\begin{array}{c} p \vee q \\ \sim p \\ \hline q \end{array}$$

We must set up a truth table for the statement $[(p \vee q) \wedge \sim p] \rightarrow q$.

p	q	$p \vee q$	$\sim p$	$(p \vee q) \wedge \sim p$	$[(p \vee q) \wedge \sim p] \rightarrow q$
T	T	T	F	F	T
T	F	T	F	F	T
F	T	T	T	T	T
F	F	F	T	F	T

The statement is a tautology and the argument is valid. Any argument of this form is valid by the law of **disjunctive syllogism.**   ∎

EXAMPLE 5 Using a Truth Table to Determine Validity

Determine whether the argument is *valid* or *invalid*.

> If it squeaks, then I use WD-40.
> If I use WD-40, then I must go to the hardware store.
> _____
> If it squeaks, then I must go to the hardware store.

Solution

Let p represent "It squeaks," let q represent "I use WD-40," and let r represent "I must go to the hardware store." The argument takes on the following form.

$$\begin{aligned} p &\to q \\ q &\to r \\ \hline p &\to r \end{aligned}$$

Make a truth table for this statement, which requires eight rows.

$$[(p \to q) \land (q \to r)] \to (p \to r)$$

p	q	r	$p \to q$	$q \to r$	$p \to r$	$(p \to q) \land (q \to r)$	$[(p \to q) \land (q \to r)] \to (p \to r)$
T	T	T	T	T	T	T	T
T	T	F	T	F	F	F	T
T	F	T	F	T	T	F	T
T	F	F	F	T	F	F	T
F	T	T	T	T	T	T	T
F	T	F	T	F	T	F	T
F	F	T	T	T	T	T	T
F	F	F	T	T	T	T	T

This argument is valid because the final statement is a tautology. This pattern of argument is called **reasoning by transitivity,** or the *law of hypothetical syllogism*. ■

Valid and Invalid Argument Forms

A summary of the valid forms of argument presented so far follows.

In a scene near the beginning of the 1974 film *Monty Python and the Holy Grail*, an amazing application of **poor logic** leads to the apparent demise of a supposed witch. Some peasants have forced a young woman to wear a nose made of wood. The convoluted argument they make is this: Witches and wood are both burned, and because witches are made of wood, and wood floats, and ducks also float, if she weighs the same as a duck, then she is made of wood and, therefore, is a witch!

VALID ARGUMENT FORMS

Modus Ponens	Modus Tollens	Disjunctive Syllogism	Reasoning by Transitivity
$p \to q$	$p \to q$	$p \lor q$	$p \to q$
$\dfrac{p}{q}$	$\dfrac{\sim q}{\sim p}$	$\dfrac{\sim p}{q}$	$\dfrac{q \to r}{p \to r}$

The following is a summary of invalid forms (or fallacies).

INVALID ARGUMENT FORMS (FALLACIES)

Fallacy of the Converse	Fallacy of the Inverse
$p \to q$	$p \to q$
$\dfrac{q}{p}$	$\dfrac{\sim p}{\sim q}$

Setting the Table Correctly If an argument has the form

$$p_1$$
$$p_2$$
$$\vdots$$
$$\underline{p_n,}$$
$$c$$

then **Step 3** in the testing process calls for the statement

$$(p_1 \wedge p_2 \wedge \ldots \wedge p_n) \to c.$$

EXAMPLE 6 Using a Truth Table to Determine Validity

Determine whether the argument is *valid* or *invalid*.

> If Eddie goes to town, then Mabel stays at home.
> If Mabel does not stay at home, then Rita will cook.
> Rita will not cook. Therefore, Eddie does not go to town.

Solution

In an argument written in this manner, the premises are given first, and the conclusion is the statement that follows the word "Therefore." Let p represent "Eddie goes to town," let q represent "Mabel stays at home," and let r represent "Rita will cook." Then the argument is symbolized as follows.

$$p \to q$$
$$\sim q \to r$$
$$\underline{\sim r}$$
$$\sim p$$

When an argument contains more than two premises, it is necessary to determine the truth values of the conjunction of *all* of them.

> ***If at least one premise in a conjunction of several premises is false, then the entire conjunction is false.***

To test validity, set up a truth table for this statement.

$$[(p \to q) \wedge (\sim q \to r) \wedge \sim r] \to \sim p$$

p	q	r	$p \to q$	$\sim q$	$\sim q \to r$	$\sim r$	$(p \to q) \wedge (\sim q \to r) \wedge \sim r$	$\sim p$	$[(p \to q) \wedge (\sim q \to r) \wedge \sim r] \to \sim p$
T	T	T	T	F	T	F	F	F	T
T	T	F	T	F	T	T	T	F	F
T	F	T	F	T	T	F	F	F	T
T	F	F	F	T	F	T	F	F	T
F	T	T	T	F	T	F	F	T	T
F	T	F	T	F	T	T	T	T	T
F	F	T	T	T	T	F	F	T	T
F	F	F	T	T	F	T	F	T	T

Because the final column does not contain all Ts, the statement is not a tautology. The argument is invalid. ∎

Arguments of Lewis Carroll

Consider the following verse, which has been around for many years.

> *For want of a nail, the shoe was lost.*
> *For want of a shoe, the horse was lost.*
> *For want of a horse, the rider was lost.*
> *For want of a rider, the battle was lost.*
> *For want of a battle, the war was lost.*
> *Therefore, for want of a nail, the war was lost.*

Each line of the verse may be written as an *if . . . then* statement. For example, the first line may be restated as "If a nail is lost, then the shoe is lost." The conclusion, "For want of a nail, the war was lost," follows from the premises, because repeated use of the law of transitivity applies. Arguments such as the one used by Lewis Carroll in the next example often take a similar form.

Alice's Adventures in Wonderland is the most famous work of **Charles Dodgson** (1832–1898), better known as **Lewis Carroll,** who was a mathematician and logician. He popularized recreational mathematics with this story and its sequel, *Through the Looking-Glass.* More than a century later, Raymond Smullyan continues this genre in his book *Alice in Puzzle-land* and many others.

EXAMPLE 7 Supplying a Conclusion to Ensure Validity

Supply a conclusion that yields a valid argument for the following premises.

> Babies are illogical.
> Nobody is despised who can manage a crocodile.
> Illogical persons are despised.

Solution

First, write each premise in the form *if . . . then. . . .*

> If you are a baby, then you are illogical.
> If you can manage a crocodile, then you are not despised.
> If you are illogical, then you are despised.

Let p represent "you are a baby," let q represent "you are logical," let r represent "you can manage a crocodile," and let s represent "you are despised." The statements can be written symbolically.

$$p \to \sim q$$
$$r \to \sim s$$
$$\sim q \to s$$

Begin with any letter that appears only once. Here p appears only once. Using the contrapositive of $r \to \sim s$, which is $s \to \sim r$, rearrange the statements as follows.

$$p \to \sim q$$
$$\sim q \to s$$
$$s \to \sim r$$

From the three statements, repeated use of reasoning by transitivity gives the conclusion

$$p \to \sim r, \text{ which leads to a valid argument.}$$

In words, the conclusion is "If you are a baby, then you cannot manage a crocodile," or, as Lewis Carroll would have written it, "Babies cannot manage crocodiles." ∎

WHEN Will I Ever USE This ?

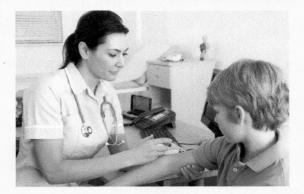

Suppose you are a pediatric nurse administering flu vaccination for a 6-year-old patient. The flowchart on the next page is a dosing algorithm provided by the CDC for children 6 months to 8 years of age.

Influenza Dosing Algorithm

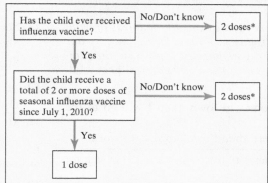

* Doses should be administered at least 4 weeks apart.
Source: cdc.gov

The patient was vaccinated for the first time last year, so you place the patient on a 2-dose regimen. Use a truth table to determine the validity of your action.

We let

p be "The child has received flu vaccine in the past,"

q be "The child has received 2 or more doses of flu vaccine since July 1, 2010,"

and r be "The child needs 2 doses this season."

Then the algorithm and your treatment decision can be expressed symbolically by the following argument.

$$\frac{\begin{array}{c}(p \wedge q) \leftrightarrow \sim r\\ \sim q\end{array}}{r}$$

Make a truth table for the argument. Since there are three component statements, we require eight rows.

p	q	r	$[((p$	$\wedge$	$q)$	$\leftrightarrow$	$\sim r)$	$\wedge$	$\sim q]$	$\rightarrow$	r
T	T	T								T	T
T	T	F	T	T	T	T	T	F	F	T	F
T	F	T								T	T
T	F	F	T	F	F	F	T	F	T	T	F
F	T	T								T	T
F	T	F	F	F	T	F	T	F	F	T	F
F	F	T								T	T
F	F	F	F	F	F	F	T	F	T	T	F
			①	②	①	④	③	⑥	⑤	⑧	⑦

The truth table shows that your argument is a tautology, so your action was valid according to the CDC.

Note that in the odd rows of the table, we used the fact that the consequent *r* was true to conclude that the conditional was true, thus avoiding the effort required to "build" those rows piece by piece. In the even rows, we used the shortcut method introduced in **Example 10** of **Section 3.2**.

Each argument either is valid by one of the forms of valid arguments discussed in this section, or is a fallacy by one of the forms of invalid arguments discussed. (See the summary boxes.) Decide whether the argument is valid *or a fallacy, and give the form that applies.*

1. If Rascal Flatts comes to town, then I will go to the concert.

If I go to the concert, then I'll call in sick for work.

If Rascal Flatts comes to town, then I'll call in sick for work.

2. If you use binoculars, then you get a glimpse of the bald eagle.

If you get a glimpse of the bald eagle, then you'll be amazed.

If you use binoculars, then you'll be amazed.

3. If Marina works hard enough, she will get a promotion.

Marina works hard enough.

She will get a promotion.

4. If Isaiah's ankle heals on time, he'll play this season.

His ankle heals on time.

He'll play this season.

5. If he doesn't have to get up at 3:00 A.M., he's ecstatic.

He's ecstatic.

He doesn't have to get up at 3:00 A.M.

6. "A mathematician is a device for turning coffee into theorems." (quote from Paul Erdos)

You turn coffee into theorems.

You are a mathematician.

7. If Clayton pitches, the Dodgers win.

The Dodgers do not win.

Clayton does not pitch.

8. If Josh plays, the opponent gets shut out.

The opponent does not get shut out.

Josh does not play.

9. "If you're going through hell, keep going." (quote from Winston Churchill)

You're not going through hell.

Don't keep going.

10. "If you can't get rid of the skeleton in your closet, you'd best teach it to dance." (quote from George Bernard Shaw)

You can get rid of the skeleton in your closet.

You'd best not teach it to dance.

11. She uses e-commerce or she pays by credit card.

She does not pay by credit card.

She uses e-commerce.

12. Mia kicks or Drew passes.

Drew does not pass.

Mia kicks.

Use a truth table to determine whether the argument is valid *or* invalid.

13. $p \vee q$
p

$\sim q$

14. $p \wedge \sim q$
p

$\sim q$

15. $\sim p \rightarrow \sim q$
q

p

16. $p \vee \sim q$
p

$\sim q$

17. $p \rightarrow q$
$q \rightarrow p$

$p \wedge q$

18. $\sim p \rightarrow q$
p

$\sim q$

19. $p \rightarrow \sim q$
q

$\sim p$

20. $p \rightarrow \sim q$
$\sim p$

$\sim q$

21. $(p \rightarrow q) \wedge (q \rightarrow p)$
p

$p \vee q$

22. $(p \wedge q) \vee (p \vee q)$
q

p

23. $(\sim p \vee q) \wedge (\sim p \rightarrow q)$
p

$\sim q$

24. $(r \wedge p) \rightarrow (r \vee q)$
$q \wedge p$

$r \vee p$

25. $(\sim p \wedge r) \rightarrow (p \vee q)$
$\sim r \rightarrow p$

$q \rightarrow r$

26. $(p \rightarrow \sim q) \vee (q \rightarrow \sim r)$
$p \vee \sim r$

$r \rightarrow p$

27. Earlier we showed how to analyze arguments using Euler diagrams. Refer to **Example 5** in this section, restate each premise and the conclusion using a quantifier, and then draw an Euler diagram to illustrate the relationship.

28. Explain in a few sentences how to determine the statement for which a truth table will be constructed so that the arguments that follow in **Exercises 29–38** can be analyzed for validity.

Determine whether each argument is valid *or* invalid.

29. Joey loves to watch movies. If Terry likes to jog, then Joey does not love to watch movies. If Terry does not like to jog, then Carrie drives a school bus. Therefore, Carrie drives a school bus.

30. If Hurricane Gustave hit that grove of trees, then the trees are devastated. People plant trees when disasters strike and the trees are not devastated. Therefore, if people plant trees when disasters strike, then Hurricane Gustave did not hit that grove of trees.

31. If Yoda is my favorite *Star Wars* character, then I hate Darth Vader. I hate Luke Skywalker or Darth Vader. I don't hate Luke Skywalker. Therefore, Yoda is not my favorite character.

32. Carrie Underwood sings or Joe Jonas is not a teen idol. If Joe Jonas is not a teen idol, then Jennifer Hudson does not win a Grammy. Jennifer Hudson wins a Grammy. Therefore, Carrie Underwood does not sing.

33. The Cowboys will make the playoffs if and only if Troy comes back to play. Jerry doesn't coach the Cowboys or Troy comes back to play. Jerry does coach the Cowboys. Therefore, the Cowboys will not be in the playoffs.

34. If I've got you under my skin, then you are deep in the heart of me. If you are deep in the heart of me, then you are not really a part of me. You are deep in the heart of me or you are really a part of me. Therefore, if I've got you under my skin, then you are really a part of me.

35. If Dr. Hardy is a department chairman, then he lives in Atlanta. He lives in Atlanta and his first name is Larry. Therefore, if his first name is not Larry, then he is not a department chairman.

36. If I were your woman and you were my man, then I'd never stop loving you. I've stopped loving you. Therefore, I am not your woman or you are not my man.

37. All men are created equal. All people who are created equal are women. Therefore, all men are women.

38. All men are mortal. Socrates is a man. Therefore, Socrates is mortal.

39. A recent DirecTV commercial had the following script: "When the cable company keeps you on hold, you feel trapped. When you feel trapped, you need to feel free. When you need to feel free, you try hang-gliding. When you try hang-gliding, you crash into things. When you crash into things, the grid goes down. When the grid goes down, crime goes up, and when crime goes up, your dad gets punched over a can of soup . . . "

(a) Use reasoning by transitivity and all the component statements to draw a valid conclusion.

(b) If we added the line, "Your dad does not get punched over a can of soup," what valid conclusion could be drawn?

40. Molly made the following observation: "If I want to determine whether an argument leading to the statement

$$[(p \rightarrow q) \land \sim q] \rightarrow \sim p$$

is valid, I only need to consider the lines of the truth table that lead to T for the column that is headed $(p \rightarrow q) \land \sim q$." Molly was very perceptive. Can you explain why her observation was correct?

In the arguments used by Lewis Carroll, it is helpful to restate a premise in if . . . then *form in order to more easily identify a valid conclusion. The following premises come from Lewis Carroll. Write each premise in* if . . . then *form.*

41. All my poultry are ducks.

42. None of your sons can do logic.

43. Guinea pigs are hopelessly ignorant of music.

44. No teetotalers are pawnbrokers.

45. No teachable kitten has green eyes.

46. Opium-eaters have no self-command.

47. I have not filed any of them that I can read.

48. All of them written on blue paper are filed.

Exercises 49–54 involve premises from Lewis Carroll. Write each premise in symbols, and then, in the final part, give a conclusion that yields a valid argument.

49. Let *p* be "it is a duck," *q* be "it is my poultry," *r* be "one is an officer," and *s* be "one is willing to waltz."

(a) No ducks are willing to waltz.

(b) No officers ever decline to waltz.

(c) All my poultry are ducks.

(d) Give a conclusion that yields a valid argument.

50. Let *p* be "one is able to do logic," *q* be "one is fit to serve on a jury," *r* be "one is sane," and *s* be "he is your son."

  (a) Everyone who is sane can do logic.

  (b) No lunatics are fit to serve on a jury.

  (c) None of your sons can do logic.

  (d) Give a conclusion that yields a valid argument.

51. Let *p* be "one is honest," *q* be "one is a pawnbroker," *r* be "one is a promise-breaker," *s* be "one is trustworthy," *t* be "one is very communicative," and *u* be "one is a wine-drinker."

  (a) Promise-breakers are untrustworthy.

  (b) Wine-drinkers are very communicative.

  (c) A person who keeps a promise is honest.

  (d) No teetotalers are pawnbrokers. (*Hint:* Assume "teetotaler" is the opposite of "wine-drinker.")

  (e) One can always trust a very communicative person.

  (f) Give a conclusion that yields a valid argument.

52. Let *p* be "it is a guinea pig," *q* be "it is hopelessly ignorant of music," *r* be "it keeps silent while the *Moonlight Sonata* is being played," and *s* be "it appreciates Beethoven."

  (a) Nobody who really appreciates Beethoven fails to keep silent while the *Moonlight Sonata* is being played.

  (b) Guinea pigs are hopelessly ignorant of music.

  (c) No one who is hopelessly ignorant of music ever keeps silent while the *Moonlight Sonata* is being played.

  (d) Give a conclusion that yields a valid argument.

53. Let *p* be "it begins with 'Dear Sir'," *q* be "it is crossed," *r* be "it is dated," *s* be "it is filed," *t* be "it is in black ink,"

u be "it is in the third person," *v* be "I can read it," *w* be "it is on blue paper," *x* be "it is on one sheet," and *y* be "it is written by Brown."

  (a) All the dated letters are written on blue paper.

  (b) None of them are in black ink, except those that are written in the third person.

  (c) I have not filed any of them that I can read.

  (d) None of them that are written on one sheet are undated.

  (e) All of them that are not crossed are in black ink.

  (f) All of them written by Brown begin with "Dear Sir."

  (g) All of them written on blue paper are filed.

  (h) None of them written on more than one sheet are crossed.

  (i) None of them that begin with "Dear Sir" are written in the third person.

  (j) Give a conclusion that yields a valid argument.

54. Let *p* be "he is going to a party," *q* be "he brushes his hair," *r* be "he has self-command," *s* be "he looks fascinating," *t* be "he is an opium-eater," *u* be "he is tidy," and *v* be "he wears white kid gloves."

  (a) No one who is going to a party ever fails to brush his hair.

  (b) No one looks fascinating if he is untidy.

  (c) Opium-eaters have no self-command.

  (d) Everyone who has brushed his hair looks fascinating.

  (e) No one wears white kid gloves unless he is going to a party. (*Hint:* "*a* unless *b*" ≡ ~*b* → *a*.)

  (f) A man is always untidy if he has no self-command.

  (g) Give a conclusion that yields a valid argument.

CHAPTER 3   **SUMMARY**

KEY TERMS

3.1

symbolic logic
truth value
statement
compound
  statement
component
  statements
connectives
negation
quantifiers

3.2

conjunction
truth table
disjunction
equivalent statements

3.3

conditional statement
antecedent
consequent
tautology

3.4

converse
inverse
contrapositive
biconditional

3.5

argument
premises
conclusion
valid

fallacy
Euler diagram

3.6

modus ponens
modus tollens
disjunctive syllogism
fallacy of the converse
fallacy of the inverse
reasoning by
  transitivity

NEW SYMBOLS

∨ disjunction
∧ conjunction
~ negation

→ implication
↔ biconditional
≡ equivalence

TEST YOUR WORD POWER

See how well you have learned the vocabulary in this chapter.

1. A **statement** is
   A. a sentence that asks a question, the answer to which may be true or false.
   B. a directive giving specific instructions.
   C. a sentence declaring something that is either true or false, but not both at the same time.
   D. a paradoxical sentence with no truth value.

2. A **disjunction** (inclusive) is
   A. a compound statement that is true only if both of its component statements are true.
   B. a compound statement that is true if one or both of its component statements is/are true.
   C. a compound statement that is false if either of its component statements is false.
   D. a compound statement that is true if exactly one of its component statements is true.

3. A **conditional** statement is
   A. a statement that may be true or false, depending on some condition.
   B. an idea that can be stated only under certain conditions.
   C. a statement using the connective *if . . . then*.
   D. a statement the antecedent of which is implied by the consequent.

4. The **inverse** of a conditional statement is
   A. the result when the antecedent and consequent are negated.
   B. the result when the antecedent and consequent are interchanged.
   C. the result when the antecedent and consequent are interchanged and negated.
   D. logically equivalent to the conditional.

5. A **fallacy** is
   A. an argument with a false conclusion.
   B. an argument whose conclusion is not supported by the premises.
   C. a valid argument.
   D. an argument containing at least one false premise.

6. **Fallacy of the converse** is
   A. the reason the converse of a conditional is not equivalent to the conditional.
   B. an invalid argument form that assumes the converse of a premise.
   C. an invalid argument form that denies the converse of a premise.
   D. an invalid argument form that assumes the inverse of a premise.

ANSWERS
1. C 2. B 3. C 4. A 5. B 6. B

QUICK REVIEW

Concepts	Examples

3.1 Statements and Quantifiers

A **statement** is a declarative sentence that is either true or false (not both simultaneously).

A **compound statement** is made up of two or more **component statements** joined by **connectives** (*not, and, or, if . . . then*).

Quantifiers indicate how many members in a group being considered exhibit a particular property or characteristic. Universal quantifiers indicate *all* members, and existential quantifiers indicate *at least one* member.

The **negation** of a statement has the opposite truth value of that statement in all cases.

Consider the following statement.

"If it rains this month, then we'll have a green spring."

It is a compound statement made up of the following two component statements joined by the connective *if . . . then*.

"It rains this month" and "We'll have a green spring,"

The statement

"All five of those birds can fly"

contains a universal quantifier. Its negation is

"At least one of those five birds cannot fly,"

which contains an existential quantifier.

Concepts   *Examples*

Given two component statements p and q, their **conjunction** is symbolized $p \wedge q$ and is true only when both component statements are true.

p	q	$p \wedge q$	$p \vee q$
T	T	T	T
T	F	F	T
F	T	F	T
F	F	F	F

Their **disjunction**, symbolized $p \vee q$, is false only when both component statements are false.

If p represents "$7 < 10$" and q represents "$4 < 3$," then the second row of the truth table above shows that $p \wedge q$ is false and $p \vee q$ is true.

The truth value of a compound statement is found by substituting T or F for each component statement, and then working from inside parentheses out, determining truth values for larger parts of the overall statement, until the entire statement has been evaluated.

When this process is carried out for all possible combinations of truth values for the component statements, a **truth table** results.

The truth table for the statement $\sim p \vee (q \wedge p)$ is shown below, with circled numbers indicating the order in which columns were determined.

p	q	$\sim p$	$\vee$	(q	$\wedge$	p)
T	T	F	T	T	T	T
T	F	F	F	F	F	T
F	T	T	T	T	F	F
F	F	T	T	F	F	F
		①	③	①	②	①

Equivalent statements have the same truth value for all combinations of truth values for the component statements. To determine whether two statements are equivalent, construct truth tables for both and see if the final truth values agree in all rows.

The statements $\sim(p \wedge q)$ and $\sim p \vee \sim q$ are equivalent, as shown in the table.

p	q	$\sim$	(p	$\wedge$	q)	$\sim p$	$\vee$	$\sim q$
T	T	F	T	T	T	F	F	F
T	F	T	T	F	F	F	T	T
F	T	T	F	F	T	T	T	F
F	F	T	F	F	F	T	T	T

De Morgan's laws can be used to quickly find negations of disjunctions and conjunctions.

$$\sim(p \vee q) \equiv \sim p \wedge \sim q$$

$$\sim(p \wedge q) \equiv \sim p \vee \sim q$$

To find the negation of the statement "I love chess and I had breakfast," let p represent "I love chess" and let q represent "I had breakfast." Then the above statement becomes $p \wedge q$. Its negation $\sim(p \wedge q) \equiv \sim p \vee \sim q$ translates to

"I don't love chess or I didn't have breakfast."

A **conditional statement** uses the *if . . . then* connective and is symbolized $p \rightarrow q$, where p is the **antecedent** and q is the **consequent.**

If p represents "You are mighty" and q represents "I am flighty," then the conditional statement $p \rightarrow q$ is expressed as

"*If* you are mighty, *then* I am flighty."

The conditional is false if the antecedent is true and if the consequent is false. Otherwise, the conditional is true. This is because q is only *required* to be true on the *condition* that p is true, but q may "voluntarily" be true even if p is false. That is, p is sufficient for q, but not necessary.

The statement $(6 < 1) \rightarrow (3 = 7)$ is true because the antecedent is false.

The statement "If you are reading this book, then it is the year 1937" is false, because the antecedent is true and the consequent is false.

| Concepts | Examples |

The conditional $p \rightarrow q$ is equivalent to the disjunction $\sim p \vee q$, and its negation is $p \wedge \sim q$, as shown by a comparison of their truth tables.

p	q	p	$\rightarrow$	q	$\sim p$	$\vee$	q	p	$\wedge$	$\sim q$
T	T	T	T	T	F	T	T	T	F	F
T	F	T	F	F	F	F	F	T	T	T
F	T	F	T	T	T	T	T	F	F	F
F	F	F	T	F	T	T	F	F	F	T

The statement "All mice love cheese" can be stated, "*If* it's a mouse, *then* it loves cheese." This is equivalent to saying, "It's not a mouse or it loves cheese." The negation of this statement is "It's a mouse and it does not love cheese."

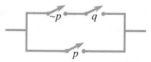

This corresponds to the logical statement $p \vee (\sim p \wedge q)$. Current will flow from one end to the other if p is true *or* if p is false and q is true. This statement is equivalent to

$$(p \vee \sim p) \wedge (p \vee q), \quad \text{which simplifies to} \quad p \vee q.$$

Electrical circuits are analogous to logical statements, with *parallel* circuits corresponding to disjunctions, and *series* circuits corresponding to conjunctions. Each switch (modeled by an arrow) represents a component statement. When a switch is closed, it allows current to pass through. The circuit represents a true statement when current flows from one end of the circuit to the other.

3.4 The Conditional and Related Statements

Given a conditional statement $p \rightarrow q$, its **converse, inverse,** and **contrapositive** are defined as follows.

Converse: $q \rightarrow p$

Inverse: $\sim p \rightarrow \sim q$

Contrapositive: $\sim q \rightarrow \sim p$

Consider the statement "If it's a pie, it tastes good."

Converse: "If it tastes good, it's a pie.

Inverse: "If it's not a pie, it doesn't taste good."

Contrapositive: "If it doesn't taste good, it's not a pie."

The conditional $p \rightarrow q$ can be translated in many ways:

If p, then q.	p is sufficient for q.
If p, q.	q is necessary for p.
p implies q.	All p are q.
p only if q.	q if p.

Statement	If . . . then form
You'll be sorry if I go.	If I go, then you'll be sorry.
Today is Tuesday only if yesterday was Monday.	If today is Tuesday, then yesterday was Monday.
All nurses wear comfortable shoes.	If you are a nurse, then you wear comfortable shoes.

For the **biconditional** statement "p if and only if q,"

$$p \leftrightarrow q \equiv (p \rightarrow q) \wedge (q \rightarrow p).$$

It is true only when p and q have the same truth value.

The statement "$5 < 9$ if and only if $3 > 7$" is false because the component statements have opposite truth values. The first is true, while the second is false.

Summary of Basic Truth Tables

1. $\sim p$, the **negation** of p, has truth value opposite that of p.
2. $p \wedge q$, the **conjunction,** is true only when both p and q are true.
3. $p \vee q$, the **disjunction,** is false only when both p and q are false.
4. $p \rightarrow q$, the **conditional,** is false only when p is true and q is false.
5. $p \leftrightarrow q$, the **biconditional,** is true only when both p and q have the same truth value.

p	$\sim p$
T	F
F	T

p	q	p	$\wedge$	q	p	$\vee$	q	p	$\rightarrow$	q	p	$\leftrightarrow$	q
T	T	T	T	T	T	T	T	T	T	T	T	T	T
T	F	T	F	F	T	T	F	T	F	F	T	F	F
F	T	F	F	T	F	T	T	F	T	T	F	F	T
F	F	F	F	F	F	F	F	F	T	F	F	T	F

Concepts	Examples

3.5 Analyzing Arguments with Euler Diagrams

A logical **argument** consists of premises and a conclusion. An argument is considered **valid** if the truth of the premises forces the conclusion to be true. Otherwise, it is **invalid.**

Euler diagrams can be used to determine whether an argument is valid or invalid.

To draw a Euler diagram, follow these steps:

1. Use the first premise to draw regions. (Arguments with multiple premises may involve multiple regions.)

2. Place an *x* in the diagram to represent the subject of the argument.

Consider this argument. Notice the universal quantifier "all."

All dogs are animals.

Dotty is a dog.

Dotty is an animal.

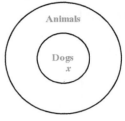

x represents Dotty.

We see from the Euler diagram that the truth of the premises forces the conclusion, that Dotty is an animal, to be true. Thus the argument is valid.

Consider the following argument. Notice the existential quantifier "some."

Some animals are warmblooded.

Albie is an animal.

Albie is warmblooded.

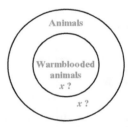

x represents Albie.

We see from the Euler diagram that the location of *x* is uncertain, so the truth of the premises does not force the conclusion to be true. Thus, the argument is invalid.

3.6 Analyzing Arguments with Truth Tables

An argument with premises $p_1, p_2, \ldots, p_n$ and conclusion c can be tested for validity by constructing a truth table for the statement

$$(p_1 \wedge p_2 \wedge \ldots \wedge p_n) \to c.$$

If all rows yield T for this statement (that is, if it is a tautology), then the argument is valid. Otherwise, the argument is invalid.

Valid Argument Forms

Modus Ponens	Modus Tollens	Disjunctive Syllogism	Reasoning by Transitivity
$p \to q$	$p \to q$	$p \vee q$	$p \to q$
p	$\sim q$	$\sim p$	$q \to r$
q	$\sim p$	q	$p \to r$

Consider this argument. "If I eat ice cream, I regret it later. I didn't regret it later. Therefore, I didn't eat ice cream."

Let p represent "I eat ice cream" and q represent "I regret it later." Then the argument can be expressed as the compound statement

$$[(p \to q) \wedge \sim q] \to \sim p.$$

Test its validity using a truth table, which shows that the statement is a tautology. The argument is valid (by **modus tollens**).

p	q	[(p	$\to$	q)	$\wedge$	$\sim q$]	$\to$	$\sim p$
T	T				F	F	T	F
T	F	T	F	F	F	T	T	F
F	T						T	T
F	F						T	T

Concepts	**Examples**

Invalid Argument Forms

Fallacy of the Converse	Fallacy of the Inverse
$p \rightarrow q$	$p \rightarrow q$
q	$\sim p$
p	$\sim q$

Consider this argument.

> If I drink coffee, I get jittery.
> I didn't drink coffee.
> _____
> I don't get jittery.

Let p represent "I drink coffee" and q represent "I get jittery."

Test the argument, using a truth table for the statement

$$[(p \rightarrow q) \wedge \sim p] \rightarrow \sim q.$$

p	q	[(p	$\rightarrow$	q)	$\wedge$	$\sim p$]	$\rightarrow$	$\sim q$
T	T		T		F	F	T	F
T	F						T	T
F	T		T		T	T	F	F
F	F						T	T

This argument is invalid by **fallacy of the inverse.**

CHAPTER 3 | TEST

Write a negation for each statement.

1. $6 - 3 = 3$

2. All men are created equal.

3. Some members of the class went on the field trip.

4. If I fall in love, it will be forever.

5. She applied and did not get a student loan.

Let p represent "You will love me" and let q represent "I will love you." Write each statement in symbols.

6. If you won't love me, then I will love you.

7. I will love you if you will love me.

8. I won't love you if and only if you won't love me.

Using the same statements as for Exercises 6–8, write each of the following in words.

9. $\sim p \wedge q$ **10.** $\sim (p \vee \sim q)$

In each of the following, assume that p is true and that q and r are false. Find the truth value of each statement.

11. $\sim q \wedge \sim r$ **12.** $r \vee (p \wedge \sim q)$

13. $r \rightarrow (s \vee r)$ (The truth value of the statement s is unknown.)

14. $p \leftrightarrow (p \rightarrow q)$

15. Explain in your own words why, if p is a statement, the biconditional $p \leftrightarrow \sim p$ must be false.

16. State the necessary conditions for each of the following.
  (a) a conditional statement to be false
  (b) a conjunction to be true
  (c) a disjunction to be false
  (d) a biconditional to be true

Construct a truth table for each of the following.

17. $p \wedge (\sim p \vee q)$

18. $\sim (p \wedge q) \rightarrow (\sim p \vee \sim q)$

Decide whether each statement is true *or* false.

19. Some negative integers are whole numbers.

20. All irrational numbers are real numbers.

Write each conditional statement in if . . . then form.

21. All integers are rational numbers.

22. Being a rhombus is sufficient for a polygon to be a quadrilateral.

23. Being divisible by 2 is necessary for a number to be divisible by 4.

24. She digs dinosaur bones only if she is a paleontologist.

For each statement in Exercises 25 and 26, write **(a)** *the converse,* **(b)** *the inverse, and* **(c)** *the contrapositive.*

25. If a picture paints a thousand words, the graph will help me understand it.

26. $\sim p \to (q \wedge r)$ (Use one of De Morgan's laws as necessary.)

27. Use an Euler diagram to determine whether the argument is *valid* or *invalid*.

All members of that athletic club save money.

Don is a member of that athletic club.

Don saves money.

28. Match each argument in parts (a)–(d) in the next column with the law that justifies its validity, or the fallacy of which it is an example, in choices A–F.

  A. Modus ponens

  B. Modus tollens

  C. Reasoning by transitivity

  D. Disjunctive syllogism

  E. Fallacy of the converse

  F. Fallacy of the inverse

(a) If he eats liver, then he'll eat anything.

He eats liver.

He'll eat anything.

(b) If you use your seat belt, you will be safer.

You don't use your seat belt.

You won't be safer.

(c) If I hear *Mr. Bojangles,* I think of her.

If I think of her, I smile.

If I hear *Mr. Bojangles,* I smile.

(d) She sings or she dances.

She does not sing.

She dances.

Use a truth table to determine whether each argument is valid or invalid.

29. If I write a check, it will bounce. If the bank guarantees it, then it does not bounce. The bank guarantees it. Therefore, I don't write a check.

30. $\sim p \to \sim q$

$q \to p$

$p \vee q$

Geometry

9

Programmers of video games, flight simulators, and other virtual reality applications use software programs to render objects in their virtual world in three dimensions. The software can track the location of objects in the "world" and then show only the ones in the part of the world where the user is looking.

Some of the concepts from this chapter are foundational to the rendering process involved in such applications.

9.1 POINTS, LINES, PLANES, AND ANGLES

The Geometry of Euclid

Let no one unversed in geometry enter here.
—Motto over the door of Plato's Academy

To the ancient Greeks, mathematics meant geometry above all—a rigid kind of geometry from a modern-day point of view. The Greeks studied the properties of figures identical in shape and size (congruent figures) as well as figures identical in shape but not necessarily in size (similar figures). They absorbed ideas about area and volume from the Egyptians and Babylonians and established general formulas. The Greeks were the first to insist that statements in geometry be given rigorous proof.

The most basic ideas of geometry are **point, line,** and **plane.** In fact, it is not really possible to define them with other words. Euclid defined a point as "that which has no part," but this definition is vague. He defined a line as "that which has breadthless length." Again, this definition is vague. Based on our experience, however, we know what Euclid meant. The drawings that we use for points are dots. Lines have properties of no thickness and no width, and they extend indefinitely in two directions.

Euclid's definition of a plane, "a surface which lies evenly with the straight lines on itself," is represented by a flat surface, such as a tabletop or a page in a book.

Points, Lines, and Planes

There are certain universally accepted conventions and symbols used to represent points, lines, and planes. A capital letter usually represents a point. A line may be named by two capital letters representing points that lie on the line, or by a single (usually lowercase) letter, such as ℓ. Subscripts are sometimes used to distinguish one line from another when a lowercase letter is used. For example, ℓ_1 and ℓ_2 would represent two distinct lines. A plane may be named by three capital letters representing points that lie in the plane, or by a letter of the Greek alphabet, such as α (alpha), β (beta), or γ (gamma).

Figure 1 depicts a plane that may be represented either as α or as plane ADE. Contained in the plane is the line DE (or, equivalently, line ED), which is also labeled ℓ in the figure.

Selecting any point on a line divides the line into three parts: the point itself, and two **half-lines,** one on each side of the point. For example, point A divides the line shown in **Figure 2** into three parts, A itself and two half-lines. Point A belongs to neither half-line. As the figure suggests, each half-line extends indefinitely in the direction opposite the other half-line.

Euclid's *Elements* as translated by Billingsley appeared in 1570 and was the first English-language translation of the text—the most influential geometry text ever written.

Unfortunately, no copy of *Elements* exists that dates back to the time of Euclid (circa 300 B.C.), and most current translations are based on a revision of the work prepared by Theon of Alexandria.

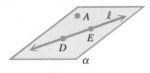

Figure 1

Figure 2

Figure 3

Including an initial point with a half-line gives a **ray.** A ray is named with two letters, one for the initial point of the ray, and one for another point contained in the half-line. In **Figure 3** ray AB has initial point A and extends in the direction of B. On the other hand, ray BA has B as its initial point and extends in the direction of A.

Given any three points that are not in a straight line, a plane can be passed through the points. That is why **camera tripods** have three legs—no matter how irregular the surface, the tips of the three legs determine a plane. A camera support with four legs would wobble unless all four legs were carefully extended just the right amount.

A **line segment** includes both endpoints and is named by its endpoints. **Figure 3** shows line segment AB, which may also be designated as line segment BA.

Table 1 shows these figures along with the symbols used to represent them.

Table 1

Name	Figure	Symbol
Line AB or line BA		$\overleftrightarrow{AB}$ or $\overleftrightarrow{BA}$
Half-line AB		$\overset{\circ}{\overrightarrow{AB}}$
Half-line BA		$\overset{\circ}{\overleftarrow{BA}}$
Ray AB		$\overset{\bullet}{\overrightarrow{AB}}$
Ray BA		$\overset{\bullet}{\overleftarrow{BA}}$
Segment AB or segment BA		$\overset{\bullet\;\bullet}{AB}$ or $\overset{\bullet\;\bullet}{BA}$

For a line, the symbol above the two letters shows two arrowheads, indicating that the line extends indefinitely in both directions. For half-lines and rays, only one arrowhead is used because these extend in only one direction. An open circle is used for a half-line to show that the endpoint is not included, while a solid circle is used for a ray to indicate the inclusion of the endpoint. Since a segment includes both endpoints and does not extend in either direction, solid circles are used to indicate endpoints of line segments.

The geometric definitions of "parallel" and "intersecting" apply to two or more lines or planes. (See **Figure 4.**) **Parallel lines** lie in the same plane and never meet, no matter how far they are extended. However, **intersecting lines** do meet.

If two distinct lines intersect, they intersect in one and only one point.

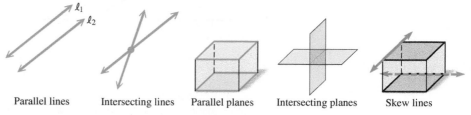

Parallel lines   Intersecting lines   Parallel planes   Intersecting planes   Skew lines

Figure 4

We use the symbol ∥ to denote parallelism. If ℓ_1 and ℓ_2 are parallel lines, as in **Figure 4,** then this may be indicated as

$$\ell_1 \parallel \ell_2.$$

Parallel planes also never meet, no matter how far they are extended. Two distinct **intersecting planes** form a straight line, the one and only line they have in common. **Skew lines** do not lie in a common plane, so they are neither parallel nor intersecting.

Angles are the key to the study of **geodesy,** the measurement of distances on the earth's surface.

Angles

An **angle** is the union of two rays that have a common endpoint. See **Figure 5.** The angle is formed by points on the rays themselves, and no other points. In **Figure 5,** point *X* is *not* a point on the angle. (It is said to be in the *interior* of the angle.)

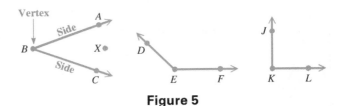

Figure 5

The rays forming an angle are its **sides.** The common endpoint of the rays is the **vertex** of the angle. There are two standard ways of naming angles using letters. If no confusion will result, an angle can be named with the letter marking its vertex. Using this method, the angles in **Figure 5** can be named, respectively, angle *B*, angle *E*, and angle *K*.

Angles also can be named with three letters: the first letter names a point on one side of the angle; the middle letter names the vertex; the third names a point on the other side of the angle. In this system, the angles in the figure can be named angle *ABC*, angle *DEF*, and angle *JKL*. The symbol for representing an angle is ∡. Rather than writing "angle *ABC*," we may write "∡*ABC*."

An angle can be associated with an amount of rotation. For example, in **Figure 6(a),** we let $\overrightarrow{BA}$ first coincide with $\overrightarrow{BC}$—as though they were the same ray. We then rotate $\overrightarrow{BA}$ (the endpoint remains fixed) in a counterclockwise direction to form ∡*ABC*.

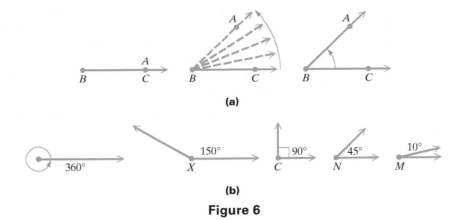

Figure 6

Why 360? The use of the number 360 goes back to the Babylonian culture. There are several theories regarding why 360 was chosen for the number of degrees in a complete rotation around a circle. One says that 360 was chosen because it is close to the number of days in a year and because it is conveniently divisible by 2, 3, 4, 5, 6, 8, 9, 10, 12, and other numbers.

Angles are measured by the amount of rotation, using a system that dates back to the Babylonians. Babylonian astronomers chose the number 360 to represent a complete rotation of a ray back onto itself. **One degree,** written 1°, is defined to be $\frac{1}{360}$ of a complete rotation. **Figure 6(b)** shows angles of various degree measures.

Angles are classified and named with reference to their degree measures. An angle whose measure is between 0° and 90° is an **acute angle.** Angles *M* and *N* in **Figure 6(b)** are acute. An angle that measures 90° is a **right angle.** Angle *C* in the figure is a right angle. The squared symbol ⌐ at the vertex denotes a right angle. Angles that measure more than 90° but less than 180° are said to be **obtuse angles** (angle *X*, for example). An angle that measures 180° is a **straight angle.** Its sides form a straight line.

A **protractor** is a tool used to measure angles. **Figure 7** shows a protractor measuring an angle whose measure is 135°.

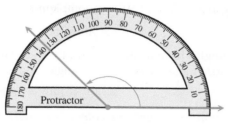

To use a protractor, position the hole (or dot) of the protractor on the vertex of the angle. With the 0-degree measure on the protractor placed on one side of the angle, the other side will show the degree measure of the angle.

Figure 7

When two lines intersect to form right angles, they are called **perpendicular lines**. In **Figure 8**, the sides of ⊀*NMP* have been extended to form another angle, ⊀*RMQ*. The pair ⊀*NMP* and ⊀*RMQ* are called **vertical angles.** Another pair of vertical angles have been formed at the same time. They are ⊀*NMQ* and ⊀*PMR*.

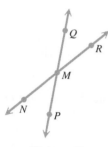

Figure 8

PROPERTY OF VERTICAL ANGLES

Vertical angles have equal measures.

EXAMPLE 1 Finding Angle Measures

Find the measure of each marked angle in the given figure.

(a) Figure 9   **(b) Figure 10**

Solution

(a) Because the marked angles are vertical angles, they have the same measure.

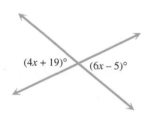

Figure 9

$$4x + 19 = 6x - 5 \qquad \text{Set measures equal.}$$
$$4x + 19 - 4x = 6x - 5 - 4x \qquad \text{Subtract } 4x.$$
$$19 = 2x - 5 \qquad \text{Combine like terms.}$$
$$19 + 5 = 2x - 5 + 5 \qquad \text{Add 5.}$$
$$24 = 2x \qquad \text{Add.}$$

Don't stop here. $\qquad 12 = x \qquad \text{Divide by 2.}$

Since $x = 12$, one angle has measure $4(12) + 19 = 67$ degrees. The other has the same measure, because $6(12) - 5 = 67$ as well. Each angle measures 67°.

(b) The measures of the marked angles must add to 180°. They form a straight angle.

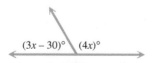

Figure 10

$$(3x - 30) + 4x = 180 \qquad \text{The angle sum is 180.}$$
$$7x - 30 = 180 \qquad \text{Combine like terms.}$$
$$7x - 30 + 30 = 180 + 30 \qquad \text{Add 30.}$$
$$7x = 210 \qquad \text{Add.}$$

Don't stop here. $\qquad x = 30 \qquad \text{Divide by 7.}$

To find the measures of the angles, replace x with 30 in the two expressions.

$$3x - 30 = 3(30) - 30 = 90 - 30 = 60$$
$$4x = 4(30) = 120$$

The two angle measures are 60° and 120°.

If the sum of the measures of two acute angles is 90°, the angles are said to be **complementary,** and each is called the *complement* of the other. For example, angles measuring 40° and 50° are complementary angles, because

$$40° + 50° = 90°.$$

If two angles have a sum of 180°, they are **supplementary.** The *supplement* of an angle whose measure is 40° is an angle whose measure is 140°, because

$$40° + 140° = 180°.$$

If x represents the degree measure of an angle, 90 − x represents the measure of its complement, and 180 − x represents the measure of its supplement.

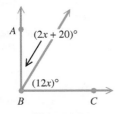

Figure 11

EXAMPLE 2   Finding Angle Measures

Find the measures of the angles in **Figure 11,** given that $\angle ABC$ is a right angle.

Solution

The sum of the measures of the two acute angles is 90° (that is, they are complementary), because they form a right angle.

$$(2x + 20) + 12x = 90 \quad \text{The angle measures sum to 90°.}$$
$$14x + 20 = 90 \quad \text{Combine like terms.}$$
$$14x = 70 \quad \text{Subtract 20.}$$
$$x = 5 \quad \text{Divide by 14.}$$

The value of x is 5. Therefore, replace x with 5 in the two expressions.

$$2x + 20 = 2(5) + 20 = 30$$
$$12x = 12(5) = 60$$

The measures of the two angles are 30° and 60°. ∎

EXAMPLE 3   Using Complementary and Supplementary Angles

The supplement of an angle measures 10° more than three times its complement. Find the measure of the angle.

Solution

Let $x =$ the degree measure of the angle.

Then $180 - x =$ the degree measure of its supplement,

and $90 - x =$ the degree measure of its complement.

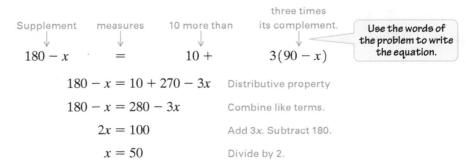

$$180 - x = 10 + 270 - 3x \quad \text{Distributive property}$$
$$180 - x = 280 - 3x \quad \text{Combine like terms.}$$
$$2x = 100 \quad \text{Add 3x. Subtract 180.}$$
$$x = 50 \quad \text{Divide by 2.}$$

The angle measures 50°. Because its supplement (130°) is 10° more than three times its complement (40°) (that is, $130 = 10 + 3(40)$ is true), the answer checks. ∎

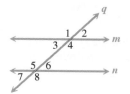

Figure 12

A set of parallel lines with equidistant spacing intersects an identical set, but at a small angle. The result is a **moiré pattern,** named after the fabric *moiré* ("watered") *silk.* Moiré patterns are related to **periodic functions,** which describe regular recurring phenomena (wave patterns such as heartbeats or business cycles). Moirés thus apply to the study of electromagnetic, sound, and water waves, to crystal structure, and to other wave phenomena.

Figure 12 shows parallel lines m and n. When a line q intersects two parallel lines, q is a **transversal.** In **Figure 12,** the transversal intersecting the parallel lines forms eight angles, indicated by numbers. Angles 1 through 8 in the figure possess some special properties regarding their degree measures, as shown in **Table 2.**

Table 2

Name	Figure	Rule
Alternate interior angles	(also 3 and 6)	Angle measures are equal.
Alternate exterior angles	(also 2 and 7)	Angle measures are equal.
Interior angles on same side of transversal	(also 3 and 5)	Angle measures add to 180°.
Corresponding angles	(also 1 and 5, 3 and 7, 4 and 8)	Angle measures are equal.

The converses of the above also are true. That is, if alternate interior angles are equal, then the lines are parallel. Similar results are valid for alternate exterior angles, interior angles on the same side of a transversal, and corresponding angles.

EXAMPLE 4 Finding Angle Measures

Find the measure of each marked angle in **Figure 13,** given that lines m and n are parallel.

Solution

The marked angles are alternate exterior angles, which are equal.

$$3x + 2 = 5x - 40 \qquad \text{Set angle measures equal.}$$
$$42 = 2x \qquad \text{Subtract } 3x. \text{ Add } 40.$$
$$21 = x \qquad \text{Divide by 2.}$$

Don't stop here.

Thus, $3x + 2 = 3 \cdot 21 + 2 = 65$ and $5x - 40 = 5 \cdot 21 - 40 = 65$.

So both angles measure 65°.

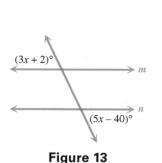

$(3x + 2)°$

$(5x - 40)°$

Figure 13

9.1 EXERCISES

Fill in each blank with the correct response.

1. The sum of the measures of two complementary angles is _____ degrees.

2. The sum of the measures of two supplementary angles is _____ degrees.

3. The measures of two vertical angles are _____.
   (equal/not equal)

4. The measures of _____ right angles add up to the measure of a straight angle.

Decide whether each statement is true *or* false.

5. A line segment has two endpoints.

6. A ray has one endpoint.

7. If A and B are distinct points on a line, then ray AB and ray BA represent the same set of points.

8. If two lines intersect, they lie in the same plane.

9. If two lines are parallel, they lie in the same plane.

10. If two lines are neither parallel nor intersecting, they cannot lie in the same plane.

11. If two lines do not intersect, they must be parallel.

12. There is no angle that is its own complement.

13. Segment AB and segment BA represent the same set of points.

14. There is no angle whose complement and supplement are the same.

15. There is no angle that is its own supplement.

16. The use of the degree as a unit of measure of an angle goes back to the Egyptians.

Exercises 17–24 name portions of the line shown. For each exercise, **(a)** *give the symbol that represents the portion of the line named, and* **(b)** *draw a figure showing just the portion named, including all labeled points.*

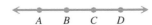

17. line segment AB

18. ray BC

19. ray CB

20. line segment AD

21. half-line BC

22. half-line AD

23. ray BA

24. line segment CA

Match each symbol in Group I with the symbol in Group II that names the same set of points, based on the figure.

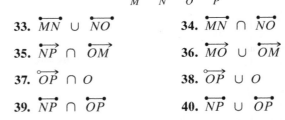

I		II	
25. $\vec{PQ}$	26. $\overset{\circ}{QR}$	A. $\overset{\circ}{QS}$	B. $\vec{RQ}$
27. $\overleftrightarrow{QR}$	28. $\vec{PQ}$	C. $\overleftrightarrow{SR}$	D. $\overset{\circ}{QS}$
29. $\vec{RP}$	30. $\overset{\circ}{SQ}$	E. $\vec{SP}$	F. $\overset{\circ}{QP}$
31. $\overset{\bullet\!-\!\bullet}{PS}$	32. $\overset{\circ}{PS}$	G. $\overleftrightarrow{RS}$	H. none of these

Lines, rays, half-lines, and segments may be considered sets of points. The **intersection** *(symbolized* ∩*) of two sets is composed of all elements common to both sets, while the* **union** *(symbolized* ∪*) of two sets is composed of all elements found in at least one of the two sets.*

Based on the figure below, specify each of the sets given in Exercises 33–40 in a simpler way.

33. $\vec{MN} \cup \vec{NO}$

34. $\vec{MN} \cap \vec{NO}$

35. $\vec{NP} \cap \vec{OM}$

36. $\vec{MO} \cup \vec{OM}$

37. $\vec{OP} \cap O$

38. $\vec{OP} \cup O$

39. $\vec{NP} \cap \vec{OP}$

40. $\vec{NP} \cup \vec{OP}$

Give the measure of the complement of each angle.

41. $28°$ 42. $32°$ 43. $89°$

44. $45°$ 45. $x°$ 46. $(90 - x)°$

Give the measure of the supplement of each angle.

47. $132°$ 48. $105°$ 49. $26°$

50. $90°$ 51. $y°$ 52. $(180 - y)°$

Complementary and Supplementary Angles *Solve each problem.*

53. If the supplement of an angle is $40°$ more than twice its complement, what is the measure of the angle?

54. If an angle measures $15°$ less than twice its complement, what is the measure of the angle?

55. Half the supplement of an angle is $12°$ less than twice the complement of the angle. Find the measure of the angle.

56. The supplement of an angle measures $25°$ more than twice its complement. Find the measure of the angle.

Name all pairs of vertical angles in each figure.

57.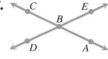

58.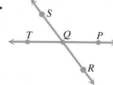

59. In Exercise 57, if ∡*ABE* has a measure of 52°, find the measures of the following angles.

   (a) ∡*CBD*   **(b)** ∡*CBE*

60. In Exercise 58, if ∡*SQP* has a measure of 126°, find the measures of the following angles.

   (a) ∡*TQR*   **(b)** ∡*PQR*

Find the measure of each marked angle.

61.

62.

63.

64.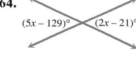

65.

66.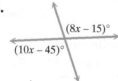

67.

68.

In Exercises 69–72, assume that lines m and n are parallel, and find the measure of each marked angle.

69.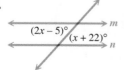

70.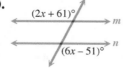

71.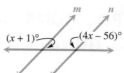

72.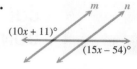

73. The sketch shows parallel lines *m* and *n* cut by a transversal *q*. Complete the steps to prove that alternate exterior angles have the same measure.

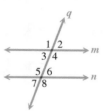

   (a) Measure of ∡2 = measure of ∡ _____ , since they are vertical angles.

   (b) Measure of ∡3 = measure of ∡ _____ , since they are alternate interior angles.

   (c) Measure of ∡6 = measure of ∡ _____ , since they are vertical angles.

   (d) By the results of parts (a), (b), and (c), the measure of ∡2 must equal the measure of ∡ _____ , showing that alternate _____ angles have equal measures.

74. Use the sketch to find the measure of each numbered angle. Assume that *m* ∥ *n*.

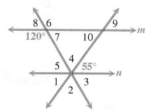

75. Complete these steps in the proof that vertical angles have equal measures. In this exercise, m (∡*x*) means "the measure of the angle *x*." Use the figure at the right.

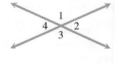

   (a) m(∡1) + m(∡2) = _____ °

   (b) m(∡2) + m(∡3) = _____ °

   (c) Subtract the equation in part (b) from the equation in part (a) to get [m(∡1) + m(∡2)] − [m(∡2) + m(∡3)] = _____ ° − _____ °.

   (d) m(∡1) + m(∡2) − m(∡2) − m(∡3) = _____ °

   (e) m(∡1) − m(∡3) = _____ °

   (f) m(∡1) = m(∡ _____)

<table>
<tr><td>**9.2**</td><td>**CURVES, POLYGONS, CIRCLES, AND GEOMETRIC CONSTRUCTIONS**</td></tr>
</table>

OBJECTIVES

1 Classify curves.

2 Identify and classify triangles and quadrilaterals.

3 Learn the vocabulary of circles.

4 Perform geometric constructions.

Curves

The term *curve* is used for describing figures in the plane.

SIMPLE CURVE AND CLOSED CURVE

A **simple curve** can be drawn without lifting the pencil from the paper and without passing through any point twice.

A **closed curve** has its starting and ending points the same and is drawn without lifting the pencil from the paper.

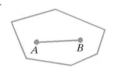

Convex

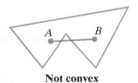

Not convex

Figure 15

Some examples are shown in **Figure 14.**

Simple; closed   Simple; not closed   Not simple; closed   Not simple; not closed

Figure 14

A simple closed figure is said to be **convex** if, for any two points A and B inside the figure, the line segment AB (that is, $\overrightarrow{AB}$) is always completely inside the figure. **Figure 15** shows a convex figure and one that is not convex.

Among the most common types of curves in mathematics are those that are both simple and closed, and perhaps the most important of these are *polygons*. A **polygon** is a simple closed curve made up only of straight line segments. The line segments are the *sides*, and the points at which the sides meet are the *vertices* (singular: *vertex*).

Polygons are classified according to the number of line segments used as sides. **Table 3** gives the special names. ***In general, if a polygon has n sides, and no particular value of n is specified, it is called an n-gon.***

Some examples of polygons are shown in **Figure 16.** A polygon may or may not be convex. Polygons with all sides equal and all angles equal are **regular polygons.**

Table 3 Classification of Polygons According to Number of Sides

Number of Sides	Name
3	triangle
4	quadrilateral
5	pentagon
6	hexagon
7	heptagon
8	octagon
9	nonagon
10	decagon

Convex   Not convex

Polygons are simple closed curves made up of straight line segments.

Regular polygons have equal sides and equal angles.

Figure 16

The puzzle game above comes from China, where it has been a popular amusement for centuries. Each figure above is a **tangram.** Any tangram is composed of the same set of seven tans (the pieces making up the figure).

Mathematicians have described various properties of tangrams. While each tan is convex, only 13 convex tangrams are possible. All others, like the figure on the left, are not convex.

Triangles and Quadrilaterals

Triangles are classified by measures of angles as well as by number of equal sides, as shown in the following box. (Notice that tick marks are used in the bottom three figures to show how side lengths are related.)

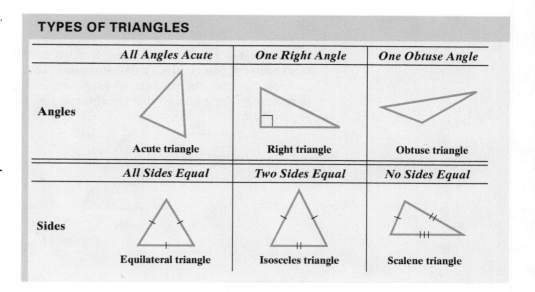

TYPES OF TRIANGLES

	All Angles Acute	*One Right Angle*	*One Obtuse Angle*
Angles	Acute triangle	Right triangle	Obtuse triangle
	All Sides Equal	*Two Sides Equal*	*No Sides Equal*
Sides	Equilateral triangle	Isosceles triangle	Scalene triangle

Quadrilaterals are classified by sides and angles. An important distinction involving quadrilaterals is whether one or more pairs of sides are parallel.

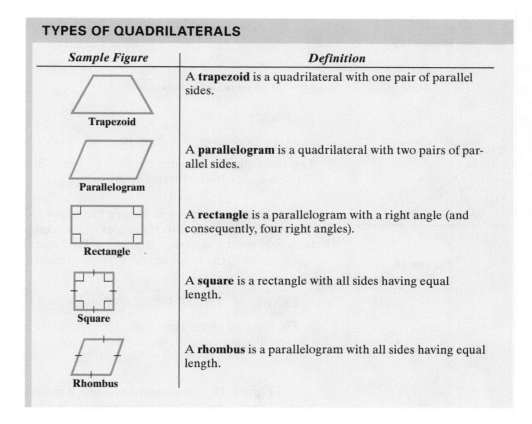

TYPES OF QUADRILATERALS

Sample Figure	*Definition*
Trapezoid	A **trapezoid** is a quadrilateral with one pair of parallel sides.
Parallelogram	A **parallelogram** is a quadrilateral with two pairs of parallel sides.
Rectangle	A **rectangle** is a parallelogram with a right angle (and consequently, four right angles).
Square	A **square** is a rectangle with all sides having equal length.
Rhombus	A **rhombus** is a parallelogram with all sides having equal length.

An important property of triangles that was first proved by the Greek geometers deals with the sum of the measures of the angles of any triangle.

ANGLE SUM OF A TRIANGLE

The sum of the measures of the interior angles of any triangle is $180°$.

While it is not an actual proof, a rather convincing argument for the truth of this statement can be given using any size triangle cut from a piece of paper. Tear each corner from the triangle, as suggested in **Figure 17(a)**. You should be able to rearrange the pieces so that the three angles form a straight angle, as shown in **Figure 17(b)**.

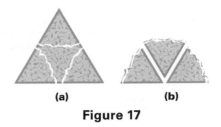

(a)   (b)

Figure 17

EXAMPLE 1 Finding Angle Measures in a Triangle

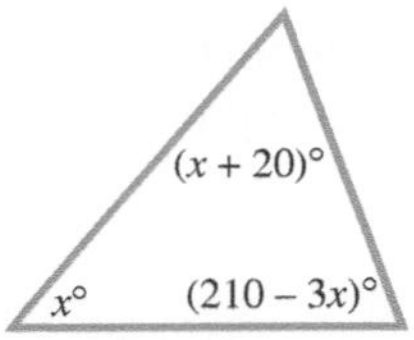

Find the measure of each angle in the triangle of **Figure 18.**

Figure 18

Solution

By the angle sum relationship, the three angle measures must add up to $180°$.

$$x + (x + 20) + (210 - 3x) = 180 \qquad \text{Sum is 180.}$$
$$-x + 230 = 180 \qquad \text{Combine like terms.}$$
$$-x = -50 \qquad \text{Subtract 230.}$$
$$x = 50 \qquad \text{Divide by } -1.$$

There are two more values to find.

Because $x = 50$,

$$x + 20 = 50 + 20 = 70 \quad \text{and} \quad 210 - 3x = 210 - 3(50) = 60.$$

The three angles measure $50°$, $70°$, and $60°$. Because $50° + 70° + 60° = 180°$, the answers satisfy the angle sum relationship. ∎

In the triangle shown in **Figure 19,** angles 1, 2, and 3 are **interior angles,** while angles 4, 5, and 6 are **exterior angles** of the triangle. Using the fact that the sum of the angle measures of any triangle is $180°$, and the fact that a straight angle also measures $180°$, the following property may be deduced.

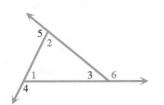

Figure 19

EXTERIOR ANGLE MEASURE

The measure of an exterior angle of a triangle is equal to the sum of the measures of the two opposite interior angles.

In **Figure 19,** the measure of angle 6 is equal to the sum of the measures of angles 1 and 2. Two other such statements can be made.

EXAMPLE 2 Finding Interior and Exterior Angle Measures

Find the measures of interior angles A, B, and C of the triangle in **Figure 20**, and the measure of exterior angle BCD.

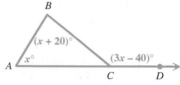

Figure 20

Solution

By the property concerning exterior angles, the sum of the measures of interior angles A and B must equal the measure of angle BCD.

$$x + (x + 20) = 3x - 40$$

$$2x + 20 = 3x - 40 \qquad \text{Combine like terms.}$$

$$-x = -60 \qquad \text{Subtract } 3x. \text{ Subtract } 20.$$

$$x = 60 \qquad \text{Divide by } -1.$$

Because the value of x is 60, we have the following.

> m(angle A) denotes the measure of angle A.

$\text{m}(\text{Interior angle } A) = 60°$

$\text{m}(\text{Interior angle } B) = (60 + 20)° = 80°$

$\text{m}(\text{Interior angle } C) = 180° - (60° + 80°) = 40°$

$\text{m}(\text{Exterior angle } BCD) = [3(60) - 40]° = 140°$ ∎

Circles

A circle is a simple closed curve defined as follows.

CIRCLE

A **circle** is a set of points in a plane, each of which is the same distance from a fixed point.

A circle may be physically constructed with a compass, where the spike leg remains fixed and the other leg swings around to construct the circle. A string may also be used to draw a circle. For example, loop a piece of chalk on one end of a piece of string. Hold the other end in a fixed position on a chalkboard, and pull the string taut. Then swing the chalk end around to draw a circle.

A circle, along with several lines and segments, is shown in **Figure 21**. The points P, Q, and R lie on the circle. Each lies the same distance from point O, which is the **center** of the circle. (It is the "fixed point" referred to in the definition.) $\overleftrightarrow{OP}$, $\overleftrightarrow{OQ}$, and $\overleftrightarrow{OR}$ are segments whose endpoints are the center and a point on the circle. Each is a **radius** of the circle (plural: *radii*). $\overleftrightarrow{PQ}$ is a segment whose endpoints both lie on the circle and is an example of a **chord.** The segment $\overleftrightarrow{PR}$ is a chord that passes through the center and is a **diameter** of the circle. Notice that the measure of a diameter is twice that of a radius. A diameter such as $\overleftrightarrow{PR}$ in **Figure 21** divides a circle into two parts of equal size, each of which is a **semicircle.**

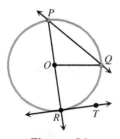

Figure 21

Figure 21 (repeated)

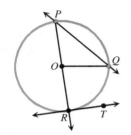

Thales is credited with the first proof of the **inscribed angle theorem.** Legend records that he studied for a time in Egypt and then introduced geometry to Greece, where he attempted to apply the principles of Greek logic to his newly learned subject.

In **Figure 21,** $\overleftrightarrow{RT}$ is a line that touches (intersects) the circle in only one point, R, and is a **tangent** to the circle. R is the point of tangency. $\overleftrightarrow{PQ}$, which intersects the circle in two points, is a **secant** line. (What is the distinction between a chord and a secant?)

The portion of the circle shown in red in **Figure 21** is an **arc** of the circle. It consists of two endpoints (P and Q) and all points on the circle "between" these endpoints. The colored portion is arc PQ (or QP), denoted in symbols as $\overset{\frown}{PQ}$ (or $\overset{\frown}{QP}$). An angle such as QPR, which has its vertex P on the circle and its sides $\overrightarrow{PQ}$ and $\overrightarrow{PR}$, is said to be **inscribed** in the circle, and it **intercepts** arc QR.

The Greeks were the first to insist that all propositions, or **theorems,** about geometry be given rigorous proofs before being accepted. One of the theorems receiving such a proof was this one.

INSCRIBED ANGLE

Any angle inscribed in a circle has degree measure half of that of its intercepted arc.

Figure 22(a) states this theorem symbolically. For example, if *arc PR* measures $80°$, then inscribed angle PQR measures $\left(\frac{80}{2}\right)° = 40°$. A special case of this theorem is indicated in **Figure 22(b)**. *Any angle inscribed in a semicircle is a right angle.*

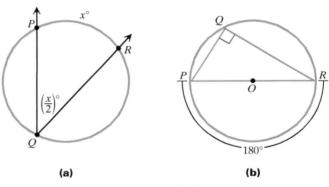

(a)   (b)

Figure 22

Geometric Constructions

To the Greeks, geometry was the highest expression of mathematics. It is no surprise then that they required **geometric constructions** to have abstract beauty. This was achieved by allowing only a minimal set of tools: a compass (also called compasses, or a pair of compasses) for drawing circles and arcs of circles, and an unmarked straightedge for drawing straight line segments.

Here are three basic constructions. Their justifications are based on the *congruence properties* of **Section 9.3.**

A **compass** may be used to:
1. Swing a circular arc with given center and radius.
2. Reproduce a given length. (The Greeks used "collapsing" compasses, which would not allow distances to be copied directly. But Proposition II from Book I of Euclid's *Elements* provides a construction for transferring distances using a collapsing compass. Thus for our purposes, we will use a "fixed" compass.)

Perpendicular Bisector **Construct the perpendicular bisector of a given line segment.**

Let the segment have endpoints A and B. Adjust the compass for any radius greater than half the length of AB. Place the point of the compass at A and draw an arc; then draw another arc of the same size at B. The line drawn through the points of intersection of these two arcs is the desired perpendicular bisector. See **Figure 23**.

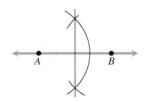

Figure 23

In his first effort as a director, Mel Gibson starred in the 1993 movie *The Man Without a Face.* As disfigured former teacher Justin McLeod, he tutors teenager Chuck Norstadt (portrayed by Nick Stahl). McLeod explains to Norstadt how to find the center of a circle using any three points on the circle as he sketches the diagram on a windowpane. His explanation is based on the fact that the **perpendicular bisector** of any chord of a circle passes through the center of the circle. See the figure.

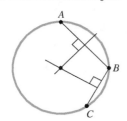

Perpendicular to a Line **Construct a perpendicular from a point off a line to the line.**

1. Let *A* be the point, *r* the line. Place the point of the compass at *A* and draw an arc, cutting *r* in two points.

2. Swing arcs of equal radius from each of the two points on *r* that were constructed in (1). The line drawn through the intersection of the two arcs and point *A* is perpendicular to *r*. See **Figure 24.**

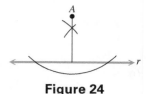

Figure 24

Copied Angle **Copy an angle.**

1. In order to copy an angle *ABC* on line *r*, place the point of the compass at *B* and draw an arc. Then place the point of the compass on *r'* at some point *P* and draw the same arc, as in **Figure 25.**

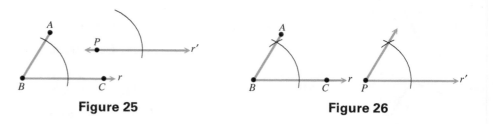

Figure 25   **Figure 26**

2. Measure, with your compass, the distance between the points where the arc intersects the angle, and transfer this distance, as shown in **Figure 26.** Use a straightedge to join *P* to the point of intersection. The angle is now copied.

There are other basic constructions that can be found in books on plane geometry.

9.2   EXERCISES

Fill in each blank with the correct response.

1. A segment joining two points on a circle is called a(n) _____.

2. A segment joining the center of a circle and a point on the circle is called a(n) _____.

3. A regular triangle is called a(n) _____ triangle.

4. A chord that contains the center of a circle is called a(n) _____.

Decide whether each statement is true *or* false.

5. A rhombus is an example of a regular polygon.

6. If a triangle is isosceles, then it is not scalene.

7. A triangle can have more than one obtuse angle.

8. A square is both a rectangle and a parallelogram.

9. A square must be a rhombus.

10. A rhombus must be a square.

11. In your own words, explain the distinction between a chord and a secant.

12. What common traffic sign in the United States is in the shape of an octagon?

Identify each curve as simple, closed, both, *or* neither.

13.   14.

15.   16.

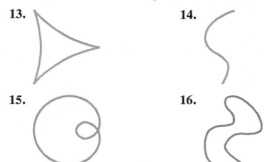

17.

18.

19.

20.

Decide whether each figure is convex *or* not convex.

21.

22.

23.

24.

25.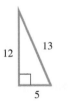

26.

Classify each triangle as acute, right, *or* obtuse. *Also classify each as* equilateral, isosceles, *or* scalene.

27.

28.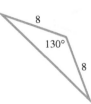

29.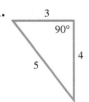

30.

31.

32.

33.

34.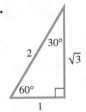

35.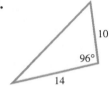

36.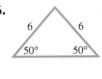

37. Give a definition of *isosceles right triangle.*

38. Can a triangle be both right and obtuse?

Find the measure of each angle in triangle ABC.

39.

40.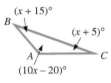

41.

42.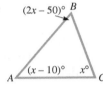

43. *Angle Measures* In triangle ABC, angles A and B have the same measure, while the measure of angle C is 15 degrees larger than the measure of each of A and B. What are the measures of the three angles?

44. *Angle Measures* In triangle ABC, the measure of angle A is 3 degrees more than the measure of angle B. The measure of angle B is the same as the measure of angle C. Find the measure of each angle.

In each triangle, find the measure of exterior angle BCD.

45.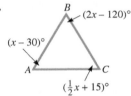

46.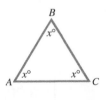

47. Find the sum, in degrees, of the six labeled angles. (*Source: Mathematics Teacher*)

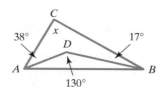

48. In $\triangle ABC$ shown, D is some interior point, and x is the measure of $\angle C$, in degrees. Find x. (*Source: Mathematics Teacher*)

49. Using the points, segments, and lines in the figure, list all parts of the circle.

    (a) center

    (b) radii

    (c) diameters

    (d) chords

    (e) secants

    (f) tangents

50. In the classic 1939 movie *The Wizard of Oz*, the Scarecrow, upon getting a brain, says the following:

> *"The sum of the square roots of any two sides of an isosceles triangle is equal to the square root of the remaining side."*

Give an example to show that his statement is incorrect.

In Exercises 51 and 52, construct the perpendicular bisector of segment PQ.

51.

52. r

In Exercises 53 and 54, construct a perpendicular from P to the line r.

53.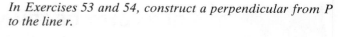

54.

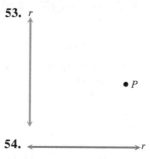

In Exercises 55 and 56, construct a perpendicular through the line r at P.

55.

56. r

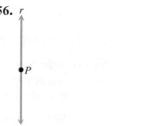

In Exercises 57 and 58, copy the given angle.

57.   **58.**

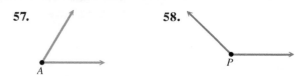

59. Investigate Proposition II of Book I of Euclid's *Elements,* and explain why the construction it provides enables us to use a "fixed" compass without guilt.

60. Use a software program to duplicate any of the constructions in **Exercises 51–58.** Print your results and show your instructor. There are some excellent free programs (www.geogebra.org, for example) available online.

> ## 9.3 THE GEOMETRY OF TRIANGLES: CONGRUENCE, SIMILARITY, AND THE PYTHAGOREAN THEOREM

OBJECTIVES

1 Recognize congruent triangles.

2 Determine similar triangles.

3 Learn and apply the Pythagorean theorem.

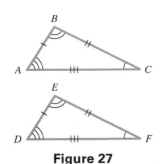

Figure 27

Congruent Triangles

Triangles that are both the same size and the same shape are **congruent triangles.** Informally speaking, if two triangles are congruent, then it is possible to pick up one of them and place it on top of the other so that they coincide exactly. As an everyday example of congruent triangles, consider the triangular supports for a child's swing set, machine-produced with exactly the same dimensions each time.

We use the symbol $\triangle$ to designate triangles. **Figure 27** illustrates two congruent triangles, $\triangle ABC$ and $\triangle DEF$. The symbol $\cong$ denotes congruence, so

$$\triangle ABC \cong \triangle DEF.$$

Notice how the angles and sides are marked to indicate which angles are congruent and which sides are congruent. (Using precise terminology, we refer to angles or sides as being *congruent,* while the *measures* of congruent angles or congruent sides are *equal.* We will often use the terms "equal angles" and "equal sides" to describe angles of equal measure and sides of equal measure.)

In geometry the following properties are used to prove that two triangles are congruent.

CONGRUENCE PROPERTIES

Side-Angle-Side (SAS)   If two sides and the included angle of one triangle are equal, respectively, to two sides and the included angle of a second triangle, then the triangles are congruent.

Angle-Side-Angle (ASA)   If two angles and the included side of one triangle are equal, respectively, to two angles and the included side of a second triangle, then the triangles are congruent.

Side-Side-Side (SSS)   If three sides of one triangle are equal, respectively, to three sides of a second triangle, then the triangles are congruent.

EXAMPLE 1 Proving Congruence

Refer to **Figure 28.**

Given: $CE = ED$

$AE = EB$

Prove: $\triangle ACE \cong \triangle BDE$

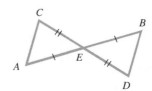

Figure 28

PROOF	STATEMENTS	REASONS
	1. $CE = ED$	1. Given
	2. $AE = EB$	2. Given
	3. $\angle CEA = \angle DEB$	3. Vertical angles are equal.
	4. $\triangle ACE \cong \triangle BDE$	4. SAS congruence property

EXAMPLE 2 **Proving Congruence**

Refer to **Figure 29**.

Given: $\angle ADB = \angle CBD$

$\angle ABD = \angle CDB$

Prove: $\triangle ADB \cong \triangle CBD$

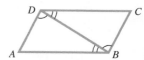

Figure 29

PROOF

STATEMENTS	REASONS
1. $\angle ADB = \angle CBD$	1. Given
2. $\angle ABD = \angle CDB$	2. Given
3. $DB = DB$	3. Reflexive property (a quantity is equal to itself)
4. $\triangle ADB \cong \triangle CBD$	4. ASA congruence property

EXAMPLE 3 **Proving Congruence**

Refer to **Figure 30**.

Given: $AD = CD$

$AB = CB$

Prove: $\triangle ABD \cong \triangle CBD$

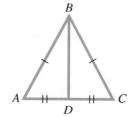

Figure 30

PROOF

STATEMENTS	REASONS
1. $AD = CD$	1. Given
2. $AB = CB$	2. Given
3. $BD = BD$	3. Reflexive property
4. $\triangle ABD \cong \triangle CBD$	4. SSS congruence property

Isosceles triangles (**Example 3** and **Figure 31**) have several important features.

Figure 31

IMPORTANT STATEMENTS ABOUT ISOSCELES TRIANGLES

If $\triangle ABC$ is an isosceles triangle with $AB = CB$, and if D is the midpoint of the base AC (that is, $AD = DC$), then the following properties hold.

1. The base angles A and C are equal.

2. Angles ABD and CBD are equal.

3. Angles ADB and CDB are both right angles.

Similar Triangles

Similar triangles are pairs of triangles that are exactly the same shape but not necessarily the same size. **Figure 32** shows three pairs of similar triangles. (*Note:* The triangles do not need to be oriented in the same fashion in order to be similar.)

Figure 32

Suppose that a correspondence between two triangles ABC and DEF is set up.

$\angle A$ corresponds to $\angle D$ side AB corresponds to side DE

$\angle B$ corresponds to $\angle E$ side BC corresponds to side EF

$\angle C$ corresponds to $\angle F$ side AC corresponds to side DF

For triangle ABC to be similar to triangle DEF, these conditions must hold.

1. Corresponding angles must have the same measure.

2. The ratios of the corresponding sides must be constant. That is, the corresponding sides are proportional.

By showing that either of these conditions holds in a pair of triangles, we may conclude that the triangles are similar.

EXAMPLE 4 Verifying Similarity

In **Figure 33**, $\overleftrightarrow{AB}$ is parallel to $\overleftrightarrow{ED}$. Verify that $\triangle ABC$ is similar to $\triangle EDC$.

Solution

Because $\overleftrightarrow{AB}$ is parallel to $\overleftrightarrow{ED}$, the transversal $\overleftrightarrow{BD}$ forms equal alternate interior angles ABC and EDC. Also, transversal $\overleftrightarrow{AE}$ forms equal alternate interior angles BAC and DEC. We know that $\angle ACB = \angle ECD$, because they are vertical angles. Because the corresponding angles have the same measures in triangles ABC and EDC, the triangles are similar. ∎

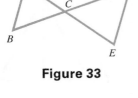

Figure 33

Once we have shown that two angles of one triangle are equal to the two corresponding angles of a second triangle, it is not necessary to show the same for the third angle. In any triangle the sum of the angles equals 180°, so the measures of the remaining angles *must* be equal. This leads to the following property.

ANGLE-ANGLE (AA) SIMILARITY PROPERTY

If the measures of two angles of one triangle are equal to those of two corresponding angles of a second triangle, then the two triangles are similar.

EXAMPLE 5 Finding Side Lengths in Similar Triangles

In **Figure 34**, $\triangle EDF$ is similar to $\triangle CAB$. Find the unknown side lengths in $\triangle EDF$.

Solution

Side DF of the small triangle corresponds to side AB of the larger one, and sides DE and AC correspond. The fact that similar triangles have corresponding sides in proportion leads to the following equation.

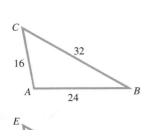

Figure 34

$$\frac{8}{16} = \frac{DF}{24}$$

Using algebra, set the two cross products equal. (As an alternative method of solution, multiply both sides by 48, the least common multiple of 16 and 24.)

$$8(24) = 16DF \quad \text{Cross products are equal.}$$

$$192 = 16DF \quad \text{Multiply.}$$

$$12 = DF \quad \text{Divide by 16.}$$

Side DF has length 12.

Side *EF* corresponds to side *CB*. This leads to another proportion.

$$\frac{8}{16} = \frac{EF}{32}$$

$$\frac{1}{2} = \frac{EF}{32} \quad \tfrac{8}{16} = \tfrac{1}{2}$$

$$EF = 16 \quad \text{Multiply by 32.}$$

Side *EF* has length 16. ■

EXAMPLE 6 Finding Unknown Measures in Similar Triangles

Find the measures of the unknown parts of the similar triangles *STU* and *ZXY* in **Figure 35**.

Solution

Here angles *X* and *T* correspond, as do angles *Y* and *U*, and angles *Z* and *S*. Since angles *Z* and *S* correspond and since angle *S* is 52°, angle *Z* also must be 52°. The sum of the angles of any triangle is 180°. In the larger triangle, *X* = 71° and *Z* = 52°.

$$X + Y + Z = 180 \quad \text{The angle sum is 180°.}$$

$$71 + Y + 52 = 180 \quad \text{Substitute, and solve for } Y.$$

$$123 + Y = 180 \quad \text{Add.}$$

$$Y = 57 \quad \text{Subtract 123.}$$

Angle *Y* measures 57°. Because angles *Y* and *U* correspond, *U* = 57° also.

Now find the unknown sides. Sides *SU* and *ZY* correspond, as do *TS* and *XZ*, and *TU* and *XY*, leading to the following proportions.

$\dfrac{SU}{ZY} = \dfrac{TS}{XZ}$	$\dfrac{XY}{TU} = \dfrac{ZY}{SU}$	Write the proportions.
$\dfrac{48}{144} = \dfrac{TS}{126}$	$\dfrac{XY}{40} = \dfrac{144}{48}$	Substitute.
$\dfrac{1}{3} = \dfrac{TS}{126}$	$\dfrac{XY}{40} = \dfrac{3}{1}$	Lowest terms
$3TS = 126$	$XY = 120$	Cross products are equal.
$TS = 42$		Solve.

Side *TS* has length 42, and side *XY* has length 120. ■

The Pythagorean Theorem

In a right triangle, the side opposite the right angle (the longest side) is the **hypotenuse.** The other two sides, which are perpendicular, are the **legs.**

Figure 35

PYTHAGOREAN THEOREM

If the two legs of a right triangle have lengths *a* and *b*, and the hypotenuse has length *c*, then

$$a^2 + b^2 = c^2.$$

That is, the sum of the squares of the lengths of the legs is equal to the square of the hypotenuse.

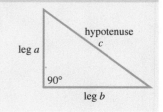

Figure 36

Pythagoras did not actually discover the theorem that was named after him. There is evidence that the Babylonians knew the concept quite well.

Figure 36 illustrates the theorem by using a tile pattern. The side of the square along the hypotenuse measures 5 units. Those along the legs measure 3 and 4 units. If $a = 3$, $b = 4$, and $c = 5$, the equation of the Pythagorean theorem is satisfied.

$$a^2 + b^2 = c^2 \qquad \text{Pythagorean theorem}$$
$$3^2 + 4^2 = 5^2 \qquad \text{Substitute.}$$
$$9 + 16 = 25 \qquad \text{Square.}$$
$$25 = 25 \;\checkmark \qquad \text{Add.}$$

The natural numbers 3, 4, and 5 form the **Pythagorean triple** (3, 4, 5) because they satisfy the equation of the Pythagorean theorem. There are infinitely many such triples.

WHEN Will I Ever USE This ?

Suppose you work for the Department of Forestry and have been called in to cut down a diseased tree at a summer camp. The tree is quite tall and is in an area surrounded by cabins. You measure the distance from the base of the tree to the nearby cabins, and you find that the cabins will be safe if the tree falls within 140 feet of its base.

Is it safe to cut the tree at ground level? If not, how high up the trunk must you cut to guarantee that the tip of the tree will hit the ground within the safe zone?

Assume that the tree stays "hinged" at the location of the cut.

In early afternoon, you find that a 72-inch fence post casts an 18-inch. shadow at the same time the diseased tree casts a 50-foot shadow. See **Figure 37.**

Let y be the height of the tree. Solve the proportion.

$$\frac{y}{50} = \frac{72}{18}$$

$$\frac{y}{50} = 4 \qquad \text{Reduce: } \tfrac{72}{18} = \tfrac{4}{1}.$$

$$y = 200 \qquad \text{Multiply by 50.}$$

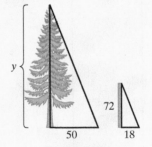

Figure 37

Since the tree is 200 feet tall, you cannot cut it at ground level. Refer to **Figure 38.**

Let z be the height above the ground at which to cut. We can use the Pythagorean theorem to find z.

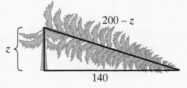

Figure 38

$$z^2 + 140^2 = (200 - z)^2$$

$$z^2 + 19{,}600 = 40{,}000 - 400z + z^2 \qquad \text{FOIL method from \textbf{Chapter 8}}$$

$$19{,}600 = 40{,}000 - 400z \qquad \text{Subtract } z^2.$$

$$400z = 20{,}400 \qquad \text{Add } 400z \text{ and subtract } 19{,}600.$$

$$z = 51 \qquad \text{Divide by 400.}$$

You need to cut the tree 51 feet above the ground.

EXAMPLE 7 Using the Pythagorean Theorem

Find the length a in the right triangle shown in **Figure 39.**

Solution

$$a^2 + b^2 = c^2 \qquad \text{Pythagorean theorem}$$

$$a^2 + 36^2 = 39^2 \qquad b = 36, \, c = 39$$

$$a^2 + 1296 = 1521 \qquad \text{Square.}$$

$$a^2 = 225 \qquad \text{Subtract 1296 from both sides.}$$

$$a = 15 \qquad \text{Choose the positive square root, because } a > 0.$$

Figure 39

Verify that $(15, 36, 39)$ is a Pythagorean triple as a check. ■

The statement of the Pythagorean theorem is an *if . . . then* statement. If the antecedent (the statement following the word "if") and the consequent (the statement following the word "then") are interchanged, the new statement is the *converse* of the original. Although the converse of a true statement may not be true, the *converse* of the Pythagorean theorem *is* also a true statement and can be used to determine whether a triangle is a right triangle, given the lengths of the three sides.

CONVERSE OF THE PYTHAGOREAN THEOREM

If a triangle has sides of lengths a, b, and c, where c is the length of the longest side, and if $a^2 + b^2 = c^2$, then the triangle is a right triangle.

EXAMPLE 8 Applying the Converse of the Pythagorean Theorem

Jonathan has been contracted to complete an unfinished 8-foot-by-12-foot laundry room in an existing house. He finds that the previous contractor built the floor so that the length of its diagonal is 14 feet, 8 inches. Is the floor "squared off" properly?

Solution

Because 14 feet, 8 inches $= 14\frac{2}{3}$ feet, he must check to see whether the following statement is true.

$$8^2 + 12^2 \stackrel{?}{=} \left(14\frac{2}{3}\right)^2 \qquad a^2 + b^2 = c^2$$

$$8^2 + 12^2 \stackrel{?}{=} \left(\frac{44}{3}\right)^2 \qquad 14\frac{2}{3} = \frac{44}{3}$$

$$208 \stackrel{?}{=} \frac{1936}{9} \qquad \text{Simplify.}$$

$$208 \neq 215\frac{1}{9} \qquad \text{The two values are not equal.}$$

He needs to fix the problem, since the diagonal, which measures 14 feet, 8 inches, should actually measure $\sqrt{208} \approx 14.4 \approx 14$ feet, 5 inches. ■

Following **Hurricane Katrina** in August 2005, the pine trees of southeastern Louisiana provided thousands of examples of **right triangles.** See the photo.

Suppose the vertical distance from the base of a broken tree to the point of the break is 55 inches. The length of the broken part is 144 inches. How far along the ground is it from the base of the tree to the point where the broken part touches the ground?

FOR FURTHER THOUGHT

Proving the Pythagorean Theorem

The Pythagorean theorem has probably been proved in more different ways than any theorem in mathematics. A book titled *The Pythagorean Proposition*, by Elisha Scott Loomis, was first published in 1927. It contained more than 250 different proofs of the theorem.

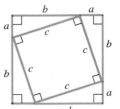

One of the most popular proofs of the theorem follows. This proof requires two formulas for area. The area $\mathcal{A}$ of a square is given by

$$\mathcal{A} = s^2,$$

where s is the length of a side of the square. The area $\mathcal{A}$ of a triangle is given by

$$\mathcal{A} = \frac{1}{2}bh,$$

where b is the base of the triangle and h is the height corresponding to that base.

For Group or Individual Investigation

In the figure given in the next column, the area of the large square must always be the same.

It is made up of four right triangles and a smaller square.

(a) The length of a side of the large square is _____, so its area is (_____)^2, or _____.

(b) The area of the large square can also be found by obtaining the sum of the areas of the four right triangles and the smaller square. The area of each right triangle is _____, so the sum of the areas of the four right triangles is _____. The area of the smaller square is _____.

(c) The sum of the areas of the four right triangles and the smaller square is _____.

(d) Since the areas in (a) and (c) represent the area of the same figure, the expressions there must be equal. Setting them equal to each other, we obtain

_____ = _____.

(e) Subtract $2ab$ from each side of the equation in (d) to obtain the desired result:

_____ = _____.

9.3   EXERCISES

*In Exercises 1–6, provide a STATEMENTS/REASONS proof similar to the ones in **Examples 1–3.***

1. Given: $AC = BD$; $AD = BC$
Prove: $\triangle ABD \cong \triangle BAC$

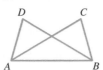

2. Given: $AC = BC$; D is the midpoint of AB.
Prove: $\triangle ADC \cong \triangle BDC$

3. Given: $\measuredangle BAC = \measuredangle DAC$; $\measuredangle BCA = \measuredangle DCA$
Prove: $\triangle ABC \cong \triangle ADC$.

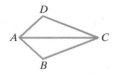

4. Given: $BC = BA$; $\measuredangle 1 = \measuredangle 2$
Prove: $\triangle DBC \cong \triangle DBA$

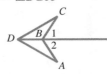

5. Given: $\overleftrightarrow{DB}$ is perpendicular to $\overleftrightarrow{AC}$; $AB = BC$
Prove: $\triangle ABD \cong \triangle CBD$

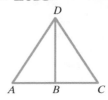

6. Given: $BO = OE$; $\overleftrightarrow{OB}$ is perpendicular to $\overleftrightarrow{AC}$; $\overleftrightarrow{OE}$ is perpendicular to $\overleftrightarrow{DF}$
Prove: $\triangle AOB \cong \triangle FOE$.

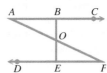

Exercises 7–10 refer to the given figure, which includes an isosceles triangle with AB = BC.

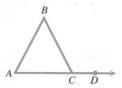

7. What is the measure of ∡BCD if ∡B measures 40°?

8. If ∡C measures 52°, what is the measure of ∡B ?

9. If ∡B measures 46°, then ∡A measures _____ and ∡C measures _____.

10. What is the measure of ∡B if ∡BCD measures 100°?

Write a short explanation for each of the following.

11. Explain why all equilateral triangles must be similar.

12. Explain how this figure demonstrates why the Congruence Properties just before **Example 1** did *not* include a Side-Side-Angle (SSA) property.

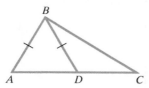

Name the corresponding angles and the corresponding sides for each of the following pairs of similar triangles.

13.

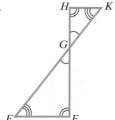

14.

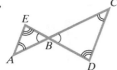

15.

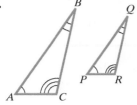

16.

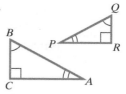

Find all unknown angle measures in each pair of similar triangles.

17.

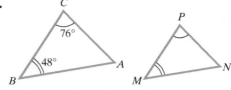

18.   **19.**

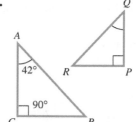   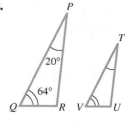

20.   **21.**

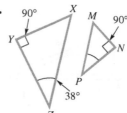   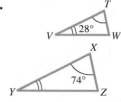

22.

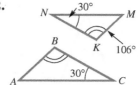

Find the unknown side lengths in each pair of similar triangles.

23.   **24.**

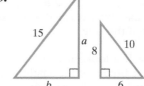   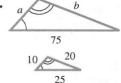

25.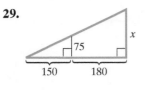

26.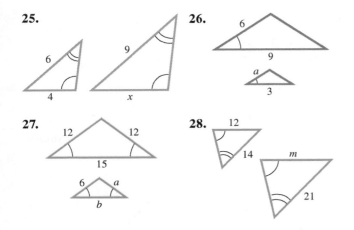

27.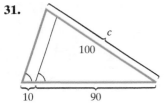

28.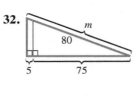

In each diagram, there are two similar triangles. Find the unknown measurement in each. (Hint: In the figure for Exercise 29, the side of length 150 in the smaller triangle corresponds to a side of length

$$150 + 180 = 330$$

in the larger triangle.)

29.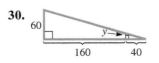

30.

31.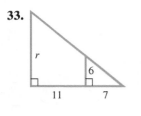

32.

33.

34.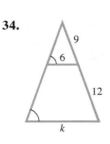

Solve each problem.

35. *Height of a Tree*   A tree casts a shadow 45 m long. At the same time, the shadow cast by a vertical 4-m stick is 3 m long. Find the height of the tree.

36. *Height of a Tower*   A forest fire lookout tower casts a shadow 80 ft long at the same time that the shadow of a 9-ft truck is 5 ft long. Find the height of the tower.

37. *Lengths of Sides of a Photograph*   On a photograph of a triangular piece of land, the lengths of the three sides are 4 cm, 5 cm, and 7 cm, respectively. The shortest side of the actual piece of land is 200 m long. Find the lengths of the other two sides.

38. *Height of a Lighthouse Keeper*   The Santa Cruz lighthouse is 14 m tall and casts a shadow 28 m long at 7 P.M. At the same time, the shadow of the lighthouse keeper is 3.5 m long. How tall is she?

39. *Height of a Building*   A house is 15 ft tall. Its shadow is 40 ft long at the same time the shadow of a nearby building is 300 ft long. Find the height of the building.

40. *Height of the World's Tallest Human*   Robert Wadlow was the tallest human being ever recorded. When a 6-ft stick cast a shadow 24 in., Robert would cast a shadow 35.7 in. How tall was he?

When proportional relationships are expressed graphically, similar triangles result. In Exercises 41 and 42, use similar triangles to answer the question.

41. *Feeding an Army*   A cake recipe that serves 6 calls for $1\frac{1}{2}$ cups of flour. How many cups of flour will be needed if the chef must serve 40 people?

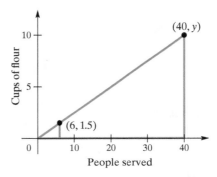

42. *How Much Herbicide?*   A landscape maintenance service is spraying for weed control. Eight ounces of the chemical being used treats 500 square feet of lawn. How many ounces of the chemical will be needed for treating 3250 square feet of lawn?

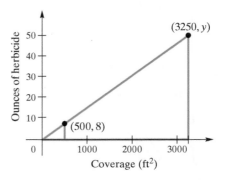

In Exercises 43–50, a and b represent the two legs of a right triangle, and c represents the hypotenuse. Find the lengths of the unknown sides.

43.
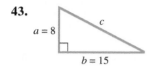
$a = 8$, c, $b = 15$

44.
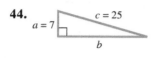
$a = 7$, $c = 25$, b

45. a, $c = 85$, $b = 84$

46. $a = 11$, $c = 61$, b

47. $a = 14$ m; $b = 48$ m

48. $a = 28$ km; $c = 100$ km

49. $b = 21$ in.; $c = 29$ in.

50. $b = 120$ ft; $c = 169$ ft

51. Refer to **Exercise 50** in **Section 9.2.** Correct the Scarecrow's statement, using language similar to his.

52. Show that if $a^2 + b^2 = c^2$, then it is not necessarily true that $a + b = c$.

There are various formulas that will generate Pythagorean triples. For example, if we choose positive integers r and s, with r > s, then the set of equations

$$a = r^2 - s^2, \quad b = 2rs, \quad c = r^2 + s^2$$

generates a Pythagorean triple (a, b, c). Use the values of r and s given in each of Exercises 53–56 to generate a Pythagorean triple using this method.

53. $r = 2, s = 1$

54. $r = 3, s = 2$

55. $r = 4, s = 3$

56. $r = 4, s = 2$

57. Show that the formula given for **Exercises 53–56** actually satisfies $a^2 + b^2 = c^2$.

58. It can be shown that if $(x, x + 1, y)$ is a Pythagorean triple, then so is

$$(3x + 2y + 1, \quad 3x + 2y + 2, \quad 4x + 3y + 2).$$

Use this idea to find three more Pythagorean triples, starting with $(3, 4, 5)$. *(Hint:* Here, $x = 3$ and $y = 5$.)

If m is an odd positive integer greater than 1, then

$$\left(m, \frac{m^2 - 1}{2}, \frac{m^2 + 1}{2} \right)$$

is a Pythagorean triple. Use this to find the Pythagorean triple generated by each value of m in Exercises 59–62.

59. $m = 3$

60. $m = 5$

61. $m = 7$

62. $m = 9$

63. Show that the expressions in the directions for **Exercises 59–62** actually satisfy $a^2 + b^2 = c^2$.

64. Show why $(6, 8, 10)$ is the only Pythagorean triple consisting of consecutive even numbers.

For any integer n greater than 1,

$$(2n, \ n^2 - 1, \ n^2 + 1)$$

is a Pythagorean triple. Use this pattern to find the Pythagorean triple generated by each value of n in Exercises 65–68.

65. $n = 2$

66. $n = 3$

67. $n = 4$

68. $n = 5$

69. Show that the expressions in the directions for **Exercises 65–68** actually satisfy $a^2 + b^2 = c^2$.

70. Can an isosceles right triangle have sides with integer lengths? Why or why not?

Solve each problem. (You may wish to review quadratic equations from algebra.)

71. *Side Length of a Triangle*   The hypotenuse of a right triangle is 1 m more than the longer leg, and the shorter leg is 7 m. Find the length of the longer leg.

72. *Side Lengths of a Triangle*   The hypotenuse of a right triangle is 3 cm more than twice the shorter leg, and the longer leg is 3 cm less than three times the shorter leg. Find the lengths of the three sides of the triangle.

73. *Height of a Tree*   At a point on the ground 24 ft from the base of a tree, the distance to the top of the tree is 6 ft less than twice the height of the tree. Find the height of the tree.

74. *Dimensions of a Rectangle*   The length of a rectangle is 2 in. less than twice the width. The diagonal is 5 in. Find the length and width of the rectangle.

75. *Height of a Break in Bamboo*   (Problem of the broken bamboo, from the Chinese work *Arithmetic in Nine Sections*, 1261) There is a bamboo 10 ft high, the upper end of which, being broken, reaches the ground 3 ft from the stem. Find the height of the break.

76. Depth of a Pond (Adapted from *Arithmetic in Nine Sections*) There grows in the middle of a circular pond 10 ft in diameter a reed that projects 1 ft out of the water. When it is drawn down, it just reaches the edge of the pond. How deep is the water?

Squaring Off a Floor under Construction *Imagine that you are a carpenter building the floor of a rectangular room. What must the diagonal of the room measure if your floor is to be squared off properly, given the dimensions in Exercises 77–80? Give your answer to the nearest inch.*

77. 12 ft by 15 ft   **78.** 14 ft by 20 ft

79. 16 ft by 24 ft   **80.** 20 ft by 32 ft

81. Proof of the Pythagorean Theorem by Similar Triangles In the figure, right triangles ABC, CBD, and ACD are similar. This may be used to prove the Pythagorean theorem. Fill in the blanks with the appropriate responses.

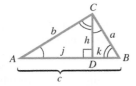

(a) By proportion, we have $\frac{c}{b} =$ ____ /j.

(b) By proportion, we also have $\frac{c}{a} = a/$____.

(c) From part (a), $b^2 =$ ____.

(d) From part (b), $a^2 =$ ____.

(e) From the results of parts (c) and (d) and factoring, $a^2 + b^2 = c($____$)$. Since ____ $= c$, it follows that _____.

82. Animated Proof of the Pythagorean Theorem Go to

  www.davis-inc.com/pythagor/proof2.html

to view an animation that provides a proof of the Pythagorean theorem.

Exercises 83–90 require ingenuity, but all can be solved using the concepts presented so far in this chapter.*

83. Value of a Measure in a Triangle
In right triangle ABC, if

$$AD = DB + 8,$$

what is the value of CD?

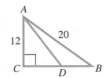

84. Angle Measure in a Triangle (A segment that *bisects* an angle divides the angle into two equal angles.) In the figure, angle A measures $50°$. OB bisects angle ABC, and OC bisects angle ACB. What is the measure of angle BOC?

85. Unknown Length In triangle VWZ, point X lies on $\overleftrightarrow{VZ}$ and point Y lies on $\overleftrightarrow{WZ}$ with $\overleftrightarrow{XY}$ parallel to $\overleftrightarrow{VW}$. If $VZ = 10$, $XZ = 8$, and $WY = 4$, find the length ZY.

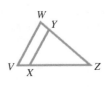

86. Unknown Length In right triangle ABC with right angle C, $BC = 4$ ft and $AC = 3$ ft. Point R is on $\overleftrightarrow{BC}$, equidistant from A and B. Find the length CR.

87. Unknown Angle Measure In the figure, $\triangle ABC$ has a right angle at B and $\angle A = 20°$. If CD is the bisector of $\angle ACB$, find $\angle CDB$.

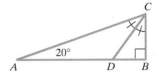

88. Unknown Length Triangle CDE is equilateral with $DE = 60$ units. A is the foot of the perpendicular from D to $\overleftrightarrow{CE}$, and B is the midpoint of $\overleftrightarrow{DA}$. Find the length CB.

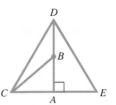

89. Unknown Angle Sum The three squares shown in the figure each share a side of $\triangle ABC$. Find the sum

$$\angle EAF + \angle DCJ + \angle GBH.$$

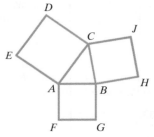

90. Unknown Length In the right triangle ACD with right angle C,

$$AB + AD = BC + DC.$$

If $BC = 8$ and $DC = 10$, find the length AB.

*In Exercises 91–93, verify that the following constructions from **Section 9.2** are valid. Use a STATEMENTS/ REASONS proof.*

91. Perpendicular Bisector

92. Perpendicular to a Line

93. Copied Angle

94. Given a line m and a point A on m, construct a line perpendicular to m through A. Prove that your construction is valid.

---

*These and other, similar problems in this chapter have been adapted from Mathematics Teacher *calendar problems.*

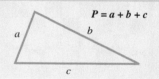

9.4 PERIMETER, AREA, AND CIRCUMFERENCE

OBJECTIVES

1 Determine the perimeter of a polygon.

2 Determine the areas of polygons and circles.

3 Determine the circumference of a circle.

Perimeter of a Polygon

When working with a polygon, we are sometimes required to find its "distance around," or *perimeter*.

PERIMETER

The **perimeter** of any polygon is the sum of the measures of the line segments that form its sides. Perimeter is measured in *linear units*.

The simplest polygon is a triangle. If a triangle has sides of lengths a, b, and c, then to find its perimeter we simply find the sum of a, b, and c, as shown below.

PERIMETER OF A TRIANGLE

The perimeter P of a triangle with sides of lengths a, b, and c is given by the following formula.

$$P = a + b + c$$

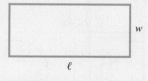

Because a rectangle is made up of two pairs of sides with the two sides in each pair equal in length, the formula for the perimeter of a rectangle may be stated as follows.

PERIMETER OF A RECTANGLE

The perimeter P of a rectangle with length ℓ and width w is given by the following formula.

$$P = 2\ell + 2w, \quad \text{or, equivalently,} \quad P = 2(\ell + w)$$

$P = 2\ell + 2w$, or $P = 2(\ell + w)$

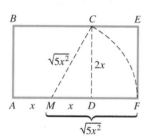

To construct a **golden rectangle,** one in which the ratio of the length to the width is equal to the ratio of the length plus the width to the length, begin with a square $ABCD$. With the point of the compass at M, the midpoint of $\overset{\bullet\bullet}{AD}$, swing an arc of radius $\overset{\bullet\bullet}{MC}$ to intersect the extension of $\overset{\bullet\bullet}{AD}$ at F. Construct a perpendicular at F, and have it intersect the extension of $\overset{\bullet\bullet}{BC}$ at E. $ABEF$ is a golden rectangle with ratio $(1 + \sqrt{5})/2$. (See **Section 5.5** for more on the golden ratio.)

To verify this construction, let $AM = x$, so that $AD = CD = 2x$. Then, by the Pythagorean theorem,

$$MC = \sqrt{x^2 + (2x)^2} = \sqrt{x^2 + 4x^2}$$
$$= \sqrt{5x^2} = x\sqrt{5}.$$

Because CF is an arc of the circle with radius MC, $MF = MC = x\sqrt{5}$. Then the ratio of length AF to width EF is

$$\frac{AF}{EF} = \frac{x + x\sqrt{5}}{2x}$$

$$= \frac{x(1 + \sqrt{5})}{2x}$$

$$= \frac{1 + \sqrt{5}}{2}.$$

Similarly, it can be shown that

$$\frac{AF + EF}{AF} = \frac{1 + \sqrt{5}}{2}.$$

EXAMPLE 1 **Using Perimeter to Determine Amount of Fencing**

A plot of land is in the shape of a rectangle. If it has length 50 feet and width 26 feet, how much fencing would be needed to completely enclose the plot?

Solution

We must find the distance around the plot of land.

$$P = 2\ell + 2w \qquad \text{Perimeter formula}$$
$$P = 2(50) + 2(26) \qquad \ell = 50, \; w = 26$$
$$P = 100 + 52 \qquad \text{Multiply.}$$
$$P = 152 \qquad \text{Add.}$$

The perimeter is 152 feet, so 152 feet of fencing is required. ∎

A square is a rectangle with four sides of equal length. The formula for the perimeter of a square is a special case of the formula for the perimeter of a rectangle.

PERIMETER OF A SQUARE

The perimeter P of a square with all sides of length s is given by the following formula.

$$P = 4s$$

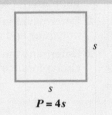

s

s

$P = 4s$

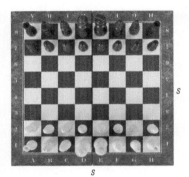

s

s

Figure 40

EXAMPLE 2 Using the Formula for Perimeter of a Square

A square chess board has perimeter 34 inches. See **Figure 40.** What is the length of each side?

Solution

$$P = 4s \qquad \text{Perimeter formula}$$
$$34 = 4s \qquad P = 34$$
$$s = 8.5 \qquad \text{Divide by 4.}$$

Each side has a measure of 8.5 inches. ∎

EXAMPLE 3 Finding Length and Width of a Rectangle

The length of a basketball court is 6 feet less than twice the width. The perimeter is 288 feet. Find the length and width.

Solution

Step 1 **Read the problem.** We must find the length and width.

Step 2 **Assign a variable.** Let w represent the width. Then $2w - 6$ can represent the length, because the length is 6 less than twice the width. **Figure 41** shows a diagram of the basketball court.

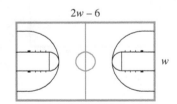

$2w - 6$

w

Figure 41

Step 3 **Write an equation.** In the formula $P = 2\ell + 2w$, replace ℓ with $2w - 6$, and replace P with 288, because the perimeter is 288 feet.

$$288 = 2(2w - 6) + 2w$$

Step 4 **Solve the equation.**

$$288 = 2(2w - 6) + 2w$$
$$288 = 4w - 12 + 2w \qquad \text{Distributive property}$$
$$288 = 6w - 12 \qquad \text{Combine like terms.}$$
$$300 = 6w \qquad \text{Add 12.}$$
$$50 = w \qquad \text{Divide by 6.}$$

Step 5 **State the answer.** Because $w = 50$, the width is 50 feet and the length is $2w - 6 = 2(50) - 6 = 94$ feet.

Step 6 **Check.** Because 94 is 6 less than twice 50, and because the perimeter is $2(94) + 2(50) = 288$, the answer is correct. ∎

> **Problem-Solving Strategy**
>
> The six-step method of solving an applied problem from **Section 7.2** can be used to solve problems involving geometric figures, as shown in **Example 3.**

Area of a Polygon

> **AREA**
>
> The amount of plane surface covered by a polygon is its **area.** Area is measured in *square units.*

Metric units will be used extensively in this chapter. Help with the **metric system,** including unit conversion, is available in MyMathLab or at www.pearsonhighered.com/mathstatsresources.

Defining the **area** of a figure requires a basic *unit of area.* One that is commonly used is the *square centimeter,* abbreviated cm^2. One square centimeter, or $1\ cm^2$, is the area of a square one centimeter on a side. In place of $1\ cm^2$, the basic unit of area could be $1\ in.^2$, $1\ ft^2$, $1\ m^2$, or any appropriate unit.

As an example, we calculate the area of the rectangle shown in **Figure 42(a).** Using the basic 1-cm^2 unit, **Figure 42(b)** shows that four squares, each 1 cm on a side, can be laid off horizontally while six such squares can be laid off vertically. A total of $4 \cdot 6 = 24$ of the small squares are needed to cover the large rectangle. Thus, the area of the large rectangle is $24\ cm^2$.

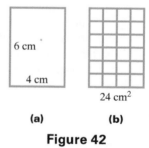

(a)　　　**(b)**

Figure 42

We generalize to obtain a formula for the area of a rectangle.

> **AREA OF A RECTANGLE**
>
> The area $\mathcal{A}$ of a rectangle with length ℓ and width w is given by the following formula.
>
> $$\mathcal{A} = \ell w$$
>
>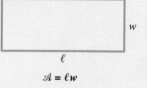

The formula for the area of a rectangle $\mathcal{A} = \ell w$ can be used to find formulas for the areas of other figures.

> **AREA OF A SQUARE**
>
> The area $\mathcal{A}$ of a square with all sides of length s is given by the following formula.
>
> $$\mathcal{A} = s^2$$
>
>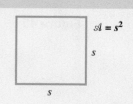

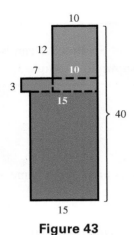

Figure 43

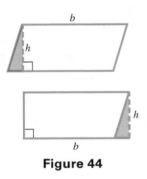

Figure 44

EXAMPLE 4 Using Area to Determine Amount of Carpet

Figure 43 shows the floor plan of a building, made up of various rectangles. If each length given is in meters, how many square meters of carpet would be required to carpet the building?

Solution

The dashed lines in the figure break up the floor area into rectangles. The areas of the various rectangles that result are as follows.

$$10 \text{ m} \cdot 12 \text{ m} = 120 \text{ m}^2, \qquad 3 \text{ m} \cdot 10 \text{ m} = 30 \text{ m}^2,$$

$$3 \text{ m} \cdot 7 \text{ m} = 21 \text{ m}^2, \qquad 15 \text{ m} \cdot 25 \text{ m} = 375 \text{ m}^2$$

$$40 - 12 - 3 = 25$$

$$(120 + 30 + 21 + 375) \text{ m}^2 = 546 \text{ m}^2$$

The amount of carpet needed is 546 m². ∎

A **parallelogram** is a four-sided figure with both pairs of opposite sides parallel. Because a parallelogram need not be a rectangle, the formula for the area of a rectangle cannot be used directly for a parallelogram. However, this formula can be used indirectly, as shown in **Figure 44.** Cut off the triangle in color, and slide it to the right end. The resulting figure is a rectangle with the same area as the original parallelogram.

The *height* of the parallelogram is the perpendicular distance between the top and bottom and is denoted by h in the figure. The width of the rectangle equals the height of the parallelogram, and the length of the rectangle is the base b of the parallelogram, so

$$\mathcal{A} = \text{length} \cdot \text{width} \quad \text{becomes} \quad \mathcal{A} = \text{base} \cdot \text{height}.$$

AREA OF A PARALLELOGRAM

The area $\mathcal{A}$ of a parallelogram with height h and base b is given by the following formula.

$$\mathcal{A} = bh$$

(*Note:* h represents the length of the perpendicular between the parallel sides. If the parallelogram is not a rectangle, then h is not the length of a side.)

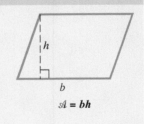

$\mathcal{A} = bh$

---

6 cm

15 cm

Figure 45

EXAMPLE 5 Using the Formula for Area of a Parallelogram

Find the area of the parallelogram in **Figure 45.**

Solution

$$\mathcal{A} = bh \qquad \text{Area formula}$$

$$= 15 \text{ cm} \cdot 6 \text{ cm} \qquad b = 15 \text{ cm}, \ h = 6 \text{ cm}$$

$$= 90 \text{ cm}^2 \qquad \text{Multiply.}$$

The area of the parallelogram is 90 cm². ∎

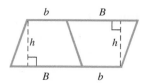

Figure 46

Figure 46 shows how we can find a formula for the area of a trapezoid. Notice that the figure as a whole is a parallelogram. It is made up of two trapezoids, each having height h, shorter base b, and longer base B. The area of the parallelogram is found by multiplying the height h by the base of the parallelogram, $b + B$—that is, $h(b + B)$. Because the area of the parallelogram is twice the area of each trapezoid, the area of each trapezoid is *half* the area of the parallelogram.

AREA OF A TRAPEZOID

The area $\mathcal{A}$ of a trapezoid with parallel bases b and B and height h is given by the following formula.

$$\mathcal{A} = \frac{1}{2}h(b + B)$$

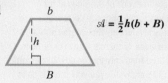

$\mathcal{A} = \frac{1}{2}h(b + B)$

EXAMPLE 6 **Using the Formula for Area of a Trapezoid**

Find the area of the trapezoid in **Figure 47.**

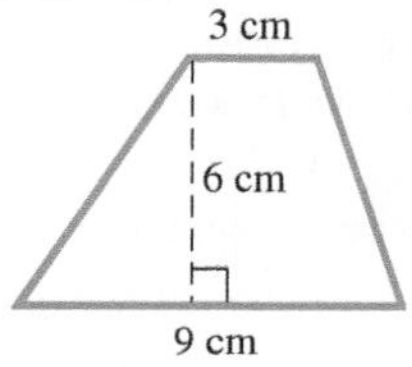

Solution

$$\mathcal{A} = \frac{1}{2}h(B + b) \qquad \text{Area formula}$$

$$= \frac{1}{2}(6 \text{ cm})(9 \text{ cm} + 3 \text{ cm}) \qquad h = 6 \text{ cm}, B = 9 \text{ cm}, b = 3 \text{ cm}$$

$$= \frac{1}{2}(6 \text{ cm})(12 \text{ cm}) \qquad \text{Add.}$$

$$= 36 \text{ cm}^2 \qquad \text{Multiply.}$$

The area of the trapezoid is 36 cm². ∎

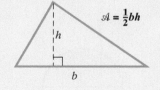

Figure 47

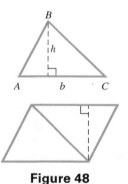

Figure 48

The formula for the area of a triangle can be found from the formula for the area of a parallelogram. In **Figure 48,** the triangle with vertices A, B, and C has been combined with another copy of itself, rotated 180° about the midpoint of $\overleftrightarrow{BC}$, to form a parallelogram. The area of this parallelogram is

$$\mathcal{A} = \text{base} \cdot \text{height}, \quad \text{or} \quad \mathcal{A} = bh.$$

However, the parallelogram has *twice* the area of the triangle, so the area of the triangle is *half* the area of the parallelogram.

AREA OF A TRIANGLE

The area $\mathcal{A}$ of a triangle with height h and base b is given by the following formula.

$$\mathcal{A} = \frac{1}{2}bh$$

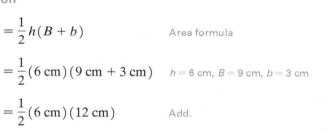

$\mathcal{A} = \frac{1}{2}bh$

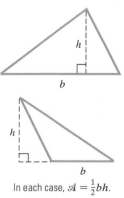

In each case, $\mathcal{A} = \frac{1}{2}bh$.

Figure 49

When applying the formula for the area of a triangle, remember that the height is the perpendicular distance between a vertex and the opposite side (or the extension of that side). See **Figure 49.**

To use the formula for the area of a triangle, $\mathcal{A} = \frac{1}{2}bh$, we must know the height from one of the sides of the triangle to the opposite vertex. Suppose that we know only the lengths of the three sides. Is there a way to determine the area from only this given information?

The answer is yes, and it leads us to the formula known as **Heron's formula.** Heron of Alexandria lived during the second half of the first century A.D., and although the formula is named after him, there is evidence that it was known to Archimedes several centuries earlier.

Let a, b, and c be lengths of the sides of any triangle. Let

$$s = \tfrac{1}{2}(a + b + c)$$

represent the **semiperimeter.** Then the area $\mathcal{A}$ of the triangle is given by the formula

$$\mathcal{A} = \sqrt{s(s - a)(s - b)(s - c)}.$$

The Vietnam Veterans Memorial in Washington, D.C., is in the shape of an unenclosed isosceles triangle. The walls form a "V-shape," and each wall measures 246.75 feet. The distance between the ends of the walls is 438.14 feet. Use Heron's formula to show that the area enclosed by the triangular shape is approximately 24,900 ft².

EXAMPLE 7 Finding the Height of a Triangular Sail

The area of a triangular sail of a sailboat is 126 ft². The base of the sail is 12 ft. Find the height of the sail.

Solution

Step 1 **Read the problem.** We must find the height of the triangular sail.

Step 2 **Assign a variable.** Let $h =$ the height of the sail in feet. See **Figure 50**.

Step 3 **Write an equation.** Using the information given in the problem, we substitute 126 ft² for $\mathcal{A}$ and 12 ft for b in the formula for the area of a triangle.

$$\mathcal{A} = \frac{1}{2}bh \qquad \text{Area formula}$$

$$126 \text{ ft}^2 = \frac{1}{2}(12 \text{ ft})h \qquad \mathcal{A} = 126 \text{ ft}^2,\ b = 12 \text{ ft}$$

Step 4 **Solve.** $\qquad 126 \text{ ft}^2 = 6h \text{ ft} \qquad \text{Multiply.}$

$\qquad\qquad\qquad\qquad 21 \text{ ft} = h \qquad \text{Divide by 6 ft.}$

Step 5 **State the answer.** The height of the sail is 21 ft.

Step 6 **Check** to see that the values $\mathcal{A} = 126$ ft², $b = 12$ ft, and $h = 21$ ft satisfy the formula for the area of a triangle. ∎

Figure 50

Circumference of a Circle

The distance around a circle is its **circumference** (rather than its perimeter). To understand the formula for the circumference of a circle, use a piece of string to measure the distance around a circular object. Then find the object's diameter and divide the circumference by the diameter. The quotient is the same, no matter what the size of the circular object is, and it will be an approximation for the number π.

$$\pi = \frac{\text{circumference}}{\text{diameter}} = \frac{C}{d}, \quad \text{or, alternatively,} \quad C = \pi d$$

Recall that π is not a rational number. **Figure 51** shows that it takes slightly more than three (about 3.14) diameters to make the circumference. In this chapter we will use 3.14 as an approximation for π when one is required.

Figure 51

CIRCUMFERENCE OF A CIRCLE

The circumference C of a circle of diameter d is given by the following formula.

$$C = \pi d$$

Also, since $d = 2r$, the circumference C of a circle of radius r is given by the following formula.

$$C = 2\pi r$$

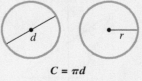

$C = \pi d$

$C = 2\pi r$

On March 8, 2014, Malaysia Airlines Flight 370 (a Boeing 777) disappeared while en route from Malaysia to China. Officials estimated that the plane had about a half-hour of fuel left when satellites received last contact over the Indian Ocean.

If a Boeing 777 can fly 950 km/hr at top speed, and if the plane's flight direction was unknown after its last known location, approximately how large an area should be searched? The answer can be found on the next page.

EXAMPLE 8 Finding the Circumference of a Circle

Find the circumference of each circle described. Use $\pi \approx 3.14$.

(a) A circle with diameter 12.6 centimeters

(b) A circle with radius 1.70 meters

Solution

(a)

$$C = \pi d \qquad \text{Circumference formula}$$

$$\approx (3.14)(12.6 \text{ cm}) \qquad \pi \approx 3.14, d = 12.6 \text{ cm}$$

$$= 39.6 \text{ cm} \qquad \text{Multiply.}$$

The circumference is about 39.6 centimeters, rounded to the nearest tenth.

(b)

$$C = 2\pi r \qquad \text{Circumference formula}$$

$$\approx 2(3.14)(1.70 \text{ m}) \qquad \pi \approx 3.14, r = 1.70 \text{ m}$$

$$= 10.7 \text{ m} \qquad \text{Multiply.}$$

The circumference is approximately 10.7 meters. ∎

Area of a Circle

Start with a circle as shown in **Figure 52(a)**, divided into many equal pie-shaped pieces **(sectors)**. Rearrange the pieces into an approximate rectangle as shown in **Figure 52(b)**. The circle has circumference $2\pi r$, so the "length" of the approximate rectangle is one-half of the circumference, or $\frac{1}{2}(2\pi r) = \pi r$, while its "width" is r. The area of the approximate rectangle is length times width, or $(\pi r)r = \pi r^2$. As we choose smaller and smaller sectors, the figure becomes closer and closer to a rectangle, so its area becomes closer and closer to πr^2.

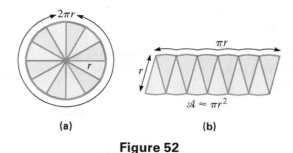

(a)   (b)

Figure 52

AREA OF A CIRCLE

The area $\mathcal{A}$ of a circle with radius r is given by the following formula.

$$\mathcal{A} = \pi r^2$$

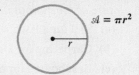

$\mathcal{A} = \pi r^2$

Problem-Solving Strategy

The formula for the area of a circle can be used to determine the best value for your money the next time you purchase a pizza. The next example uses the idea of unit pricing.

EXAMPLE 9 Using Area to Determine Better Value for Pizza

Paw-Paw Johnny's delivers pizza. The price of an 8-inch-diameter pizza is $6.99, and the price of a 16-inch-diameter pizza is $13.98. Which is the better buy?

Solution

To determine which pizza is the better value for the money, we must first find the area of each, and divide the price by the area to determine the price per square inch.

8-inch-diameter pizza area $= \pi(4 \text{ in.})^2 \approx 50.2 \text{ in.}^2$ Radius is $\frac{1}{2}(8 \text{ in.}) = 4 \text{ in.}$

16-inch-diameter pizza area $= \pi(8 \text{ in.})^2 \approx 201 \text{ in.}^2$ Radius is $\frac{1}{2}(16 \text{ in.}) = 8 \text{ in.}$

The price per square inch for the 8-inch pizza is

$$\frac{\$6.99}{50.2} \approx 13.9\,\cent,$$

and the price per square inch for the 16-inch pizza is

$$\frac{\$13.98}{201} \approx 7.0\,\cent.$$

Therefore, the 16-inch pizza is the better buy, since it costs approximately half as much per square inch. ∎

Solution to Margin Note problem

If the plane travels at full speed of 950 km/hr for half an hour in an unknown direction, then the search area would be a circle centered at the last known location with a radius of

$$r = \frac{950}{2} = 475 \text{ km}.$$

The area of this circle would be

$$\mathcal{A} = \pi(475 \text{ km})^2$$
$$\approx 710{,}000 \text{ km}^2.$$

9.4   EXERCISES

In Exercises 1–5, fill in each blank with the correct response.

1. The perimeter of an equilateral triangle with side length equal to ____ inches is the same as the perimeter of a rectangle with length 20 inches and width 16 inches.

2. A square with area 49 cm² has perimeter ____ cm.

3. If the area of a certain triangle is 40 square inches, and the base measures 8 inches, then the height must measure ____ inches.

4. If the radius of a circle is tripled, then its area is multiplied by a factor of ____.

5. Circumference is to a circle as _____ is to a polygon.

6. **Perimeter or Area?** *Decide whether perimeter or area would be used to solve a problem concerning the measure of the quantity.*

   (a) Sod for a lawn

   (b) Carpeting for a bedroom

   (c) Baseboards for a living room

   (d) Fencing for a yard

   (e) Fertilizer for a garden

   (f) Tile for a bathroom

   (g) Determining the cost of planting rye grass in a lawn for the winter

   (h) Determining the cost of replacing a linoleum floor with a wood floor

Use the formulas of this section to find the area of each figure. In Exercises 17–20, use 3.14 as an approximation for π, and in Exercises 18–20 round to the nearest unit.

7.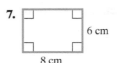
6 cm
8 cm

8.
4 cm
4 cm

9.
3 cm
$3\frac{1}{3}$ cm

10.
3 cm
1 cm

11.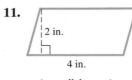
2 in.
4 in.
(a parallelogram)

12.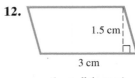
1.5 cm
3 cm
(a parallelogram)

13.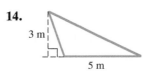
38 mm
22 mm

14.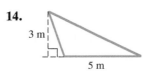
3 m
5 m

15.

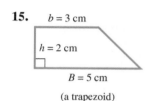

b = 3 cm
h = 2 cm
B = 5 cm
(a trapezoid)

16.

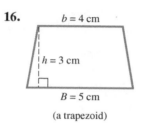

b = 4 cm
h = 3 cm
B = 5 cm
(a trapezoid)

17.

1 cm
O

18.

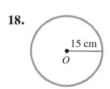

15 cm
O

19.

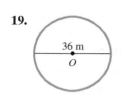

36 m
O

20.

12 m
O

Solve each problem.

21. Window Side Length A stained-glass window in a church is in the shape of a rhombus. The perimeter of the rhombus is 7 times the length of a side in meters, decreased by 12. Find the length of a side of the window.

22. Dimensions of a Rectangle A video rental machine has a rectangular display beside it advertising several movies inside. The display's length is 18 in. more than the width, and the perimeter is 180 in. What are the dimensions of the display?

23. Dimensions of a Lot A lot is in the shape of a triangle. One side is 100 ft longer than the shortest side, while the third side is 200 ft longer than the shortest side. The perimeter of the lot is 1200 ft. Find the lengths of the sides of the lot.

24. Pennant Side Lengths A wall pennant is in the shape of an isosceles triangle. Each of the two equal sides measures 18 in. more than the third side, and the perimeter of the triangle is 54 in. What are the lengths of the sides of the pennant?

25. Radius of a Circular Foundation A hotel is in the shape of a cylinder, with a circular foundation. The circumference of the foundation is 6 times the radius, increased by 14 ft. Find the radius of the circular foundation. (Use 3.14 as an approximation for π.)

26. Radius of a Circle If the radius of a certain circle is tripled, with 8.2 cm then added, the result is the circumference of the circle. Find the radius of the circle. (Use 3.14 as an approximation for π.)

27. Area of Two Lots The survey plat in the figure below shows two lots that form a trapezoid. The measures of the parallel sides are 115.80 ft and 171.00 ft. The height of the trapezoid is 165.97 ft. Find the combined area of the two lots. Round your answer to the nearest hundredth of a square foot.

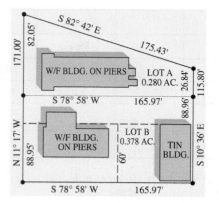

28. Area of a Lot Lot A in the figure is in the shape of a trapezoid. The parallel sides measure 26.84 ft and 82.05 ft. The height of the trapezoid is 165.97 ft. Find the area of Lot A. Round your answer to the nearest hundredth of a square foot.

29. Search Area A search plane carries radar equipment that can detect metal objects (like submarine periscopes or plane wreckage) on the ocean surface up to 15.5 miles away. If the plane completes a circular flight pattern of 471 miles in circumference, how much area will it search? (Use 3.14 as an approximation for π, and round to the nearest 100 mi^2.)

30. Flight Path If the search plane from **Exercise 29** needs to search a circular swath with an area of 20,000 square miles, how far will the plane need to fly (in a circle)? (Round to the nearest mile.)

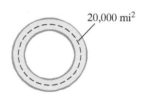

20,000 mi^2

In the chart below, the value of r (radius), d (diameter), C (circumference), or A (area) is given for a particular circle. Find the remaining three values. Leave π in your answers.

	r	d	C	A
31.	6 in.			
32.	9 in.			
33.		10 ft		
34.		40 ft		
35.			12π cm	
36.			18π cm	
37.				100π in.^{2}
38.				256π in.^{2}
39.				$\frac{400}{\pi}$ yd^2
40.			60 m	

Each figure has the perimeter indicated. (Figures are not necessarily to scale.) Find the value of x.

41. P = 58

42. P = 42

43. P = 38

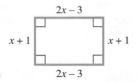

44. P = 278

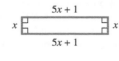

Each figure has the area indicated. Find the value of x.

45. A = 32.49

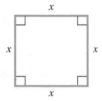

46. A = 28

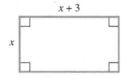

47. A = 21

48. A = 30

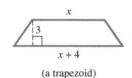

(a trapezoid)

Each circle has the circumference or area indicated. Find the value of x. Use 3.14 as an approximation for π.

49. C = 37.68

50. C = 54.95

51. A = 28.26

52. A = 18.0864

53. Work the parts of this exercise in order, and make a generalization concerning areas of rectangles.

(a) Find the area of a rectangle 4 cm by 5 cm.

(b) Find the area of a rectangle 8 cm by 10 cm.

(c) Find the area of a rectangle 12 cm by 15 cm.

(d) Find the area of a rectangle 16 cm by 20 cm.

(e) The rectangle in part (b) had sides twice as long as the sides of the rectangle in part (a). Divide the larger area by the smaller. Doubling the sides made the area increase _____ times.

(f) To get the rectangle in part (c), each side of the rectangle in part (a) was multiplied by _____. This made the larger area _____ times the size of the smaller area.

(g) To get the rectangle of part (d), each side of the rectangle of part (a) was multiplied by _____. This made the area increase to _____ times what it was originally.

(h) In general, if the length of each side of a rectangle is multiplied by *n*, the area is multiplied by _____.

54. Use the logic of **Exercise 53** to answer the following: If the height of a triangle is multiplied by *n* and the base length remains the same, then the area of the triangle is multiplied by _____.

55. Use the logic of **Exercise 53** to answer the following: If the radius of a circle is multiplied by *n*, then the area of the circle is multiplied by _____.

*Job Cost   Use the results of **Exercise 53** to solve each problem.*

56. A ceiling measuring 9 ft by 15 ft can be painted for $60. How much would it cost to paint a ceiling 18 ft by 30 ft?

57. Suppose carpet for a room 10 ft by 12 ft costs $200. Find the cost to carpet a room 20 ft by 24 ft.

58. A carpet cleaner uses 8 oz of shampoo to clean an area 31 ft by 31 ft. How much shampoo would be needed for an area 93 ft by 93 ft?

Total Area as the Sum of Areas *By considering total area as the sum of the areas of all of its parts, we can determine the area of a figure such as those in Exercises 59–62. Find the total area of each figure. Use 3.14 as an approximation for π in Exercises 61 and 62, and round to the nearest hundredth.*

59.
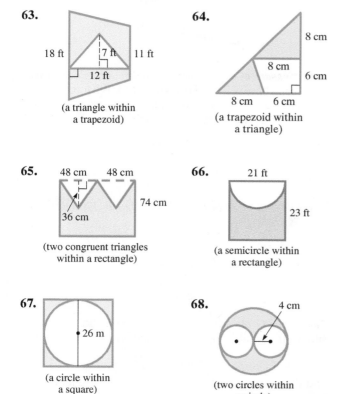
10

6

4

(a parallelogram
and a triangle)

60.
9

4   10

3

(a triangle, a rectangle,
and a parallelogram)

61.
8

3

3

(a rectangle and
two semicircles)

62.
8

8   8

8

(a square and
four semicircles)

Area of a Shaded Portion of a Plane Figure *The shaded areas of the figures in Exercises 63–68 may be found by subtracting the area of the unshaded portion from the total area of the figure. Use this approach to find the area of the shaded portion. Use 3.14 as an approximation for π in Exercises 66–68, and round to the nearest hundredth.*

63.
18 ft   7 ft   11 ft

12 ft

(a triangle within
a trapezoid)

64.
8 cm

8 cm

6 cm

8 cm   6 cm

(a trapezoid within
a triangle)

65.
48 cm   48 cm

74 cm

36 cm

(two congruent triangles
within a rectangle)

66.
21 ft

23 ft

(a semicircle within
a rectangle)

67.
26 m

(a circle within
a square)

68.
4 cm

(two circles within
a circle)

Pizza Pricing *The following exercises show prices actually charged by Old Town Pizza, a local pizzeria. The dimension is the diameter of the pizza. Find the best buy.*

Menu Item	Prices			
	10-in.	**12-in.**	**14-in.**	**16-in.**
69. Cheese pizza with one topping	$10	$14	$17	$20
70. Cheese pizza with two toppings	$11.50	$15.75	$19	$22.25
71. Choo Choo Chicken	$15	$19	$22	$25
72. Steam Engine + two toppings	$18	$22.50	$26	$29.50

James Garfield's Proof of the Pythagorean Theorem *James A. Garfield, the twentieth president of the United States, provided a proof of the Pythagorean theorem using the figure below. Supply the required information in each of Exercises 73–76, in order, to follow his proof.*

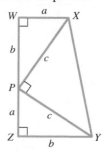

73. Find the area of the trapezoid $WXYZ$ using the formula for the area of a trapezoid.

W a X

b

c

P

a c

Z b Y

74. Find the area of each of the right triangles PWX, PZY, and PXY.

75. Because the sum of the areas of the three right triangles must equal the area of the trapezoid, set the expression from **Exercise 73** equal to the sum of the three expressions from **Exercise 74.**

76. Simplify the terms of the equation from **Exercise 75** as much as possible. What is the result?

A polygon can be inscribed within a circle or circumscribed about a circle. In the figure, triangle ABC is inscribed within the circle, while square WXYZ is circumscribed about it. These ideas will be used in some of the remaining exercises in this section and later in this chapter.

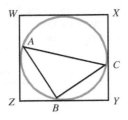

Exercises 77–88 require some ingenuity, but all may be solved using the concepts presented so far in this chapter.

77. Diameter of a Circle Given the circle with center O and rectangle $ABCO$, find the diameter of the circle.

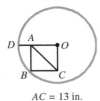

$AC = 13$ in.
$AD = 3$ in.

78. Perimeter of a Triangle What is the perimeter of $\triangle AEB$ if $AD = 20$ in., $DC = 30$ in., and $AC = 34$ in.?

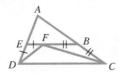

79. Area of a Square The area of square $PQRS$ is 1250 square feet. T, U, V, and W are the midpoints of PQ, QR, RS, and SP, respectively. What is the area of square $TUVW$?

80. Area of a Quadrilateral The rectangle $ABCD$ has length twice the width. If P, Q, R, and S are the midpoints of the sides, and the perimeter of $ABCD$ is 96 in., what is the area of quadrilateral $PQRS$?

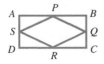

81. Area of Shaded Region If the area of $\triangle ACE$ is 10 cm², the area of $\triangle BDE$ is 16 cm², and the area of $\triangle ADE$ is 20 cm², determine the area of the shaded region.

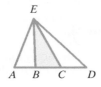

82. Area of Trapezoid The three squares have the dimensions indicated in the diagram. What is the area of the shaded trapezoid?

83. Area of a Shaded Region Express the area of the shaded region in terms of r, given that the circle is inscribed in the square.

84. Area of a Pentagon In the figure, pentagon $PQRST$ is formed by a square and an equilateral triangle such that $PQ = QR = RS = ST = PT$. The perimeter of the pentagon is 80. Find the area of the pentagon.

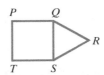

85. Area of a Quadrilateral Find the area of quadrilateral $ABCD$ if angles A and C are right angles.

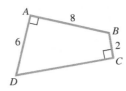

86. Base Measure of an Isosceles Triangle An isosceles triangle has a base of 24 and two sides of 13. What other base measure can an isosceles triangle with equal sides of 13 have and still have the same area as the given triangle?

Exercises 87 and 88 refer to the given figure. The center of the circle is O.

87. Radius of a Circle If $\overset{\frown}{AC}$ measures 6 in. and $\overset{\frown}{BC}$ measures 8 in., what is the radius of the circle?

88. Lengths of Chords of a Circle If $\overset{\frown}{AB}$ measures 13 cm, and the length of $\overset{\frown}{BC}$ is 7 cm more than the length of $\overset{\frown}{AC}$, what are the lengths of $\overset{\frown}{BC}$ and $\overset{\frown}{AC}$?

OBJECTIVES

1 Classify space figures.

2 Calculate surface area and volume of common space figures.

Space Figures

Thus far, this chapter has discussed only **plane figures**—figures that can be drawn completely in the plane of a sheet of paper. However, it takes the three dimensions of space to represent the solid world around us. For example, **Figure 53** shows a "box" (a **rectangular parallelepiped**). The *faces* of a box are rectangles. The faces meet at *edges;* the "corners" are *vertices* (plural of *vertex*—the same word that is used for the "corner" of an angle).

Vertex

Face

Edge

Rectangular parallelepiped (box)

Figure 53

Boxes are one kind of **space figure** belonging to an important group called **polyhedra,** the faces of which are made only of polygons. Perhaps the most interesting polyhedra are the *regular polyhedra*. Recall that a *regular polygon* is a polygon with all sides equal and all angles equal. A regular polyhedron is a space figure, the faces of which are only one kind of regular polygon. It turns out that there are only five different regular polyhedra. They are shown in **Figure 54**. A **tetrahedron** is composed of four equilateral triangles, each three of which meet in a point. Use the figure to verify that there are four faces, four vertices, and six edges.

Polyhedral dice such as the ones shown here are often used in today's role-playing games.

The five regular polyhedra are also known as **Platonic solids,** named for the Greek philosopher Plato. He considered them as "building blocks" of nature and assigned fire to the tetrahedron, earth to the cube, air to the octahedron, and water to the icosahedron. Because the dodecahedron is different from the others due to its pentagonal faces, he assigned to it the cosmos (stars and planets). (*Source:* http://platonicrealms.com/encyclopedia/Platonic-solid) An animated view of the Platonic solids can be found at http://www.wikipedia.org/wiki/Platonic_solid.

The image above is from an Android app (*Dice,* by Teazel.com) that simulates the rolling of polyhedral dice.

Tetrahedron　　Hexahedron (cube)　　Octahedron　　Dodecahedron　　Icosahedron

Figure 54

The four remaining regular polyhedra are the **hexahedron,** the **octahedron,** the **dodecahedron,** and the **icosahedron.** The hexahedron, or cube, is composed of six squares, each three of which meet at a point. The octahedron is composed of groups of four regular (i.e., equilateral) triangles meeting at a point. The dodecahedron is formed by groups of three regular pentagons, and the icosahedron is made up of groups of five regular triangles.

Two other types of polyhedra are familiar space figures: pyramids and prisms. **Pyramids** are made of triangular sides and a polygonal base. **Prisms** have two faces in parallel planes; these faces are congruent polygons. The remaining faces of a prism are all parallelograms. (See **Figures 55(a)** and **(b)** on the next page.) By this definition, a box is also a prism.

Figure 55(c) shows space figures made up in part of circles, including *right circular cones* and *right circular cylinders*. It also shows how a circle can generate a *torus,* a doughnut-shaped solid that has interesting topological properties. See **Section 9.7.**

Tetrahedron

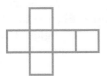

Hexahedron (cube)

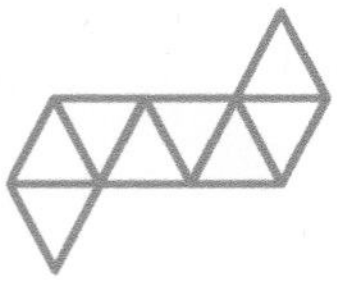

Octahedron

Dodecahedron

Icosahedron

Patterns such as these may be used to construct three-dimensional models of the **regular polyhedra**. See

http://www.korthalsaltes.com

for some examples.

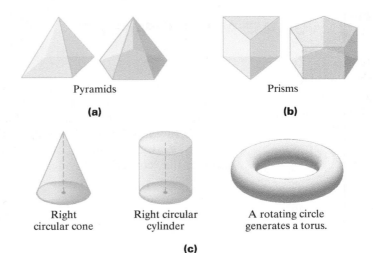

Pyramids

(a)

Prisms

(b)

Right circular cone

Right circular cylinder

A rotating circle generates a torus.

(c)

Figure 55

Volume and Surface Area of Space Figures

While area is a measure of surface covered by a plane figure, **volume** is a measure of capacity of a space figure. Volume is measured in *cubic* units. For example, a cube with edge measuring 1 cm has volume 1 cubic centimeter, which is also written as 1 cm³, or 1 cc. The **surface area** is the total area that would be covered if the space figure were "peeled" and the peel laid flat. Surface area is measured in *square* units.

VOLUME AND SURFACE AREA OF A BOX

Suppose that a box has length ℓ, width w, and height h. Then the volume V and the surface area S are given by the following formulas.

$$V = \ell wh \quad \text{and} \quad S = 2\ell w + 2\ell h + 2hw$$

If the box is a cube with edge of length s, the formulas are as follows.

$$V = s^3 \quad \text{and} \quad S = 6s^2$$

$V = \ell wh$

$S = 2\ell w + 2\ell h + 2hw$

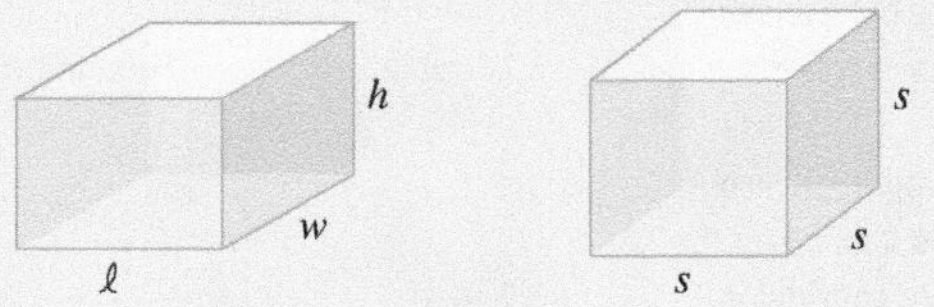

$V = s^3$

$S = 6s^2$

EXAMPLE 1 **Using the Formulas for a Box**

Find the volume V and the surface area S of the box shown in **Figure 56.**

Solution

$$
\begin{aligned}
V &= \ell wh &&\text{Volume formula} \\
&= 14 \cdot 7 \cdot 5 &&\text{Substitute.} \\
&= 490 &&\text{Multiply.}
\end{aligned}
$$

Volume is measured in cubic units, so the volume of the box is 490 cubic centimeters, or 490 cm³.

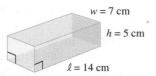

$w = 7$ cm

$h = 5$ cm

$\ell = 14$ cm

Figure 56

$$S = 2\ell w + 2\ell h + 2hw \qquad \text{Surface area formula}$$
$$= 2(14)(7) + 2(14)(5) + 2(5)(7) \qquad \text{Substitute.}$$
$$= 196 + 140 + 70 \qquad \text{Multiply.}$$
$$= 406 \qquad \text{Add.}$$

Surface areas of space figures are measured in square units, so the surface area of the box is 406 square centimeters, or 406 cm^2. ■

A typical tin can is an example of a **right circular cylinder.**

VOLUME AND SURFACE AREA OF A RIGHT CIRCULAR CYLINDER

If a right circular cylinder has height h and the radius of its base is equal to r, then the volume V and the surface area S are given by the following formulas.

$$V = \pi r^2 h$$

and $\qquad S = 2\pi rh + 2\pi r^2$

(In the formula for S, the areas of the top and bottom are included.)

$V = \pi r^2 h$
$S = 2\pi rh + 2\pi r^2$

EXAMPLE 2 **Using the Formulas for a Right Circular Cylinder**

In **Figure 57,** the volume of medication in the syringe is 10 mL (which is equivalent to 10 cm^3). Find each measure. Use 3.14 as an approximation for π.

(a) the radius of the cylindrical syringe (round to the nearest 0.1 cm)

(b) the surface area of the medication (round to the nearest 0.1 cm^2)

Solution

(a)
$$V = \pi r^2 h \qquad \text{Volume formula}$$
$$10 = \pi r^2 (5.0) \qquad V = 10,\ h = 5.0$$
$$\frac{2}{\pi} = r^2 \qquad \text{Divide by } 5.0\pi.$$
$$r = \sqrt{\frac{2}{\pi}} \approx 0.8 \qquad \text{Take the square root and approximate.}$$

The radius is approximately 0.8 cm.

(b)
$$S = 2\pi rh + 2\pi r^2 \qquad \text{Surface area formula}$$
$$= 2\pi(0.8)(5.0) + 2\pi(0.8)^2 \qquad r = 0.8,\ h = 5.0$$
$$= 9.28\pi \qquad \text{Multiply; add.}$$
$$\approx 29.1 \qquad \text{Approximate, using 3.14 for } \pi.$$

The surface area is approximately 29.1 cm^2. ■

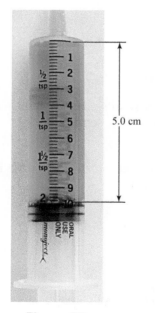

5.0 cm

Figure 57

The three-dimensional analogue of a circle is a **sphere.** It is defined by replacing the word "plane" with "space" in the definition of a circle (**Section 9.2**).

VOLUME AND SURFACE AREA OF A SPHERE

If a sphere has radius r, then the volume V and the surface area S are given by the following formulas.

$$V = \frac{4}{3}\pi r^3 \quad \text{and} \quad S = 4\pi r^2$$

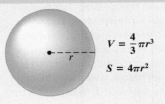

$$V = \frac{4}{3}\pi r^3$$

$$S = 4\pi r^2$$

A cone with circular base having its apex (highest point) directly above the center of its base is a **right circular cone.**

VOLUME AND SURFACE AREA OF A RIGHT CIRCULAR CONE

If a right circular cone has height h and the radius of its circular base is r, then the volume V and the surface area S are given by the following formulas.

$$V = \frac{1}{3}\pi r^2 h$$

and $$S = \pi r \sqrt{r^2 + h^2} + \pi r^2$$

(In the formula for S, the area of the circular base is included.)

$$V = \frac{1}{3}\pi r^2 h$$

$$S = \pi r \sqrt{r^2 + h^2} + \pi r^2$$

EXAMPLE 3 Comparing Volumes Using Ratios

Figure 58 shows a right circular cone inscribed in a semi-sphere of radius r. What is the ratio of the volume of the cone to the volume of the semi-sphere?

Figure 58

Solution

First, use the formula for the volume of a cone. Note that because the cone is inscribed in the semi-sphere, its height is equal to its radius.

$$V_1 = \text{Volume of the cone} = \frac{1}{3}\pi r^2 h = \frac{1}{3}\pi r^3 \quad \text{Use } h = r.$$

The semi-sphere will have half the volume of a sphere of radius r.

$$V_2 = \text{Volume of the semi-sphere} = \frac{1}{2} \cdot \frac{4}{3}\pi r^3 = \frac{2}{3}\pi r^3$$

Now find the ratio of the first volume to the second.

$$\frac{V_1}{V_2} = \frac{\frac{1}{3}\pi r^3}{\frac{2}{3}\pi r^3} = \frac{1}{2}$$

The ratio is $\frac{1}{2}$.

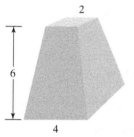

2

6

4

A problem concerning the **frustum of a pyramid** like the one shown above is included in the **Moscow papyrus,** which dates back to about 1850 B.C. Problem 14 in the document reads:

You are given a truncated pyramid of 6 for the vertical height by 4 on the base by 2 on the top. You are to square this 4, result 16. You are to double 4, result 8. You are to square 2, result 4. You are to add the 16, the 8, and the 4, result 28. You are to take one-third of 6, result 2. You are to take 28 twice, result 56. See, it is 56. You will find it right.

The formula for finding the volume of the frustum of a pyramid with square bases is

$$V = \frac{1}{3}h(B^2 + Bb + b^2),$$

where B is the side length of the lower base, b is the side length of the upper base, and h is the height (or altitude).

A **pyramid** is a space figure having a polygonal base and triangular sides. **Figure 59** shows a pyramid with a square base.

Pyramid

Figure 59

VOLUME OF A PYRAMID

If B represents the area of the base of a pyramid, and h represents the height (that is, the perpendicular distance from the top, or apex, to the base), then the volume V is given by the following formula.

$$V = \frac{1}{3}Bh$$

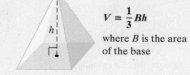

$V = \frac{1}{3}Bh$

where B is the area of the base

EXAMPLE 4 **Using the Volume Formula for a Pyramid**

The Great Pyramid at Giza has a square base. When originally constructed, its base measured about 230 meters on a side, and it was about 147 meters high. What was its volume?

Solution

Use the formula for the volume of a pyramid.

$$V = \frac{1}{3}Bh$$

Since the base is square, the area of the base is the square of the side length.

$$V = \frac{1}{3}(230)^2(147) = 2{,}592{,}100 \text{ m}^3 \qquad \blacksquare$$

9.5   EXERCISES

Decide whether each statement is true *or* false.

1. A cube with volume 125 cubic inches has surface area 150 square inches.

2. A tetrahedron has the same number of faces as vertices.

3. A sphere with a 1-unit radius has three times as many units of surface area as it has units of volume.

4. Each face of an octahedron is an octagon.

5. If you double the length of the edge of a cube, the new cube will have a volume that is four times the volume of the original cube.

6. A dodecahedron can be used as a model for a calendar for a given year, where each face of the dodecahedron contains a calendar for a single month, and there are no faces left over.

Find **(a)** *the volume and* **(b)** *the surface area of each space figure. When necessary, use 3.14 as an approximation for* π, *and round answers to the nearest hundredth.*

7.

$2\frac{1}{4}$ m

4 m

$2\frac{1}{2}$ m

(a box)

8.

3 in.

5 in.

6 in.

(a box)

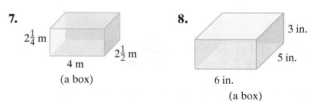

9.

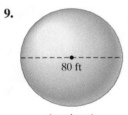

80 ft

(a sphere)

10.

14.8 cm

(a sphere)

11.

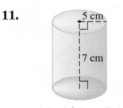

5 cm

7 cm

(a right circular cylinder)

12.

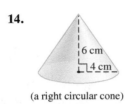

12 m

4 m

(a right circular cylinder)

13.

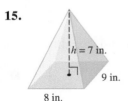

3 m

7 m

(a right circular cone)

14.

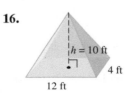

6 cm

4 cm

(a right circular cone)

Find the volume of each pyramid. In each case, the base is a rectangle.

15.

$h = 7$ in.

9 in.

8 in.

16.

$h = 10$ ft

4 ft

12 ft

Volumes of Common Objects   *Find each volume. Use 3.14 as an approximation for π when necessary.*

17. a coffee can, radius 6.3 cm and height 15.8 cm

18. a soup can, radius 3.2 cm and height 9.5 cm

19. a pork-and-beans can, diameter 7.2 cm and height 10.5 cm

20. a cardboard mailing tube, diameter 2 in. and height 40 in.

21. a coffee mug, diameter 9 cm and height 8 cm

22. a bottle of glue, diameter 3 cm and height 4.3 cm

23. the Red Pyramid at Dahshur, near Cairo—its base is a square 220 m on a side, and its height is 105 m

24. a grain silo in the shape of a right circular cylinder with a base radius of 7 m and a height of 25 m

25. a road construction marker, a cone with height 2 m and base radius $\frac{1}{2}$ m

26. the conical portion of a witch's hat for a Halloween costume, with height 12 in. and base radius 4 in.

In the chart below, the value of r (radius), V (volume), or S (surface area) is given for a particular sphere. Find the remaining two values. Leave π in your answers.

	r	*V*	*S*
27.	6 in.		
28.	9 in.		
29.		$\frac{32}{3}\pi$ cm³	
30.		$\frac{256}{3}\pi$ cm³	
31.			4π m²
32.			144π m²

Solve each problem.

33. Volume or Surface Area?   In order to determine the amount of liquid a spherical tank will hold, would you need to use volume or surface area?

34. Volume or Surface Area?   In order to determine the amount of leather it would take to manufacture a basketball, would you need to use volume or surface area?

35. Irrigation Tank   An irrigation tank is formed of a concrete "box" that is 5 ft wide, 5 ft deep, and 10 ft long, along with two cylindrical sleeves, each 2 ft high and 2.5 ft in diameter. What is the total volume of the tank? (Use 3.14 as an approximation for π, and round to the nearest cubic foot.)

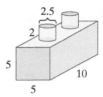

36. Underground Bunker   An underground bunker is to be made of concrete 2 ft thick. It will be semi-spherical with outer radius of 20 feet. How many cubic feet of concrete will be needed to construct the bunker? (Use 3.14 as an approximation for π, and round to the nearest cubic foot.)

37. Side Length of a Cube One of the three famous construction problems of Greek mathematics required the construction of an edge of a cube with twice the volume of a given cube. If the length of each side of the given cube is x, what would be the length of each side of a cube with twice the original volume?

38. Work through the parts of this exercise in order, and use them to make a generalization concerning volumes of spheres. Leave answers in terms of π.

(a) Find the volume of a sphere having radius of 1 m.

(b) Suppose the radius is doubled to 2 m. What is the volume?

(c) When the radius was doubled, by how many times did the volume increase? (To find out, divide the answer for part (b) by the answer for part (a).)

(d) Suppose the radius of the sphere from part (a) is tripled to 3 m. What is the volume?

(e) When the radius was tripled, by how many times did the volume increase?

(f) In general, if the radius of a sphere is multiplied by n, the volume is multiplied by ____ .

Cost to Fill a Spherical Tank *If a spherical tank 2 m in diameter can be filled with a liquid for $300, find the cost to fill tanks of each diameter.*

39. 6 m   **40.** 8 m   **41.** 10 m

42. Use the logic of **Exercise 38** to answer the following: If the radius of a sphere is multiplied by n, then the surface area of the sphere is multiplied by ____ .

43. Volume Decrease The radius of a sphere is decreased by 30%. By what percent does the volume decrease? Round to the nearest 0.1%.

44. Surface Area Decrease The length of each edge of a cube is decreased by 40%. By what percent does the surface area decrease?

Each of the following figures has the volume indicated. Find the value of x.

45. $V = 60$

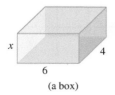

6
(a box)

46. $V = 450$

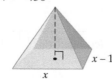

x
$h = 15$
Base is a rectangle.
(a pyramid)

47. $V = 36\pi$

(a sphere)

48. $V = 245\pi$

15

x
(a right circular cone)

Exercises 49–58 require some ingenuity, but all can be solved using the concepts presented so far in this chapter.

49. Volume of a Box The areas of the sides of a rectangular box are 30 in.^{2}, 35 in.^{2}, and 42 in.^{2}. What is the volume of the box?

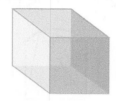

50. Ratio of Volumes Three tennis balls are stacked in a cylindrical container that touches the stack on all sides, on the top, and on the bottom. What is the ratio of the volume filled with tennis balls to the volume of empty space in the container?

51. Equal Area and Volume The inhabitants of Planet Volarea have a unit of distance called a *volar*. The number of square volars in the planet's surface area is the same as the number of cubic volars in the planet's volume. If the diameter of Volarea is 1800 miles, how many miles are in a volar?

52. Change in Volume If the height of a right circular cylinder is halved and the diameter is tripled, how is the volume changed?

h

d

53. Ratio of Areas What is the ratio of the area of the circumscribed square to the area of the inscribed square?

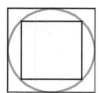

54. *Perimeter of a Square* Suppose the diameter of the circle shown is 8 in. What is the perimeter of the inscribed square $ABCD$?

55. *Value of a Sum* In the circle shown with center O, the radius is 6. $QTSR$ is an inscribed square. Find the value of

$$PQ^2 + PT^2 + PR^2 + PS^2.$$

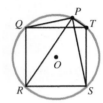

56. *Ratio of Side Lengths* The square $JOSH$ is inscribed in a semicircle. What is the ratio of x to y?

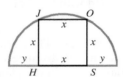

57. *Frustum of a Pyramid* The feature "When Will I Ever Use This?" on the next page shows an application of the *frustum* of a pyramid. Use the figure below to help verify the formula for the volume of the frustum of a pyramid with square base. (Note that, in this formula, B and b are the lengths of the sides of the bases, *not* the areas of the bases.)

$$V = \frac{1}{3} h \left(B^2 + Bb + b^2\right)$$

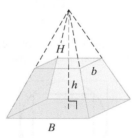

58. *Ratio of Surface Area to Base Area* The figure shows a pyramid with square base and with height equal to the side length of the base. Find the ratio of the entire surface area to the area of the base.

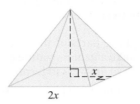

Euler's Formula *Many crystals and some viruses are constructed in the shapes of regular polyhedra.*

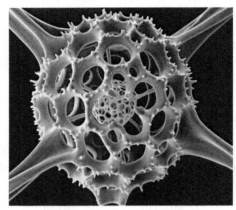

Radiolara virus

Leonhard Euler investigated a remarkable relationship among the numbers of faces (F), vertices (V), and edges (E) for the five regular polyhedra. Complete the chart in Exercises 59–63, and then draw a conclusion in Exercise 64.

Polyhedron	Faces (F)	Vertices (V)	Edges (E)	Value of F + V − E
59. Tetrahedron				
60. Hexahedron (cube)				
61. Octahedron				
62. Dodecahedron				
63. Icosahedron				

64. Euler's formula is $F + V - E = $ _____ .

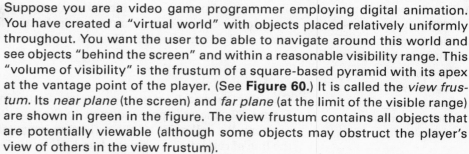

WHEN Will I Ever USE This ?

Suppose you are a video game programmer employing digital animation. You have created a "virtual world" with objects placed relatively uniformly throughout. You want the user to be able to navigate around this world and see objects "behind the screen" and within a reasonable visibility range. This "volume of visibility" is the frustum of a square-based pyramid with its apex at the vantage point of the player. (See **Figure 60.**) It is called the *view frustum*. Its *near plane* (the screen) and *far plane* (at the limit of the visible range) are shown in green in the figure. The view frustum contains all objects that are potentially viewable (although some objects may obstruct the player's view of others in the view frustum).

Suppose the screen is square, measuring about $\frac{1}{3}$ meter on a side, and is about 1 meter away from the user's eye. If the range of visibility is 300 meters, what is the volume of the view frustum? If the entire virtual world can be represented by a circular cylinder of radius 1000 meters and height 200 meters, what percentage of the world is contained within a single view frustum?

The view frustum is shown in detail in **Figure 61.** Since it has square bases, its volume is given (see the margin note on **page 493**) by

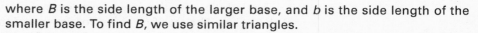

$$V = \frac{1}{3}h(B^2 + Bb + b^2), \quad \text{Volume formula}$$

Figure 60

where B is the side length of the larger base, and b is the side length of the smaller base. To find B, we use similar triangles.

$$\frac{300}{1} = \frac{B}{\frac{1}{3}} \qquad \text{Ratios of corresponding sides are equal.}$$

$$100 = B \qquad \text{Multiply using cross products.}$$

We now substitute values for h, B, and b into the formula.

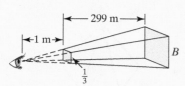

Figure 61

$$V = \frac{1}{3}h(B^2 + Bb + b^2) \qquad \text{Volume formula}$$

$$= \frac{1}{3}(299)\left(100^2 + 100\left(\frac{1}{3}\right) + \left(\frac{1}{3}\right)^2\right) \qquad h = 299, B = 100, b = \frac{1}{3}$$

$$\approx 1{,}000{,}000 \qquad \text{Simplify.}$$

The volume of the view frustum is about 1,000,000 m³.

The volume of the entire virtual world is

$$V = \pi r^2 h \qquad \text{Volume of a right circular cylinder}$$

$$= \pi(1000)^2(200) \qquad r = 1000, h = 200$$

$$\approx 3.14(1{,}000{,}000)(200) \qquad \pi \approx 3.14; \text{ multiply.}$$

$$= 628{,}000{,}000 \qquad \text{Multiply.}$$

A single view frustum contains about $\frac{1}{628} \approx 0.16\%$ of the entire virtual world.

The software you are using for rendering three-dimensional objects allows for *frustum culling*, which instructs the graphics hardware to render only the objects in the view frustum, rather than *all* of the objects in the virtual world. This allows for a much more efficient use of memory and processor speed, which lead to shorter loading times and a better player experience.

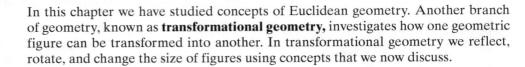

9.6 TRANSFORMATIONAL GEOMETRY

In this chapter we have studied concepts of Euclidean geometry. Another branch of geometry, known as **transformational geometry,** investigates how one geometric figure can be transformed into another. In transformational geometry we reflect, rotate, and change the size of figures using concepts that we now discuss.

Reflections

One way to transform one geometric figure into another is by **reflection.** In **Figure 62,** line m is perpendicular to the line segment AA' and bisects this line segment. We call point A' the **reflection image** of point A about line m. Line m is the **line of reflection** for points A and A'. In the figure, we use a dashed line to connect points A and A' to show that these two points are images of each other under this transformation.

Point A' is the reflection image of point A only for line m. If a different line were used, A would have a different reflection image. Think of the reflection image of a point A about a line m as follows:

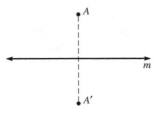

Figure 62

> Place a drop of ink at point A, and fold the paper along line m. The spot made by the ink on the other side of m is the reflection image of A. If A' is the image of A about line m, then A is the image of A' about the same line m.

To find the reflection image of a figure, find the reflection image of each point of the figure. The set of all reflection images of the points of the original figure is the reflection image of the figure. **Figure 63** shows several figures (in black) and their reflection images (in color) about the lines shown.

An example of a **reflection.**

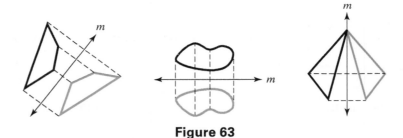

Figure 63

Each point in a plane has exactly one reflection image point with respect to a given line of reflection. Also, each reflection image point has exactly one original point. Thus, two distinct points cannot have the same reflection image. This means there is a *1-to-1 correspondence* between the set of points of the plane and the image points with respect to a given line of reflection. Any operation, such as reflection, in which there is a 1-to-1 correspondence between the points of the plane and their image points is a **transformation.** We call reflection about a line the **reflection transformation.**

If a point A and its image, A', under a certain transformation are the same point, then point A is an **invariant point** of the transformation. The only invariant points of the reflection transformation are the points of the line of reflection.

Three points that lie on the same straight line are **collinear.** In **Figure 64,**

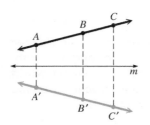

Figure 64

points A, B, and C are collinear,

and it can be shown that the reflection images A', B', and C' are also collinear. Thus, the reflection image of a line is also a line. We express this by saying that **reflection preserves collinearity.**

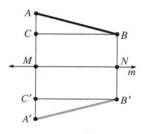

Figure 65

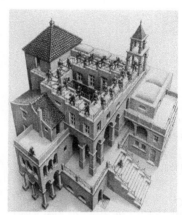

M. C. Escher (1898–1972) was a Dutch graphic artist, most recognized for spatial illusions, impossible buildings, repeating geometric patterns (tessellations), and his incredible techniques in woodcutting and lithography. He was a humble man who considered himself neither an artist nor a mathematician.

The lithograph pictured here, called *Ascending and Descending*, gives the illusion that the stairs near the top of this building are both ascending and descending simultaneously.

How many kinds of **symmetry** do you see here?

Distance is also preserved by the reflection transformation. Thus, in **Figure 65,** the distance between points A and B, written $|AB|$, is equal to the distance between the reflection images A' and B', or

$$|AB| = |A'B'|.$$

To prove this, we can use the definition of reflection image to verify that

$$|AM| = |MA'|, \quad \text{and} \quad |BN| = |NB'|.$$

Construct segments CB and $C'B'$, each perpendicular to BB'. Note that $CBB'C'$ is a rectangle. Because the opposite sides of a rectangle are equal and parallel, we have

$$|CB| = |C'B'|. \qquad \text{(Side)} \quad \textbf{(1)}$$

Because $CBB'C'$ is a rectangle, we can also say

$$m \angle ACB = m \angle A'C'B' = 90°, \qquad \text{(Angle)} \quad \textbf{(2)}$$

where we use $m \angle ACB$ to represent the measure of angle ACB.

We know $|AM| = |MA'|$ and can show $|CM| = |MC'|$, so that

$$|AC| = |A'C'|. \qquad \text{(Side)} \quad \textbf{(3)}$$

From statements (1), (2), and (3) above, we conclude that in triangles ABC and $A'B'C'$, two sides and the included angle of one are equal in measure to the corresponding two sides and angle of the other and, thus, are congruent by SAS (**Section 9.3**). Corresponding sides of congruent triangles are equal in length, so

$$|AB| = |A'B'|,$$

which is what we wanted to show. Hence, the distance between two points equals the distance between their reflection images, and thus, reflection preserves distance. (The proof we have given is not really complete, because we have tacitly assumed that AB is not parallel to $A'B'$, and that A and B are on the same side of the line of reflection. Some modification would have to be made in the proof above to include these other cases.)

The figures shown in **Figure 66** are their own reflection images about the lines of reflection shown. In this case, the line of reflection is a **line of symmetry** for the figure. **Figure 66(a)** has three lines of symmetry. A circle has every line through its center as a line of symmetry.

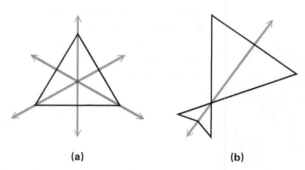

(a)   (b)

Figure 66

Translations and Rotations

We shall use the symbol r_m to represent a reflection about line m, and let us use $r_n \cdot r_m$ to represent a reflection about line m followed by a reflection about line n. We call $r_n \cdot r_m$ the **composition,** or **product,** of the two reflections r_n and r_m. **Figure 67** on the next page shows two examples of the composition of two reflections. In **Figure 67(a),** lines m and n are parallel, whereas they intersect in **Figure 67(b).**

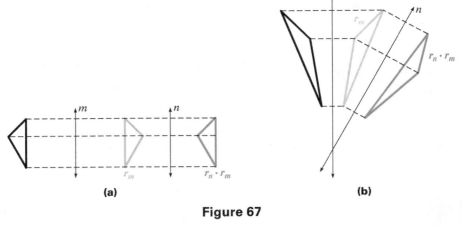

(a)   **(b)**

Figure 67

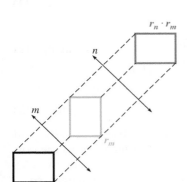

Figure 68

In **Figure 67(a)** both the original figure and its image under the composition of the two reflections appear to be oriented the same way and to have the same "tilt." In fact, it appears that the original figure could be slid along the dashed lines of **Figure 67(a)**, with no rotation, so as to cover the image. This composite transformation is a **translation. Figure 68** shows a translation, and the image can be obtained as a composition of two reflections about parallel lines. Check that the distance between a point and its image under a translation is twice the distance between the two parallel lines. The distance between a point and its image under a translation is the **magnitude** of the translation.

A translation of magnitude 0 leaves every point of the plane unchanged and, thus, is the **identity translation.** A translation of magnitude k, followed by a similar translation of magnitude k but of opposite direction, returns a point to its original position, so these two translations are **inverses** of each other. Check that there are no invariant points in a translation of magnitude $k > 0$.

A translation preserves collinearity (three points on the same line have image points that also lie on a line) and distance (the distance between two points is the same as the distance between the images of the points).

In **Figure 67(b)**, the original figure could be rotated so as to cover the image. Hence, we call the composition of two reflections about nonparallel lines a **rotation.** The point of intersection of these two nonparallel lines is the **center of rotation.** The black triangle of **Figure 69** was reflected about line m and then reflected about line n, resulting in a rotation with center at B. The dashed lines in color represent the paths of the vertices of the triangle under the rotation. It can be shown that $m \angle ABA'$ is twice as large as $m \angle MBN$. The measure of angle ABA' is the **magnitude** of the rotation.

This **Escher pattern** fills (tiles) the entire plane if we start with one fish, one duck, and one lizard, and then perform repeated translations in opposite directions.

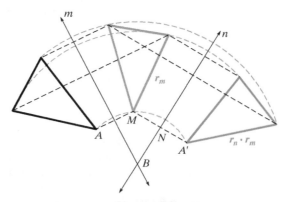

Figure 69

Rotations also preserve collinearity and distance. The identity transformation here is a rotation of 0° or 360°, and rotations of, say, 240° and 120° (or, in general, $x°$ and $360° - x°$, $0 \leq x \leq 360°$) are inverses of each other. The center of rotation is the only invariant point of any rotation except the identity rotation.

We have defined rotations as the composition of two reflections about nonparallel lines of reflection. We can also define a rotation by specifying its center, the angle of rotation, and a direction of rotation, as shown by the following example.

EXAMPLE 1 Finding an Image under a Rotation

Find the image of a point P under a rotation transformation having center at a point Q and magnitude 135° clockwise.

Solution

To find P', the image of P, first draw angle PQM having measure 135°. Then draw an arc of a circle with center at Q and radius $|PQ|$. The point where this arc intersects side QM is P'. See **Figure 70**.

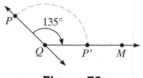

Figure 70

Figure 71 shows a rotation transformation having center Q and magnitude 180° clockwise. Point Q bisects the line segment from a point A to its image A', and for this reason this rotation is sometimes called a **point reflection.**

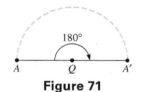

Figure 71

EXAMPLE 2 Finding Point Reflection Images

Find the point reflection images about point Q for each of the following figures.

(a)   **(b)**

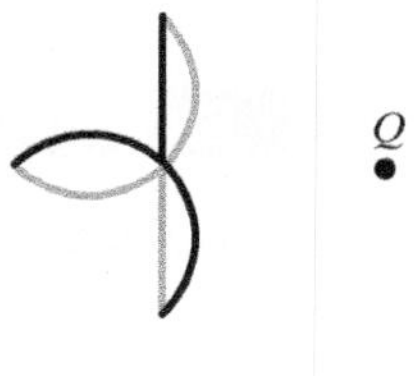

Solution

(a) 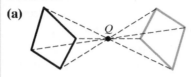   **(b)**

The point reflection images are shown in color.

Let r_m be a reflection about line m, and let T be a translation having nonzero magnitude and a direction parallel to m. Then the composition of T and r_m is a **glide reflection,** as seen in **Figure 72**. Here a reflection followed by a translation is the same as a translation followed by a reflection, so in this case,

$$T \cdot r_m = r_m \cdot T.$$

Because a translation is the composition of *two* reflections, a glide reflection is the composition of *three* reflections. Because it is required that the translation have nonzero magnitude, there is no identity glide transformation.

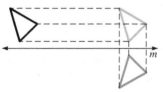

Figure 72

All the transformations of this section discussed so far are **isometries,** or transformations in which the image of a figure has the same size and shape as the original figure. Any isometry is either a reflection or the composition of two or more reflections.

Size Transformations

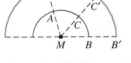
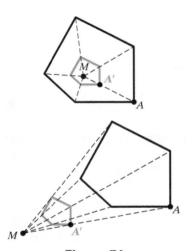

Figure 73

Figure 73 shows a semicircle in black, a point M, and an image semicircle in color. Distance $A'M$ is twice the distance AM and distance $B'M$ is twice the distance BM. In fact, every point of the image semicircle, such as C', was obtained by drawing a line through M and C, and then locating C' such that $|MC'| = 2|MC|$.

Such a transformation is a **size transformation** with center M and magnitude 2. We shall assume that a size transformation can have any positive real number k as magnitude. A size transformation having magnitude $k > 1$ is a **dilation,** or **stretch.** A size transformation having magnitude $k < 1$ is a **contraction,** or **shrink.**

EXAMPLE 3 Applying Size Transformations

Apply a size transformation with center M and magnitude $\frac{1}{3}$ to the two pentagons shown in black in **Figure 74.**

Solution

To find the images of these pentagons, we can find the image points of some sample points. For example, if we select point A on each of the original pentagons, we can find the image points by drawing a line through A and M, and locating a point A' such that $|MA'| = \frac{1}{3}|MA|$. By doing this for all points of each of the black pentagons, we get the images shown in color in **Figure 74.** ■

Figure 74

The identity transformation is a size transformation of magnitude 1, while size transformations of magnitude k and $\frac{1}{k}$, having the same center, are inverses of each other. The only invariant point of a size transformation of magnitude $k \neq 1$ is the center of the transformation.

EXAMPLE 4 Investigating Size Transformations

Does a size transformation **(a)** preserve collinearity? **(b)** preserve distance?

Solution

(a) **Figure 75** shows three collinear points, A, B, and C, and their images under two different size transformations with center at M: one of magnitude 3 and one of magnitude $\frac{1}{3}$. In each case the image points appear to be collinear, and it can be proved that they are, using similar triangles. In fact, the image of a line not through the center of the transformation is a line parallel to the original line.

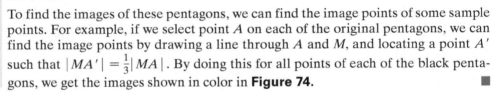

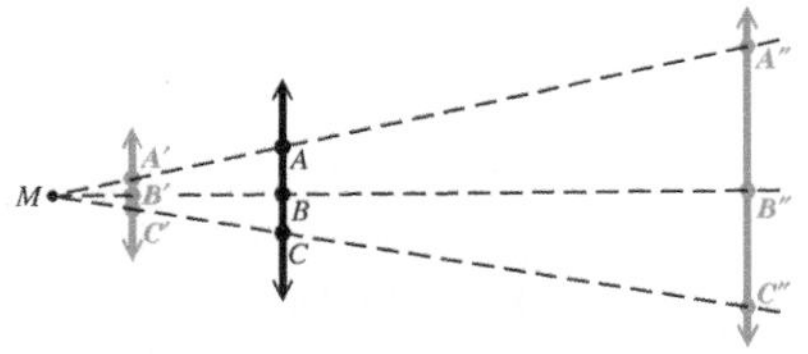

Figure 75

(b) As shown in **Figure 75,** $|AB| \neq |A'B'|$. Thus, a size transformation of magnitude $k \neq 1$ does not preserve distance and is not an isometry.

Transformations are summarized in Table 4 on page 505. ■

FOR FURTHER THOUGHT

Tessellations

The authors wish to thank Suzanne Alejandre for permission to reprint this article on tessellations, which first appeared at www.mathforum.org/sum95/suzanne/whattess.html.

tessellate (verb), **tessellation** (noun): from Latin *tessera* "a square tablet" or "a die used for gambling." Latin tessera may have been borrowed from Greek *tessares*, meaning "four," since a square tile has four sides. The diminutive of *tessera* was *tessella*, a small, square piece of stone or a cubical tile used in mosaics. Since a mosaic extends over a given area without leaving any region uncovered, the geometric meaning of the word "tessellate" is "to cover the plane with a pattern in such a way as to leave no region uncovered." By extension, space or hyperspace may also be tessellated.

Definition

A dictionary will tell you that the word "tessellate" means to form or arrange small squares in a checkered or mosaic pattern. The word "tessellate" is derived from the Ionic version of the Greek word "tesseres," which in English means "four." The first tilings were made from square tiles.

A regular polygon has 3 or 4 or 5 or more sides and angles, all equal. A **regular tessellation** means a tessellation made up of congruent regular polygons. [Remember: *Regular* means that the sides of the polygon are all the same length. *Congruent* means that the polygons that you put together are all the same size and shape.]

Only three regular polygons tessellate in the Euclidean plane: triangles, squares, or hexagons. We can't show the entire plane, but imagine that these are pieces taken from planes that have been tiled. Here are examples of

a tessellation of triangles

a tessellation of squares

a tessellation of hexagons

When you look at these three samples you can easily notice that the squares are lined up with each other while the triangles and hexagons are not.

Also, if you look at six triangles at a time, they form a hexagon, so the tiling of triangles and the tiling of hexagons are similar and they cannot be formed by directly lining shapes up under each other—a slide (or a glide!) is involved.

You can work out the interior measure of the angles for each of these polygons:

Shape	Angle Measure in Degrees
triangle	60
square	90
pentagon	108
hexagon	120
more than six sides	more than 120 degrees

Since the regular polygons in a tessellation must fill the plane at each vertex, the interior angle must be an exact divisor of 360 degrees. This works for the triangle, square, and hexagon, and you can show working tessellations for these figures. For all the others, the interior angles are not exact divisors of 360 degrees, and, therefore, those figures cannot tile the plane.

Naming Conventions

A tessellation of squares is named "4.4.4.4." Here's how: choose a vertex, and then look at one of the polygons that touches that vertex. How many sides does it have?

Since it's a square, it has four sides, and that's where the first "4" comes from. Now keep going around the vertex in either direction, finding the number of sides of the polygons until you get back to the polygon you started with. How many polygons did you count?

There are four polygons, and each has four sides.

4.4.4.4

For a tessellation of regular congruent hexagons, if you choose a vertex and count the sides of the polygons that touch it, you'll see that there are three polygons and each has six sides, so this tessellation is called "6.6.6":

6.6.6

A tessellation of triangles has six polygons surrounding a vertex, and each of them has three sides: "3.3.3.3.3.3."

3.3.3.3.3.3

Semi-regular Tessellations

You can also use a variety of regular polygons to make **semi-regular tessellations.**

A semi-regular tessellation has two properties, which are:

1. It is formed by regular polygons.
2. The arrangement of polygons at every vertex point is identical.

Here are the **eight** semi-regular tessellations:

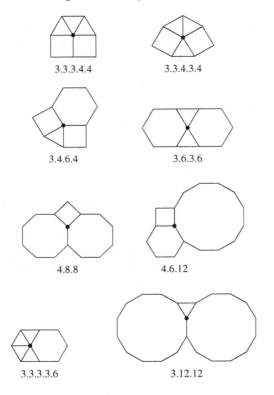

3.3.3.4.4   3.3.4.3.4

3.4.6.4   3.6.3.6

4.8.8   4.6.12

3.3.3.3.6   3.12.12

Interestingly, there are other combinations that seem like they should tile the plane because the arrangements of the regular polygons fill the space around a point. For example:

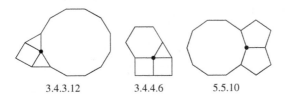

3.4.3.12   3.4.4.6   5.5.10

If you try tiling the plane with these units of tessellation you will find that they cannot be extended infinitely.

There is an infinite number of tessellations that can be made of patterns that do not have the same combination of angles at every vertex point. There are also tessellations made of polygons that do not share common edges and vertices.

For Group or Individual Investigation

1. Use the naming conventions to name each of these semi-regular tessellations.

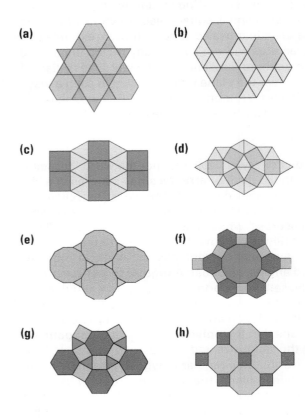

(a)   (b)

(c)   (d)

(e)   (f)

(g)   (h)

2. Why isn't this a semi-regular tessellation?

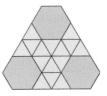

Tessellations (a) through (h) are courtesy of www.coolmath.com.

Table 4 Summary of Transformations

	Reflection	Translation	Rotation	Glide Reflection	Size Transformation
Example	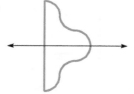				
Preserve collinearity?	Yes	Yes	Yes	Yes	Yes
Preserve distance?	Yes	Yes	Yes	Yes	No
Identity transformation?	None	Magnitude 0	Magnitude 360°	None	Magnitude 1
Inverse transformation?	None	Same magnitude; opposite direction	Same center; magnitude $360° - x°$	None	Same center; magnitude $\frac{1}{k}$
Composition of n reflections?	$n = 1$	$n = 2$, parallel	$n = 2$, nonparallel	$n = 3$	No
Isometry?	Yes	Yes	Yes	Yes	No
Invariant points?	Line of reflection	None	Center of rotation	None	Center of transformation

9.6 EXERCISES

Find the reflection images of the given figures about the given lines.

1.

2.

3.

4.

5.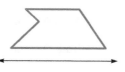

6.

7.

8.

Find any lines of symmetry of the given figures.

9.

10.

11.

12.

First reflect the given figure about line m. Then reflect about line n.

13.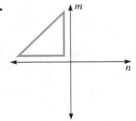

14.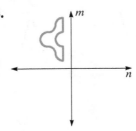

15.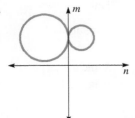

16.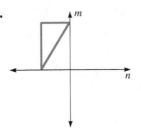

17.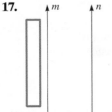

18.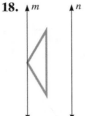

19.

20.

In Exercises 21–34, let T be a translation having magnitude 1.5 cm to the right in a direction parallel to the bottom edge of the page. Let r_m be a reflection about line m, and let R_P be a rotation about point P having magnitude 60° clockwise. In each of Exercises 21–32, perform the given transformations on point A of the figure below to obtain final image point A'.

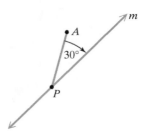

21. r_m **22.** R_P **23.** T

24. $r_m \cdot r_m$ **25.** $T \cdot T$ **26.** $R_P \cdot R_P$

27. $T \cdot R_P$ **28.** $T \cdot r_m$ **29.** $r_m \cdot T$

30. $R_P \cdot r_m$ **31.** $r_m \cdot R_P$ **32.** $R_P \cdot T$

33. Is $T \cdot r_m$ a glide reflection here?

34. Is $T \cdot r_m = r_m \cdot T$ true?

35. Suppose a rotation is given by $r_m \cdot r_n$, as shown in the figure below. Find the images of A, B, and C.

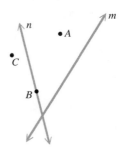

36. Does a glide reflection preserve
   (a) collinearity?   **(b)** distance?

Find the point reflection images of each of the following figures with the given point Q as center.

37.

38.

39.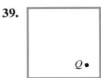

40.

Perform the indicated size transformation.

41. magnitude 2; center M

42. magnitude $\frac{1}{2}$; center M

43. magnitude $\frac{1}{2}$; center M

44. magnitude 2; center M

45. magnitude $\frac{1}{3}$; center M

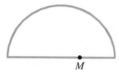

46. magnitude $\frac{1}{3}$; center M

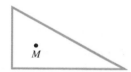

Exercises 47–50 refer to the figure in the next column, which consists of a sequence of quadrilaterals spiraling toward a single point P. Each successive quadrilateral is obtained by a clockwise 60° rotation about P, followed by a contraction of magnitude $\frac{4}{5}$ with center P. We will call the rotation R_P and the contraction C_P.

47. A composition of _____ clockwise rotations of 60° results in an identically oriented quadrilateral.

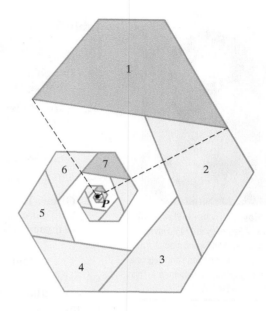

48. Quadrilateral 1 may be transformed into Quadrilateral 7 by the composition

$$C_P \cdot R_P \cdot C_P \cdot R_P \cdot C_P \cdot R_P \cdot C_P \cdot R_P \cdot C_P \cdot R_P \cdot C_P \cdot R_P.$$

Use your conclusion from **Exercise 47** to simplify this to a single contraction. Express the magnitude as a fraction.

49. Quadrilateral 1 may be transformed into Quadrilateral $6n + 1$ by repeating C_P $6n$ times. This can be expressed concisely as $C_P{}^{6n}$. Find a similar concise expression for the transformation of Quadrilateral 1 into Quadrilateral $6n + 3$.

50. What transformation will transform Quadrilateral n into Quadrilateral $n + 3$?

9.7 NON-EUCLIDEAN GEOMETRY AND TOPOLOGY

OBJECTIVES

1. Consider Euclid's postulates and axioms.
2. Understand the parallel postulate.
3. Investigate the origins of non-Euclidean geometry.
4. Project Euclidean objects onto a sphere.
5. Understand the concept of duality in projective geometry.
6. Determine the topological equivalence of figures.

Euclid's Postulates and Axioms

The *Elements* of Euclid is quite possibly the most influential mathematics book ever written. (See the margin note on **page 450.**) It begins with definitions of basic ideas such as

point, line, and plane.

Euclid then gives five postulates providing the foundation of all that follows.

Next, Euclid lists five axioms that he views as general truths and not just facts about geometry. See **Table 5** on the next page. (To some of the Greek writers, postulates were truths about a particlar field, while axioms were general truths. Today, "axiom" is used in either case.) Using only these ten statements and the basic rules of logic, Euclid was able to prove a large number of "propositions" about geometric figures.

John Playfair (1748–1819) wrote his *Elements of Geometry* in 1795. Playfair's Axiom is: Given a line *k* and a point *P* not on the line, there exists one and only one line *m* through *P* that is parallel to *k*. This is equivalent to Euclid's Postulate 5.

Table 5

Euclid's Postulates	Euclid's Axioms
1. Two points determine one and only one straight line.	**6.** Things equal to the same thing are equal to each other.
2. A straight line extends indefinitely far in either direction.	**7.** If equals are added to equals, the sums are equal.
3. A circle may be drawn with any given center and any given radius.	**8.** If equals are subtracted from equals, the remainders are equal.
4. All right angles are equal.	**9.** Figures that can be made to coincide are equal.
5. Given a line *k* and a point *P* not on the line, there exists one and only one line *m* through *P* that is parallel to *k*.	**10.** The whole is greater than any of its parts.

The statement for Postulate 5 given above is actually known as Playfair's axiom on parallel lines, which is equivalent to Euclid's fifth postulate. To understand why this postulate caused trouble for so many mathematicians for so long, we must examine the original formulation.

The Parallel Postulate (Euclid's Fifth Postulate)

In its original form, Euclid's fifth postulate states the following:

*If two lines (k and m in **Figure 76**) are such that a third line, n, intersects them so that the sum of the two interior angles (A and B) on one side of line n is less than (the sum of) two right angles, then the two lines, if extended far enough, will meet on the same side of n that has the sum of the interior angles less than (the sum of) two right angles.*

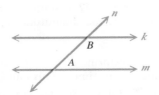

Figure 76

Euclid's parallel postulate is quite different from the other nine postulates and axioms we listed. It is long and wordy, and difficult to understand without a sketch. It was commonly believed that this was not a postulate at all but a theorem to be proved. For more than 2000 years, mathematicians tried repeatedly to prove it.

The most dedicated attempt came from an Italian Jesuit, Girolamo Saccheri (1667–1733). He attempted to prove the parallel postulate in an indirect way, by so-called "reduction to absurdity." He would assume the postulate to be false and then show that the assumption leads to a contradiction of something true (an absurdity). Such a contradiction would thus prove the statement true. Saccheri began with a quadrilateral, as in **Figure 77**. He assumed angles *A* and *B* to be right angles and sides *AD* and *BC* to be equal. His plan was as follows:

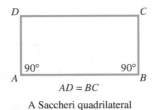

AD = BC

A Saccheri quadrilateral

Figure 77

1. To assume that angles *C* and *D* are obtuse angles, and to show that this leads to a contradiction.

2. To assume that angles *C* and *D* are acute angles, and to show that this also leads to a contradiction.

3. Then if *C* and *D* can be neither acute nor obtuse angles, they must be right angles.

4. If *C* and *D* are both right angles, then it can be proved that the fifth postulate is true. It thus is a theorem rather than a postulate.

Saccheri had no trouble with part 1. However, he did not actually reach a contradiction in the second part but produced some theorems so "repugnant" that he convinced himself he had vindicated Euclid. In fact, he published a book called in English *Euclid Freed of Every Flaw*. However, today we know that the fifth postulate is indeed an axiom and not a theorem. It is *consistent* with Euclid's other axioms.

A song titled simply **Lobachevsky** appears on the CD *Tom Lehrer Revisited.* The songwriter described this song as an account of "one way to get ahead in mathematics (which happens to be the author's own academic specialty) or any other academic field." Lehrer's music is available for download. Listen to *Lobachevsky,* and see what Lehrer suggests!

The ten axioms of Euclid describe the world around us with remarkable accuracy. We now realize that the fifth postulate is necessary in Euclidean geometry to establish *flatness.* That is, the axioms of Euclid describe the geometry of *plane surfaces.* By changing the fifth postulate, we can describe the geometry of other surfaces. So, other geometric systems exist as much as Euclidean geometry exists, and they can even be demonstrated in our world. A system of geometry in which the fifth postulate is changed is a **non-Euclidean geometry.**

The Origins of Non-Euclidean Geometry

One non-Euclidean system was developed by three people working separately at about the same time. Early in the nineteenth century, Carl Friedrich Gauss worked out a consistent geometry replacing Euclid's fifth postulate. He never published his work, however, because he feared the ridicule of people who could not free themselves from habitual ways of thinking.

Nikolai Ivanovich Lobachevski (1793–1856) published a similar system in 1830 in the Russian language. At the same time, Janos Bolyai (1802–1860), a Hungarian army officer, worked out a similar system, which he published in 1832, not knowing about Lobachevski's work. Bolyai never recovered from the disappointment of not being the first and did no further work in mathematics.

Lobachevski replaced Euclid's fifth postulate with the following.

> *Angles C and D in the quadrilateral of Saccheri are acute angles.*
>
> Lobachevski's replacement

This postulate of Lobachevski can be rephrased as follows.

> *Through a point P off a line k* (**Figure 78**), *at least two different lines can be drawn parallel to k.*

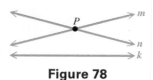

Figure 78

Compare this form of Lobachevski's postulate to the geometry of Euclid, where only one line can be drawn through *P* and parallel to *k.* At first glance, the postulate of Lobachevski does not agree with what we know about the world around us. But this is only because we think of our immediate surroundings as being flat.

Many of the theorems of Euclidean geometry are valid for the geometry of Lobachevski, but many are not. For example, in Euclidean geometry, the sum of the measures of the angles in any triangle is 180°. In Lobachevskian geometry, the sum of the measures of the angles in any triangle is *less* than 180°. Also, triangles of different sizes can never have equal angles, so similar triangles do not exist.

The geometry of Euclid can be represented on a plane. Since any portion of the earth that we are likely to see looks flat, Euclidean geometry is very useful for describing the everyday world around us. The non-Euclidean geometry of Lobachevski can be represented as a surface called a **pseudosphere.** This surface is formed by revolving a curve called a **tractrix** about the line *AB* in **Figure 79.**

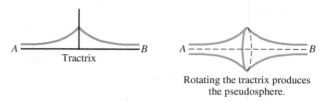

Figure 79

A second non-Euclidean system was developed by Georg Riemann (1826–1866). He pointed out the difference between a line that continues indefinitely and a line having infinite length. For example, a circle on the surface of a sphere continues indefinitely but does not have infinite length. Riemann developed the idea of geometry on a sphere and replaced Euclid's fifth postulate with the following.

Angles C and D of the Saccheri quadrilateral are obtuse angles.

Riemann's replacement

In terms of parallel lines, Riemann's postulate is stated this way.

Through a point P off a line k, no line can be drawn that is parallel to k.

Riemannian geometry is important in navigation. "Lines" in this geometry are really *great circles,* or circles whose centers are at the center of the sphere. The shortest distance between two points on a sphere lies along an arc of a great circle. Great circle routes on a globe don't look at all like the shortest distance when the globe is flattened out to form a map, but this is part of the distortion that occurs when the earth is represented as a flat surface. See **Figure 80.** The sides of a triangle drawn on a sphere would be arcs of great circles. And, in Riemannian geometry, the sum of the measures of the angles in any triangle is *more* than 180°.

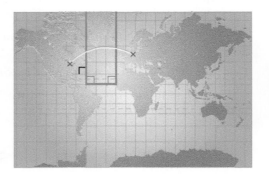
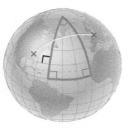

Figure 80

Projective Geometry

Beginning in the fifteenth century, artists led by Leone Battista Alberti (1404–1472), Leonardo da Vinci (1452–1519), and Albrecht Dürer (1471–1528) began to study the problems of representing three dimensions in two. What artists initiated, mathematicians developed into another non-Euclidean geometry, that of **projective geometry.**

Gerard Desargues (1591–1661), a French architect and engineer, published in 1636 and 1639 a treatise and proposals about **perspective,** thus inventing projective geometry. However, these innovations were hidden for nearly 200 years until a manuscript by Desargues was discovered in 1840, about 30 years after projective geometry had been revived by Jean-Victor Poncelet (1788–1867).

Although there are many projective geometries, an example of one that projects three-dimensional space onto a **projective sphere** is depicted in **Figure 81** on the next page. The projected image of a point *P* is the pair of points of intersection of the sphere with the line passing through *P* and the center of the sphere. These two points (labeled *P′* and *P″* in the figure) are **antipodal points** and are considered undistinguishable (that is, they are treated as a single point). The eye of the observer is thought to be at the center of the sphere, and the images of objects in space are projected onto the spherical "screen." Notice that parallel lines *m* and *n* in Euclidean space correspond to two great circles in the sphere that intersect on the "equator" of the sphere. In this configuration, the equator corresponds to infinity, which is just another great circle (line) in this geometry.

How should artists paint a realistic view of **railroad tracks vanishing into the horizon?** In reality, the tracks are always a constant distance apart, but they cannot be drawn that way except from overhead. The artist must make the tracks converge at a "vanishing point" to show how things look from the perspective of an observer.

Georg Friedrich Bernhard Riemann (1826–1866) was a German mathematician. Though he lived a short time and published few papers, his work forms a basis for much modern mathematics. He made significant contributions to the theory of functions and the study of complex numbers, as well as to geometry. Most calculus books today use the idea of a "Riemann sum" in defining the integral.

Riemann achieved a complete understanding of the non-Euclidean geometries of his day, expressing them on curved surfaces and showing how to extend them to higher dimensions.

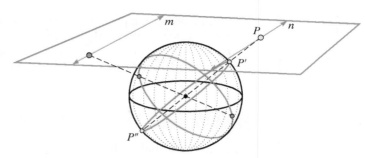

Figure 81

Figure 82 shows that intersecting lines in Euclidean space are also mapped to great circles that intersect at a single point (antipodal pair).

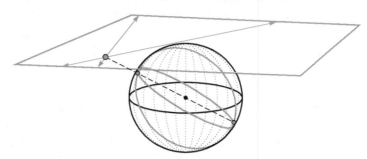

Figure 82

Projective geometries preserve points and intersections, but not distances. **Figure 82** demonstrates that a point of intersection in Euclidean space will be projected to a point of intersection in the projective plane. But **Figure 81** illustrates that distance (such as that between parallel lines) in Euclidean space does not survive the projection process.

EXAMPLE 1 Determining the Projective Image of a Plane Figure

Given a triangle in Euclidean space, draw a picture showing how the triangle would be projected onto the projective sphere.

Solution

Since antipodal points are not distinguished, we use a hemisphere for simplicity. We begin with a triangle contained in a plane above the hemisphere, and draw segments from the vertices of the triangle to the center of the sphere. We then do our best to estimate the three points where those segments intersect the sphere. Remembering that lines in the projective geometry are great circles, we connect the three points with arcs of great circles. The finished drawing is shown in **Figure 83.** ∎

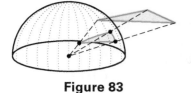

Figure 83

Consider the following statements.

Any two distinct points are contained in a unique line.

Any two distinct lines contain a unique point.

The first of these statements is true in Euclidean plane geometry, but the second is not. However, projective geometry removes the obstacle of non-intersecting parallel lines. As shown in **Figures 81 and 82,** every pair of lines (great circles) has a point of intersection. Surfaces for which both of the above statements are true are **projective planes.** Notice that these statements are identical, except that the instances of "point" and "line" are interchanged, and the containment relationship is exchanged for its inverse.

The preceding pair of statements is one example of the **duality** that is characteristic of projective geometry. Every true statement about a relationship between points and lines in the projective plane has its dual—a statement formed by interchanging "point" with "line" and replacing the relationship with its inverse.

EXAMPLE 2 Expressing a Dual

Express the dual of the following statement.

There are four distinct points, no three of which are contained in the same line.

Solution

We interchange "point" and "line" in the statement, and exchange the relationship "contained in" with its inverse, "contains." These changes give this statement.

There are four distinct lines, no three of which contain the same point. ∎

Topology

The plane and space figures studied in the Euclidean system are carefully distinguished by differences in size, shape, angularity, and so on. For a given figure such properties are permanent, and, thus, we can ask sensible questions about congruence and similarity. Suppose we studied "figures" made of rubber bands, as it were: "figures" that could be stretched, bent, or otherwise distorted without tearing or scattering. **Topology** does just that.

Topological questions concern the basic structure of objects rather than size or arrangement. A typical topological question has to do with the number of holes in an object, a basic structural property that does not change during deformation. Consider these examples.

- We cannot deform a rubber ball to get a rubber band without tearing it—making a hole in it. Thus the two objects are not topologically equivalent.

- On the other hand, a doughnut and a coffee cup are topologically equivalent, because one could be stretched to form the other without changing the basic structural property.

EXAMPLE 3 Determining Topological Equivalence

Decide whether the figures in each pair are topologically equivalent.

(a) a football and a cereal box   **(b)** a doughnut and an unzipped coat

Solution

(a) If we assume that a football is made of a perfectly elastic substance such as rubber or dough, it could be twisted or kneaded into the same shape as a cereal box. Thus, the two figures are topologically equivalent.

(b) A doughnut has one hole, while the coat has two (the sleeve openings). Thus, a doughnut could not be stretched and twisted into the shape of the coat without tearing another hole in it. Because of this, a doughnut and the coat are not topologically equivalent. ∎

Topology and geometry software, including games for users age 10 and up, can be found at www.geometrygames.org, a site developed by Jeff Weeks. Included are Torus Games, Kali, KaleidoTile, and investigations into Curved Spaces.

In topology, figures are classified according to their **genus**—that is, the number of cuts that can be made without cutting the figures into two pieces. The genus of an object is the number of holes in it. See **Figure 84** on the next page.

Torus One of the most useful figures in topology is the torus, a doughnut-like surface. Its properties are different from those of a sphere, for example. Imagine a sphere covered with hair. You cannot comb the hairs in a completely smooth way. One fixed point remains, as you can find on your own head. In the same way, on the surface of the earth the winds are not a smooth system. There is a calm point somewhere. However, the hair on a torus could be combed smooth.

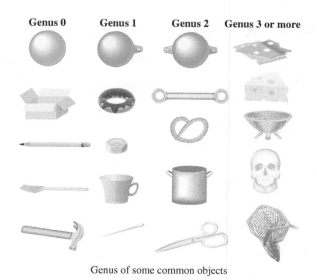

Genus of some common objects

Figure 84

FOR FURTHER THOUGHT

Two Interesting Topological Surfaces

Two examples of topological surfaces are the **Möbius strip** and the **Klein bottle**. The Möbius strip is a single-sided surface named after August Ferdinand Möbius (1790–1868), a pupil of Gauss.

To construct a Möbius strip, cut out a rectangular strip of paper, perhaps 3 cm by 25 cm. Paste together the two 3-cm ends after giving the paper a half-twist. To see how the strip now has only one side, mark an x on the strip and then mark another x on what appears to be the other "side." Begin at one of the x's you have drawn, and trace a path along the strip. You will eventually come to the other x without crossing the edge of the strip.

A branch of chemistry called chemical topology studies the structures of chemical configurations. A recent advance in this area was the synthesis of the first molecular Möbius strip, which was formed by joining the ends of a double-stranded strip of carbon and oxygen atoms.

A mathematician confided

That a Möbius strip is one-sided.

And you'll get quite a laugh

If you cut one in half,

For it stays in one piece when divided.

Möbius strip

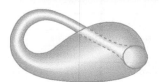

Klein bottle

Whereas a Möbius strip results from giving a paper *strip* a half-twist and then connecting it to itself, if we could do the same thing with a paper *tube* we would obtain a Klein bottle, named after Felix Klein (1849–1925). Klein produced important results in several areas, including non-Euclidean geometry and the early beginnings of group theory.

A mathematician named Klein

Thought the Möbius strip was divine.

Said he, "If you glue

The edges of two

You'll get a weird bottle like mine."

For Group or Individual Investigation

1. The Möbius strip has other interesting properties. With a pair of scissors, cut the strip lengthwise. Do you get two strips? Repeat the process with what you have obtained from the first cut. What happens?

2. Now construct another Möbius strip, and start cutting lengthwise about $\frac{1}{3}$ of the way from one edge. What happens?

3. What would be the advantage of a conveyor belt with the configuration of a Möbius strip?

9.7 EXERCISES

Study the chart below, and use it to respond to Exercises 1–10.

1. In which geometry is the sum of the measures of the angles of a triangle equal to 180°?

2. In which geometry is the sum of the measures of the angles of a triangle greater than 180°?

3. In which geometry is the sum of the measures of the angles of a triangle less than 180°?

4. In a quadrilateral *ABCD* in Lobachevskian geometry, the sum of the measures of the angles must be _____ 360°.
(less than/greater than)

5. In a quadrilateral *ABCD* in Riemannian geometry, the sum of the measures of the angles must be _____ 360°.
(less than/greater than)

6. Suppose *m* and *n* represent lines through *P* that are both parallel to *k*. In which geometry is this possible?

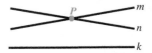

7. Suppose *m* and *n* below *must* meet at a point. In which geometry is this possible?

_____ *m*

_____ *n*

8. A globe representing the earth is a model for a surface in which geometry?

9. In which geometry is this statement possible? "Triangle *ABC* and triangle *DEF* are such that ∡*A* = ∡*D*, ∡*B* = ∡*E*, and ∡*C* = ∡*F*, and they have different perimeters."

EUCLIDEAN	NON-EUCLIDEAN	
Dates back to about 300 B.C.	Lobachevskian (about 1830)	Riemannian (about 1850)
Lines have *infinite* length.		Lines have *finite* length.
Geometry on a plane	Geometry on a surface like a pseudosphere	Geometry on a sphere
Angles *C* and *D* of a Saccheri quadrilateral are *right* angles.	Angles *C* and *D* are *acute* angles.	Angles *C* and *D* are *obtuse* angles.
Given point *P* off line *k*, exactly *one* line can be drawn through *P* and parallel to *k*.	*More than one* line can be drawn through *P* and parallel to *k*.	*No* line can be drawn through *P* and parallel to *k*.
Typical triangle *ABC*	Typical triangle *ABC*	Typical triangle *ABC*
Two triangles with the same size angles can have different size sides (similarity as well as congruence).	Two triangles with the same size angles must have the same size sides (congruence only).	

10. Draw a figure (on a sheet of paper) as best you can showing the shape formed by the north pole N and two points A and B lying at the equator of a model of the earth.

In Exercises 11 and 12, project the given shape onto the hemisphere.

11.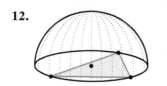

12.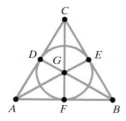

*Exercises 13–18 refer to the **Fano Plane,** shown here. It is a finite projective geometry containing seven points and seven lines.*

Points: A, B, C, D, E, F, and G

Lines: ADC, AFB, AGE, BEC, BGD, CGF, and DEF

(*Note: There is no requirement that a line be "straight" as in Euclidean geometry.*)

Verify that the Fano Plane satisfies each of the following statements, and state the dual in each case.

13. Any two distinct points have at least one line in common.

14. No two distinct points have more than one line in common.

15. Any two lines in a plane have at least one point of the plane in common.

16. There is at least one line on a plane.

17. Every line contains at least three points of the plane.

18. Not all of the points are contained in the same line.

Topological Equivalence   *Someone once described a topologist as "a mathematician who doesn't know the difference between a doughnut and a coffee cup." This is because both are of genus 1—they are topologically equivalent! Based on this interpretation, would a topologist know the difference between each pair of objects in Exercises 19–22?*

19. a spoon and a fork

20. a mixing bowl and a colander

21. a slice of American cheese and a slice of Swiss cheese

22. a compact disc and a phonograph record

In Exercises 23–30 each figure may be topologically equivalent to none or some of the objects labeled A–E. List all topological equivalences (by letter) for each figure.

A.

B.

C.

D.

E.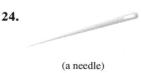

23.

(a pair of scissors)

24.

(a needle)

25.

(a carrot)

26.

(a calculator)

27.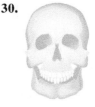

(a nut)

28.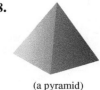

(a pyramid)

29.

(a coin)

30.

(a skull)

Give the genus of each object.

31. a compact disc

32. a phonograph record

33. a sheet of loose-leaf paper made for a three-ring binder

34. a sheet of loose-leaf paper made for a two-ring binder

35. a wedding band

36. a postage stamp

37. Pappus, a Greek mathematician in Alexandria about A.D. 320, wrote a commentary on the geometry of the times. We will work out a theorem of his about a hexagon inscribed in two intersecting lines.

First we define an old word in a new way: a **hexagon** consists of any six lines in a plane, no three of which meet in the same point. In the figure, the vertices of several hexagons are labeled with numbers. Thus 1–2 represents a line segment joining vertices 1 and 2. Segments 1–2 and 4–5 are opposite sides of a hexagon, as are 2–3 and 5–6, and 3–4 and 6–1.

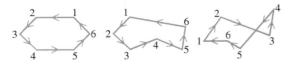

(a) Draw an angle less than 180°.

(b) Choose three points on one side of the angle. Label them 1, 5, 3 in that order, beginning with the point nearest the vertex.

(c) Choose three points on the other side of the angle. Label them 6, 2, 4 in that order, beginning with the point nearest the vertex.

(d) Draw line segments 1–6 and 3–4. Draw lines through the segments so that they extend to meet in a point. Call it *N*.

(e) Let lines through 1–2 and 4–5 meet in point *M*.

(f) Let lines through 2–3 and 5–6 meet in point *P*.

(g) Draw a straight line through points *M*, *N*, and *P*.

(h) Write in your own words a theorem generalizing your result.

38. The following theorem comes from projective geometry:

Theorem of Desargues in a Plane In a plane, if two triangles are placed so that lines joining corresponding vertices meet in a point, then corresponding sides, when extended, will meet in three collinear points. (*Collinear* points are points lying on the same line.)

Draw a figure that illustrates Desargues' theorem.

9.8	**CHAOS AND FRACTAL GEOMETRY**

OBJECTIVES

1 Investigate the origins and meaning of chaos.

2 Understand the basics of fractal geometry.

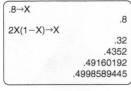

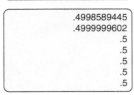

These two screens show how the TI-83 calculator can produce the sequence described. (The TI-84 plus produces a slightly different display, with the same results.)

Chaos

Does Chaos Rule the Cosmos?
—One of the ten great unanswered questions of science, as found in the November 1992 issue of *Discover*

Consider the equation

$$y = kx(1 - x).$$

Choosing $k = 2$ gives the equation

$$y = 2x(1 - x),$$

which can be "iterated" by starting with an arbitrary x-value between 0 and 1, calculating the resulting y-value, substituting that y-value back in as x, calculating the resulting y-value, substituting that y-value back in as x, calculating another y-value, and so on. For example, a starting value of $x = 0.8$ produces the following sequence (which you can verify with a calculator):

$$0.8, \ 0.32, \ 0.435, \ 0.492, \ 0.500, \ 0.500, \ 0.500, \quad \text{and so on.}$$

The sequence seems to begin randomly but quickly stabilizes at the value 0.500. A different initial x-value would produce another sequence that would also "converge" to 0.500. The value 0.500 can be called an *attractor* for the sequence generated by the equation $y = 2x(1 - x)$. The values of the sequence are "attracted" toward 0.500.

n	$u(n)$	
0	.7	
1	.63	
2	.6993	
3	.63084	
4	.69864	

$u(n) = 3u(n-1)(1-...$

n	$u(n)$	
14	.69588	
15	.63489	
16	.69542	
17	.63544	
18	.69497	
19	.63596	
20	.69454	

$u(n) = .6945436475$

These screens support the results of **Example 1.**

EXAMPLE 1 Finding Attractors

For the equation $y = kx(1 - x)$ with $k = 3$, begin with $x = 0.7$ and iterate with a calculator. What pattern emerges? How many attractors are there?

Solution

Using a TI-83/84 Plus calculator, we find that the seventeenth through twentieth iterations give this sequence of terms.

$$0.6354387337, \quad 0.6949690482, \quad 0.6359612107, \quad 0.6945436475$$

The sequence apparently converges in a manner different from the initial discussion, alternating between values near 0.636 and 0.695. Therefore, for $k = 3$, the sequence tends alternately toward *two* distinct attractors. ∎

It happens that the equation in **Example 1** exhibits the same behavior for any initial value of x between 0 and 1. You are asked to show this for several cases in the exercises.

n	$u(n)$	
0	.7	
1	.735	
2	.68171	
3	.75943	
4	.63943	

$u(n) = 3.5u(n-1)(...$

n	$u(n)$	
45	.82694	
46	.50088	
47	.875	
48	.38282	
49	.82694	
50	.50088	
51	.875	

$u(n) = .8749972636$

These screens support the discussion in **Example 2.**

EXAMPLE 2 Finding Attractors

In the equation of **Example 1,** change the multiplier k to 3.5, and find the forty-fourth through fifty-first terms. What pattern emerges? How many attractors are there?

Solution

Again, using a TI-83/84 Plus calculator and rounding to three decimal places, we get

$$0.383, 0.827, 0.501, 0.875, 0.383, 0.827, 0.501, 0.875.$$

This sequence seems to stabilize around *four* alternating attractors, approximately 0.383, 0.827, 0.501, and 0.875. ∎

Notice that in our initial discussion, for $k = 2$, the sequence converged to *one* attractor. In **Example 1,** for $k = 3$, it converged to *two* attractors, and in **Example 2,** for $k = 3.5$, it converged to *four* attractors.

It turns out that as k is increased further, the number of attractors doubles over and over again, more and more often. In fact, this doubling has occurred infinitely many times before k even gets as large as 4. When we look closely at groups of these doublings, we find that they are always similar to earlier groups but on a smaller scale. This is called *self-similarity,* or *scaling,* an idea that is not new but has taken on new significance in recent years. Somewhere before k reaches 4, the resulting sequence becomes apparently totally random, with no attractors and no stability. This type of condition is one instance of what has come to be known in the scientific community as **chaos.** This name came from an early paper by the mathematician James A. Yorke, of the University of Maryland at College Park.

The equation $y = kx(1 - x)$ does not look all that complicated, but the intricate behavior exhibited by it and similar equations has occupied some of the brightest minds (not to mention computers) in various fields—ecology, biology, physics, genetics, economics, mathematics—since about 1960. Such an equation might represent, for example, the population of some animal species, where the value of k is determined by factors (such as food supply or predators that prey on the species) that affect the increase or decrease of the population. Under certain conditions there is a long-run steady-state population (a single attractor). Under other conditions the population will eventually fluctuate between two alternating levels (two attractors), or four, or eight, and so on. But after a certain value of k, the long-term population becomes totally chaotic and unpredictable.

John Nash, a notable modern American mathematician (born in 1928), first came to the attention of the general public through his biography *A Beautiful Mind* (and the movie of the same name). In 1958 Nash narrowly lost out to René Thom (pictured below), topologist and inventor of catastrophe theory, for the Fields Medal. This is the mathematical equivalent of the Nobel prize.

Although his brilliant career was sadly interrupted by mental illness for a period of about thirty years, in 1994 Nash was awarded "the Central Bank of Sweden Prize in Economic Science in Memory of Alfred Nobel," generally regarded as equivalent to the Nobel prize. This award was for Nash's equilibrium theorem, published in his doctoral thesis in 1950. It turned out that Nash's work established a significant new way of analyzing rational conflict and cooperation in economics and other social sciences.

As long as k is small enough, there will be some number of attractors, and the long-term behavior of the sequence (or population) is the same regardless of the initial x-value. But once k is large enough to cause chaos, the long-term behavior of the system will change drastically when the initial x-value is changed only slightly. For example, consider the following two sequences, both generated from $y = 4x(1 - x)$.

0.600, 0.960, 0.154, 0.520, 0.998, 0.006, 0.025, . . .   Starting with $x = 0.600$

0.610, 0.952, 0.184, 0.601, 0.959, 0.157, 0.529, . . .   Starting with $x = 0.610$

The fact that the two sequences wander apart from one another is partly due to roundoff errors along the way. But Yorke and others have shown that even "exact" calculations of the iterates would quickly produce divergent sequences just because of the slightly different initial values. This type of "sensitive dependence on initial conditions" was discovered (accidentally) back in the 1960s by Edward Lorenz when he was looking for an effective computerized model of weather patterns. He discerned the implication that any long-range weather-predicting schemes might well be hopeless.

Patterns like those in the sequences above are more than just numerical oddities. Similar patterns apply to a great many phenomena in the physical, biological, and social sciences, many of them seemingly common natural systems that have been studied for hundreds of years. The measurement of a coastline; the description of the patterns in a branching tree, or a mountain range, or a cloud formation, or intergalactic cosmic dust; the prediction of weather patterns; the turbulent behavior of fluids of all kinds; the circulatory and neurological systems of the human body; fluctuations in populations and economic systems—these and many other phenomena remain mysteries, concealing their true nature somewhere beyond the reach of even our brightest minds and our biggest and fastest computers.

Continuous phenomena are easily dealt with. A change in one quantity produces a predictable change in another. (For example, a little more pressure on the gas pedal produces a little more speed.) Mathematical functions that represent continuous events can be graphed by unbroken lines or curves, or perhaps smooth, gradually changing surfaces. The governing equations for such phenomena are "linear," and extensive mathematical methods of solving them have been developed. On the other hand, erratic events associated with certain other equations are harder to describe or predict. The science of chaos, made possible by modern computers, continues to open up new ways to deal with such events.

One early attempt to deal with discontinuous processes in a new way, generally acknowledged as a forerunner of chaos theory, was that of the French mathematician René Thom, who, in the 1960s, applied the methods of topology. To emphasize the feature of sudden change, Thom referred to events such as a heartbeat, a buckling beam, a stock market crash, a riot, or a tornado as *catastrophes.* He proved that all catastrophic events (in our four-dimensional space-time) are combinations of seven elementary catastrophes. (In higher dimensions the number quickly approaches infinity.)

Each of the seven elementary catastrophes has a characteristic topological shape. Two examples are shown in **Figure 85.** The figure on the left is called a *cusp.* The figure on the right is an *elliptic umbilicus* (a belly button with an oval cross-section). Thom's work became known as **catastrophe theory.**

René Thom

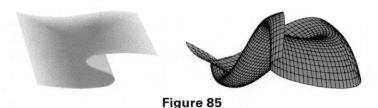

Figure 85

Computer graphics have been indispensable in the study of chaotic processes. The plotting of large numbers of points has revealed patterns that would otherwise not have been observed. (The underlying reasons for many of these patterns, however, have still not been explained.) The images shown in **Figure 86** were created using chaotic processes.

The surface of the earth, consisting of continents, mountains, oceans, valleys, and so on, has **fractal dimension** 2.2.

Aside from providing a geometric structure for chaotic processes in nature, fractal geometry is viewed by many as a significant art form. (To appreciate why, see the 1986 publication *The Beauty of Fractals,* by H. O. Peitgen and P. H. Richter, which contains 184 figures, many in color.) Peitgen and others have also published *Fractals for the Classroom: Strategic Activities Volume One* (Springer-Verlag, 1991).

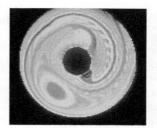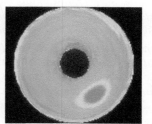

Figure 86

Fractals

If there is one structure that has provided a key for the new study of nonlinear processes, it is **fractal geometry,** developed over a period of years mainly by the IBM mathematician Benoit Mandelbrot (1924–2010). For his work in this field, and at the recommendation of the National Science Foundation, Columbia University awarded him the 1985 Bernard Medal for Meritorious Service to Science.

Lines have a single dimension. Plane figures have two dimensions, and we live in a three-dimensional spatial world. In a paper published in 1967, Mandelbrot investigated the idea of measuring the length of a coastline. He concluded that such a shape defies conventional Euclidean geometry and that, rather than having a natural number dimension, it has a "fractional dimension." A coastline is an example of a *self-similar shape*—a shape that repeats itself over and over on different scales. From a distance, the bays and inlets cannot be individually observed, but as one moves closer they become more apparent. The branching of a tree, from twig to limb to trunk, also exhibits a shape that repeats itself.

In the early twentieth century, the German mathematician H. von Koch investigated the so-called Koch snowflake. It is shown in **Figure 87.** Starting with an equilateral triangle, each side then gives rise to another smaller equilateral triangle. The process continues over and over, indefinitely, and a curve of infinite length is produced. The mathematics of Koch's era was not advanced enough to deal with such figures. However, using Mandelbrot's theory, it is shown that the Koch snowflake has dimension of about 1.26. This figure is obtained using a formula that involves logarithms. (Logarithms were introduced briefly in **Chapter 8.**)

Figure 87

The theory of fractals today finds application in many areas of science and technology. It has been used to analyze the turbulence of liquids, the branching of rivers, and price variation in economics—and even to identify certain types of cancer cells. Hollywood has used fractals in the special effects found in some blockbuster movies.

The image above is a **fractal** design generated by *Fractoid,* one of several fractal-generating apps available free in the Android market. This particular application allows the user to select the generating equation and choose among several color-assigning algorithms.

An interesting account of the science of chaos is found in the popular 1987 book *Chaos,* by James Gleick. Mandelbrot published two books on fractals. They are *Fractals: Form, Chance, and Dimension* (1975) and *The Fractal Geometry of Nature* (1982).

Exercises 1–25 are taken from an issue of Student Math Notes, *published by the National Council of Teachers of Mathematics. They were written by Dr. Tami S. Martin, Mathematics Department, Illinois State University, and the authors wish to thank N.C.T.M. and Tami Martin for permission to reproduce this activity. Because the exercises should be done in numerical order, answers to all exercises (both even- and odd-numbered) appear in the answer section of the student edition of this text.*

Most of the mathematical objects you have studied have dimensions that are whole numbers. For example, such solids as cubes and icosahedrons have dimension three. Squares, triangles, and many other planar figures are two-dimensional. Lines are one-dimensional, and points have dimension zero. Consider a square with side of length one. Gather several of these squares by cutting out or using patterning blocks.

(a square)

The size of a figure is calculated by counting the number of replicas (small pieces) that make it up. Here, a replica is the original square with edges of length one.

1. What is the least number of these squares that can be put together edge to edge to form a larger square?

The original square is made up of one small square, so its size is one.

2. What is the size of the new square?

3. What is the length of each edge of the new square?

*Similar figures have the same shape but are not necessarily the same size. The **scale factor** between two similar figures can be found by calculating the ratio of corresponding edges:*

$$\frac{\text{new length}}{\text{old length}}.$$

4. What is the scale factor between the large square and the small square?

5. Find the ratio $\frac{\text{new size}}{\text{old size}}$ for the two squares.

6. Form an even larger square that is three units long on each edge. Compare this square to the small square.

What is the scale factor between the two squares? What is the ratio of the new size to the old size?

7. Form an even larger square that is four units long on each edge. Compare this square to the small square. What is the scale factor between the two squares? What is the ratio of the new size to the old size?

8. Complete the table for squares.

Scale factor	2	3	4	5	6	10
Ratio of new size to old size						

9. How are the two rows in the table related?

Consider an equilateral triangle. The length of an edge of the triangle is one unit. The size of this triangle is one.

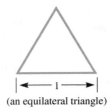

(an equilateral triangle)

10. What is the least number of equilateral triangles that can be put together edge to edge to form a similar larger triangle?

11. Complete the table for triangles.

Scale factor	2	3	4	5	6	10
Ratio of new size to old size						

12. How does the relationship between the two rows in this table compare with the one you found in the table for squares?

One way to define the dimension, d, of a figure relates the scale factor, the new size, and the old size:

$$(\text{scale factor})^d = \frac{\text{new size}}{\text{old size}}.$$

Using a scale factor of two for squares or equilateral triangles, we can see that $2^d = \frac{4}{1}$; that is, $2^d = 4$. Because $2^2 = 4$, the dimension, d, must be two. This definition of dimension confirms what we already know—that squares and equilateral triangles are two-dimensional figures.

13. Use this definition and your completed tables to confirm that the square and the equilateral triangle are two-dimensional figures for scale factors other than two.

Consider a cube, with edges of length one. Let the size of the cube be one.

14. What is the least number of these cubes that can be put together face to face to form a larger cube?

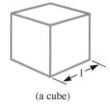

(a cube)

15. What is the scale factor between these two cubes? What is the ratio of the new size to the old size for the two cubes?

16. Complete the table for cubes.

Scale factor	2	3	4	5	6	10
Ratio of new size to old size						

17. How are the two rows in the table related?

18. Use the definition of dimension and a scale factor of two to verify that a cube is a three-dimensional object.

We have explored scale factors and sizes associated with two- and three-dimensional figures. Is it possible for mathematical objects to have fractional dimensions? Consider each figure formed by replacing the middle third of a line segment of length one by one upside-down V, each of whose two sides is equal in length to the segment removed. The first four stages in the development of this figure are shown.

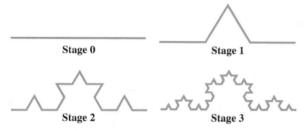

Stage 0   Stage 1

Stage 2   Stage 3

Finding the scale factor for this sequence of figures is difficult, because the overall length of a representative portion of the figure remains the same while the number of pieces increases. To simplify the procedure, follow these steps.

Step 1 Start with any stage (e.g., Stage 1).

Step 2 Draw the next stage (e.g., Stage 2) of the sequence and "blow it up" so that it contains an exact copy of the preceding stage (in this example, Stage 1).

Notice that Stage 2 contains four copies, or replicas, of Stage 1 and is three times as long as Stage 1.

Length = 1, size = 1 (1 replica)   Length = 3, size = 4 (4 replicas)
Stage 1   Stage 2

19. The scale factor is equal to the ratio $\frac{\text{new length}}{\text{old length}}$ between any two consecutive stages. The scale factor between Stage 1 and Stage 2 is _____.

20. The size can be determined by counting the number of replicas of Stage 1 found in Stage 2. Old size = 1, new size = ___.

Use the definition of dimension to compute the dimension, d, of the figure formed by this process: $3^d = \frac{4}{1}$; that is, $3^d = 4$. Since $3^1 = 3$ and $3^2 = 9$, for $3^d = 4$ the dimension of the figure must be greater than one but less than two:

$$1 < d < 2.$$

21. Use your calculator to estimate d. Remember that d is the exponent that makes 3^d equal 4. For example, because d must be between 1 and 2, try $d = 1.5$. But $3^{1.5} = 5.196\ldots$, which is greater than 4; thus, d must be smaller than 1.5. Continue until you approximate d to three decimal places. (Use logarithms for maximum accuracy.)

*The original figure was a one-dimensional line segment. By iteratively adding to the line segment, an object of dimension greater than one but less than two was generated. Objects with fractional dimension are known as **fractals**. Fractals are infinitely self-similar objects formed by repeated additions to, or removals from, a figure. The object attained at the limit of the repeated procedure is the fractal.*

Next consider a two-dimensional object with sections removed iteratively. In each stage of the fractal's development, a triangle is removed from the center of each triangular region.

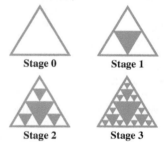

Stage 0   Stage 1

Stage 2   Stage 3

Use the process from the last example to help answer the following questions.

22. What is the scale factor of the fractal?

23. Old size = 1, new size = ___.

24. The dimension of the fractal is between what two whole number values?

25. Use the definition of dimension and your calculator to approximate the dimension of this fractal to three decimal places.

Use a calculator to determine the pattern of attractors for the equation

$$y = kx(1 - x)$$

for the given value of k and the given initial value of x.

26. $k = 3.25,$
$x = 0.7$

27. $k = 3.4,$
$x = 0.8$

28. $k = 3.55,$
$x = 0.7$

CHAPTER 9 SUMMARY

KEY TERMS

9.1

point
line
plane
half-line
ray
line segment
parallel lines
intersecting lines
parallel planes
intersecting planes
skew lines
angle
sides
vertex
one degree
acute angle
right angle
obtuse angle
straight angle
protractor
perpendicular lines
vertical angles
complementary
supplementary
transversal
alternate interior angles
alternate exterior angles
interior angles on same
   side of transversal
corresponding angles

9.2

simple curve
closed curve
convex
polygon
regular polygon
acute triangle
right triangle
obtuse triangle
equilateral triangle
isosceles triangle
scalene triangle
trapezoid
parallelogram
rectangle
square
rhombus
interior angle
exterior angle
circle
center
radius
chord
diameter
semicircle
tangent
secant
arc
inscribed
geometric construction
compass
perpendicular bisector

9.3

congruent triangles
similar triangles
hypotenuse
legs
Pythagorean triple

9.4

perimeter
area
circumference

9.5

plane figure
rectangular parallelopiped
space figure
polyhedra
tetrahedron
hexahedron
octahedron
dodecahedron
icosahedron
pyramid
prism
volume
surface area
right circular cylinder
sphere
right circular cone

9.6

transformational geometry
reflection

reflection image
line of reflection
transformation
invariant point
collinear
line of symmetry
composition
translation
magnitude
identity translation
inverses
rotation
center of rotation
point reflection
glide reflection
isometry
size transformation
dilation
contraction

9.7

pseudosphere
tractrix
perspective
projective sphere
antipodal points
projective plane
duality
genus

9.8

chaos
catastrophe theory
fractal

NEW SYMBOLS

$\longleftrightarrow$	line	$\parallel$	parallel	$\triangle$	triangle
$\circ\!\!\longrightarrow$	half-line	$\sphericalangle$	angle	$\cong$	congruence
$\bullet\!\!\longrightarrow$	ray	$\neg$	right angle	A'	image of A
$\bullet\!\!-\!\!\bullet$	segment	$\frown$	arc		

TEST YOUR WORD POWER

See how well you have learned the vocabulary in this chapter.

1. Vertical angles are
  A. angles whose measures add up to 180 degrees.
  B. formed by intersecting lines and have equal measure.
  C. formed by intersecting lines and do not have equal measure.
  D. angles with one side pointing vertically upward.

2. A scalene triangle is
  A. a triangle having at least two equal sides.
  B. a triangle that cannot possibly be a right triangle.
  C. a triangle having no two sides equal.
  D. a regular polygon having three sides.

3. A **Pythagorean triple** is
   A. a special triangle with side length ratio 1:2:3.
   B. an ordered triple (a, b, c) for which $a^2 + b^2 = c^2$.
   C. a triangle with largest angle having measure three times that of the smallest angle.
   D. a triangle with base equaling triple the height.

4. A **tetrahedron** is
   A. a regular polyhedron having four sides.
   B. a pyramid with a square base.
   C. a space figure having two faces in parallel planes.
   D. a space figure with parallelogram faces.

5. An **invariant point** of a transformation is a point
   A. that is its own image under the transformation.
   B. whose image is the same distance from the line of reflection as the point itself.
   C. contained in both the image and the original figure.
   D. that cannot be changed by any transformation.

6. In topology, the **genus** of a figure is
   A. the area of its cross section.
   B. the shape of its image projected onto the unit sphere.
   C. the number of distinct surfaces it has.
   D. the number of cuts that can be made without cutting it into two pieces.

ANSWERS

1. B **2.** C **3.** B **4.** A **5.** A **6.** D

QUICK REVIEW

Concepts	Examples

9.1 Points, Lines, Planes, and Angles

A **point** is represented by a dot. A **line** extends indefinitely in two directions, has no width, and is determined by two distinct points. A **plane** is represented by a flat surface and is determined by three points not all on the same line.

A **ray** has a starting point and extends indefinitely in one direction, and a **half-line** is a ray without a starting point. A **line segment** includes a starting point, an ending point, and all points between them.

Two lines are **parallel** if they are in the same plane but never intersect. Lines not in the same plane are **skew**.

An **angle** is made up of two rays with a common endpoint (**vertex**). The measure of an angle is given in **degrees,** where 1 degree (1°) is $\frac{1}{360}$ of a full rotation.

- An angle measuring less than 90° is an **acute angle.**
- An angle measuring between 90° and 180° is an **obtuse angle.**
- An angle measuring exactly 90° is a **right angle.**
- An angle measuring 180° is a **straight angle.**
- Two angles whose measures add to 90° are **complementary angles.**
- Two angles whose measures add to 180° are **supplementary angles.**

Lines intersecting at 90° angles are **perpendicular lines.**

A line intersecting parallel lines is a **transversal.**

Intersecting lines create two pairs of **vertical angles.**

Vertical angles have equal measure.

The figure shows a line passing through points A and B, and a plane determined by points A, B, and C.

- Ray AB ($\overrightarrow{AB}$) consists of point A and all points on the line to the right of point A.
- Half-line $A\overset{\circ}{B}$ consists only of the points to the right of point A.
- Line segment $\overline{AB}$ contains the two endpoints and all points in between.

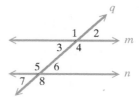

In the figure above, lines m and n are parallel. The transversal q, along with lines m and n, form eight angles.

∡1 is an **obtuse angle,** and ∡2 is an **acute angle.**

∡1 and ∡2 are **supplementary angles,** and together they form a **straight angle.**

∡1 and ∡4 are **vertical angles.**

∡1 and ∡5 are **corresponding angles** and have equal measure.

∡3 and ∡6 are **alternate interior angles** and have equal measure.

∡2 and ∡7 are **alternate exterior angles** and have equal measure.

∡3 and ∡5 are **interior angles on the same side of the transversal** and are supplementary.

Concepts	Examples

9.2 Curves, Polygons, Circles, and Geometric Constructions

Simple curves can be drawn without lifting the pencil from the paper and without passing through the same point twice. A **closed curve** has the same starting and ending point, and it can be drawn without lifting the pencil from the paper.

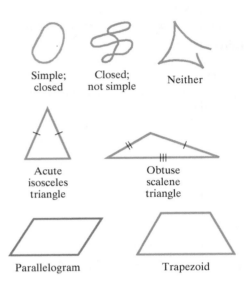

Simple; closed   Closed; not simple   Neither

A **polygon** is a simple closed curve made up of straight line segments; it is **regular** if all sides are equal and all angles are equal.

Triangles are three-sided polygons classified by the number of equal sides and by the measures of their angles relative to 90°.

Acute isosceles triangle   Obtuse scalene triangle

Quadrilaterals have four sides and are classified by characteristics of their sides and angles. For example, a **rhombus** is a parallelogram (a quadrilateral having two pairs of parallel sides) with all sides having equal lengths.

Parallelogram   Trapezoid

The sum of the interior angles of any triangle is 180°.

Any exterior angle has measure equal to the sum of the two opposite interior angles.

Solve for x.

The triangle has angles $(3x)°$, $(2x-5)°$, and exterior angle $(3x+41)°$.

$$3x + 2x - 5 = 3x + 41$$
$$5x - 5 = 3x + 41 \quad \text{Combine like terms.}$$
$$2x = 46 \quad \text{Subtract } 3x. \text{ Add 5.}$$
$$x = 23 \quad \text{Divide by 2.}$$

A **circle** is a set of points in the plane that are equidistant from a fixed point called the **center**. A **chord** is a line segment having endpoints on the circle, and the part of the circle between the endpoints of a chord, along with the endpoints themselves, form an **arc.** A chord passing through the center is a **diameter.**

The circle on the left shows the inscribed angle PQR with vertex Q on the circle, and chords PQ and QR. If chord PQ is a diameter, use a geometric construction to find the center of the circle.

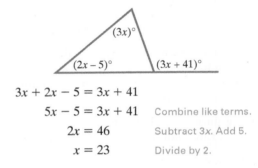

An angle with its vertex on a circle and its sides passing through two (other) points on the circle is said to be **inscribed** in the circle. Any inscribed angle has a measure equal to half the intercepted arc.

A straightedge and compass can be used to complete **geometric constructions.**

On the right, construct the perpendicular bisector of the chord QR. The center of the circle is the point where this bisector intersects the diameter PQ.

The construction reveals the point O to be the center of the circle. (*Note:* The center O could also be found by constructing the perpendicular bisector of the diameter PQ.)

Concepts	**Examples**

9.3 | The Geometry of Triangles: Congruence, Similarity, and the Pythagorean Theorem

Congruent triangles have exactly the same shape and size. This means that corresponding sides have equal length and corresponding angles have equal measure.

$$\triangle ABC \cong \triangle DEF$$

Congruence is often verified in a two-column proof.

Similar triangles have the same shape (corresponding angles are equal) but not necessarily the same size. Corresponding sides are proportional.

Properties of similar triangles can be used to solve for unknown parts of triangles, and this has many applications.

Given: $AC = BC$; $\angle ACD = \angle BCD$
Prove: $\triangle ADC \cong \triangle BDC$

Statements	**Reasons**
1. $AC = BC$	1. Given
2. $\angle ACD = \angle BCD$	2. Given
3. $CD = CD$	3. Reflexive property
4. $\triangle ADC \cong \triangle BDC$	4. SAS congruence property

In the figure shown, $\overleftrightarrow{AB}$ is parallel to $\overleftrightarrow{DE}$. Verify that $\triangle ABC$ is similar to $\triangle EDC$.

Since $\overleftrightarrow{AB}$ is parallel to $\overleftrightarrow{DE}$, $\overleftrightarrow{AE}$ is a transversal, and thus $\angle BAC = \angle DEC$ because they are alternate interior angles. Also, $\angle BCA = \angle DCE$, since they are vertical angles.

Therefore, $\triangle ABC$ is similar to $\triangle EDC$ by the Angle-Angle (AA) similarity property.

A flagpole casts a 99-ft shadow at the same time that a building 10 ft high casts an 18-ft shadow. Find the height of the flagpole.

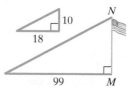

$$\frac{MN}{10} = \frac{99}{18} \qquad \text{Write a proportion using similar triangles.}$$
$$MN \cdot 18 = 10 \cdot 99 \qquad \text{Cross products}$$
$$MN = 55 \qquad \text{Solve for } MN.$$

The flagpole is 55 ft tall.

Pythagorean Theorem

If the two legs of a right triangle have lengths a and b, and the hypotenuse has length c, then

$$a^2 + b^2 = c^2.$$

Find the length of the hypotenuse of the right triangle with the flagpole above using the Pythagorean theorem. Let c be the length of the hypotenuse.

$$99^2 + (MN)^2 = c^2 \qquad a^2 + b^2 = c^2$$
$$99^2 + 55^2 = c^2 \qquad \text{Let } MN = 55.$$
$$9801 + 3025 = c^2 \qquad \text{Apply the exponents.}$$
$$12{,}826 = c^2 \qquad \text{Add.}$$
$$c = \sqrt{12{,}826} \qquad \text{Take the square root.}$$
$$c \approx 113.25 \qquad \text{Approximate.}$$

The length of the hypotenuse is approximately 113.25 ft.

Concepts   *Examples*

9.4 Perimeter, Area, and Circumference

The **perimeter** of a polygon is the sum of the lengths of its sides. The **area** of a polygon is the amount of plane surface it covers.

Polygon	Perimeter	Area
Triangle a $\;h\;$ c b	$P = a + b + c$	$\mathcal{A} = \dfrac{1}{2}bh$
Rectangle w ℓ	$P = 2\ell + 2w$	$\mathcal{A} = \ell w$
Square s s	$P = 4s$	$\mathcal{A} = s^2$
Parallelogram h b		$\mathcal{A} = bh$
Trapezoid b h B		$\mathcal{A} = \dfrac{1}{2}h(B + b)$

The distance around a circle is its **circumference.**

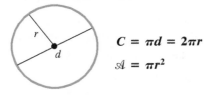

$C = \pi d = 2\pi r$

$\mathcal{A} = \pi r^2$

Find the perimeter of the entire figure and the area of the shaded region.

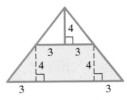

The hypotenuse of each triangle with legs of length 3 and 4 is $\sqrt{3^2 + 4^2} = \sqrt{25} = 5.$

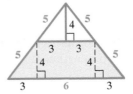

The *entire figure* is an isosceles triangle with side lengths of 12, 10, and 10.

$$P = 12 + 10 + 10 = 32$$

The shaded region is a trapezoid, with $B = 12$, $b = 6$, and $h = 4.$

$$\mathcal{A} = \frac{1}{2}h(B + b) = \frac{1}{2}(4)(12 + 6) = 36$$

Find the perimeter and area of the following figure.

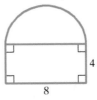

The figure is made up of a rectangle and a semicircle.

$$P = (4 + 8 + 4) + \left(\frac{1}{2} \cdot \pi \cdot 8\right) = 4\pi + 16$$

$$\mathcal{A} = (8 \cdot 4) + \left(\frac{1}{2} \cdot \pi \cdot 4^2\right) = 8\pi + 32$$

Concepts   **Examples**

9.5 Volume and Surface Area

Space figures occupy three-dimensional space and have both **volume** and **surface area.** A **polyhedron** is a space figure, the faces of which are polygons. A *regular* poly-hedron is one for which all faces are a copy of a single regular polygon. There are only five regular polyhedra.

The **volume** of a space figure is a measure of its capacity. The **surface area** is the total area that would be covered if the space figure were "peeled" and the peel laid flat.

Space Figure	Volume and Surface Area
Box	$V = \ell wh$ $S = 2\ell w + 2\ell h + 2hw$
Cube	$V = s^3$ $S = 6s^2$
Right Circular Cylinder	$V = \pi r^2 h$ $S = 2\pi rh + 2\pi r^2$
Sphere	$V = \dfrac{4}{3}\pi r^3$ $S = 4\pi r^2$
Right Circular Cone	$V = \dfrac{1}{3}\pi r^2 h$ $S = \pi r\sqrt{r^2 + h^2} + \pi r^2$
Pyramid	$V = \dfrac{1}{3}Bh$ (*B* is the area of the base.)

Regular Polyhedra

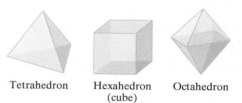

Tetrahedron   Hexahedron   Octahedron
               (cube)

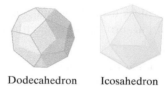

Dodecahedron   Icosahedron

Find the volume and surface area of the box.

$$V = \ell \cdot w \cdot h$$
$$= (8)(6)(4)$$
$$= 192 \text{ cm}^3$$

4 cm   8 cm   6 cm

$$S = 2\ell w + 2\ell h + 2hw$$
$$= 2(8)(6) + 2(8)(4) + 2(4)(6)$$
$$= 96 + 64 + 48$$
$$= 208 \text{ cm}^2$$

The grain silo consists of a half-sphere on top of a right circular cylinder. Find its volume and surface area (using $\pi \approx 3.14$).

$$V = \frac{1}{2} \cdot \frac{4}{3}\pi(4)^3 + \pi(4)^2(8)$$
$$\approx 535.89 \text{ cubic units}$$

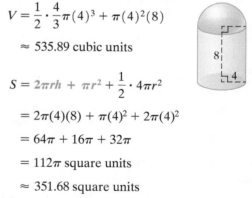

8

4

$$S = 2\pi rh + \pi r^2 + \frac{1}{2} \cdot 4\pi r^2$$
$$= 2\pi(4)(8) + \pi(4)^2 + 2\pi(4)^2$$
$$= 64\pi + 16\pi + 32\pi$$
$$= 112\pi \text{ square units}$$
$$\approx 351.68 \text{ square units}$$

Note that in the portion of surface area for the cylinder (shown in red), the formula included πr^2 instead of $2\pi r^2$, because the top of the cylinder is not an exposed surface in this case.

Concepts

Examples

9.6 Transformational Geometry

One geometric figure can be transformed into another by one or more geometric **transformations.**

- A **reflection** gives the mirror image of a figure about a **line of reflection.**

- A **translation** "slides" a copy of a figure to a new location. It is equivalent to two reflections about parallel lines.

- A **rotation** revolves a figure about a point called the **center of rotation** through an angle (the **magnitude of rotation**).

- A **glide reflection** is the composition of a reflection and a translation along the line of reflection.

- A **size transformation** stretches (or shrinks) a figure away from (or toward) a point (the center).

The figure shows $\triangle ABC$ **reflected** about line m. The image $\triangle A'B'C'$ is then **translated** parallel to line m. The image of this translation, $\triangle A''B''C''$, is then **rotated** clockwise around point H through an angle of 45°, resulting in the image $\triangle A'''B'''C'''$. Finally, this triangle is **stretched** (or **dilated**) by a factor of 2 using M as the center of the size transformation, resulting in the image $\triangle JKL$.

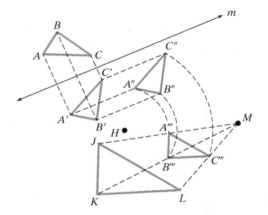

9.7 Non-Euclidean Geometry and Topology

Euclidean geometry is based on five postulates and five axioms. The fifth postulate is equivalent to "Given a line k and a point P not on the line, there exists one and only one line m through P that is parallel to k." When this postulate is changed, a **non-Eulcidean geometry** results.

Lobachevskian geometry replaces Euclid's fifth postulate with the statement "Through a point P off a line k, at least two different lines can be drawn parallel to k."

Riemannian geometry uses as its parallel postulate "Through a point P off a line k, no line can be drawn that is parallel to k."

Projective geometries exhibit **duality,** in that for each statement that holds true about points and lines in a projective plane, another true statement can be formed by interchanging "point" and "line" in the original statement.

Topology deals with properties of figures that are preserved under distortions that do not involve separating (puncturing or tearing) the figures. The topological **genus** of a figure is equal to the number of holes in the figure.

The figure shows the projection of a Euclidean triangle and line onto the sphere. The image is a Riemannian triangle with interior angles summing to more than 180°, and half of a great circle, which is a line in this projective geometry.

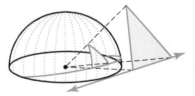

The *dual* of the statement "Every pair of distinct points determine a line" is the statement

"Every pair of distinct lines determine a point."

A sphere and a cone both have genus 0, and a torus has genus 1.

Concepts   **Examples**

9.8 Chaos and Fractal Geometry

Chaos theory deals with systems that may become unstable with very small changes in governing parameter values.

Fractals are infinitely self-similar objects formed by repeated additions to, or removals from, a figure. The object attained at the limit of the procedure is the fractal.

The sequence generated by the equation

$$y = 2.5x(1 - x),$$

with intial value of $x = 0.5$, has one attractor at 0.6.

CHAPTER 9   TEST

1. Consider a 42° angle. Answer each of the following.
   (a) What is the measure of its complement?
   (b) What is the measure of its supplement?
   (c) Classify it as acute, obtuse, right, or straight.

Find the measure of each marked angle.

2.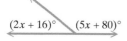
   $(2x + 16)°$ $(5x + 80)°$

3.
   $(7x - 25)°$ $(4x + 5)°$

4.
   $(4x + 6)°$
   $(10x)°$

In Exercises 5 and 6, assume that lines m and n are parallel, and find the measure of each marked angle.

5.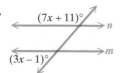
   $(7x + 11)°$ n
   $(3x - 1)°$ m

6.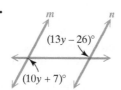
   m   n
   $(13y - 26)°$
   $(10y + 7)°$

7. Explain why a rhombus must be a quadrilateral, but a quadrilateral might not be a rhombus.

8. Which one of the statements A–D is false?
   A. A square is a rhombus.
   B. The acute angles of a right triangle are complementary.
   C. A triangle may have both a right angle and an obtuse angle.
   D. A trapezoid may have nonparallel sides of the same length.

Identify each of the following curves as simple, closed, both, *or* neither.

9.

10.

11. Find the measure of each angle in the triangle.
    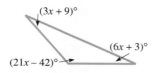
    $(3x + 9)°$
    $(6x + 3)°$
    $(21x - 42)°$

Find the area of each of the following figures.

12.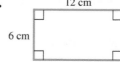
    12 cm
    6 cm

13.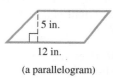
    5 in.
    12 in.
    (a parallelogram)

14.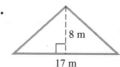
    8 m
    17 m

15.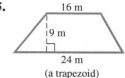
    16 m
    9 m
    24 m
    (a trapezoid)

16. **Area of a Shaded Figure** What is the area (to the nearest square unit) of the colored portion of the figure? Use 3.14 as an approximation for π.
    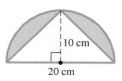
    10 cm
    20 cm
    (a triangle within a semicircle)

17. Circumference of a Circle If a circle has area 144π square inches, what is its circumference?

18. Circumference of a Dome The Rogers Centre in Toronto, Canada, is the first stadium with a hard-shell, retractable roof. The steel dome is 630 feet in diameter. To the nearest foot, what is the circumference of this dome?

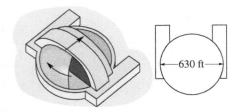

—630 ft—

19. Given: $\angle CAB = \angle DBA$; $DB = CA$
Prove: $\triangle ABD \cong \triangle BAC$

20. Height of a Building If an 8-ft stop sign casts a 5-ft shadow at the same time a building casts a 40-ft shadow, how tall is the building?

21. Diagonal of a Rectangle What is the measure of a diagonal of a rectangle that has width 20 m and length 21 m?

22. Reflect the given figure first about line n and then about line m.

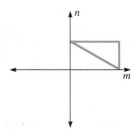

23. Find the point reflection image of the given figure with the given point as center.

$\bullet Q$

*Find **(a)** the volume and **(b)** the surface area of each of the following space figures. When necessary, use 3.14 as an approximation for π. In Exercises 24 and 26, round to the nearest hundredth.*

24.

6 in.

(a sphere)

25.

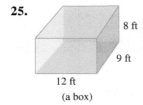

8 ft

9 ft

12 ft

(a box)

26.

6 m

14 m

(a right circular cylinder)

27. List several main distinctions between Euclidean geometry and non-Euclidean geometry.

28. Topological Equivalence Are the following pairs of objects topologically equivalent?

(a) a page of a book and the cover of the same book

(b) a pair of glasses with the lenses removed, and the Mona Lisa

29. Projection Image A line segment of length 7 cm is projected onto a sphere with radius 1 cm. Will the image also have a length of 7 cm?

30. Use a calculator to determine the attractors for the sequence generated by the equation

$$y = 2.1x(1 - x),$$

with initial value of $x = 0.6$.

Counting Methods

10

When he was just a youngster, Howard became fascinated with cooking. He knew very early in life that he wanted to start his own restaurant one day. His specialty was hamburgers—people often told him that his burgers were the best they ever ate.

He got his restaurant management degree, and his small business loan soon followed. His dream had come true, and he eagerly began the process of opening Howard's Up and Down Hamburgers. Howard knew he wanted a very limited menu so that he could concentrate on ensuring the highest quality in the small number of items he offered. He decided that for his hamburger orders, he would offer his customers the following 8 choices of extras to add to the basic bun and meat patty:

a second patty, cheese, mustard, mayonnaise, lettuce, tomato, onion, pickle.

A customer could choose none, some but not others, or all of these extras.

During construction of his restaurant, Howard needed to have a sign custom-made to let customers know that they could have their hamburger however they wanted. He recalled, from visits to Sonic and Waffle House, that he had seen large numbers indicating how many different combinations of extras their customers could select. The question became

"What number applies to my situation?"

It was easy to count the special cases:

1 way of ordering *no extras,*

8 ways of ordering only *1 extra,*

and   1 way of ordering *all 8 extras.*

Number of Extras	Number of Ways to Order
0	1
1	8
2	28
3	56
4	70
5	56
6	28
7	8
8	1

Using concepts from the chapter on counting that he studied in his college mathematics class, Howard was able to determine the other numbers of ways. See the table in the margin.

He added up all the numbers (in other words, all the combinations of 8 things taken a particular number at a time), and told his sign maker to come up with a sign indicating that Howard's Up and Down burgers can be chosen in 256 different ways.

10.1   COUNTING BY SYSTEMATIC LISTING

OBJECTIVES

1 Use a systematic approach to perform a one-part counting task.

2 Use a product table to perform a two-part counting task.

3 Use a tree diagram to perform a multiple-part counting task.

4 Use systematic listing in a counting task that involves a geometric figure.

Counting

In this chapter, **counting** means finding the number of objects, of some certain type, that exist. The methods of counting presented in this section involve listing the possible results for a given task. This approach is practical only for fairly short lists. When listing possible results, it is extremely important to use a *systematic* approach, so that no possibilities are missed.

One-Part Tasks

The results for simple *one-part tasks* can often be listed easily. An example of a **one-part task** is tossing a single fair coin. The list here is *heads, tails,* with two possible results. If the task is to roll a single fair die (a cube with faces numbered 1 through 6), the different results are

1, 2, 3, 4, 5, 6,   a total of six possibilities.

EXAMPLE 1 Selecting a Club President

Consider a club *N* with five members:

$N = \{$ Alan, Bill, Cathy, David, Evelyn $\}$,   abbreviated as $N = \{A, B, C, D, E\}$.

In how many ways can this group select a president? (All members are eligible.)

Solution

The task in this case is to select one of the five members as president. There are five possible results.

A, B, C, D, and E ∎

Product Tables for Two-Part Tasks

We now consider **two-part tasks.**

EXAMPLE 2   Building Numbers from a Set of Digits

Determine the number of two-digit numbers that can be written using only the digits 1, 2, and 3.

Solution

This task consists of two parts.

Part 1   Choose a first digit.

Part 2   Choose a second digit.

The results for a two-part task can be pictured in a **product table** such as **Table 1**. From the table we obtain our list of possible results.

$$11, \ 12, \ 13, \ 21, \ 22, \ 23, \ 31, \ 32, \ 33$$

There are nine possibilities. ■

Table 1

	Second Digit		
First Digit	**1**	**2**	**3**
1	11	12	13
2	21	22	23
3	31	32	33

EXAMPLE 3   Rolling a Pair of Dice

Determine the number of different possible results when two ordinary dice are rolled.

Solution

Assume the dice are easily distinguishable. Perhaps one is red and the other green. Then the task consists of two parts.

Part 1   Roll the red die.

Part 2   Roll the green die.

The product table in **Table 2** shows that there are thirty-six possible results.

Table 2   Rolling Two Fair Dice

		Green Die					
		1	**2**	**3**	**4**	**5**	**6**
Red Die	**1**	(1, 1)	(1, 2)	(1, 3)	(1, 4)	(1, 5)	(1, 6)
	2	(2, 1)	(2, 2)	(2, 3)	(2, 4)	(2, 5)	(2, 6)
	3	(3, 1)	(3, 2)	(3, 3)	(3, 4)	(3, 5)	(3, 6)
	4	(4, 1)	(4, 2)	(4, 3)	(4, 4)	(4, 5)	(4, 6)
	5	(5, 1)	(5, 2)	(5, 3)	(5, 4)	(5, 5)	(5, 6)
	6	(6, 1)	(6, 2)	(6, 3)	(6, 4)	(6, 5)	(6, 6)

36 possible results

■

You will want to refer to **Table 2** *when various dice-rolling problems occur in the remainder of this chapter and the next.*

WHEN Will I Ever USE This ?

One of today's most popular sports-related pastimes is that of fantasy leagues. Members of the league draft a team and compete against other "owners," relying on the modern-day immediate availability of statistics via technology. But before the advent of fantasy leagues, a similar hobby provided hours of enjoyment for rabid sports fans (and still does for many). An author of this text spent many hours playing table-top baseball in his youth.

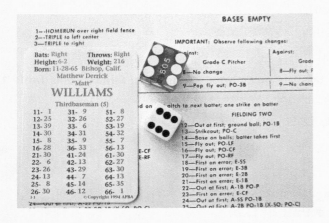

In 1951, a young entrepreneur named Richard Seitz transformed his love for baseball and its statistics into a successful game company that he called APBA. It was located in Lancaster, Pennsylvania, and in 2011 moved to Alpharetta, Georgia, where it still operates. His idea spawned numerous competitors over the years (such as the popular Strat-o-Matic game) that feature simulation of athletes performing according to their actual statistics. To initiate the action in a random fashion, the classic Parker Brothers game Monopoly (for example) uses the sum of a roll of two dice. But certain sums occur more than others. Therefore, to ensure that the results are equally likely, in APBA Major League Baseball, the action is begun by rolling two dice of different sizes (and colors) and reading the results in such a way that every result has an equal chance to occur. Specifically, the number that will activate play is found by reading the face of the large die followed by that of the small die. (See **Table 2** on the preceding page, which illustrates this same idea.)

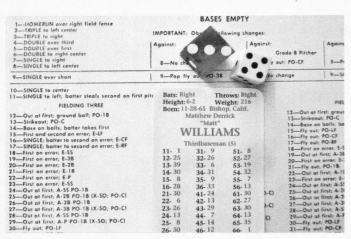

As an illustration of how this game works, see the photo of a play board and the batter card for Matt Williams, a third baseman for the San Francisco Giants in the 1990s who later went on to become manager of the Washington Nationals.

A larger red-die result of 3 followed by a small-die result of 5 is read 35. This number is located on the player card, and it corresponds to a different number, which in this case is 9. That latter number is then found on the applicable game board with a description of the play. As seen on the board, Matt gets a single over shortstop. (When their teams are at bat, APBA managers love to roll 66, because that number always leads to the best possible outcome for the batter.) In Matt's case, a roll of 66 would lead to 1, which would be a home run over the right field fence. The well-established formula devised years ago by the company for constructing batters' cards ensures that in the long run, their results in the game will accurately reflect their actual performances.

EXAMPLE 4 Electing Two Club Officers

In **Example 1,** we considered club N consisting of five members.

$$N = \{A, B, C, D, E\}$$

Find the number of ways that the club can elect both a president and a secretary. Assume that all members are eligible, but that no one can hold both offices.

Solution

Again, the required task has two parts.

Part 1 Determine the president.

Part 2 Determine the secretary.

Constructing **Table 3** gives us the possibilities (where, for example, AB denotes president A and secretary B, while BA denotes president B and secretary A).

Table 3   Electing Two Officers

		Secretary				
		A	**B**	**C**	**D**	**E**
President	**A**		AB	AC	AD	AE
	B	BA		BC	BD	BE
	C	CA	CB		CD	CE
	D	DA	DB	DC		DE
	E	EA	EB	EC	ED	

20 possible results

Notice that entries down the main diagonal, from upper left to lower right, are omitted from the table because the cases AA, BB, and so on would imply one person holding both offices. Altogether, there are twenty possibilities. ∎

EXAMPLE 5 Selecting Committees for a Club

Find the number of ways that club N from **Example 4** can appoint a committee of two members to represent them at an association conference.

Solution

The required task again has two parts. In fact, we can refer to **Table 3** again, but this time, the order of the two letters (people) in a given pair really makes no difference. For example, BD and DB are the same committee. In **Example 4,** BD and DB were different results since the two people would be holding different offices.

In the case of committees, we can eliminate not only the main diagonal entries but also all entries below the main diagonal. The resulting list contains ten possibilities.

$$AB, \quad AC, \quad AD, \quad AE, \quad BC, \quad BD, \quad BE, \quad CD, \quad CE, \quad DE$$ ∎

Tree Diagrams for Multiple-Part Tasks

Problem-Solving Strategy

A task that has more than two parts is not easy to analyze with a product table. Another helpful device is the **tree diagram.**

Bone dice were unearthed in the remains of a Roman garrison, Vindolanda, near the border between England and Scotland. Life on the Roman frontier was occupied with gaming as well as fighting. Some of the Roman dice were loaded in favor of 6 and 1.

Life on the American frontier was reflected in cattle brands that were devised to keep alive the memories of hardships, feuds, and romances. A rancher named Ellis from Paradise Valley in Arizona designed his cattle brand in the shape of a pair of dice. You can guess that the pips were 6 and 1.

EXAMPLE 6 Building Numbers from a Set of Digits

Find the number of three-digit numbers that can be written using only the digits 1, 2, and 3, assuming that

(a) repeated digits are allowed **(b)** repeated digits are not allowed.

Solution

(a) The task of constructing such a number has three parts.

Part 1 Select the first digit.

Part 2 Select the second digit.

Part 3 Select the third digit.

As we move from left to right through the tree diagram in **Figure 1,** the tree branches at the first stage to all possibilities for the first digit. Then each first-stage branch again branches, or splits, at the second stage, to all possibilities for the second digit. Finally, the third-stage branching shows the third-digit possibilities. The list of twenty-seven possible results is shown in the right-hand column.

(b) For the case of nonrepeating digits, we could construct a whole new tree diagram, as in **Figure 2,** or we could simply go down the list of numbers from the first tree diagram and strike out any that contain repeated digits. In either case we obtain only six possibilities.

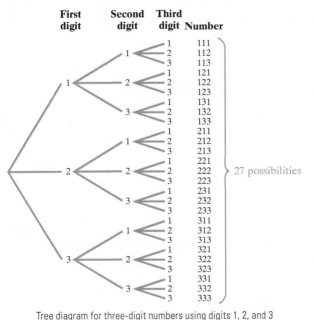

Tree diagram for three-digit numbers using digits 1, 2, and 3

Figure 1

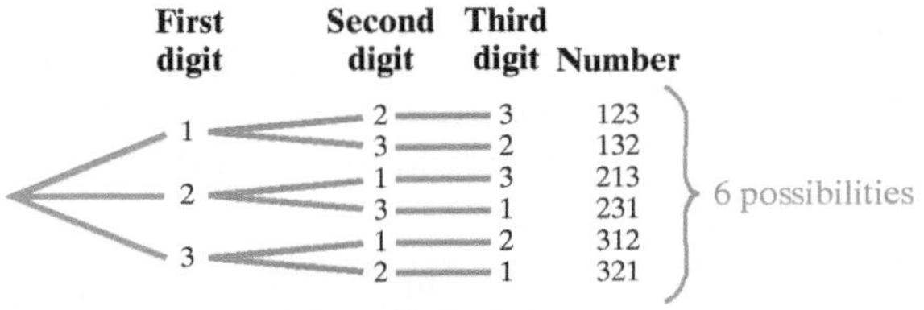

Tree diagram for nonrepeating three-digit numbers using digits 1, 2, and 3

Figure 2

Notice the distinction between parts (a) and (b) of **Example 6.** There are twenty-seven possibilities when "repetitions (of digits) are allowed," but only six possibilities when "repetitions are not allowed."

Here is another way to phrase the problem of **Example 6.**

> *A three-digit number is to be determined by placing three slips of paper (marked 1, 2, and 3) into a hat and drawing out three slips in succession. Find the number of possible results if the drawing is done* **(a)** *with replacement* **and (b)** *without replacement.*

Drawing "with replacement" means drawing a slip, recording its digit, and replacing the slip into the hat so that it is again available for subsequent draws.

> *Drawing "with replacement" has the effect of "allowing repetitions," while drawing "without replacement" has the effect of "not allowing repetitions."*

The words "repetitions" and "replacement" are important in the statement of a problem. In **Example 2,** no restrictions were stated, so we assumed that *repetitions (of digits) were allowed,* or, equivalently, that digits were to be selected *with replacement.*

EXAMPLE 7 Selecting Switch Settings on a Printer

Pamela's computer printer allows for optional settings with a panel of four on-off switches in a row. How many different settings can she select if no two adjacent switches can both be off?

Solution

This situation is typical of user-selectable options on various devices, including computer equipment, garage door openers, and other appliances. In **Figure 3,** we denote "on" and "off" with 1 and 0, respectively. The number of possible settings is eight.

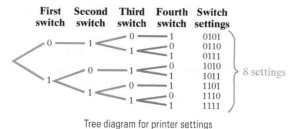

Tree diagram for printer settings

Figure 3

Notice that each time a switch is indicated as off (0), the next switch can only be on (1). This is to satisfy the restriction that no two adjacent switches can both be off.

EXAMPLE 8 Seating Attendees at a Concert

Arne, Bobbette, Chuck, and Deirdre have tickets for four reserved seats in a row at a concert. In how many different ways can they seat themselves so that Arne and Bobbette will sit next to each other?

Solution

Here we have a four-part task:

Assign people to the first, second, third, and fourth seats.

Let A, B, C, and D represent the four people. The tree diagram in **Figure 4** avoids repetitions, because no person can occupy more than one seat. Also, once A or B appears in the tree, the other one *must* occur at the next stage. No splitting occurs from stage three to stage four because by that time there is only one person left unassigned. The right column in the figure shows the twelve possible seating arrangements.

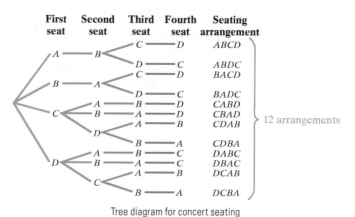

Tree diagram for concert seating

Figure 4

Although we have applied tree diagrams only to tasks with three or more parts, they can also be used for two-part or even simple, one-part tasks. Product tables, on the other hand, are practical only for two-part tasks.

Other Systematic Listing Methods

There are additional systematic ways, besides product tables and tree diagrams, to produce complete listings of possible results.

In **Example 4,** where we used a product table (**Table 3**) to list all possible president-secretary pairs for the club $N = \{A, B, C, D, E\}$, we could have systematically constructed the same list using a sort of alphabetical or left-to-right approach.

First, consider the results where A is president. Any of the remaining members (B, C, D, or E) could then be secretary. That gives us the pairs AB, AC, AD, and AE. Next, assume B is president. The secretary could then be A, C, D, or E. We get the pairs BA, BC, BD, and BE. Continuing in order, we get the complete list just as in **Example 4.**

$$AB, \quad AC, \quad AD, \quad AE, \quad BA, \quad BC, \quad BD, \quad BE, \quad CA, \quad CB,$$

$$CD, \quad CE, \quad DA, \quad DB, \quad DC, \quad DE, \quad EA, \quad EB, \quad EC, \quad ED$$

EXAMPLE 9 **Counting Triangles in a Figure**

How many different triangles (of any size) can be traced in **Figure 5?**

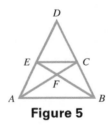

Figure 5

Solution

One systematic approach is to label points as shown, begin with A, and proceed in alphabetical order to write all three-letter combinations, and then cross out the ones that are not triangles in the figure.

$$ABC, \quad ABD, \quad ABE, \quad ABF, \quad ACD, \quad ACE, \quad \cancel{ACF}, \quad \cancel{ADE}, \quad \cancel{ADF}, \quad AEF,$$

$$\cancel{BCD}, \quad BCE, \quad BCF, \quad BDE, \quad \cancel{BDF}, \quad \cancel{BEF}, \quad CDE, \quad \cancel{CDF}, \quad CEF, \quad \cancel{DEF}$$

Finally, there are twelve different triangles in the figure. ACB and CBF (and many others) are not included in the list, because they have already been considered.

Another method might be first to identify the triangles consisting of a single region each: DEC, ECF, AEF, BCF, ABF. Then list those consisting of two regions each: AEC, BEC, ABE, ABC; and those with three regions each: ACD, BED. There are no triangles with four regions, but there is one with five: ABD. The total is again twelve. Can you think of other systematic ways of getting the same list? ∎

Notice that in the first method shown in **Example 9,** the labeled points were considered in alphabetical order. In the second method, the single-region triangles were listed by using a top-to-bottom and left-to-right order. Using a definite system helps to ensure that we get a complete list.

Counting methods can be used to find the number of moves required to solve a **Rubik's Cube.** The scrambled cube must be modified so that each face is a solid color. Rubik's royalties from sales of the cube in Western countries made him Hungary's richest man.

Although the craze over the cube of the early 1980s has waned, certain groups have remained intensely interested in not only solving the scrambled cube, but also doing so as quickly as possible. And the 30-year search for an exact number of moves (called face turns) that is guaranteed to suffice in all cases, while no smaller number will suffice, finally ended in July 2010. That number is now known to be 20.

10.1 EXERCISES

Electing Officers of a Club Refer to **Examples 1 and 4**, *involving the club*

$$N = \{ \text{Alan, Bill, Cathy, David, Evelyn} \}.$$

Assuming that all members are eligible, but no one can hold more than one office, list and count the different ways the club could elect each group of officers. (Cathy and Evelyn are women, and the others are men.)

1. a president and a treasurer

2. a president and a treasurer if the president must be a female

3. a president and a treasurer if the two officers must be the same sex

4. a president, a secretary, and a treasurer, if the president and treasurer must be women

5. a president, a secretary, and a treasurer, if the president must be a man and the other two must be women

6. a president, a secretary, and a treasurer, if all three officers must be men

Appointing Committees List and count the ways club N could appoint a committee of three members under each condition.

7. There are no restrictions.

8. The committee must include more men than women.

Refer to **Table 2** (the product table for rolling two dice). Of the 36 possible outcomes, determine the number for which the sum (for both dice) is the following.

9. 2   10. 3   11. 4

12. 5   13. 6   14. 7

15. 8   16. 9   17. 10

18. 11   19. 12   20. 13

21. odd   22. even   23. prime

24. composite

25. from 5 through 10 inclusive

26. from 6 through 8 inclusive

27. between 6 and 10

28. less than 5   29. greater than 4

30. Construct a product table showing all possible two-digit numbers using digits from the set

$$\{2, 3, 5, 7\}.$$

*Of the sixteen numbers in the product table for **Exercise 30**, list the ones that belong to each category.*

31. numbers with repeating digits

32. even numbers

33. prime numbers

34. multiples of 3

35. Construct a tree diagram showing all possible results when three fair coins are tossed. Then list the ways of getting each result.

    (a) at least two heads

    (b) more than two heads

    (c) no more than two heads

    (d) fewer than two heads

36. Extend the tree diagram of **Exercise 35** for four fair coins. Then list the ways of getting each result.

    (a) more than three tails

    (b) fewer than three tails

    (c) at least three tails

    (d) no more than three tails

Determine the number of triangles (of any size) in each figure.

37.   38.

39.   40.

Determine the number of squares (of any size) in each figure.

41.   42.

43.    **44.**

Consider only the smallest individual cubes and assume solid stacks (no gaps). Determine the number of cubes in each stack that are not visible from the perspective shown.

45. 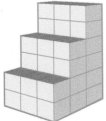   **46.**

47. 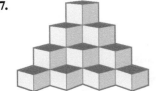   **48.**

49. Find the number of paths from *A* to *B* in the figure illustrated here if the directions on various segments are restricted as shown.

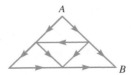

50. In the plane figure illustrated here, only movement that tends downward is allowed. Find the total number of paths from *A* to *B*.

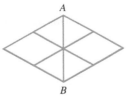

Work each problem.

51. *Rolling Unusual Dice* An unusual die has the numbers

2, 2, 3, 3, 5, and 8

on its six faces. Two of these dice are rolled, and the two numbers on the top faces are added. How many different sums are possible? (*Mathematics Teacher* calendar problem)

52. *Shaking Hands in a Group* A group of six strangers sat in a circle, and each one got acquainted only with the person to the left and the person to the right. Then all six people stood up and each one shook hands (once) with each of the others who was still a stranger. How many handshakes occurred?

53. *Number of Games in a Chess Tournament* Fifty people enter a single-elimination chess tournament. If you lose one game, you're out. Assuming no ties occur, what is the number of games required to determine the tournament champion?

54. *Sums of Digits* How many positive integers less than 100 have the sum of their digits equal to a perfect square?

55. *Sums of Digits* How many three-digit numbers have the sum of their digits equal to 22?

56. *Integers Containing the Digit 2* How many integers between 100 and 400 contain the digit 2?

57. *Filling an Order* A customer ordered fifteen Zingers. Zingers are placed in packages of four, three, or one. In how many different ways can this order be filled? (*Mathematics Teacher* calendar problem)

58. *Selecting Dinner Items* Michael and several friends are dining this evening at the Clam Shell Restaurant, where a complete dinner consists of three items.

> *Choice 1* soup (clam chowder or minestrone) or salad (fresh spinach or shrimp),
>
> *Choice 2* sourdough rolls or bran muffin, and
>
> *Choice 3* entree (lasagna, lobster, or roast turkey).

Michael selects his meal subject to the following restrictions. He cannot stomach more than one kind of seafood at a sitting. Also, whenever he tastes minestrone, he cannot resist having lasagna as well. Use a tree diagram to determine the number of different choices Michael has.

Setting Options on a Computer Printer For Exercises 59–61, refer to **Example 7**. How many different settings could Pamela choose in each case?

59. No restrictions apply to adjacent switches.

60. No two adjacent switches can be off *and* no two adjacent switches can be on.

61. There are five switches rather than four, and no two adjacent switches can be on.

Work each problem.

62. *Building Numbers from Sets of Digits* Determine the number of odd, nonrepeating three-digit numbers that can be written using only the digits 0, 1, 2, and 3.

63. *Lattice Points on a Line Segment* A line segment joins the points

(8, 12)   and   (53, 234)

in the Cartesian plane. Including its endpoints, how many lattice points does this line segment contain? (A *lattice point* is a point with integer coordinates.)

64. *Lengths of Segments Joining Lattice Points* In the pattern that follows, dots are one unit apart horizontally and vertically. If a segment can join any two dots, how many segments can be drawn with each length?

(a) 1 (b) 2 (c) 3 (d) 4 (e) 5

65. *Patterns in Floor Tiling* A square floor is to be tiled with square tiles as shown. There are blue tiles on the main diagonals and red tiles everywhere else. In all cases, both blue and red tiles must be used, and the two diagonals must have a common blue tile at the center of the floor.

(a) If 81 blue tiles will be used, how many red tiles will be needed?

(b) For what numbers in place of 81 would this problem still be solvable?

(c) Find an expression in k giving the number of red tiles required in general.

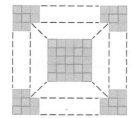

66. *Counting Matchsticks in a Grid* Uniform-length matchsticks are used to build a rectangular grid as shown here. If the grid is 12 matchsticks high and 25 matchsticks wide, how many matchsticks are used?

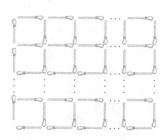

67. *Shaking Hands in a Group* Chris and his son were among four father-and-son pairs who gathered to trade baseball cards. As each person arrived, he shook hands with anyone he had not known previously. Each person ended up making a different number of new acquaintances (0–6), except Chris and his son, who each met the same number of people. How many hands did Chris shake?

68. *Sum of Primes* Determine the different number of ways the given composite number can be written as the sum of two prime numbers. (*Hint:* Consider a sum such as 2 + 3 the same as 3 + 2.)

(a) 30

(b) 40

(c) 95

In Exercises 69 and 70, restate the given counting problem in two ways, first (a) *using the word* repetition, *and then* (b) *using the word* replacement.

69. Example 2

70. Example 4

10.2 USING THE FUNDAMENTAL COUNTING PRINCIPLE

OBJECTIVES

1 Know the meaning of uniformity in counting, and understand the fundamental counting principle.

2 Use the fundamental counting principle to solve counting problems.

3 Determine the factorial of a whole number.

4 Use factorials to determine the number of arrangements, including distinguishable arrangements, of a given number of objects.

Uniformity and the Fundamental Counting Principle

In **Section 10.1,** we obtained complete lists of all possible results for various tasks. However, if the total number of possibilities is all we need to know, then an actual listing usually is unnecessary and often is difficult or tedious to obtain, especially when the list is long.

Figure 6 shows all possible nonrepeating three-digit numbers using only the digits 1, 2, and 3.

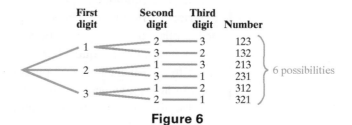

Figure 6

Richard Dedekind (1831–1916) studied at the University of Göttingen, where he was Gauss's last student. His work was not recognized during his lifetime, but his treatment of the infinite and of what constitutes a real number are influential even today.

While on vacation in Switzerland, Dedekind met Georg Cantor. Dedekind was interested in Cantor's work on infinite sets. Perhaps because both were working in new and unusual fields of mathematics, such as number theory, and because neither received the professional attention he deserved during his lifetime, the two struck up a lasting friendship.

The tree diagram in **Figure 6** is "uniform" in the sense that a given part of the task can be done in the same number of ways, no matter which choices were selected for previous parts. For example, there are always two choices for the second digit. (If the first digit is 1, the second can be 2 or 3. If the first is 2, the second can be 1 or 3. If the first is 3, the second can be 1 or 2.)

Example 6(a) of **Section 10.1** addressed the same basic situation:

> *Find the number of three-digit numbers that can be written using the digits 1, 2, and 3.*

In that case repetitions were allowed. With repetitions allowed, there were many more possibilities (27 rather than 6—see **Figure 1** of **Section 10.1**). But the uniformity criterion mentioned above still applied. No matter what the first digit is, there are three choices for the second (1, 2, 3). And no matter what the first and second digits are, there are three choices for the third. This uniformity criterion can be stated in general as follows.

UNIFORMITY CRITERION FOR MULTIPLE-PART TASKS

A multiple-part task is said to satisfy the **uniformity criterion** if the number of choices for any particular part is the same *no matter which choices were selected for previous parts.*

The uniformity criterion is not always satisfied. Refer to **Example 7** and **Figure 3** of **Section 10.1**. After the first switch (two possibilities), other switches had either one or two possible settings depending on how previous switches were set. This "nonuniformity" arose, in that case, from the requirement that no two adjacent switches could both be off.

In the many cases where uniformity does hold, we can avoid having to construct a tree diagram by using the **fundamental counting principle,** stated as follows.

FUNDAMENTAL COUNTING PRINCIPLE

When a task consists of k separate parts and satisfies the uniformity criterion, if the first part can be done in n_1 ways, the second part can then be done in n_2 ways, and so on through the kth part, which can be done in n_k ways, then the total number of ways to complete the task is given by the following product.

$$n_1 \cdot n_2 \cdot n_3 \cdot \ldots \cdot n_k$$

Problem-Solving Strategy

A problem-solving strategy suggested in **Chapter 1** was *"If a formula applies, use it."* The fundamental counting principle provides a formula that applies to a variety of problems. The strategy is to visualize the "task" at hand as being accomplished in a sequence of two or more separate parts.

A helpful technique when applying the fundamental counting principle is to write out all the separate parts of the task, with a blank for each one. Reason out how many ways each part can be done, and enter these numbers in the blanks. Finally, multiply these numbers together.

EXAMPLE 1 Counting the Two-Digit Numbers

How many two-digit numbers are there in our (base-ten) system of counting numbers? (*Hint:* 40 is a two-digit number, but 04 is not.)

Solution

Our "task" here is to select, or construct, a two-digit number. Work as follows.

Part of task	Select first digit	Select second digit
Number of ways	_____	_____

There are nine choices for the first digit (1 through 9). Since there were no stated or implied restrictions, we assume that repetition of digits is allowed. Therefore, no matter which nonzero digit is used as the first digit, all nine choices are available for the second digit. Also, unlike the first digit, the second digit may be zero, so we have ten choices for the second digit. We can now fill in the blanks and multiply.

Part of task	Select first digit	Select second digit
Number of ways	9 ·	10	= 90

There are 90 two-digit numbers. (As a check, notice that they are the numbers from 10 through 99, a total of $99 - 10 + 1 = 90$.) ∎

EXAMPLE 2 Building Two-Digit Numbers with Restrictions

Find the number of two-digit numbers that do not contain repeated digits.

Solution

The basic task is again to select a two-digit number, and there are two parts.

Part 1 Select the first digit.   *Part 2* Select the second digit.

But a new restriction applies—no repetition of digits. There are nine choices for the first digit (1 through 9). Then nine choices remain for the second digit, since one nonzero digit has been used and cannot be repeated, but zero is now available. The total number is $9 \cdot 9 = 81$. ∎

EXAMPLE 3 Electing Club Officers with Restrictions

In how many ways can Club *N*, of **Examples 1** and **4** in the previous section, elect a president and a secretary if no one may hold more than one office and the secretary must be a man?

Solution

Recall that $N = \{A, B, C, D, E\} = \{$Alan, Bill, Cathy, David, Evelyn$\}$. Considering president first, there are five choices (no restrictions). But now we have a problem with finding the number of choices for secretary. If a woman was selected president (*C* or *E*), there are three choices for secretary (*A*, *B*, and *D*). If a man was selected president, only two choices (the other two men) remain for secretary. *In other words, the uniformity criterion is not met, and our attempt to apply the fundamental counting principle has failed.*

All is not lost, however. To find the total number of ways, we can consider secretary first. There are three choices: *A*, *B*, and *D*. Now, no matter which man was chosen secretary, both of the other men and both women are available for president, with four choices in every case. In this order, we satisfy the uniformity criterion and can use the fundamental counting principle. The total number of ways to elect a president and a secretary is $3 \cdot 4 = 12$. ∎

To the Student

In Club *N*,
  Alan is a man.
  Bill is a man.
  Cathy is a woman.
  David is a man.
  Evelyn is a woman.

Problem-Solving Strategy

Example 3 suggests a useful problem-solving strategy: Whenever one or more parts of a task have special restrictions, try considering that part (or those parts) before other parts.

EXAMPLE 4 Counting Three-Digit Numbers with Restrictions

How many nonrepeating odd three-digit counting numbers are there?

Solution

The most restricted digit is the third, since it must be odd. There are five choices (1, 3, 5, 7, and 9). Next, consider the first digit. It can be any nonzero digit except the one already chosen as the third digit. There are eight choices. Finally, the second digit can be any digit (including 0) except for the two nonzero digits already used. There are eight choices.

Part of task	Select third digit		Select first digit		Select second digit	
Number of ways	5	·	8	·	8	= 320

There are 320 nonrepeating odd three-digit counting numbers. ∎

EXAMPLE 5 Counting License Plates

In some states, auto license plates have contained three letters followed by three digits. How many such licenses are possible?

Solution

The basic task is to design a license plate with three letters followed by three digits. There are six component parts to this task. There are no restrictions on letters or digits, so the fundamental counting principle gives

$$26 \cdot 26 \cdot 26 \cdot 10 \cdot 10 \cdot 10 = 26^3 \cdot 10^3 = 17{,}576{,}000 \text{ possible licenses.}$$

In practice, a few of the possible sequences of letters are considered undesirable and are not used. ∎

EXAMPLE 6 Building Numbers with Specified Digits

A four-digit number is to be constructed using only the digits 1, 2, and 3.

(a) How many such numbers are possible?

(b) How many of these numbers are odd and less than 2000?

Solution

(a) To construct such a number, we must select four digits, in succession, from the given set of three digits, where the selection is done with replacement (since repetition of digits is apparently allowed). The number of possibilities is

$$3 \cdot 3 \cdot 3 \cdot 3 = 3^4 = 81. \quad \text{Fundamental counting principle}$$

(b) The number is less than 2000 only if the first digit is 1 (just one choice) and is odd only if the fourth digit is 1 or 3 (two choices). The second and third digits are unrestricted (three choices for each). The answer is

$$1 \cdot 3 \cdot 3 \cdot 2 = 18.$$

As a check, you may want to list the eighteen possibilities. ∎

EXAMPLE 7 Distributing Golf Clubs

Vern has four antique golf clubs that he wants to give to his three sons, Mark, Chris, and Scott.

(a) How many ways can the clubs be distributed?

(b) How many choices are there if the power driver must go to Mark and the number 3 wood must go to either Chris or Scott?

Solution

(a) The task is to distribute four clubs among three sons. Consider the clubs in succession, and, for each one, ask how many sons could receive it. In effect, we must select four sons, in succession, from the list Mark, Chris, Scott, selecting with replacement. Compare this with **Example 6(a)**, in which we selected four digits, in succession, from the digits 1, 2, and 3, selecting with replacement. In this case, we are selecting sons rather than digits, but the pattern is the same and the numbers are the same. Again our answer is

$$3^4 = 81.$$

(b) Just as in **Example 6(b)**, one part of the task is now restricted to a single choice, and another part is restricted to two choices. As in that example, the number of possibilities is

$$1 \cdot 3 \cdot 3 \cdot 2 = 18. \qquad \blacksquare$$

EXAMPLE 8 Seating Attendees at a Concert

This is a repeat of **Example 8** in **Section 10.1**.

Arne, Bobbette, Chuck, and Deirdre have tickets for four reserved seats in a row at a concert. In how many different ways can they seat themselves so that Arne and Bobbette will sit next to each other?

Solution

Arne, Bobbette, Chuck, and Deirdre (A, B, C, and D) are to seat themselves in four adjacent seats (say 1, 2, 3, and 4) so that A and B are side-by-side. One approach to accomplish this task is to make three successive decisions as follows.

1	2	3	4
X	X	—	—
—	X	X	—
—	—	X	X

Seats available to *A* and *B*

1. *Which pair of seats should A and B occupy?* There are *three* choices: 1 and 2, 2 and 3, 3 and 4, as illustrated in the margin.

2. *Which order should A and B take?* There are *two* choices: A left of B, or B left of A.

3. *Which order should C and D take?* There are *two* choices: C left of D, or D left of C, not necessarily right next to each other.

The fundamental counting principle now gives the total number of choices.

$$3 \cdot 2 \cdot 2 = 12 \quad \text{Same result as in \textbf{Section 10.1}} \qquad \blacksquare$$

Factorials

Short Table of Factorials Factorial values increase rapidly. The value of 100! is a number with 158 digits.

$$0! = 1$$
$$1! = 1$$
$$2! = 2$$
$$3! = 6$$
$$4! = 24$$
$$5! = 120$$
$$6! = 720$$
$$7! = 5040$$
$$8! = 40,320$$
$$9! = 362,880$$
$$10! = 3,628,800$$

This section began with a discussion of nonrepeating three-digit numbers using digits 1, 2, and 3. The number of possibilities was

$$3 \cdot 2 \cdot 1 = 6. \quad \text{Fundamental counting principle}$$

That product can also be thought of as the total number of distinct *arrangements* of the three digits 1, 2, and 3. Similarly, the number of distinct arrangements of four objects (say A, B, C, and D) is

$$4 \cdot 3 \cdot 2 \cdot 1 = 24. \quad \text{Fundamental counting principle}$$

Because this type of product occurs so commonly in applications, we give it a special name and symbol. For any counting number n, the product of *all* counting numbers from n down through 1 is called **n factorial,** and is denoted **$n!$.**

> ## FACTORIAL FORMULA
>
> For any counting number **n**, the quantity **n factorial** is defined as follows.
>
> $$n! = n \cdot (n - 1) \cdot (n - 2) \cdot \ldots \cdot 2 \cdot 1$$

The first few factorial values are easily found by simple multiplication, but they rapidly become very large. The use of a calculator is advised in most cases.

> ### Problem-Solving Strategy
>
> Sometimes expressions involving factorials can be evaluated easily by observing that, in general, $n! = n \cdot (n - 1)!$, $n! = n \cdot (n - 1) \cdot (n - 2)!$, and so on. For example,
>
> $$8! = 8 \cdot 7!, \quad 12! = 12 \cdot 11 \cdot 10 \cdot 9!, \quad \text{and so on.}$$
>
> This pattern is especially helpful in evaluating quotients of factorials.
>
> $$\frac{10!}{8!} = \frac{10 \cdot 9 \cdot 8!}{8!} = 10 \cdot 9 = 90$$

EXAMPLE 9 Evaluating Expressions Containing Factorials

Evaluate each expression.

(a) $3!$ **(b)** $6!$ **(c)** $(6 - 3)!$ **(d)** $6! - 3!$

(e) $\dfrac{6!}{3!}$ **(f)** $\left(\dfrac{6}{3}\right)!$ **(g)** $15!$ **(h)** $100!$

Solution

(a) $3! = 3 \cdot 2 \cdot 1 = 6$

(b) $6! = 6 \cdot 5 \cdot 4 \cdot 3 \cdot 2 \cdot 1 = 720$

(c) $(6 - 3)! = 3! = 6$

(d) $6! - 3! = 720 - 6 = 714$

(e) $\dfrac{6!}{3!} = \dfrac{6 \cdot 5 \cdot 4 \cdot 3!}{3!} = 6 \cdot 5 \cdot 4 = 120$ Note application of the Problem-Solving Strategy.

(f) $\left(\dfrac{6}{3}\right)! = 2! = 2 \cdot 1 = 2$

```
6!
                    720
6!-3!
                    714
15!
          1.307674368E12
```

The results of **Example 9(b), (d), and (g)** are illustrated in this calculator screen.

(g) $15! = 1.307674368000 \times 10^{12}$ ← Done on a calculator

(h) $100! = 9.332621544 \times 10^{157}$ ← Too large for most calculators

Notice the distinction between parts (c) and (d) and between parts (e) and (f). ■

So that factorials will be defined for all whole numbers, including zero, we define 0! as follows.

DEFINITION OF ZERO FACTORIAL

$$0! = 1$$

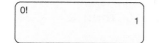

The definition 0! = 1 is illustrated here.

(We will see later that this special definition makes other results easier to state.)

Arrangements of Objects

When finding the total number of ways to *arrange* a given number of distinct objects, we can use a factorial. The fundamental counting principle would do, but factorials provide a shortcut.

ARRANGEMENTS OF *n* DISTINCT OBJECTS

The total number of different ways to arrange n distinct objects is $n!$.

EXAMPLE 10 Arranging Essays

Michelle has seven essays to include in her English 1A folder. In how many different orders can she arrange them?

Solution

The number of ways to arrange seven distinct objects is

$$7! = 5040.$$ ■

EXAMPLE 11 Arranging Preschoolers

Tricia is taking thirteen preschoolers to the park. How many ways can the children line up, in single file, to board the van?

Solution

Thirteen children can be arranged in

$$13! = 6{,}227{,}020{,}800 \text{ different ways.}$$ ■

Distinguishable Arrangements

D_1AD_2

D_2AD_1

D_1D_2A

D_2D_1A

AD_1D_2

AD_2D_1

In counting arrangements of objects that contain look-alikes, the normal factorial formula must be modified to find the number of truly different arrangements. For example, the number of distinguishable arrangements of the letters of the word DAD is not $3! = 6$ but rather $\frac{3!}{2!} = 3$. The listing in the margin shows how the six total arrangements consist of just three groups of two, where the two in a given group look alike.

ARRANGEMENTS OF *n* OBJECTS CONTAINING LOOK-ALIKES

The number of **distinguishable arrangements** of *n* objects, where one or more subsets consist of look-alikes (say n_1 are of one kind, n_2 are of another kind, ..., and n_k are of yet another kind), is given by

$$\frac{n!}{n_1! \cdot n_2! \cdot \ldots \cdot n_k!}.$$

EXAMPLE 12 Counting Distinguishable Arrangements

Determine the number of distinguishable arrangements of the letters in each word.

(a) ATTRACT   **(b)** NIGGLING

Solution

(a) For the letters of ATTRACT, the number of distinguishable arrangements is

7 letters total $\longrightarrow$
3 *T*'s, 2 *A*'s $\longrightarrow$ $\dfrac{7!}{3! \cdot 2!} = 420.$

(b) For the letters of NIGGLING, the number of distinguishable arrangements is

8 letters total $\longrightarrow$
2 *N*'s, 2 *I*'s, 3 *G*'s $\longrightarrow$ $\dfrac{8!}{2! \cdot 2! \cdot 3!} = 1680.$ ∎

FOR FURTHER THOUGHT

Stirling's Approximation for *n*!

Although all factorial values are counting numbers, they can be approximated using **Stirling's formula,**

$$n! \approx \sqrt{2\pi n} \cdot n^n \cdot e^{-n},$$

which involves two important irrational numbers, π and *e*. For example, while the exact value of 5! is $5 \cdot 4 \cdot 3 \cdot 2 \cdot 1 = 120$, the corresponding approximation, using Stirling's formula, is

$$5! \approx \sqrt{2\pi \cdot 5} \cdot 5^5 \cdot e^{-5} \approx 118.019168,$$

which is off by less than 2, an error of only 1.65%.

For Group or Individual Investigation

Use a calculator to fill in the table on the right. The column values are defined as follows.

$C = n!$ (exact value, by calculator)

$S \approx n!$ (Stirling's approximation, by calculator)

$D =$ Difference $(C - S)$

$P =$ Percentage difference $\left(\dfrac{D}{C} \cdot 100\% \right)$

n	C	S	D	P
10				
15				
20				
25				
30				

Try to obtain percentage differences accurate to two decimal places. Based on your calculations, answer each of the following.

1. In general, is Stirling's approximation too low or too high?

2. Observe the values in the table as *n* grows larger.

  (a) Do the differences (*D*) get larger or smaller?

  (b) Do the percentage differences (*P*) get larger or smaller?

  (c) Does Stirling's formula become more accurate or less accurate as *n* increases?

3. An even better approximation is given by

$$n! \approx \sqrt{\left(2n + \tfrac{1}{3}\right)\pi} \cdot n^n e^{-n}.$$

Show that this formula gives a closer approximation to 5! than Stirling's formula.

10.2   EXERCISES

Evaluate each expression without using a calculator.

1. $4!$

2. $6!$

3. $\dfrac{9!}{7!}$

4. $\dfrac{16!}{14!}$

5. $\dfrac{5!}{(5-2)!}$

6. $\dfrac{6!}{(6-3)!}$

7. $\dfrac{8!}{6!(8-6)!}$

8. $\dfrac{9!}{7!(9-7)!}$

9. $\dfrac{10!}{9!(10-9)!}$

10. $\dfrac{100!}{99!(100-99)!}$

11. $\dfrac{50!}{48! \cdot 2!}$

12. $\dfrac{37!}{35! \cdot 2!}$

For the given values of n and r, evaluate

(a) $\dfrac{n!}{(n-r)!}$ *and*   **(b)** $\dfrac{n!}{r!(n-r)!}.$

13. $n = 10, r = 3$

14. $n = 11, r = 2$

15. $n = 18, r = 2$

16. $n = 20, r = 3$

Use a calculator to evaluate each expression.

17. $10!$

18. $14!$

19. $\dfrac{12!}{5!}$

20. $\dfrac{14!}{8!}$

21. $\dfrac{16!}{(16-9)!}$

22. $\dfrac{13!}{(13-6)!}$

23. $\dfrac{20!}{10! \cdot 10!}$

24. $\dfrac{19!}{9! \cdot 10!}$

25. $\dfrac{n!}{(n-r)!}$, where $n = 17$ and $r = 8$

26. $\dfrac{n!}{(n-r)!}$, where $n = 20$ and $r = 4$

27. $\dfrac{n!}{r!(n-r)!}$, where $n = 24$ and $r = 18$

28. $\dfrac{n!}{r!(n-r)!}$, where $n = 26$ and $r = 20$

Arranging Letters   Find the number of distinguishable arrangements of the letters of each word or phrase.

29. GOOGOL

30. BANANA

31. HEEBIE-JEEBIES

32. VICE VERSA

Settings on a Switch Panel   A panel containing three on-off switches in a row is to be set.

33. Assuming no restrictions on individual switches, use the fundamental counting principle to find the total number of possible panel settings.

34. Assuming no restrictions, construct a tree diagram to list all the possible panel settings of **Exercise 33.**

35. Now assume that no two adjacent switches can both be off. Explain why the fundamental counting principle does not apply.

36. Construct a tree diagram to list all possible panel settings under the restriction of **Exercise 35.**

37. *Rolling Dice*   **Table 2** in the previous section shows that there are 36 possible outcomes when two fair dice are rolled. How many outcomes would there be if three fair dice were rolled?

38. *Counting Five-Digit Numbers*   How many five-digit numbers are there in our system of counting numbers?

39. *Bowling*   After the rolling of the first ball of a frame in a game of 10-pin bowling, how many different pin configurations can remain (assuming all configurations are physically possible)? (*Mathematics Teacher* calendar problem)

40. *Bowling*   Answer the question of **Exercise 39** assuming that pins 4, 7, and 8 were knocked down on the first roll.

Matching Club Members with Tasks   Recall the club

$N = \{$ Alan, Bill, Cathy, David, Evelyn $\}.$

In how many ways could they do each of the following?

41. line up all five members for a photograph

42. schedule one member to work in the office on each of five different days, assuming members may work more than one day

43. select a male and a female to decorate for a party

44. select two members, one to open their next meeting and one to close it, given that Bill will not be present

Building Numbers with Specified Digits   *In Exercises 45–48, counting numbers are to be formed using only the digits 3, 4, and 5. Determine the number of different possibilities for each type of number described.*

45. two-digit numbers

46. odd three-digit numbers

47. four-digit numbers with one pair of adjacent 4s and no other repeated digits

(*Hint:* You may want to split the task of designing such a number into three parts, such as *Part 1* position the pair of 4s, *Part 2* position the 3, and *Part 3* position the 5.)

48. five-digit numbers beginning and ending with 3 and with unlimited repetitions allowed

Selecting Dinner Items   *The Gourmet de Coeur Restaurant offers*

five choices in the soup and salad category (two soups and three salads),

two choices in the bread category,

and   four choices in the entrée category.

Find the number of dinners available in each case.

49. One item should be included from each of the three categories.

50. Only salad and entrée are to be included.

Selecting Answers on a Test   *Determine the number of possible ways to mark your answer sheet (with an answer for each question) for each test.*

51. a six-question true-or-false test

52. a ten-question multiple-choice test with five answer choices for each question

Selecting a College Class Schedule   *Jessica's class schedule for next semester must consist of exactly one class from each of the four categories shown in the table.*

For each situation in Exercises 53–58 in the next column, use the table to determine the number of different sets of classes Jessica can take.

Category	Choices	Number of Choices
Economics	Free Markets Controlled Markets	2
Mathematics	History of Mathematics College Algebra Finite Mathematics	3
Education	Classroom Technology Group Dynamics Language Supervision Parent/Teacher Relations	4
Sociology	Social Problems Sociology of the Middle East Aging in America Minorities in America Women in American Culture	5

53. All classes shown are available.

54. She is not eligible for Free Markets or for Group Dynamics.

55. All sections of Minorities in America and Women in American Culture already are filled.

56. She does not have the prerequisites for Controlled Markets, College Algebra, or Language Supervision.

57. Funding has been withdrawn for three of the Education courses and for two of the Sociology courses.

58. She must complete Finite Mathematics and Social Problems to fulfill her degree requirements.

59. Selecting Clothing   Don has two pairs of shoes, four pairs of pants, and six shirts. If all items are compatible, how many different outfits can he wear?

60. Selecting Music Equipment   A music equipment outlet stocks ten different guitars, three guitar cases, six amplifiers, and five special effects processors, with all items mutually compatible and all suitable for beginners. How many different complete setups could Lionel choose to start his musical career?

61. Counting ZIP Codes   Tonya's ZIP code is 85726. How many ZIP codes altogether could be formed, each one using those same five digits?

62. *Listing Phone Numbers* Raj keeps the phone numbers for his seven closest friends (three men and four women) in his digital phone memory. (Refer to **Example 8.**) How many ways can he list them for the following conditions?

(a) men are listed before women

(b) men are all listed together

(c) no two men are listed next to each other?

63. *Counting Telephone Area Codes* Until 1995, the rules for three-digit area codes in the United States were as follows:

• The first digit could not be 0 or 1.

• The second digit had to be 0 or 1.

• The third digit had no such restrictions.

In 1995, the restriction on the second digit of area codes was removed. How many area codes are possible? (*Mathematics Teacher* calendar problem)

64. *Repeated Digits* Repeat **Example 4,** but this time allow repeated digits. Does the order in which digits are considered matter in this case?

*Seating Arrangements at a Theater In Exercises 65–68, Arne, Bobbette, Chuck, Deirdre, Ed, and Fran have reserved six seats in a row at the theater, starting at an aisle seat. (Refer to **Example 8.**)*

65. In how many ways can they arrange themselves? (*Hint:* Divide the task into the series of six parts shown below, performed in order.)

(a) If *A* is seated first, how many seats are available for him?

(b) Now, how many are available for *B*?

(c) Now, how many for *C*?

(d) Now, how many for *D*?

(e) Now, how many for *E*?

(f) Now, how many for *F*?

Now multiply your six answers above.

66. In how many ways can they arrange themselves so that Arne and Bobbette will be next to each other?

1	2	3	4	5	6
X	*X*				
	X	*X*			
		X	*X*		
			X	*X*	
				X	*X*

Seats available to *A* and *B*

(*Hint:* Answer the questions in parts (a)–(f), in order.)

(a) How many pairs of adjacent seats can *A* and *B* occupy?

(b) Now, given the two seats for *A* and *B*, in how many orders can they be seated?

(c) Now, how many seats are available for *C*?

(d) Now, how many for *D*?

(e) Now, how many for *E*?

(f) Now, how many for *F*?

Now multiply your six answers above.

67. In how many ways can they arrange themselves if the men and women are to alternate seats and a man must sit on the aisle? Arne, Chuck, and Ed are men, and the others are women. (*Hint:* First answer the following six questions in order.)

(a) How many choices are there for the person to occupy the first seat, next to the aisle? (It must be a man.)

(b) How many choices of people may occupy the second seat from the aisle? (It must be a woman.)

(c) Now, how many for the third seat? (one of the remaining men)

(d) Now, how many for the fourth seat? (a woman)

(e) Now, how many for the fifth seat? (a man)

(f) Now, how many for the sixth seat? (a woman)

Now multiply your six answers above.

68. In how many ways can they arrange themselves if the men and women are to alternate with either a man or a woman on the aisle? Arne, Chuck, and Ed are men, and the others are women. (*Hint:* First answer the following six questions in order.)

(a) How many choices of people are there for the aisle seat?

(b) Now, how many are there for the second seat? (This person must not be of the same gender as the person on the aisle.)

(c) Now, how many choices are there for the third seat?

(d) Now, how many for the fourth seat?

(e) Now, how many for the fifth seat?

(f) Now, how many for the sixth seat?

Now multiply your six answers above.

Work each problem.

69. *Six-Digit Numbers* If all the six-digit numbers formed by using the digits

1, 2, 3, 4, 5, and 6,

without repetition, are listed from least to greatest, which number will be 500th in the list? (*Mathematics Teacher* calendar problem)

70. *Palindromes* How many of the anagrams (arrangements of the letters) of

INDIANA

are palindromes, that is arrangements that read the same forward and backward? *Hint:* One such palindrome is

INADANI.

(*Mathematics Teacher* calendar problem)

71. *Divisibility* The number $2^7 \cdot 3^4 \cdot 5 \cdot 7^2 \cdot 11^3$ is divisible by many perfect squares. How many? (*Mathematics Teacher* calendar problem)

72. *Distinguishability* How many distinguishable rearrangements of the letters in the word

CONTEST

start with the two vowels? (*Mathematics Teacher* calendar problem)

10.3 USING PERMUTATIONS AND COMBINATIONS

OBJECTIVES

1 Solve counting problems involving permutations and the fundamental counting principle.

2 Solve counting problems involving combinations and the fundamental counting principle.

3 Solve counting problems that require deciding whether to use permutations or combinations.

Permutations

Again recall the club

$$N = \{\text{Alan, Bill, Cathy, David, Evelyn}\} = \{A, B, C, D, E\}$$

and consider two questions.

1. How many ways can all the club members arrange themselves in a row for a photograph?
2. How many ways can the club elect a president, a secretary, and a treasurer if no one can hold more than one office?

From **Section 10.2,** the answer to the first question above is

$$5! = 5 \cdot 4 \cdot 3 \cdot 2 \cdot 1 = 120,$$

the number of possible arrangements of 5 distinct objects. We answered questions like the second one using a tree diagram or the fundamental counting principle.

$$5 \cdot 4 \cdot 3 = 60$$

A good way to think of the second question is as follows.

> ***How many arrangements are there of five things taken three at a time?***

The factors begin with 5 and proceed downward, just as in a factorial product, but do not go all the way to 1. Here the product stops when there are three factors.

In the context of counting problems, arrangements are called **permutations.** The number of permutations of n distinct things taken r at a time is denoted $_nP_r$.*

---

*Alternative notations are $P(n, r)$ and P_r^n.

The number of objects being arranged cannot exceed the total number available, so we assume that $r \leq n$. Applying the fundamental counting principle gives

$$_nP_r = n(n-1)(n-2)\ldots[n-(r-1)].$$

The first factor is $n - 0$, the second is $n - 1$, the third is $n - 2$, and so on. The rth factor, the last one in the product, will be the one with $r - 1$ subtracted from n, as shown above. We can express permutations, in general, in terms of factorials, to obtain a formula as follows.

$$_nP_r = n(n-1)(n-2)\ldots[n-(r-1)]$$

$$= n(n-1)(n-2)\ldots(n-r+1) \qquad \text{Simplify the last factor.}$$

$$= \frac{n(n-1)(n-2)\ldots(n-r+1)(n-r)(n-r-1)\ldots2\cdot1}{(n-r)(n-r-1)\ldots2\cdot1} \qquad \begin{array}{l}\text{Multiply and divide by}\\ (n-r)(n-r-1)\ldots2\cdot1.\end{array}$$

$$_nP_r = \frac{n!}{(n-r)!} \qquad \text{Definition of factorial}$$

FACTORIAL FORMULA FOR PERMUTATIONS

The number of **permutations,** or *arrangements*, of n distinct things taken r at a time, where $r \leq n$, can be calculated as follows.

$$_nP_r = \frac{n!}{(n-r)!}$$

Although we sometimes refer to a symbol such as

$$_4P_2$$

as "a permutation," the symbol actually represents "the number of permutations of 4 distinct things taken 2 at a time."

EXAMPLE 1 Using the Factorial Formula for Permutations

Evaluate each permutation.

(a) $_4P_2$ **(b)** $_8P_5$ **(c)** $_5P_5$

Solution

(a) $_4P_2 = \dfrac{4!}{(4-2)!} = \dfrac{4!}{2!} = \dfrac{24}{2} = 12$

(b) $_8P_5 = \dfrac{8!}{(8-5)!} = \dfrac{8!}{3!} = \dfrac{40{,}320}{6} = 6720$

(c) $_5P_5 = \dfrac{5!}{(5-5)!} = \dfrac{5!}{0!} = \dfrac{120}{1} = 120$

```
4!/(4-2)!
                    12
8!/(8-5)!
                  6720
5!/(5-5)!
                   120
```

This screen uses factorials to support the results of **Example 1.**

Notice that $_5P_5$ is equal to 5!. The following is true for all whole numbers n.

$$_nP_n = n!$$

This is the number of arrangements of n distinct objects taken all n at a time.

Many calculators allow direct calculation of permutations.

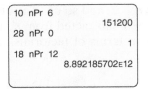

This screen uses the permutations feature to support the results of **Example 2.**

EXAMPLE 2 Calculating Permutations Directly

Evaluate each permutation.

(a) $_{10}P_6$ **(b)** $_{28}P_0$ **(c)** $_{18}P_{12}$

Solution

(a) $_{10}P_6 = 151,200$ **(b)** $_{28}P_0 = 1$ **(c)** $_{18}P_{12} = 8,892,185,702,400$

Concerning part (c), many calculators will not display this many digits, so you may obtain an answer such as 8.8921857×10^{12}. ∎

Problem-Solving Strategy

Permutations can be used any time we need to know the number of arrangements of r objects that can be selected from a collection of n objects. *The word "arrangement" implies an ordering, so we use permutations only in cases that satisfy these conditions:*

  1. *Repetitions are not allowed.*   2. *Order is important.*

Change ringing, the English way of ringing church bells, combines mathematics and music. Bells are rung first in sequence, 1, 2, 3, ... Then the sequence is permuted ("changed"). On six bells, 720 different "changes" (different permutations of tone) can be rung:
$_6P_6 = 6!$.

The church bells are swung by means of ropes attached to the wheels beside them. One ringer swings each bell, listening intently and watching the other ringers closely. If one ringer gets lost and stays lost, the rhythm of the ringing cannot be maintained; all the ringers have to stop.

A ringer can spend weeks just learning to keep a bell going and months learning to make the bell ring in exactly the right place. Errors of $\frac{1}{4}$ second mean that two bells are ringing at the same time. Even errors of $\frac{1}{10}$ second can be heard.

EXAMPLE 3 Building Numbers from a Set of Digits

How many nonrepeating three-digit numbers can be written using only the digits 3, 4, 5, 6, 7, and 8?

Solution

Repetitions are not allowed since the numbers are to be "nonrepeating." For example, 448 is not acceptable. Also, order is important. For example, 476 and 746 are *distinct* cases. So we use permutations to determine the total number. There are

$$_6P_3 = 6 \cdot 5 \cdot 4 = 120 \text{ ways.}$$ ∎

EXAMPLE 4 Designing Account Numbers

Suppose certain account numbers are to consist of two letters followed by four digits and then three more letters. Repetitions of letters or digits are not allowed *within* any of the three groups, but the last group of letters may contain one or both of those used in the first group. How many such accounts are possible?

Solution

The task of designing such a number consists of three parts.

Part 1   Determine the first set of two letters.   (There are 26 letters.)

Part 2   Determine the set of four digits.   (There are 10 digits.)

Part 3   Determine the final set of three letters.   (There are 26 letters.)

Each part requires an arrangement without repetitions, which is a permutation.

$$_{26}P_2 \cdot {}_{10}P_4 \cdot {}_{26}P_3 = \underset{\text{Part 1}}{\underline{650}} \cdot \underset{\text{Part 2}}{\underline{5040}} \cdot \underset{\text{Part 3}}{\underline{15,600}} \quad \text{Fundamental counting principle}$$

$$= 51,105,600,000$$ ∎

Combinations

Permutations involve the number of arrangements of n things taken r at a time, where repetitions are not allowed. Order is important. Recall that club

$$N = \{\text{Alan, Bill, Cathy, David, Evelyn}\}$$

could elect three officers in $_5P_3 = 60$ different ways. With three-member committees, on the other hand, order is not important. The committees B, D, E and E, B, D are not different. The possible number of committees is not the number of arrangements of size 3. Rather, it is the number of *subsets* of size 3.

Recall that in the study of sets, a **set** is a collection or group of things, commonly designated using a list within braces, as we have been designating the club

$$N = \{A, B, C, D, E\}.$$

The order of listing of the members (of any set) is unimportant. For example, $\{D, B, A, E, C\}$ is the same club. A **subset** of a set is a collection of some of the members. It may be all members of the original set, or even none of them, or anywhere in between.

Such subsets are **combinations.** The number of combinations of n things taken r at a time—that is, the number of size-r subsets, given a set of size n—is written $_nC_r$.*

> ***There are n things available and we are choosing r of them, so we can read $_nC_r$ as "n choose r."***

The size-3 committees (subsets) of the club (set) $N = \{A, B, C, D, E\}$ are

$$\{A, B, C\}, \quad \{A, B, D\}, \quad \{A, B, E\}, \quad \{A, C, D\}, \quad \{A, C, E\},$$
$$\{A, D, E\}, \quad \{B, C, D\}, \quad \{B, C, E\}, \quad \{B, D, E\}, \quad \{C, D, E\}.$$

There are ten subsets of size 3, so ten is the number of three-member committees possible. Repetitions are not allowed. For example, $\{E, E, B\}$ is not a valid three-member subset, just as EEB is not a valid three-member arrangement.

To see how to find the number of such subsets without listing them all, notice that each size-3 subset (combination) gives rise to six size-3 arrangements (permutations). For example, the single combination ADE yields these six permutations.

$$A, D, E \quad A, E, D \quad D, A, E \quad D, E, A \quad E, A, D \quad E, D, A$$

There must be six times as many size-3 permutations as there are size-3 combinations, or, equivalently, one-sixth as many combinations as permutations.

$$_5C_3 = \frac{_5P_3}{6} = \frac{60}{6} = 10$$

The 6 appears in the denominator because there are six different ways to arrange a set of three things and $3! = 3 \cdot 2 \cdot 1 = 6$. Generalizing, we obtain the following.

$$_nC_r = \frac{_nP_r}{r!} \qquad \text{\scriptsize r things can be arranged in $r!$ ways.}$$

$$= \frac{\dfrac{n!}{(n-r)!}}{r!} \qquad \text{\scriptsize Substitute the factorial formula for $_nP_r$.}$$

$$_nC_r = \frac{n!}{r!(n-r)!} \qquad \text{\scriptsize Simplify algebraically.}$$

*Alternative notations are $C(n, r)$, C_r^n, and $\binom{n}{r}$.

$\mathcal{A}$	$\mathcal{B}$	C	$\mathcal{D}$	E	F
Aaaaa	aaaab	aaaba.	aaabb.	aabaa.	aabab.
G	H	I	K	L	$\mathcal{M}$
aabba	aabbb	abaaa.	abaab.	ababa.	ababb.
$\mathcal{N}$	O	P	Q	$\mathcal{R}$	S
abbaa.	abbab.	abbba.	abbbb.	baaaa.	baaab.
T	$\mathcal{V}$	W	X	Y	Z
baaba.	baabb.	babaa.	babab.	babba.	babbb.

"Bilateral cipher" (above) was invented by **Francis Bacon** early in the seventeenth century to code political secrets. This binary code, *a* and *b* in combinations of five, has 32 permutations. Bacon's "biformed alphabet" (bottom four rows) uses two type fonts to conceal a message in some straight text. The decoder deciphers a string of *a*'s and *b*'s, groups them by fives, then deciphers letters and words. This code was applied to Shakespeare's plays in efforts to prove Bacon the rightful author.

FACTORIAL FORMULA FOR COMBINATIONS

The number of **combinations,** or *subsets,* of n distinct things taken r at a time, where $r \leq n$, can be calculated as follows.

$$_nC_r = \frac{_nP_r}{r!} = \frac{n!}{r!(n-r)!}$$

In **Examples 5 and 6,** we refer to $_nC_r$ as "a combination" even though it actually represents the number of combinations of n distinct things taken r at a time.

EXAMPLE 5 Using the Factorial Formula for Combinations

Evaluate each combination.

(a) $_9C_7$ **(b)** $_{24}C_{18}$

Solution

9!/(7!∗2!)
36
24!/(18!∗6!)
134596

This screen uses factorials to support the results of **Example 5**.

(a) $_9C_7 = \dfrac{9!}{7!(9-7)!} = \dfrac{9!}{7! \cdot 2!} = \dfrac{362{,}880}{5040 \cdot 2} = 36$

(b) $_{24}C_{18} = \dfrac{24!}{18!(24-18)!} = \dfrac{24!}{18! \cdot 6!} = 134{,}596$ ∎

EXAMPLE 6 Calculating Combinations Directly

Evaluate each combination.

(a) $_{14}C_6$ **(b)** $_{21}C_{15}$

Solution

14 nCr 6
3003
21 nCr 15
54264

This screen uses the combinations feature to support the results of **Example 6**.

(a) $_{14}C_6 = 3003$ **(b)** $_{21}C_{15} = 54{,}264$ Use a calculator in each case. ∎

Problem-Solving Strategy

Combinations share an important feature with permutations in that repetitions are not allowed, and they differ from permutations in one key distinction, which is that order is *not* important with combinations. Combinations are applied only in these situations:

   1. *Repetitions are not allowed.*   **2. *Order is not important.***

EXAMPLE 7 Finding the Number of Subsets

Find the number of different subsets of size 2 in the set $\{a, b, c, d\}$. List them.

Solution

A subset of size 2 must have two distinct elements, so repetitions are not allowed. The order in which the elements of a set are listed makes no difference,

$$_4C_2 = \frac{4!}{2!(4-2)!} = \frac{4!}{2! \cdot 2!} = 6 \quad \text{Combinations formula with } n=4 \text{ and } r=2$$

The six subsets of size 2 are $\{a, b\}, \{a, c\}, \{a, d\}, \{b, c\}, \{b, d\}, \{c, d\}$. ∎

The set of 52 playing cards in the **standard deck** has four suits.

♠ spades   ♦ diamonds
♥ hearts   ♣ clubs

Ace is the unit card. Jacks, queens, and kings are "face cards." Each suit contains thirteen denominations: ace, 2, 3, . . . , 10, jack, queen, king. In some games, ace rates above king, instead of counting as 1.

EXAMPLE 8 Finding the Number of Possible Poker Hands

A common form of poker involves "hands" (sets) of five cards each, dealt from a standard deck consisting of 52 different cards. How many different 5-card hands are possible?

Solution

A 5-card hand must contain five distinct cards, so repetitions are not allowed. Also, the order is not important because a given hand depends only on the cards it contains, and not on the order in which they were dealt or the order in which they are displayed or played.

Order does not matter, so we use combinations and a calculator.

$$_{52}C_5 = \frac{52!}{5!(52-5)!} = \frac{52!}{5! \cdot 47!} = 2{,}598{,}960$$ ■

EXAMPLE 9 Finding the Number of Subsets of Paintings

Keri would like to buy ten different paintings but she can afford only four of them. In how many ways can she make her selections?

Solution

The four paintings selected must be distinct. Repetitions are not allowed, and the order of the four chosen has no bearing in this case, so we use combinations.

$$_{10}C_4 = \frac{10!}{4!(10-4)!} = \frac{10!}{4! \cdot 6!} = 210 \text{ ways}$$ ■

Notice that, according to our formula for combinations,

$$_{10}C_6 = \frac{10!}{6!(10-6)!} = \frac{10!}{6! \cdot 4!} = 210,$$

which is the same as $_{10}C_4$. In fact, **Exercise 74** asks you to prove the following fact, in general, for all whole numbers n and r, with $r \leq n$.

$$_nC_r = {_nC_{n-r}}$$

Guidelines on Which Method to Use

The following table summarizes the similarities and differences between permutations and combinations and appropriate formulas for calculating their values.

Permutations	**Combinations**
Number of ways of selecting r items out of n items	
Repetitions are not allowed.	
Order is important.	Order is not important.
Arrangements of n items taken r at a time	Subsets of n items taken r at a time
$_nP_r = \dfrac{n!}{(n-r)!}$	$_nC_r = \dfrac{n!}{r!(n-r)!}$
Clue words: arrangement, schedule, order	Clue words: set, group, sample, selection

In cases where r items are to be selected from n items and repetitions are allowed, it is usually best to make direct use of the fundamental counting principle.

The exercises in this section will call for permutations and/or combinations. In the case of multiple-part tasks, the fundamental counting principle may also be required. *In all cases, decide carefully whether order is important, because that determines whether to use permutations or combinations.*

Problem-Solving Strategy

Many counting problems involve selecting some of the items from a given set of items. The particular conditions of the problem will determine which specific technique to use.

1. **If selected items can be repeated, use the fundamental counting principle.**
   Example: How many four-digit numbers are there?

   $$9 \cdot 10^3 = 9000$$

2. **If selected items cannot be repeated, and order is important, use permutations.**
   Example: How many ways can three of eight people line up at a ticket counter?

   $$_8P_3 = \frac{8!}{(8-3)!} = 336$$

3. **If selected items cannot be repeated, and order is *not* important, use combinations.**
   Example: How many ways can a committee of three be selected from a group of twelve people?

   $$_{12}C_3 = \frac{12!}{3!(12-3)!} = 220$$

EXAMPLE 10 Distributing Toys to Children

In how many ways can a mother distribute three different toys among her seven children if a child may receive anywhere from none to all three toys?

Solution

Because a given child can be a repeat recipient, repetitions are allowed here, so we use the fundamental counting principle. Each of the three toys can go to any of the seven children. The number of possible distributions is

$$7 \cdot 7 \cdot 7 = 343.$$ ∎

EXAMPLE 11 Selecting Committees

How many different three-member committees could club $N = \{$Alan, Bill, Cathy, David, Evelyn$\}$ appoint so that exactly one woman is on the committee?

Solution

Two members are women and three are men. Although the question mentioned only that the committee must include exactly one woman, to complete the committee two men must be selected as well. The task of selecting the committee members consists of two parts.

4. Multiply the expressions from Steps 1, 2, and 3. Explain why this product should give the total number of full house hands possible.

5. Find the three missing values in the right column of **Table 4**. (See **Table 1** in **Chapter 11**.)

6. Verify the right column total shown in **Table 4**.

Table 4   Categories of Hands in 5-Card Poker

Event E	Description of Event E	Number of Outcomes Favorable to E
Royal flush	Ace, king, queen, jack, and 10, all of the same suit	4
Straight flush	5 cards of consecutive denominations, all in the same suit (excluding royal flush)	36
Four of a kind	4 cards of the same denomination, plus 1 additional card	_____
Full house	3 cards of one denomination, plus 2 cards of a second denomination	3744
Flush	Any 5 cards all of the same suit (excluding royal flush and straight flush)	_____
Straight	5 cards of consecutive denominations (not all the same suit)	10,200
Three of a kind	3 cards of one denomination, plus 2 cards of two additional denominations	54,912
Two pairs	2 cards of one denomination, plus 2 cards of a second denomination, plus 1 card of a third denomination	_____
One pair	2 cards of one denomination, plus 3 additional cards of three different denominations	1,098,240
No pair	No two cards of the same denomination (and excluding any sort of flush or straight)	1,302,540
Total		**2,598,960**

10.3   EXERCISES

Evaluate each expression.

1. $_9P_3$
2. $_{10}P_6$
3. $_{12}P_5$

4. $_{11}P_3$
5. $_{11}C_7$
6. $_{14}C_6$

7. $_{10}C_8$
8. $_{12}C_9$

Determine the number of permutations (arrangements) of each of the following.

9. 20 things taken 4 at a time

10. 15 things taken 5 at a time

11. 16 things taken 4 at a time

12. 13 things taken 7 at a time

Determine the number of combinations (subsets) of each of the following.

13. 9 things taken 4 at a time

14. 13 things taken 6 at a time

15. 12 things taken 5 at a time

16. 11 things taken 8 at a time

Use a calculator to evaluate each expression.

17. $_{22}P_9$
18. $_{23}P_{11}$

19. $_{32}C_{12}$
20. $_{31}C_{17}$

Decide whether each object is a permutation or a combination.

21. a telephone number

22. a Social Security number

23. a hand of cards in poker

24. a committee of politicians

25. the "combination" on a student gym locker combination lock

26. a lottery choice of six numbers where the order does not matter

27. an automobile license plate number

28. an Internet password

Exercises 29–36 can be solved using permutations even though the problem statements will not always include a form of the word "permutation," or "arrangement," or "ordering."

29. *Arranging New Home Models* Tyler, a contractor, builds homes of eight different models and presently has five lots to build on. In how many different ways can he arrange homes on these lots? Assume five different models will be built.

30. *ATM PIN Numbers* An automated teller machine (ATM) requires a four-digit personal identification number (PIN), using the digits 0–9. (The first digit may be 0.) How many such PINs have no repeated digits?

31. *Electing Officers of a Club* How many ways can a president and a vice president be determined in a club with twelve members?

32. *Counting Prize Winners* First, second, and third prizes are to be awarded to three different people. If there are ten eligible candidates, how many outcomes are possible?

33. *Counting Prize Winners* How many ways can a teacher give five different prizes to five of her 25 students?

34. *Scheduling Security Team Visits* A security team visits 12 offices each night. How many different ways can the team order its visits?

35. *Placing in a Race* How many different ways could first-, second-, and third-place finishers occur in a race with six runners competing?

36. *Sums of Digits* How many counting numbers have four distinct nonzero digits such that the sum of the four digits is

(a) 10?

(b) 11?

Exercises 37–44 can be solved using combinations even though the problem statements will not always include the word "combination" or "subset."

37. *Arranging New Home Models* Tyler (the contractor) is to build six homes on a block in a new subdivision, using two different models: standard and deluxe. (All standard model homes are the same, and all deluxe model homes are the same.)

(a) How many different choices does Tyler have in positioning the six houses if he decides to build three standard and three deluxe models?

(b) If Tyler builds two deluxes and four standards, how many different positionings can he use?

38. *Sampling Cell Phones* How many ways can a sample of five cell phones be selected from a shipment of twenty-four cell phones?

39. *Detecting Defective Cell Phones* If the shipment of **Exercise 38** contains six defective phones, how many of the size-five samples would not include any of the defective ones?

40. *Committees of U.S. Senators* How many different five-member committees could be formed from the 100 U.S. senators?

41. *Selecting Hands of Cards* Refer to the standard 52-card deck pictured in the margin near **Example 8,** and notice that the deck contains four aces, twelve face cards, thirteen hearts (all red), thirteen diamonds (all red), thirteen spades (all black), and thirteen clubs (all black). Of the 2,598,960 different five-card hands possible, decide how many would consist of the following cards.

(a) all diamonds   (b) all black cards

(c) all aces

42. *Selecting Lottery Entries* In a 7/39 lottery, you select seven distinct numbers from the set 1 through 39, where order makes no difference. How many different ways can you make your selection?

43. *Number of Paths from Point to Point* In a certain city, there are seven streets going north–south and four streets going east–west. How many street paths start at the southwest corner of the city, end at the northeast corner of the city, and have the shortest possible length? (*Mathematics Teacher* calendar problem)

44. *Choosing a Monogram* Sheryl Jett wants to name her new baby so that his monogram (first, middle, and last initials) will be distinct letters in alphabetical order and he will share her last name. How many different monograms could she select?

In Exercises 45–72, use permutations, combinations, the fundamental counting principle, or other counting methods, as appropriate.

45. *Identification Numbers in Research* Subject identification numbers in a certain scientific research project consist of three letters followed by three digits and then three more letters. Assume repetitions are not allowed within any of the three groups, but letters in the first group of three may occur also in the last group of three. How many distinct identification numbers are possible?

46. *Radio Station Call Letters* Radio stations in the United States have call letters that begin with K or W. Some have three call letters, such as WBZ in Boston, WLS in Chicago, and KGO in San Francisco. Assuming no repetition of letters, how many three-letter sets of call letters are possible? (Count all possibilities even though, practically, some may be inappropriate.)

47. *Radio Station Call Letters* Most stations that were licensed after 1927 have four call letters starting with K or W, such as WXYZ in Detroit and KRLD in Dallas. Assuming no repetitions, how many four-letter sets are possible? (Count all possibilities even though, practically, some may be inappropriate.)

48. *Selecting Lottery Entries* In SuperLotto Plus, a California state lottery game, you select five distinct numbers from 1 to 47, and one MEGA number from 1 to 27, hoping that your selection will match a random list selected by lottery officials.

(a) How many different sets of six numbers can you select?

(b) Paul always includes his age and his wife's age as two of the first five numbers in his SuperLotto Plus selections. How many ways can he complete his list of six numbers?

49. *Scheduling Batting Orders in Baseball* The Coyotes, a youth league baseball team, have seven pitchers, who only pitch, and twelve other players, all of whom can play any position other than pitcher. For Saturday's game, the coach has not yet determined which nine players to use or what the batting order will be, except that the pitcher will bat last. How many different batting orders may occur?

50. *Scheduling Games in a Basketball League* Each team in an eight-team basketball league is scheduled to play each other team three times. How many games will be played altogether?

51. *Arranging a Wedding Reception Line* At a wedding reception, the bride, the groom and four attendants will form a reception line. How many ways can they be arranged in each of the following cases?

(a) Any order will do.

(b) The bride and groom must be the last two in line.

(c) The groom must be last in line with the bride next to him.

52. *Ordering Performers in a Music Recital* A music class of five girls and four boys is having a recital. If each member is to perform once, how many ways can the program be arranged in each of the following cases?

(a) All girls must perform first.

(b) A girl must perform first, and a boy must perform last.

(c) Elisa (a girl) and Doug (a boy) will perform first and last, respectively.

(d) The entire program will alternate between girls and boys.

(e) The first, fifth, and ninth performers must be girls.

53. *Dividing People into Groups* In how many ways could fifteen people be divided into five groups containing, respectively, one, two, three, four, and five people?

54. *Dividing People into Groups* In how many ways could fifteen people be divided into five groups of three people?

55. *Dividing People into Groups* In how many ways could eight people be divided into two groups of three people and a group of two people?

56. *Scheduling Daily Reading* Carole begins each day by reading from one of seven inspirational books. How many ways can she arrange her reading for one week if the selection is done

    (a) with replacement?

    (b) without replacement?

57. *Counting Card Hands* How many of the possible 5-card hands from a standard 52-card deck would consist of the following cards?

    (a) four clubs and one non-club

    (b) two face cards and three non-face cards

    (c) two red cards, two clubs, and a spade

58. *Drawing Cards* How many cards must be drawn (without replacement) from a standard deck of 52 to guarantee the following?

    (a) Two of the cards will be of the same suit.

    (b) Three of the cards will be of the same suit.

59. *Flush Hands in Poker* How many different 5-card poker hands would contain only cards of a single suit?

60. *Screening Computer Processors* A computer company will screen a shipment of 30 processors by testing a random sample of five of them. How many different samples are possible?

61. *Selecting Drivers and Passengers for a Trip* Natalie, her husband, her son, and four additional friends are driving in two vehicles to the seashore.

    (a) If all seven people can drive, how many ways can the two drivers be selected? (Everyone wants to drive the sports car, so it is important which driver gets which car.)

    (b) If the sports car must be driven by Natalie, her husband, or their son, how many ways can the drivers now be determined?

    (c) If the sports car will accommodate only two people, and there are no other restrictions, how many ways can both drivers and passengers be assigned to both cars?

62. *Points and Lines in a Plane* If any two points determine a line, how many lines are determined by seven points in a plane, no three of which are collinear?

63. *Points and Triangles in a Plane* How many triangles are determined by twenty points in a plane, no three of which are collinear?

64. *Counting Possibilities on a Combination Lock* How many different three-number "combinations" are possible on a combination lock having 40 numbers on its dial? (*Hint:* "Combination" is a misleading name for these locks since repetitions are allowed and order makes a difference.)

65. *Winning the Trifecta in Horse Racing* Many race tracks offer a "trifecta" race. You win by selecting the correct first-, second-, and third-place finishers. If eight horses are entered, how many tickets must you purchase to guarantee that one of them will be a trifecta winner?

66. *Winning the Daily Double in Horse Racing* At a horse race, you win the "daily double" by purchasing a ticket and selecting the winners of two specific races. If there are six and eight horses running in those races, respectively, how many tickets must you buy to guarantee a win?

67. *Selecting Committees* Nine people are to be distributed among three committees of two, three, and four members, and a chairperson is to be selected for each committee. How many ways can this be done? (*Hint:* Break the task into the following sequence of parts.)

    Part 1 Select the members of the two-person committee.

    Part 2 Select the members of the three-person committee.

    Part 3 Select the chair of the two-person committee.

    Part 4 Select the chair of the three-person committee.

    Part 5 Select the chair of the four-person committee.

68. *Selecting Committee Members* Repeat **Exercise 67** in the case where the three committees are to have three members each. (*Hint:* Use the same general sequence of task parts, but remember to adjust for *unwanted ordering* of the three committees.)

69. *Arranging New Home Models* (See **Exercise 37.**) Because of his good work, Tyler gets a contract to build homes on three additional blocks in the subdivision, with six homes on each block. He decides to build nine deluxe homes on these three blocks: two on the first block, three on the second, and four on the third. The remaining nine homes will be standard.

    (a) Altogether on the three-block stretch, how many different choices does Tyler have for positioning the eighteen homes? (*Hint:* Consider the three blocks separately, and use the fundamental counting principle.)

    (b) How many choices would he have if he built 2, 3, and 4 deluxe models on the three different blocks as before, but not necessarily on the first, second, and third blocks in that order?

70. *Sums of Digits*   How many counting numbers consist of four distinct nonzero digits such that the sum of the four digits is the given number?

    (a) 12

    (b) 13

71. *Building Numbers from Sets of Digits*   Recall that the counting numbers are

$$1, 2, 3, 4, \ldots .$$

    (a) How many six-digit counting numbers use all six digits 4, 5, 6, 7, 8, and 9?

    (b) Suppose all these numbers were arranged in increasing order:

$$456{,}789; \quad 456{,}798; \quad \text{and so on.}$$

    Which number would be 364th in the list?

72. *Arranging Five-letter Words*   The 120 permutations of AHSME are arranged in dictionary order, as if each were an ordinary five-letter word. Find the last letter of the 86th word in the list. (*Mathematics Teacher* calendar problem)

73. Verify that $_{12}C_9 = {_{12}C_3}$.

74. Use the factorial formula for combinations to prove that in general,

$$_nC_r = {_nC_{n-r}}.$$

10.4   USING PASCAL'S TRIANGLE

OBJECTIVES

1 Construct Pascal's triangle and recognize the relationship between its entries and values of $_nC_r$.

2 Use Pascal's triangle to solve applications involving combinations.

Pascal's Triangle

The triangular array in **Figure 7** represents what we can call "random walks" that begin at START and proceed downward according to the following rule:

> *At each circle (branch point), a coin is tossed. If it lands heads, we go downward to the left. If it lands tails, we go downward to the right. At each point, left and right are equally likely.*

In each circle we have recorded the number of different routes that could bring us to that point. For example, the colored 3 can be reached as the result of three different coin-tossing sequences.

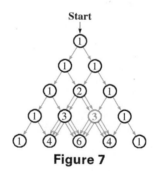

Figure 7

htt,   tht,   and   tth   Ways to get to ③

Another way to generate the same pattern of numbers is to begin with 1s down both diagonals and then fill in the interior entries by adding the two numbers just above a given position (to the left and right). For example, the green 28 in **Table 5** on the next page is the result of adding 7 and 21 in the row above it.

By continuing to add pairs of numbers, we extend the array indefinitely downward, always beginning and ending each row with 1s. The table shows just rows 0 through 10. This unending triangular array of numbers is called **Pascal's triangle,** because Blaise Pascal wrote a treatise about it in 1653. There is evidence, though, that it was known as early as around 1100 and may have been studied in China or India still earlier.

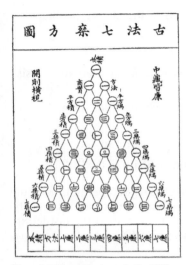

"Pascal's" triangle is shown in the 1303 text **Szu-yuen Yu-chien** (*The Precious Mirror of the Four Elements*) by the Chinese mathematician Chu Shih-chieh.

Table 5   Pascal's Triangle

Row Number													Row Sum
0							1						1
1						1		1					2
2					1		2		1				4
3				1		3		3		1			8
4			1		4		6		4		1		16
5		1		5		10		10		5		1	32
6	1		6		15		20		15		6	1	64
7	1	7	21		35		35		21		7	1	128
8	1	8	28	56		70		56		28	8	1	256
9	1	9	36	84	126		126		84	36	9	1	512
10 1	10	45	120	210	252		210	120	45	10	1	1024

At any rate, the triangle possesses many interesting properties. In counting applications, the most useful property is that, in general, entry number r in row number n is equal to $_nC_r$—the number of *combinations* of n things taken r at a time. This correspondence is shown through row 8 in **Table 6**.

Table 6   Combination Values in Pascal's Triangle

Row Number									
0					$_0C_0$				
1				$_1C_0$		$_1C_1$			
2			$_2C_0$		$_2C_1$		$_2C_2$		
3		$_3C_0$		$_3C_1$		$_3C_2$		$_3C_3$	
4	$_4C_0$		$_4C_1$		$_4C_2$		$_4C_3$		$_4C_4$
5	$_5C_0$	$_5C_1$		$_5C_2$		$_5C_3$		$_5C_4$	$_5C_5$
6	$_6C_0$	$_6C_1$	$_6C_2$		$_6C_3$		$_6C_4$	$_6C_5$	$_6C_6$
7	$_7C_0$	$_7C_1$	$_7C_2$	$_7C_3$		$_7C_4$	$_7C_5$	$_7C_6$	$_7C_7$
8	$_8C_0$	$_8C_1$	$_8C_2$	$_8C_3$	$_8C_4$	$_8C_5$	$_8C_6$	$_8C_7$	$_8C_8$

The entries in color correspond to those examined earlier in **Table 5**. Having a copy of Pascal's triangle handy gives us another option for evaluating combinations. Any time we need to know the number of combinations of n things taken r at a time, we can simply read entry number r of row number n. **Keep in mind that the first row shown is row number 0.** Also, the first entry of each row can be called entry number 0. This entry gives the number of subsets of size 0, which is always 1 because there is only one empty set.

Applications

EXAMPLE 1 Applying Pascal's Triangle to Counting People

A group of ten people includes six women and four men. If five of these people are randomly selected to fill out a questionnaire, how many different samples of five people are possible?

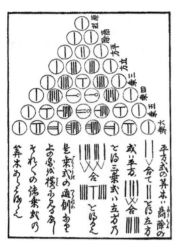

This **Japanese version** of the triangle dates from the eighteenth century. The "stick numerals" evolved from bamboo counting pieces used on a ruled board. Possibly Omar Khayyam, twelfth-century Persian mathematician and poet, may also have divined its patterns in pursuit of algebraic solutions. (The triangle lists the coefficients of the binomial expansion, explained in **For Further Thought** at the end of this section.)

Solution

This is simply a matter of selecting a subset of five from a set of ten, which is the number of combinations of ten things taken five at a time.

$$_{10}C_5 = 252 \quad \text{See row 10 of Pascal's triangle in Table 5.} \quad \blacksquare$$

EXAMPLE 2 Applying Pascal's Triangle to Counting People

Among the 252 possible samples of five people in **Example 1,** how many of them would consist of exactly two women and three men?

Solution

Two women can be selected from six women in $_6C_2$ different ways, and three men can be selected from four men in $_4C_3$ different ways. These combination values can be read from Pascal's triangle. Then, since the task of obtaining two women and three men requires both individual parts, the fundamental counting principle tells us to multiply the two values.

$$_6C_2 \cdot {}_4C_3 = 15 \cdot 4 = 60 \quad \text{Rows 6 and 4 of Pascal's triangle} \quad \blacksquare$$

EXAMPLE 3 Applying Pascal's Triangle to Coin Tossing

If five fair coins are tossed, in how many different ways could exactly three heads be obtained?

Solution

There are various "ways" of obtaining exactly three heads because the three heads can occur on different subsets of the coins. For example, hhtht and thhth are just two of many possibilities. When such a possibility is written down, exactly three positions are occupied by an h, the other two by a t. Each distinct way of choosing three positions from a set of five positions gives a different possibility. (Once the three positions for h are determined, each of the other two positions automatically receives a t.)

So our answer is just the number of size-three subsets of a size-five set—that is, the number of combinations of five things taken three at a time.

$$_5C_3 = 10 \quad \text{Row 5 of Pascal's triangle} \quad \blacksquare$$

Notice that row 5 of Pascal's triangle also provides answers to several other questions about tossing five fair coins. They are summarized in **Table 7.**

The Pascal Identity We know that each interior entry in Pascal's triangle can be obtained by adding the two numbers just above it (to the left and right). This fact, known as the "Pascal identity," can be written as

$$_nC_r = {}_{n-1}C_{r-1} + {}_{n-1}C_r.$$

The factorial formula for combinations (along with some algebra) can be used to prove the Pascal identity.

Table 7 Tossing **Five** Fair Coins

Number of Heads n	Ways of Obtaining Exactly n Heads	Listing
0	$_5C_0 = 1$	ttttt
1	$_5C_1 = 5$	htttt, thttt, tthtt, tttht, tttth
2	$_5C_2 = 10$	hhttt, hthtt, htthtt, htttth, thhtt, ththt, thtth, tthht, tthth, ttthh
3	$_5C_3 = 10$	hhhtt, hhtht, hhtth, hthht, hthth, htthh, thhht, thhth, ththh, tthhh
4	$_5C_4 = 5$	hhhht, hhhth, hhthh, hthhh, thhhh
5	$_5C_5 = 1$	hhhhh

To analyze the tossing of a different number of fair coins, we can simply take the pertinent numbers from a different row of Pascal's triangle. Repeated coin tossing is an example of a "binomial" experiment because each toss has *two* possible outcomes:

heads and tails.

FOR FURTHER THOUGHT

The Binomial Theorem

The combination values that make up Pascal's triangle also arise in a totally different mathematical context. In algebra, "binomial" refers to a two-term expression such as

$$x + y, \quad \text{or} \quad a + 2b, \quad \text{or} \quad w^3 - 4.$$

The first few powers of the binomial $x + y$ are shown here.

$$(x + y)^0 = 1$$
$$(x + y)^1 = x + y$$
$$(x + y)^2 = x^2 + 2xy + y^2$$
$$(x + y)^3 = x^3 + 3x^2y + 3xy^2 + y^3$$
$$(x + y)^4 = x^4 + 4x^3y + 6x^2y^2 + 4xy^3 + y^4$$
$$(x + y)^5 = x^5 + 5x^4y + 10x^3y^2 + 10x^2y^3$$
$$+ 5xy^4 + y^5$$

The numerical coefficients of these expansions form the first six rows of Pascal's triangle. In our study of counting, we have called these numbers combinations, but in the study of algebra, they are called **binomial coefficients** and are usually denoted

$$\binom{n}{r} \quad \text{rather than} \quad {}_nC_r.$$

Generalizing the pattern of the powers yields the important result known as the **binomial theorem**.

Binomial Theorem

For any whole number n,

$$(x + y)^n$$

$$= \binom{n}{0} \cdot x^n + \binom{n}{1} \cdot x^{n-1}y$$

$$+ \binom{n}{2} \cdot x^{n-2}y^2 + \binom{n}{3} \cdot x^{n-3}y^3 +$$

$$\cdots + \binom{n}{n-1} \cdot xy^{n-1} + \binom{n}{n} \cdot y^n.$$

Here each binomial coefficient can be calculated by the formula

$$\binom{n}{r} = \frac{n!}{r!(n - r)!}.$$

If $n = 0$, then the first coefficient shown in the expansion is, at the same time, the last coefficient, for

$$\binom{n}{0} \cdot x^n = \binom{0}{0} \cdot x^0 = \frac{0!}{0! \cdot 0!} \cdot 1 = 1,$$

and $\quad \binom{n}{n} \cdot y^n = \binom{0}{0} \cdot y^0 = \frac{0!}{0! \cdot 0!} \cdot 1 = 1.$

■■ EXAMPLE   Applying the Binomial Theorem

Write out the binomial expansion for $(2a + 5)^4$.

Solution

We take the initial coefficients from row 4 of Pascal's triangle and then simplify algebraically.

$$(2a + 5)^4$$

$$= \binom{4}{0} \cdot (2a)^4 + \binom{4}{1} \cdot (2a)^3 \cdot 5$$

$$+ \binom{4}{2} \cdot (2a)^2 \cdot 5^2 + \binom{4}{3} \cdot (2a) \cdot 5^3$$

$$+ \binom{4}{4} \cdot 5^4$$

Recall that $(xy)^n = x^n \cdot y^n$.

$$= 1 \cdot 2^4 \cdot a^4 + 4 \cdot 2^3 \cdot a^3 \cdot 5 + 6 \cdot 2^2 \cdot a^2 \cdot 5^2$$
$$+ 4 \cdot 2 \cdot a \cdot 5^3 + 1 \cdot 5^4$$
$$= 16a^4 + 160a^3 + 600a^2 + 1000a + 625 \qquad ■$$

For Group or Individual Investigation

Write out the binomial expansion for each of the following powers. (*Hint:* $-b$ can written $+(-b)$.)

1. $(x + y)^6$ 2. $(x + y)^7$

3. $(a - b)^4$ 4. $(a - b)^5$

5. $(2x + 1)^4$ 6. $(3y + 2)^3$

10.4   EXERCISES

Read each combination value directly from Pascal's triangle.

1. $_4C_2$ **2.** $_5C_3$ **3.** $_6C_3$ **4.** $_7C_5$

5. $_8C_5$ **6.** $_9C_6$ **7.** $_9C_2$ **8.** $_{10}C_7$

Selecting Committees of Congressmembers *A committee of four Congressmembers will be selected from a group of seven Democrats and three Republicans. Find the number of ways of obtaining each result.*

9. exactly one Democrat

10. exactly two Democrats

11. exactly three Democrats

12. exactly four Democrats

Tossing Coins *Suppose eight fair coins are tossed. Find the number of ways of obtaining each result.*

13. exactly three heads

14. exactly four heads

15. exactly five heads

16. exactly six heads

Selecting Classrooms *Diana is searching for her ecology class and knows that it must be in one of nine classrooms. Since the professor does not allow people to enter after the class has begun, and there is very little time left, she decides to try just four of the rooms at random.*

17. How many different selections of four rooms are possible?

18. How many of the selections of **Exercise 17** will fail to locate the class?

19. How many of the selections of **Exercise 17** will succeed in locating the class?

20. What fraction of the possible selections will lead to "success"? (Give three decimal places.)

For a set of five objects, find the number of different subsets of each size. (Use row 5 of Pascal's triangle to find the answers.)

21. 0   **22.** 1   **23.** 2

24. 3   **25.** 4   **26.** 5

27. How many subsets (of any size) are there for a set of five elements?

28. For a given row in Pascal's triangle, let n be the row number and let s be the row sum.

    (a) Write an equation relating s and n.

    (b) Explain the relationship in part (a).

29. Which rows of Pascal's triangle have a single greatest entry?

30. What is the least four-digit number in Pascal's triangle? (*Mathematics Teacher* calendar problem)

Patterns in Pascal's Triangle *Over the years, many interesting patterns have been discovered in Pascal's triangle. We explore a few of them in Exercises 31–37.*

31. Refer to **Table 5**.

    (a) Choose a row whose row number is prime. Except for the 1s in this row, what is true of all the other entries?

    (b) Choose a second prime row number and see if the same pattern holds.

    (c) Use the usual method to construct row 11 in **Table 5**. Verify that the same pattern holds.

32. Name the next five numbers of the diagonal sequence in the figure. What are these numbers called? (See **Section 1.2**.)

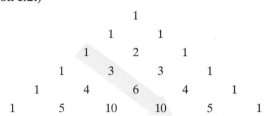

33. Complete the sequence of sums on the diagonals shown in the figure. What pattern do these sums make? What is the name of this important sequence of numbers? The presence of this sequence in the triangle apparently was not recognized by Pascal.

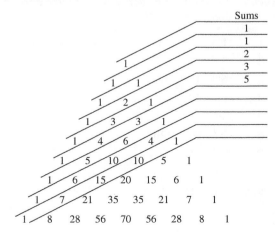

34. Construct another "triangle" by replacing every number in Pascal's triangle (rows **0** through **5**) by the remainder when it is divided by 2. What special property is shared by rows **2** and **4** of this new triangle?

35. What is the next row that would have the same property as rows **2** and **4** in **Exercise 34**?

36. (Work **Exercises 34 and 35** first.) How many even numbers are there in row **256** of Pascal's triangle?

37. The figure shows a portion of Pascal's triangle with several inverted triangular regions outlined. For any one of these regions, what can be said of the sum of the squares of the entries across its top row?

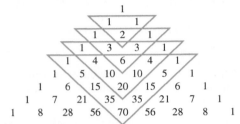

38. *Tartaglia's Rectangle* More than a century before Pascal's treatise on the triangle appeared, a work by the Italian mathematician Niccolo Tartaglia (1506–1559) came out and included the table of numbers shown here.

1	1	1	1	1	1
1	2	3	4	5	6
1	3	6	10	15	21
1	4	10	20	35	56
1	5	15	35	70	126
1	6	21	56	126	252
1	7	28	84	210	462
1	8	36	120	330	792

Explain the connection between Pascal's triangle and Tartaglia's rectangle.

Tartaglia's Rectangle The triangle that Pascal studied and published in his treatise was actually more like a truncated corner of Tartaglia's rectangle, as shown here.

1	1	1	1	1	1	1	1	1	1
1	2	3	4	5	6	7	8	9	
1	3	6	10	15	21	28	36		
1	4	10	20	35	56	84			
1	5	15	35	70	126				
1	6	21	56	126					
1	7	28	84						
1	8	36							
1	9								
1									

Each number in the truncated corner of Tartaglia's rectangle can be calculated in various ways. In each of Exercises 39–42, consider the number N to be located anywhere in the array. By checking several locations in the given array, determine how N is related to the sum of all entries in the shaded cells. Describe the relationship in words.

39.

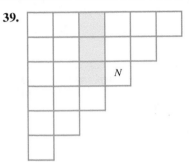

40.

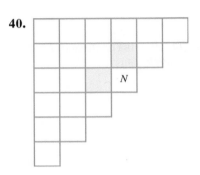

41.

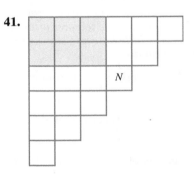

42.

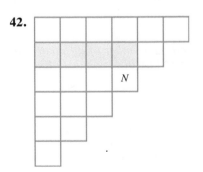

10.5 COUNTING PROBLEMS INVOLVING "NOT" AND "OR"

OBJECTIVES

1 Understand the complements principle of counting.

2 Apply the complements principle to a counting problem by considering the problem in terms of outcomes that do not occur (a "not" statement).

3 Understand the additive principle of counting.

4 Apply the additive principle to a counting problem by considering the problem in terms of the union of two outcomes (an "or" statement).

Set Theory/Logic/Arithmetic Correspondences

The counting techniques in this section, which can be thought of as *indirect techniques*, are based on some useful correspondences from **Chapters 2 and 3** among set theory, logic, and arithmetic, as shown in **Table 8**.

Table 8 Correspondences

	Set Theory	**Logic**	**Arithmetic**
Operation or Connective (Symbol)	Complement $(')$	Not $(\sim)$	Subtraction $(-)$
Operation or Connective (Symbol)	Union $(\cup)$	Or $(\vee)$	Addition $(+)$

Problems Involving "Not"

Suppose U is the set of all possible results of some type. The "universal set U" comprises all possibilities, as discussed in **Chapter 2**. Let A be the set of all those results that satisfy a given condition. For any set S, its cardinal number is written $n(S)$, and its complement is written S'. **Figure 8** suggests that

$$n(A) + n(A') = n(U).$$

Also, $\qquad n(A) = n(U) - n(A') \qquad$ and $\qquad n(A') = n(U) - n(A).$

We focus here on the form that expresses the following indirect counting principle based on the complement/not/subtraction correspondence from **Table 8**.

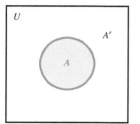

The complement of a set
Figure 8

COMPLEMENTS PRINCIPLE OF COUNTING

The number of ways in which a certain condition can be satisfied is the total number of possible results minus the number of ways the condition would **not** be satisfied. Symbolically, if A is any set within the universal set U, then the following formula holds.

$$n(A) = n(U) - n(A')$$

EXAMPLE 1 Counting the Proper Subsets of a Set

A **proper subset** of a set S is a subset that is not S itself. For the set $S = \{a, b, c, d, e, f\}$, find the number of proper subsets.

Solution

A proper subset of S is any subset with fewer than all six elements. Subsets of several different sizes would satisfy this condition. Consider the one subset that is not proper, namely S itself. From set theory, we know that set S has a total of

$$2^6 = 64 \text{ subsets.}$$

Thus, from the complements principle, the number of proper subsets is

$$64 - 1 = 63.$$

In words, the number of subsets that *are* proper is the total number of subsets minus the number of subsets that are *not* proper. ∎

Proper Subsets As an illustration, the proper subsets of $\{a, b\}$ are

$$\{a\}, \quad \{b\}, \quad \text{and} \quad \varnothing.$$

Consider the tossing of three fair coins. Since each coin will land either heads (h) or tails (t), the possible results can be listed as follows.

hhh, hht, hth, thh, htt, tht, tth, ttt   Results of tossing three fair coins

Even without the listing, we could have concluded that there would be eight possibilities. There are two possible outcomes for each coin, so the fundamental counting principle gives

$$2 \cdot 2 \cdot 2 = 2^3 = 8.$$

Suppose we wanted the number of ways of obtaining *at least* one head. In this case, "at least one" means one or two or three. Rather than dealing with all three cases, we can note that "at least one" is the opposite (or complement) of "fewer than one", which is zero. Because there is only one way to get zero heads (ttt), and there are a total of eight possibilities, the complements principle gives the number of ways of getting at least one head.

$$8 - 1 = 7 \text{ ways}$$

Indirect counting methods can often be applied to problems involving "at least," or "at most," or "less than," or "more than."

EXAMPLE 2 Counting Coin-Tossing Results

If four fair coins are tossed, in how many ways can at least one tail be obtained?

Solution

By the fundamental counting principle, $2^4 = 16$ different results are possible. Exactly one of these fails to satisfy the condition of "at least one tail," and that is hhhh. So the answer from the complements principle is

$$16 - 1 = 15.$$ ∎

EXAMPLE 3 Counting Selections of Airliner Seats

Carol and three friends are boarding an airliner. There are only ten seats left, three of which are aisle seats. How many ways can the four friends arrange themselves in available seats so that at least one of them sits on the aisle?

Solution

The word "arrange" implies that order is important, so we use permutations. "At least one aisle seat" is the opposite (complement) of "no aisle seats." The total number of ways to arrange four people among ten seats is

$$_{10}P_4 = 5040.$$

The number of ways to arrange four people among seven (non-aisle) seats is

$$_7P_4 = 840.$$

Therefore, by the complements principle, the number of arrangements with at least one aisle seat is followed by subtracting.

$$\overset{_{10}P_4}{\underset{\downarrow}{5040}} - \overset{_7P_4}{\underset{\downarrow}{840}} = 4200$$ ∎

```
(10 nPr 4)-(7 nPr 4)
                4200
(13 nCr 5)+(26 nCr 5)
               67067
```

Results in **Examples 3 and 4** are supported in this screen.

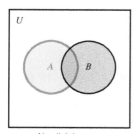

Nondisjoint sets
Figure 9

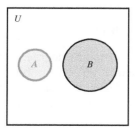

Disjoint sets
Figure 10

Problems Involving "Or"

The complements principle is one way of counting indirectly. Another technique is to count the elements of a set by breaking that set into simpler component parts. If

$$S = A \cup B,$$

the cardinal number formula from **Section 2.4** says to find the number of elements in S by adding the number in A to the number in B. We must then subtract the number in the intersection $A \cap B$ if A and B are not disjoint, as in **Figure 9**. But if A and B are disjoint, as in **Figure 10**, the subtraction is not necessary.

The following principle reflects the union/or/addition correspondence from **Table 8**.

ADDITIVE PRINCIPLE OF COUNTING

The number of ways that one **or** the other of two conditions could be satisfied is the number of ways one of them could be satisfied plus the number of ways the other could be satisfied, minus the number of ways they could both be satisfied together.

Symbolically, **if A and B are any two sets, then**

$$n(A \cup B) = n(A) + n(B) - n(A \cap B).$$

If sets A and B are disjoint, then

$$n(A \cup B) = n(A) + n(B).$$

EXAMPLE 4   **Counting Card Hands**

How many five-card poker hands consist of either all clubs or all red cards?

Solution

No hand that satisfies one of these conditions could also satisfy the other, so the two sets of possibilities (all **clubs,** all **red** cards) are disjoint. Therefore, the second formula of the additive principle applies.

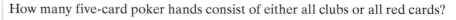

$n(\text{all }\mathbf{clubs}\text{ or all }\mathbf{red}\text{ cards}) = n(\text{all }\mathbf{clubs}) + n(\text{all }\mathbf{red}\text{ cards})$	Additive counting principle
$= {}_{13}C_5 + {}_{26}C_5$	13 clubs, 26 red cards
$= \mathbf{1287} + 65{,}780$	Substitute values.
$= 67{,}067$	Add. ∎

EXAMPLE 5   **Counting Selections from a Diplomatic Delegation**

Table 9 categorizes a diplomatic delegation of 18 congressional. members as to political party and gender. If one of the members is chosen randomly to be spokesperson for the group, in how many ways could that person be a Democrat (D) or a woman (W)?

Table 9

	Men (M)	Women (W)	Totals
Republican (R)	5	3	8
Democrat (D)	4	6	10
Totals	9	9	18

Solution

D and W are not disjoint because 6 delegates are both Democrats and women. The first formula of the additive principle is required.

$$n(D \text{ or } W) = n(D \cup W) \qquad \text{Union/or correspondence}$$
$$= n(D) + n(W) - n(D \cap W) \quad \text{Additive principle}$$
$$= 10 + 9 - 6 \qquad \text{Substitute values.}$$
$$= 13 \qquad \text{Add and subtract.} \quad \blacksquare$$

EXAMPLE 6 Counting Course Selections for a Degree Program

Chrissy needs to take twelve more specific courses for a bachelor's degree, including four in math, three in physics, three in computer science, and two in business. If five courses are randomly chosen from these twelve for next semester's program, how many of the possible selections would include at least two math courses?

Solution

Of all the information given here, what is important is that there are four math courses and eight other courses to choose from, and that five of them are being selected for next semester. If T denotes the set of selections that include at least two math courses, then we can write

$$T = A \cup B \cup C,$$

where A = the set of selections with exactly two math courses

B = the set of selections with exactly three math courses

C = the set of selections with exactly four math courses.

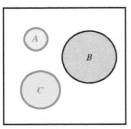

$T = A \cup B \cup C$
Figure 11

In this case, *at least two* means exactly two **or** exactly three **or** exactly four. The situation is illustrated in **Figure 11.** By previous methods, we know that

Two math courses $\longrightarrow$ $n(A) = {}_4C_2 \cdot {}_8C_3 = 6 \cdot 56 = 336$ In each case, $8 = 12 - 4$.

Three math courses $\longrightarrow$ $n(B) = {}_4C_3 \cdot {}_8C_2 = 4 \cdot 28 = 112$ In each case, the sum of the numbers in red is 5.

Four math courses $\longrightarrow$ $n(C) = {}_4C_4 \cdot {}_8C_1 = 1 \cdot 8 = 8.$

By the additive principle,

$$n(T) = 336 + 112 + 8 = 456. \qquad \blacksquare$$

EXAMPLE 7 Counting Three-Digit Numbers with Conditions

How many three-digit counting numbers are multiples of 2 or multiples of 5?

Solution

- A multiple of 2 must end in an even digit $(0, 2, 4, 6, \text{ or } 8)$, so there are $9 \cdot 10 \cdot 5 = 450$ three-digit multiples of 2.

- A multiple of 5 must end in 0 or 5, so there are $9 \cdot 10 \cdot 2 = 180$ of those.

- A multiple of both 2 and 5 is a multiple of 10 and must end in 0. There are $9 \cdot 10 \cdot 1 = 90$ of those.

By the additive principle, there are

$$450 + 180 - 90 = 540$$

possible three-digit numbers that are multiples of 2 or multiples of 5. $\qquad \blacksquare$

EXAMPLE 8 Counting Card-Drawing Results

A single card is drawn from a standard 52-card deck.

(a) In how many ways could it be a heart or a king?

(b) In how many ways could it be a club or a face card?

Solution

(a) A single card can be both a heart and a king (the king of hearts), so use the first additive formula. There are thirteen hearts, four kings, and one card that is both a heart and a king.

$$13 + 4 - 1 = 16 \quad \text{Additive principle}$$

(b) There are 13 clubs, 12 face cards, and 3 cards that are both clubs and face cards.

$$13 + 12 - 3 = 22 \quad \text{Additive principle}$$

EXAMPLE 9 Counting Subsets of a Set with Conditions

How many subsets of a 25-element set have more than three elements?

Solution

It would be a real job to count directly all subsets of size $4, 5, 6, \ldots, 25$. It is much easier to count those with three or fewer elements and apply the complements principle.

- There is $\quad\quad\quad\quad_{25}C_0 = 1 \quad\quad\quad$ size-0 subset.
- There are $\quad\quad\quad_{25}C_1 = 25 \quad\quad\quad$ size-1 subsets.
- There are $\quad\quad\quad_{25}C_2 = 300 \quad\quad\quad$ size-2 subsets.
- There are $\quad\quad\quad_{25}C_3 = 2300 \quad\quad\quad$ size-3 subsets.

Use a calculator to find that the total number of subsets of all sizes, 0 through 25, is $2^{25} = 33,554,432$. So the number with more than three elements must be

$$33,554,432 - \underbrace{(1 + 25 + 300 + 2300)}_{\text{Additive principle}} = 33,554,432 - 2626$$
$$= 33,551,806. \quad \text{Complements principle}$$

10.5 EXERCISES

How many proper subsets are there of each set?

1. $\{A, B, C, D\}$

2. $\{u, v, w, x, y, z\}$

3. $\{1, 2, 3, 4, 5, 6, 7\}$

4. $\{a, b, c, \ldots, j\}$

Tossing Coins *If you toss seven fair coins, in how many ways can you obtain each result?*

5. at least one head
("At least one" is the complement of "none.")

6. at least two heads
("At least two" is the complement of "zero or one.")

7. at least two tails

8. at least one of each (a head and a tail)

Rolling Dice *If you roll two fair dice (say red and green), in how many ways can you obtain each result? (Refer to* **Table 2** *in Section 10.1.)*

9. at least 2 on the green die

10. a sum of at least 3

11. a 4 on at least one of the dice

12. a different number on each die

Drawing Cards *If you draw a single card from a standard 52-card deck, in how many ways can you obtain each result?*

13. a card other than the ace of spades

14. a nonface card

15. a card other than a ten

16. a card other than a jack or queen

Identifying Properties of Counting Numbers *How many two-digit counting numbers meet each requirement?*

17. not a multiple of 10

18. not a multiple of 20

19. greater than 70 or a multiple of 10

20. less than 30 or a multiple of 20

21. *Choosing Country Music Albums* Jeanne's collection of ten country music albums includes *Sundown Heaven Town*, by Tim McGraw. She will choose three of her albums to play on a drive to Nashville. (Assume order is not important.)

 (a) How many different sets of three albums could she choose?

 (b) How many of these sets would not include *Sundown Heaven Town*?

 (c) How many of them would include *Sundown Heaven Town*?

22. *Choosing Broadway Hits* The ten longest Broadway runs include *The Phantom of the Opera* and *Les Misérables*. Four of the ten are chosen randomly. (Assume order is not important.)

 (a) How many ways can the four be chosen?

 (b) How many of those groups of four would include neither of the two productions mentioned?

 (c) How many of them would include at least one of the two productions mentioned?

23. *Choosing Days of the Week* How many different ways could three distinct days of the week be chosen so that at least one of them begins with the letter S? (Assume order of selection is not important.)

24. *Choosing School Assignments for Completion* Diona has nine major assignments to complete for school this week. Two of them involve writing essays. Diona decides to work on two of the nine assignments tonight. How many different choices of two would include at least one essay assignment? (Assume order is not important.)

Selecting Restaurants *Jason wants to dine at four different restaurants during a summer getaway. If three of eight available restaurants serve seafood, find the number of ways that at least one of the selected restaurants will serve seafood given the following conditions.*

25. The order of selection is important.

26. The order of selection is not important.

27. *Seating Arrangements on an Airliner* Refer to **Example 3.** If one of the group decided at the last minute not to fly, then how many ways could the remaining three arrange themselves among the ten available seats so that at least one of them would sit on the aisle?

28. *Identifying Properties of Counting Numbers* Find the number of four-digit counting numbers containing at least one zero, under each of the following conditions.

 (a) Repeated digits are allowed.

 (b) Repeated digits are not allowed.

29. *Counting Radio Call Letters* Radio stations in the United States have call letters that begin with either K or W. Some have a total of three letters, and others have four letters. How many different call letter combinations are possible? Count all possibilities even though, practically, some may be inappropriate. (*Mathematics Teacher* calendar problem) (*Hint:* Do *not* apply combinations.)?

30. *Selecting Faculty Committees* A committee of four faculty members will be selected from a department of twenty-five, which includes professors Fontana and Spradley. In how many ways could the committee include at least one of these two professors?

31. *Selecting Search-and-Rescue Teams* A Civil Air Patrol unit of twelve members includes four officers. In how many ways can four members be selected for a search-and-rescue mission such that at least one officer is included?

32. *Choosing Team Members* Three students from a class of 12 will form a math contest team that must include at least 1 boy and at least 1 girl. If 160 different teams can be formed from the 12 students, which of the following can be the difference between the number of boys and the number of girls in the class?

A. 0   **B.** 2   **C.** 4   **D.** 6   **E.** 8

(*Mathematics Teacher* calendar problem)

Drawing Cards *If a single card is drawn from a standard 52-card deck, in how many ways could it be the following? (Use the additive principle.)*

33. a club or a jack

34. a heart or a ten

35. a face card or a black card

36. an ace or a red card

Choosing Senators *The table categorizes 20 senators as to political party and gender.*

	Men (*M*)	Women (*W*)	Totals
Democrat (*D*)	8	4	12
Republican (*R*)	3	5	8
Totals	11	9	20

One member is chosen at random. In how many ways can the chosen person be as described?

37. a woman or a Republican

38. a man or a Democrat

39. a man or a Republican woman

40. a woman or a Democrat man

Counting Card Hands *Among the 2,598,960 possible 5-card poker hands from a standard 52-card deck, how many contain the following cards?*

41. at least one card that is not a heart (complement of "all hearts")

42. cards of more than one suit (complement of "all the same suit")

43. at least one face card (complement of "no face cards")

44. at least one club, but not all clubs (complement of "no clubs or all clubs")

45. *Selecting Doughnuts* A doughnut shop has a special on its Mix-n-Match selection, which allows customers to select three doughnuts from among the following varieties: plain, maple, frosted, chocolate, glazed, and jelly. How many different Mix-n-Match selections are possible? (*Mathematics Teacher* calendar problem)

46. *Rolling Three Dice* Three fair, standard six-faced dice of different colors are rolled. In how many ways can the dice be rolled such that the sum of the numbers rolled is 10? (*Mathematics Teacher* calendar problem)

The Size of Subsets of a Set *If a set has ten elements, how many of its subsets have the given numbers of elements?*

47. at most two elements

48. at least eight elements

49. more than two elements

50. from three through seven elements

51. *Counting License Numbers* If license numbers consist of two letters followed by three digits, how many different licenses could be created having at least one letter or digit repeated? (*Hint:* Use the complements principle of counting.)

52. *Drawing Cards* If two cards are drawn from a 52-card deck without replacement (that is, the first card is not replaced in the deck before the second card is drawn), in how many different ways is it possible to obtain a king on the first draw and a heart on the second? (*Hint:* Split this event into the two disjoint components "king of hearts and then another heart" and "non-heart king and then heart." Use the fundamental counting principle on each component and then apply the additive principle.)

53. Extend the additive counting principle to three overlapping sets (as in the figure) to show that

$$n(A \cup B \cup C) = n(A) + n(B) + n(C)$$
$$- n(A \cap B) - n(A \cap C)$$
$$- n(B \cap C) + n(A \cap B \cap C).$$

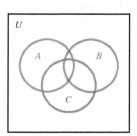

54. How many of the counting numbers 1 through 300 are *not* divisible by 2, 3, or 5? (*Hint:* Use the complements principle and the result of **Exercise 53.**)

Selecting National Monuments and Parks to Visit *Megan is planning a driving tour. Although she is interested in seeing the twelve national monuments and parks listed here, she will have to settle for seeing just three of them.*

New Mexico	Arizona	California
Gila Cliff Dwellings	Canyon de Chelly	Devils Postpile
Petroglyph	Organ Pipe Cactus	Joshua Tree
White Sands	Grand Canyon	Lava Beds
Aztec Ruins		Sequoia
		Yosemite

In how many ways could the three sites chosen include the following? (Assume that order of selection is not important.)

55. sites in only one state

56. at least one site not in California

57. sites in fewer than all three states

58. sites in exactly two of the three states

Counting Categories of Poker Hands **Table 4** *in this chapter (**For Further Thought** in **Section 10.3**) described the various kinds of hands in 5-card poker. Verify each statement in Exercises 59–62. (Explain all steps of your argument.)*

59. There are four ways to get a royal flush.

60. There are 36 ways to get a straight flush.

61. There are 10,200 ways to get a straight.

62. There are 54,912 ways to get three of a kind.

CHAPTER 10 | SUMMARY

KEY TERMS

10.1
counting
one-part task
two-part task
product table

10.2
uniformity criterion
fundamental counting
  principle
n factorial

distinguishable
  arrangements

10.3
permutation
combination

10.4
Pascal's triangle
binomial coefficients
binomial theorem

NEW SYMBOLS

$n!$	n factorial
$_nP_r, P(n, r), P_r^n$	permutations of n things taken r at a time

$_nC_r, C(n, r), C_r^n, \binom{n}{r}$	combinations of n things taken r at a time

TEST YOUR WORD POWER

See how well you have learned the vocabulary of this chapter.

1. In counting, a **product table** can be used to analyze
  A. a one-part task.
  B. a two-part task.
  C. a problem involving distinguishable
    arrangements.
  D. a problem involving Pascal's triangle.

2. The **factorial** of a natural number n is found by
  A. multiplying all the natural numbers less than or
    equal to n.
  B. adding all the natural numbers less than or equal to n.
  C. multiplying n by $n + 1$.
  D. multiplying n by $n - 1$.

3. A **permutation** of a group of objects

    A. is a subset of those objects where order is not important.

    B. is a proper subset of those objects.

    C. is an arrangement of those objects where order is important.

    D. is exemplified by a hand of cards in poker.

4. A **combination** of a group of objects

    A. is a subset of those objects.

    B. is exactly the same as a permutation of those objects.

    C. is an arrangement of those objects where order is important.

    D. is exemplified by the process of opening a combination lock.

ANSWERS

1. B   **2.** A   **3.** C   **4.** A

QUICK REVIEW

Concepts	*Examples*

10.1 Counting by Systematic Listing

Systematic Listing Methods

Two methods for listing the possible results of a two-part task are

(1) constructing a product table, and

(2) constructing a tree diagram.

Tree diagrams can be extended to tasks with three or more parts as well.

Construct a tree diagram showing all possible results when a die is rolled and a coin is tossed. How many possibilities are there?

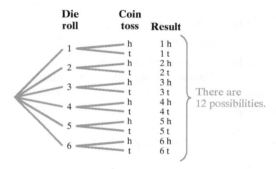

List the ways in which the die roll is even and the coin toss is heads.

$$2h, \quad 4h, \quad 6h$$

10.2 Using the Fundamental Counting Principle

Uniformity Criterion

A multiple-part task is said to satisfy the uniformity criterion if the number of choices for any particular part is the same *no matter which choices were selected for previous parts.*

If each of two adjacent switches are to be set on or off, uniformity applies if there are no restrictions. However, it does not apply if, say, they must not both be off.

Fundamental Counting Principle

When a task consists of k separate parts and satisfies the uniformity criterion, if the first part can be done in n_1 ways, the second part can then be done in n_2 ways, and so on through the kth part, which can be done in n_k ways, then the total number of ways to complete the task is given by the following product.

$$n_1 \cdot n_2 \cdot n_3 \cdot \ldots \cdot n_k$$

How many ways are there to choose a meal from 3 salads, 6 entrees, and 4 desserts?

$$3 \cdot 6 \cdot 4 = 72 \text{ ways}$$

Concepts	*Examples*
Factorial Formula For any counting number n, the quantity *n factorial* is defined as follows. $$n! = n \cdot (n-1) \cdot (n-2) \cdot \ldots \cdot 2 \cdot 1$$ By definition, $0! = 1$.	Evaluate each factorial. $$5! = 5 \cdot 4 \cdot 3 \cdot 2 \cdot 1 = 120$$ $$3! \cdot 4 = (3 \cdot 2 \cdot 1) \cdot 4 = 24$$ $$\frac{8!}{6!} = \frac{8 \cdot 7 \cdot 6 \cdot 5 \cdot 4 \cdot 3 \cdot 2 \cdot 1}{6 \cdot 5 \cdot 4 \cdot 3 \cdot 2 \cdot 1} = 8 \cdot 7 = 56$$
Arrangements of n Distinct Objects The total number of different ways to arrange n distinct objects is $n!$.	How many ways are there to arrange the letters of ROBIN? There are 5 distinct letters, so there are $$5! = 120 \text{ ways.}$$
Arrangements of n Objects Containing Look-Alikes The number of distinguishable arrangements of n objects, where one or more subsets consist of look-alikes (say n_1 are of one kind, n_2 are of another kind, . . . , and n_k are of yet another kind), is given by $$\frac{n!}{n_1! \cdot n_2! \cdot \ldots \cdot n_k!}.$$	How many distinguishable arrangements are there of the letters of MAMMOGRAM? Of the 9 letters total, 4 are M and 2 are A. So there are $$\frac{9!}{4! \cdot 2!} = 7560 \text{ distinguishable arrangements.}$$

10.3 Using Permutations and Combinations

Factorial Formula for Permutations The number of permutations, or arrangements, of n distinct things taken r at a time, where $r \leq n$, can be calculated as follows. $$_nP_r = \frac{n!}{(n-r)!}$$	How many arrangements of the letters $$W, H, I, T, E, S, U, G, A, R$$ are there if they are taken 4 at a time? There are 10 different letters. We use the permutations formula because order matters. $$_{10}P_4 = \frac{10!}{(10-4)!} = \frac{10!}{6!} = 5040$$
Factorial Formula for Combinations The number of combinations, or subsets, of n distinct things taken r at a time, where $r \leq n$, can be calculated as follows. $$_nC_r = \frac{_nP_r}{r!} = \frac{n!}{r!(n-r)!}$$	How many committees of 3 politicians can be formed from a pool of 11 politicians? We use the combinations formula because order does not matter. $$_{11}C_3 = \frac{11!}{3!\,(11-3)!} = \frac{11!}{3! \cdot 8!} = 165$$

10.4 Using Pascal's Triangle

Pascal's Triangle 1 1 1 1 2 1 1 3 3 1 1 4 6 4 1 1 5 10 10 5 1 $(6+4=10)$ 1 6 15 20 15 6 1	If six fair coins are tossed, in how many different ways can exactly two heads be obtained? The entry in green in the triangle represents $$_6C_2.$$ There are 15 ways. (The triangle entries can be expressed in terms of $_nC_r$. See **Table 6** in **Section 10.4.**)

Concepts   **Examples**

10.5 **Counting Problems Involving "Not" and "Or"**

Complements Principle of Counting

The number of ways a certain condition can be satisfied is the total number of possible results minus the number of ways the condition would **not** be satisfied. Symbolically, if A is any set within the universal set U, then

$$n(A) = n(U) - n(A').$$

If six fair coins are tossed, in how many ways can at least one head be obtained?

There are $2^6 = 64$ total ways, and only one of them (t t t t t t) does not contain a head. So there are

$$64 - 1 = 63 \text{ ways}$$

that at least one head can be obtained.

Additive Principle of Counting

The number of ways that one **or** the other of two conditions could be satisfied is the number of ways one of them could be satisfied plus the number of ways the other could be satisfied minus the number of ways they could both be satisfied together.

Symbolically, if A and B are any two sets, then

$$n(A \cup B) = n(A) + n(B) - n(A \cap B).$$

If sets A and B are disjoint, then

$$n(A \cup B) = n(A) + n(B).$$

A single card is drawn from a standard 52-card deck. In how many ways could it be black or a face card?

There are 26 black cards, 12 face cards, and 6 black face cards. So there are

$$26 + 12 - 6 = 32 \text{ ways.}$$

CHAPTER 10 | TEST

Counting Three-digit Numbers *If only the digits 0, 1, 2, 3, 4, 5, and 6 may be used, find the number of possibilities in each category.*

1. three-digit numbers

2. odd three-digit numbers

3. three-digit numbers without repeated digits

4. three-digit multiples of five without repeated digits

5. **Counting Triangles in a Figure** Determine the number of triangles (of any size) in the figure shown here.

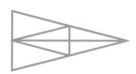

6. **Tossing Coins** Construct a tree diagram showing all possible results when a fair coin is tossed four times, if no two consecutive tosses can both be heads.

7. **Sums of Digits** How many nonrepeating four-digit numbers have the sum of their digits equal to 30?

8. **Arranging Children** Yeo has invited her sister Hae and her four best friends to her birthday party. In how many ways can the six children be arranged around a rectangular table with one child at each end and two on each side if Yeo must sit at an end seat and Hae must not sit next to Yeo?

Evaluate each expression.

9. 6!

10. $\dfrac{8!}{6!}$

11. $_{12}P_3$

12. $_8C_5$

13. **Building Words from Sets of Letters** How many five-letter "words" without repeated letters are possible using the English alphabet? (Assume that any five letters make a "word.")

14. **Building Words from Sets of Letters** Using the Russian alphabet (which has 32 letters), and allowing repeated letters, how many five-letter "words" are possible?

Scheduling Assignments *Eileen has seven homework assignments to complete. She wants to do two of them on Thursday and the other five on Saturday.*

15. In how many ways can she order Thursday's work?

16. Assuming she finishes Thursday's work successfully, in how many ways can she order Saturday's work?

17. *Arranging Letters* Find the number of distinguishable arrangements of the letters of the word PIPPIN.

Selecting Groups of Basketball Players *If there are ten players on a basketball team, find the number of choices the coach has in selecting each of the following.*

18. four players to carry the team equipment

19. two players for guard positions and two for forward positions

20. five starters and five subs

21. two groups of four

22. a group of three or more of the players

Choosing Switch Settings *Determine the number of possible settings for a row of five on–off switches under each condition.*

23. There are no restrictions.

24. The first and fifth switches must be on.

25. The first and fifth switches must be set the same.

26. No two adjacent switches can both be off.

27. No two adjacent switches can be set the same.

28. At least two switches must be on.

Choosing Subsets of Letters *Three distinct letters are to be chosen from the set*

$$\{A, B, C, D, E, F, G\}.$$

Determine the number of ways to obtain a subset that includes each of the following.

29. the letter B

30. both A and E

31. either A or E, but not both

32. letters to spell the word AD

33. more consonants than vowels

34. *Assigning Student Grades* A professor teaches a class of 60 students and another class of 40 students. Five percent of the students in each class are to receive a grade of A. How many different ways can the A grades be distributed?

35. *Number of Paths from Point to Point* A transit bus can travel in only two directions, north and east. From its starting point on the map shown, determine how many paths exist to reach the garage. (*Mathematics Teacher* calendar problem)

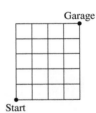

36. *Pascal's Triangle* Write down the second entry of each row of Pascal's triangle (starting with row 1). What sequence of numbers do you obtain?

Probability

11

The mathematics of *probability* occurs in various occupations and experiences in daily life. An important feature distinguishes probability from other topics in this text. For example, an equation such as

$$4x + 6 = 14$$

has a specific solution (in this case, 2) that we can state without reservation. Results found in probability are often theoretical—that is, we cannot say for sure what will actually happen in a certain case. We can only say what trends will occur "in the long run."

Here are a few examples.

Weather forecasts Meteorologists state the chances of rain based on data collected on days where the atmospheric conditions have been the same in the past. If the chance of rain is 90%, it's a good bet that rain will occur, but there is still a 10% chance that no rain will fall.

Insurance rates The rates that are charged on automobile or life insurance are based on data obtained from customers who fit the same basic profile. Actuarial science is devoted to analyzing data to provide information to insurance companies, which then make financial decisions based on those data.

Lotteries and casinos The *odds* favor the lottery commission and the gaming industry—games of chance are designed so that in the long run, "the house wins." Once in a while, the player wins (see **page 626**), but over a lifetime, the average gambler will likely lose.

Baseball manager History has shown that right-handed batters fare better against left-handed pitchers, and left-handed batters fare better against right-handed pitchers. Late in a close game, a manager will often make a pitching change based on this probability. This is only one instance of a manager or head coach making a decision based on the *law of averages*.

Court litigation One interesting application of probability, called the *calculus of negligence*, was mentioned in the cult movie *Fight Club*. A typical situation involves determination by a manufacturer whether to recall a product that has proved defective. The manufacturer may decide that it is financially feasible not to recall the product if

(the probability of loss in court) × (the amount of that loss)

is less than what it would cost to conduct the recall.

11.1 BASIC CONCEPTS

OBJECTIVES

1 Understand the basic terms in the language of probability.

2 Work simple problems involving theoretical and empirical probability.

3 Understand the law of large numbers (law of averages).

4 Find probabilities related to flower colors as described by Mendel in his genetics research.

5 Determine the odds in favor of an event and the odds against an event.

The Language of Probability

If you go to a supermarket and select five pounds of peaches at $2.49 per pound, you can easily predict the amount you will be charged at the checkout counter.

$$5 \cdot \$2.49 = \$12.45$$

This is an example of a **deterministic phenomenon.** It can be predicted exactly on the basis of obtainable information, namely, in this case, number of pounds and cost per pound.

On the other hand, consider the problem faced by the produce manager of the market, who must order peaches to have on hand each day without knowing exactly how many pounds customers will buy during the day. Customer demand is an example of a **random phenomenon.** It fluctuates in such a way that its value on a given day cannot be predicted exactly with obtainable information.

The study of probability is concerned with such random phenomena. Even though we cannot be certain whether a given result will occur, we often can obtain a good measure of its *likelihood,* or **probability.** This chapter discusses various ways of finding and using probabilities.

Any observation, or measurement, of a random phenomenon is an **experiment.** The possible results of the experiment are **outcomes,** and the set of all possible outcomes is the **sample space.**

Usually we are interested in some particular collection of the possible outcomes. Any such subset of the sample space is an **event.** See the Venn Diagram in **Figure 1.** Outcomes that belong to the event are "favorable outcomes," or "successes." Any time a success is observed, we say that the event has "occurred." The probability of an event, being a numerical measure of the event's likelihood, is determined in one of two ways: either *theoretically* (mathematically) or *empirically* (experimentally). We use the notation

$$P(E) \text{ to represent the probability of event } E.$$

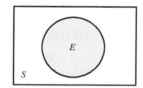

Every event *E* is a subset of the sample space *S*.

Figure 1

Examples in Probability

EXAMPLE 1 Finding Probability When Tossing a Coin

If a single coin is tossed, find the probability that it will land heads up.

Solution

There is no apparent reason for one side of a coin to land up any more often than the other (in the long run), so we assume that heads and tails are equally likely.

The experiment here is the tossing of a single fair coin, the sample space is $S = \{h, t\}$, and the event whose probability we seek is $E = \{h\}$. Since one of the two equally likely outcomes is a head, the probability of heads is the quotient of 1 and 2.

$$\text{Probability (heads)} = \frac{1}{2}, \quad \text{written} \quad P(h) = \frac{1}{2} \quad \text{or} \quad P(E) = \frac{1}{2}. \qquad \blacksquare$$

EXAMPLE 2 Finding Probability When Tossing a Cup

If a Styrofoam cup is tossed, find the probability that it will land on its top.

Solution

Intuitively, it seems that such a cup will land on its side much more often than on its top or its bottom. But just how much more often is not clear. To get an idea, we performed the experiment of tossing such a cup 50 times. It landed on its side 44 times, on its top 5 times, and on its bottom just 1 time. By the frequency of "success" in this experiment, we concluded that for the cup we used,

$$P(\text{top}) \approx \frac{5}{50} = \frac{1}{10}. \quad \boxed{\text{Write in lowest terms.}} \qquad \blacksquare$$

The Birth of Probability The basic ideas of probability arose largely in the context of games and gambling. In 1654 two French mathematicians, **Pierre de Fermat** (about 1601–1665) and **Blaise Pascal** (1623–1662) corresponded with each other regarding a problem posed by the Chevalier de Méré, a gambler and member of the aristocracy.

If the two players of a game are forced to quit before the game is finished, how should the pot be divided?

Pascal and Fermat solved the problem by developing basic methods of determining each player's chance, or probability, of winning.

In his 2010 book *The Unfinished Game: Pascal, Fermat, and the Seventeenth-Century Letter That Made the World Modern,* Keith Devlin describes how the two "struggled for several weeks" to solve the unfinished-game problem. In fact, this is no exception, but rather the rule, even for the greatest mathematicians. The reams of scratch work behind the elegant results are seldom seen and rarely published.

In **Example 1** involving the tossing of a fair coin, the number of possible outcomes was obviously two, both were equally likely, and one of the outcomes was a head. No actual experiment was required. The desired probability was obtained *theoretically.* Theoretical probabilities apply to dice rolling, card games, roulette, lotteries, and so on, and apparently to many phenomena in nature.

Laplace, in his famous *Analytic Theory of Probability,* published in 1812, gave a formula that applies to any such theoretical probability, as long as the sample space S is finite and all outcomes are equally likely. It is often referred to as the *classical definition of probability.*

THEORETICAL PROBABILITY FORMULA

If all outcomes in a sample space S are equally likely, and E is an event within that sample space, then the **theoretical probability** of event E is given by the following formula.

$$P(E) = \frac{\text{number of favorable outcomes}}{\text{total number of outcomes}} = \frac{n(E)}{n(S)}$$

WHEN Will I Ever USE This ?

The traditional coin flip is a tried-and-true method of making a decision when only two people (players) are involved. It is easy to see that each outcome of heads and tails has a probability of $\frac{1}{2}$. We sometimes say that "the chances are 50–50," meaning that each player has a 50% chance of winning. But suppose that we are faced with determining a winner among *three* players? *Can we use coin flipping in such a way that each player has an equal probability of winning?* The answer is yes.

The method is sometimes called "odd man wins." Each player flips a coin, and then the results are examined. If all three players show heads or all show tails, the experiment is repeated. (We are eliminating the outcomes hhh and ttt in our sample space this way.) There are 6 other possible outcomes, and each one shows 1 tail or 1 head. If a player has this "odd" result, that player is the winner. The tree diagram here shows that each player has a

$$\frac{2}{6}, \text{ or } \frac{1}{3}, \text{ probability of winning.}$$

Player A result	Player B result	Player C result	Outcome	Winner
h	h	h	h̶h̶h̶	—
		t	hh(t)	C
	t	h	h(t)h	B
		t	(h)tt	A
t	h	h	(t)hh	A
		t	t(h)t	B
	t	h	tt(h)	C
		t	t̶t̶t̶	—

Of the 6 equally likely outcomes considered, each player wins 2 times.

In 1827, **Robert Brown** (1773–1858), a Scottish physician and botanist, described the irregular motion of microscopic pollen grains suspended in water. Such "Brownian motion," as it came to be called, was not understood *until* 1905 when Albert Einstein explained it by treating molecular motion as a random phenomenon.

On the other hand, **Example 2** involved the tossing of a cup, where the likelihoods of the various outcomes were not intuitively clear. It took an actual experiment to arrive at a probability value of $\frac{1}{10}$, and that value, based on a portion of all possible tosses of the cup, should be regarded as an approximation of the true theoretical probability. The value was found according to the *experimental*, or *empirical*, probability formula.

EMPIRICAL PROBABILITY FORMULA

If E is an event that may happen when an experiment is performed, then an **empirical probability** of event E is given by the following formula.

$$P(E) = \frac{\text{number of times event } E \text{ occurred}}{\text{number of times the experiment was performed}}$$

Usually it is clear in applications which probability formula should be used.

EXAMPLE 3 Finding the Probability of Having Daughters

Kathy wants to have exactly two daughters. Assuming that boy and girl babies are equally likely, find her probability of success for the following cases.

(a) She has a total of two children.

(b) She has a total of three children.

Solution

(a) The equal-likelihood assumption allows the use of theoretical probability. We can determine the number of favorable outcomes and the total number of possible outcomes by using a tree diagram (see **Section 10.1**) to enumerate the possibilities, as shown in **Figure 2.** From the outcome column we obtain the sample space $S = \{gg, gb, bg, bb\}$. Only one outcome, marked with an arrow, is favorable to the event of exactly two daughters: $E = \{gg\}$.

$$P(E) = \frac{n(E)}{n(S)} = \frac{1}{4} \quad \text{Theoretical probability formula}$$

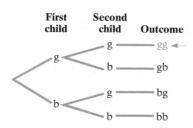

Exactly two girls among two children
Figure 2

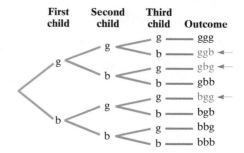

Exactly two girls among three children
Figure 3

(b) For three children altogether, we construct another tree diagram, as shown in **Figure 3.** In this case, we see that

$$S = \{ggg, ggb, gbg, gbb, bgg, bgb, bbg, bbb\} \quad \text{and} \quad E = \{ggb, gbg, bgg\},$$

so

$$P(E) = \frac{3}{8}.$$

When dealing or drawing cards, as in the next example, the dealing is generally done "without replacement." Once dealt, a card is *not* replaced in the deck. So all cards in a hand are distinct. Repetitions are *not* allowed. In many cases, such as building three-digit numbers, repetition of digits *is* allowed. For example, 255 is a legitimate three-digit number. So digit selection is done "with replacement."

EXAMPLE 4 **Finding Probability When Dealing Cards**

Find the probability of being dealt each of the following hands in five-card poker. Use a calculator to obtain answers to eight decimal places.

(a) a full house (three of one denomination and two of another)

(b) a royal flush (the five highest cards—ace, king, queen, jack, ten—of a single suit)

Solution

Table 1

Number of Poker Hands in 5-Card Poker; Nothing Wild

Event E	Number of Outcomes Favorable to E
Royal flush	4
Straight flush	36
Four of a kind	624
Full house	3744
Flush	5108
Straight	10,200
Three of a kind	54,912
Two pairs	123,552
One pair	1,098,240
No pair	1,302,540
Total	2,598,960

(a) **Table 1** summarizes the various possible kinds of five-card hands as first seen in **Section 10.3.** Because the 2,598,960 possible individual hands all are equally likely, we can enter the appropriate numbers from the table into the theoretical probability formula.

$$P(\text{full house}) = \frac{3744}{2,598,960} = \frac{6}{4165} \approx 0.00144058$$

(b) The table shows that there are four royal flush hands, one for each suit.

$$P(\text{royal flush}) = \frac{4}{2,598,960} = \frac{1}{649,740} \approx 0.00000154 \qquad ■$$

Examples 3 and 4 both utilized the theoretical probability formula because we were able to enumerate all possible outcomes and all were equally likely. In **Example 3,** however, the equal likelihood of girl and boy babies was *assumed.* While male births typically occur a little more frequently, there usually are more females living at any given time, due to higher infant mortality rates among males and longer female life expectancy in general. **Example 5** shows a way of incorporating such empirical information.

EXAMPLE 5 **Finding the Probability of the Gender of a Resident**

According to the United States Census figures, on July 1, 2012, there were an estimated 154.5 million males and 159.4 million females. If a person were selected randomly from the population in that year, what is the probability that the person would be a male? (*Source:* www.census.gov)

Solution

In this case, we calculate the empirical probability from the given experimental data.

$$P(\text{male}) = \frac{\text{number of males}}{\text{total number of persons}}$$

$$= \frac{154.5 \text{ million}}{154.5 \text{ million} + 159.4 \text{ million}}$$

$$\approx 0.492 \qquad ■$$

The Law of Large Numbers (or Law of Averages)

Recall the cup of **Example 2.** If we tossed it 50 more times, we would have 100 total tosses on which to base an empirical probability of the cup landing on its top. The new value would likely be slightly different from what we obtained before. It would still be an empirical probability, but it would be "better" in the sense that it was based on a larger set of outcomes.

If, as we increase the number of tosses, the resulting empirical probability values approach some particular number, that number can be defined as the theoretical probability of that particular cup landing on its top. We could determine this "limiting" value only as the actual number of observed tosses approached the total number of possible tosses of the cup. There are potentially an infinite number of possible tosses, so we could never actually find the theoretical probability. But we can still assume such a number exists. And as the number of actual observed tosses increases, the resulting empirical probabilities should tend ever closer to the theoretical value.

This principle is known as the **law of large numbers** or the **law of averages.**

> The **law of large numbers** (or **law of averages**) also can be stated as follows.
>
> *A theoretical probability really says nothing about one, or even a few, repetitions of an experiment, but only about the proportion of successes we would expect over the long run.*

LAW OF LARGE NUMBERS (LAW OF AVERAGES)

As an experiment is repeated more and more times, the proportion of outcomes favorable to any particular event will tend to come closer and closer to the theoretical probability of that event.

EXAMPLE 6 Graphing a Sequence of Proportions

A fair coin was tossed 35 times, producing the following sequence of outcomes.

tthhh, ttthh, hthtt, hhthh, ttthh, thttt, hhthh

Calculate the ratio of heads to total tosses after the first toss, the second toss, and so on through all 35 tosses, and plot these ratios on a graph.

Solution

After the first toss, we have 0 heads out of 1 toss, for a ratio of $\frac{0}{1} = 0.00$. After two tosses, we have $\frac{0}{2} = 0.00$. After three tosses, we have $\frac{1}{3} \approx 0.33$. Verify that the first six ratios are

0.00, 0.00, 0.33, 0.50, 0.60, 0.50.

The 35 ratios are plotted in **Figure 4.** The fluctuations away from 0.50 become smaller as the number of tosses increases, and the ratios appear to approach 0.50 toward the right side of the graph, in keeping with the law of large numbers.

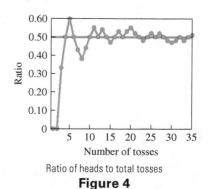

Ratio of heads to total tosses

Figure 4

COMPARING EMPIRICAL AND THEORETICAL PROBABILITIES

A series of repeated experiments provides an **empirical probability** for an event, which, by *inductive reasoning,* is an *estimate* of the event's *theoretical probability.* Increasing the number of repetitions increases the reliability of the estimate.

Likewise, an established **theoretical probability** for an event enables us, by *deductive reasoning,* to *predict* the proportion of times the event will occur in a series of repeated experiments. The prediction should be more accurate for larger numbers of repetitions.

Taking Your Chances

Smoking 1.4 cigarettes
Spending 1 hour in a coal mine
Living 2 days in New York or Boston
Eating 40 teaspoons of peanut butter
Living 2 months with a cigarette smoker
Flying 1000 miles in a jet
Traveling 300 miles in a car
Riding 10 miles on a bicycle

Risk is the probability that a harmful event will occur. Almost every action or substance exposes a person to some risk, and the assessment and reduction of risk account for a great deal of study and effort in our world. The list above, from *Calculated Risk,* by J. Rodricks, contains activities that increase a person's annual risk of death by one chance in a million.

Gregor Johann Mendel (1822–1884) came from a peasant family who managed to send him to school. By 1847 he had been ordained and was teaching at the Abbey of St. Thomas. He finished his education at the University of Vienna and returned to the abbey to teach mathematics and natural science.

Mendel began to carry out experiments on plants in the abbey garden, notably pea plants, whose distinct traits (unit characters) he had puzzled over. In 1865 he published his results. His work was not appreciated at the time, even though he had laid the foundation of **classical genetics.**

Probability in Genetics

Probabilities, both empirical and theoretical, have been valuable tools in many areas of science. An important early example was the work of the Austrian monk Gregor Mendel, who used the idea of randomness to help establish the study of genetics.

In an effort to understand the mechanism of character transmittal from one generation to the next in plants, Mendel counted the number of occurrences of various characteristics. He found that the flower color in certain pea plants obeyed this scheme:

Pure red crossed with pure white produces red.

Mendel theorized that red is "dominant," symbolized in this explanation with the capital letter R, while white is "recessive," symbolized with the lowercase letter r. The pure red parent carried only genes for red (R), and the pure white parent carried only genes for white (r). The offspring would receive one gene from each parent, hence one of the four combinations shown in the body of **Table 2.** Because every offspring receives one gene for red, that characteristic dominates, and each offspring exhibits the color red.

Table 2 First to Second Generation

		Second Parent	
		r	**r**
First Parent	**R**	Rr	Rr
	R	Rr	Rr

Table 3 Second to Third Generation

		Second Parent	
		R	**r**
First Parent	**R**	RR	Rr
	r	rR	rr

Now each of these second-generation offspring, though exhibiting the color red, still carries one of each gene. So when two of them are crossed, each third-generation offspring will receive one of the gene combinations shown in **Table 3.** Mendel theorized that each of the four possibilities would be equally likely, and he produced experimental counts that were close enough to support this hypothesis.

EXAMPLE 7 Finding Probabilities of Flower Colors

Referring to **Table 3,** determine the probability that a third-generation offspring will exhibit each flower color. Base the probabilities on the sample space of equally likely outcomes.

$$S = \{RR, Rr, rR, rr\}$$

(a) red   **(b)** white

Solution

(a) Since red dominates white, any combination with at least one gene for red (R) will result in red flowers. Since three of the four possibilities meet this criterion,

$$P(\text{red}) = \frac{3}{4}.$$

(b) Only the combination rr has no gene for red, so

$$P(\text{white}) = \frac{1}{4}.$$

■

Odds

Whereas probability compares the number of favorable outcomes to the total number of outcomes, **odds** compare the number of favorable outcomes to the number of unfavorable outcomes. Odds are commonly quoted, rather than probabilities, in horse racing, lotteries, and most other gambling situations. And the odds quoted normally are odds "against" rather than odds "in favor."

ODDS

If all outcomes in a sample space are equally likely, a of them are favorable to the event E, and the remaining b outcomes are unfavorable to E, then the

odds in favor of E are a to b, and the **odds against E** are b to a.

EXAMPLE 8 Finding the Odds of Getting an Intern Position

Theresa has been promised one of six jobs, three of which would be intern positions at the state capitol. If she has equal chances for all six jobs, find the odds *in favor* of her getting one of the intern positions.

Solution

Since three possibilities are favorable and three are not, the odds of *becoming an intern* at the capitol are 3 to 3 (or 1 to 1 in reduced terms). Odds of 1 to 1 are often termed

"even odds," or a "50–50 chance." ∎

EXAMPLE 9 Finding the Odds of Winning a Raffle

Bob has purchased 12 tickets for an office raffle in which the winner will receive an iPad. If 104 tickets were sold altogether and each has an equal chance of winning, what are the odds *against* Bob's winning the iPad?

Solution

Bob has 12 chances to win and $104 - 12 = 92$ chances to lose, so the odds *against* winning are

92 to 12.

In practice, we often use the fact that each number can be divided by their greatest common factor, to express the odds in lower terms. Dividing each of 92 and 12 by 4 gives the equivalent odds of

23 to 3. Lowest terms ∎

CONVERTING BETWEEN PROBABILITY AND ODDS

Let E be an event.

- If $P(E) = \frac{a}{b}$, then the odds in favor of E are a to $(b - a)$.

- If the odds in favor of E are a to b, then $P(E) = \frac{a}{a + b}$.

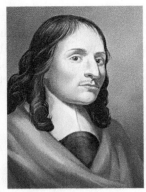

EXAMPLE 10 Converting from Probability to Odds

There is a 30% chance of rain tomorrow. Give this information in terms of odds.

Solution

$$P(\text{rain}) = 0.30 = \frac{30}{100} = \frac{3}{10}$$

Convert the decimal fraction to a quotient of integers and reduce.

By the first conversion formula, if $P(E) = \frac{a}{b}$, then the odds *in favor* of rain tomorrow are a to $(b - a)$—that is,

$$3 \text{ to } (10 - 3)$$

or

$$3 \text{ to } 7. \quad \text{Odds in favor of rain}$$

We can also say that the odds *against* rain tomorrow are

$$7 \text{ to } (10 - 7)$$

or

$$7 \text{ to } 3. \quad \text{Odds against rain} \qquad \blacksquare$$

EXAMPLE 11 Converting from Odds to Probability

In a certain sweepstakes, your odds of winning are 1 to 99,999. What is the probability that you will win?

Solution

Use the second conversion formula $P(E) = \frac{a}{a + b}$.

$$P(\text{win}) = \frac{1}{1 + 99,999} = \frac{1}{100,000} = 0.00001 \qquad \blacksquare$$

11.1 EXERCISES

In Exercises 1–4, give the probability that the spinner shown would land on **(a)** *red,* **(b)** *yellow, and* **(c)** *blue.*

1.

2.

3.

4.

Solve each probability problem.

5. **Using Spinners to Generate Numbers** Suppose the spinner shown here is spun once, to determine a single-digit number, and we are interested in the event E that the resulting number is odd. Give each of the following.

   (a) the sample space

   (b) the number of favorable outcomes

   (c) the number of unfavorable outcomes

   (d) the total number of possible outcomes

   (e) the probability of an odd number

   (f) the odds in favor of an odd number

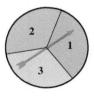

6. ***Lining Up Preschool Children*** Kim's group of preschool children includes nine girls and seven boys. If she randomly selects one child to be first in line, with *E* being the event that the one selected is a girl, give each of the following.

   (a) the total number of possible outcomes

   (b) the number of favorable outcomes

   (c) the number of unfavorable outcomes

   (d) the probability of event *E*

   (e) the odds in favor of event *E*

7. ***Using Spinners to Generate Numbers*** The spinner of **Exercise 5** is spun twice in succession to determine a two-digit number. Give each of the following.

   (a) the sample space

   (b) the probability of an odd number

   (c) the probability of a number with repeated digits

   (d) the probability of a number greater than 30

   (e) the probability of a prime number

8. ***Probabilities in Coin Tossing*** Two fair coins are tossed (say a dime and a quarter). Give each of the following.

   (a) the sample space

   (b) the probability of heads on the dime

   (c) the probability of heads on the quarter

   (d) the probability of getting both heads

   (e) the probability of getting the same outcome on both coins

9. ***Random Selection of Fifties Music*** Butch has fifty vinyl records from the fifties, including exactly one by Smiley Lewis, two by The Drifters, three by Bobby Darin, four by The Coasters, and five by Fats Domino. If he randomly selects one from his collection of fifty, find the probability it will be by each of the following.

   (a) Smiley Lewis

   (b) The Drifters

   (c) Bobby Darin

   (d) The Coasters

   (e) Fats Domino

10. ***Probabilities in Coin Tossing*** Three fair coins are tossed.

    (a) Write out the sample space.

    Determine the probability of each event.

    (b) no heads   (c) exactly one head

    (d) exactly two heads   (e) three heads

11. ***Number Sums for Rolling Two Dice*** The sample space for the rolling of two fair dice appeared in **Table 2** of **Section 10.1.** Reproduce that table, but replace each of the 36 equally likely ordered pairs with its corresponding sum (for the two dice). Then find the probability of rolling each sum.

    (a) 2   (b) 3   (c) 4

    (d) 5   (e) 6   (f) 7

    (g) 8   (h) 9   (i) 10

    (j) 11   (k) 12

12. ***Probabilities of Two Daughters among Four Children*** In **Example 3,** what would be Kathy's probability of having exactly two daughters if she were to have four children altogether? (You may want to use a tree diagram to construct the sample space.)

Probabilities of Poker Hands *In 5-card poker, find the probability of being dealt each of the following. Give each answer to eight decimal places. (Refer to* **Table 1.***)*

13. a straight flush

14. two pairs

15. four of a kind

16. four queens

17. a hearts flush (*not* a royal flush or a straight flush)

18. no pair

In Exercises 19 and 20, give answers to three decimal places.

19. ***Probability of Seed Germination*** In a hybrid corn research project, 200 seeds were planted, and 175 of them germinated. Find the empirical probability that any particular seed of this type will germinate.

20. ***Probability of Forest Land in California*** According to *The World Almanac and Book of Facts,* California has 155,959 square miles of land area, 51,250 square miles of which are forested. Find the probability that a randomly selected location in California will be forested.

Selecting Class Reports *Assuming that Ben, Jill, and Pam are three of the 26 members of the class, and that three of the class members will be chosen randomly to deliver their reports during the next class meeting, find the probability (to six decimal places) of each event.*

21. Ben, Jill, and Pam are selected, in that order.

22. Ben, Jill, and Pam are selected, in any order.

23. *Probabilities in Olympic Curling*
In Olympic curling, the scoring area (shown here) consists of four concentric circles on the ice with radii of 6 inches, 2 feet, 4 feet, and 6 feet. If a team member lands a (43-pound) stone *randomly* within the scoring area, find the probability that it ends up centered on the given color.

(a) red   **(b)** white   **(c)** blue

24. *Probabilities in Dart Throwing* If a dart hits the square target shown here at random, what is the probability that it will hit in a colored region? (*Hint:* Compare the area of the colored regions to the total area of the target.)

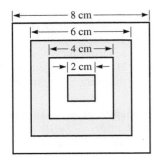

Genetics in Snapdragons *Mendel found no dominance in snapdragons (in contrast to peas) with respect to red and white flower color. When pure red and pure white parents are crossed (see* **Table 2***), the resulting* Rr *combination (one of each gene) produces second-generation offspring with pink flowers. These second-generation pinks, however, still carry one red and one white gene, so when they are crossed, the third generation is still governed by* **Table 3.**

Find each probability for third-generation snapdragons.

25. *P*(red)   **26.** *P*(pink)   **27.** *P*(white)

Genetics in Pea Plants *Mendel also investigated various characteristics besides flower color. For example, round peas are dominant over recessive wrinkled peas. First, second, and third generations can again be analyzed using* **Tables 2 and 3,** *where* R *represents round and* r *represents wrinkled.*

28. Explain why crossing pure round and pure wrinkled first-generation parents will always produce round peas in the second-generation offspring.

29. When second-generation round pea plants (each of which carries both R and r genes) are crossed, find the probability that a third-generation offspring will have the following.

(a) round peas   **(b)** wrinkled peas

Genetics of Cystic Fibrosis *Cystic fibrosis is one of the most common inherited diseases in North America (including the United States), occurring in about 1 of every 2000 Caucasian births and about 1 of every 250,000 non-Caucasian births. Even with modern treatment, victims usually die from lung damage by their early twenties.*

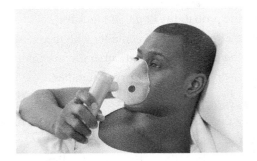

If we denote a cystic fibrosis gene with a c *and a disease-free gene with a* C *(since the disease is recessive), then only a* cc *person will actually have the disease. Such persons would ordinarily die before parenting children, but a child can also inherit the disease from two* Cc *parents (who themselves are healthy—that is, have no symptoms but are "carriers" of the disease). This is like a pea plant inheriting white flowers from two red-flowered parents that both carry genes for white.*

30. Find the empirical probability (to four decimal places) that cystic fibrosis will occur in a randomly selected infant birth among U.S. Caucasians.

31. Find the empirical probability (to six decimal places) that cystic fibrosis will occur in a randomly selected infant birth among U.S. non-Caucasians.

32. Among 150,000 North American Caucasian births, about how many occurrences of cystic fibrosis would you expect?

Suppose that both partners in a marriage are cystic fibrosis carriers (a rare occurrence). Construct a chart similar to **Table 3** *and determine the probability of each of the following events.*

33. Their first child will have the disease.

34. Their first child will be a carrier.

35. Their first child will neither have nor carry the disease.

Suppose a child is born to one cystic fibrosis carrier parent and one non-carrier parent. Find the probability of each of the following events.

36. The child will have cystic fibrosis.

37. The child will be a healthy cystic fibrosis carrier.

38. The child will neither have nor carry the disease.

Genetics of Sickle-Cell Anemia *Sickle-cell anemia occurs in about 1 of every 500 black baby births and about 1 of every 160,000 non-black baby births. It is ordinarily fatal in early childhood. There is a test to identify carriers. Unlike cystic fibrosis, which is recessive, sickle-cell anemia is* **codominant.** *This means that inheriting two sickle-cell genes causes the disease, while inheriting just one sickle-cell gene causes a mild (non-fatal) version (which is called* **sickle-cell trait***). This is similar to a snapdragon plant manifesting pink flowers by inheriting one red gene and one white gene.*

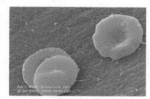

In Exercises 39 and 40, find the empirical probabilities of the given events.

39. A randomly selected black baby will have sickle-cell anemia. (Give your answer to three decimal places.)

40. A randomly selected non-black baby will have sickle-cell anemia. (Give your answer to six decimal places.)

41. Among 80,000 births of black babies, about how many occurrences of sickle-cell anemia would you expect?

In Exercises 42–44, find the theoretical probability of each condition in a child both of whose parents have sickle-cell trait.

42. The child will have sickle-cell anemia.

43. The child will have sickle-cell trait.

44. The child will be healthy.

Drawing Balls from an Urn Anne Kelly randomly chooses a single ball from the urn shown here. Find the odds against each event.

45. red   **46.** yellow

47. blue   **48.** red or yellow

49. yellow or blue   **50.** red or blue

Random Selection of Club Officers *Five people (Alan, Bill, Cathy, David, and Evelyn) form a club:* $N = \{A, B, C, D, E\}$. *Cathy and Evelyn are women, and the others are men. If they choose a president randomly, find the odds against each of the following becoming president.*

51. Cathy   **52.** a woman

53. a person whose name begins with a consonant

54. a man

In Exercises 55 and 56, assume that the probability of an event E is

$$P(E) = 0.37.$$

Find each of the following.

55. the odds in favor of E **56.** the odds against E

Make the requested conversions in Exercises 57 and 58.

57. If the odds in favor of event E are 12 to 19, find $P(E)$.

58. If the odds against event E are 10 to 3, find $P(E)$.

59. Women's 100-Meter Run In the history of track and field, no woman has broken the 10-second barrier in the 100-meter run.

(a) From the statement above, find the empirical probability that a woman runner will break the 10-second barrier next year.

(b) Can you find the theoretical probability for the event of part (a)?

(c) Is it possible that the event of part (a) will occur?

60. On page 27 of their book *Descartes' Dream*, Philip Davis and Reuben Hersh ask the question, "Is probability real or is it just a cover-up for ignorance?" What do you think?

The remaining exercises require careful thought to determine n(E) and n(S). (In some cases, you may want to employ counting methods from Chapter 10, such as the fundamental counting principle, permutations, or combinations.)

Probabilities of Seating Arrangements *Six people (three married couples) arrange themselves randomly in six consecutive seats in a row. In Exercises 61–64,*

(a) *determine the number of ways in which the described event can occur, and*

(b) *determine the probability of the event.*

(Hint: In each case the denominator of the probability fraction will be 6! = 720, the total number of ways to arrange six items.)

61. Each man will sit immediately to the left of his wife.

62. Each man will sit immediately to the left of a woman.

63. The women will be in three adjacent seats.

64. The women will be in three adjacent seats, as will the men.

Solve each problem.

65. *Altered Dice* A six-sided die has been altered so that the side that had been a single dot is now a blank face. Another die has a blank face instead of the face with four dots. What is the probability that a sum of 7 is rolled when the two dice are thrown? (*Mathematics Teacher* calendar problem)

66. *Location in a Tunnel* Mr. Davis is driving through a tunnel that is eight miles long. At this instant, what is the probability that he is at least six miles from one end of the tunnel? (*Mathematics Teacher* calendar problem)

67. *Slopes* Two lines, neither of which is vertical, are perpendicular if and only if their slopes are negative reciprocals (as are $\frac{2}{3}$ and $-\frac{3}{2}$). If two distinct numbers are chosen randomly from the set

$$\left\{-2, -\frac{4}{3}, -\frac{1}{2}, 0, \frac{1}{2}, \frac{3}{4}, 3\right\},$$

find the probability that they will be the slopes of two perpendicular lines.

68. *Drawing Cards* When drawing cards without replacement from a standard 52-card deck, find the maximum number of cards you could possibly draw and still get the following.

(a) fewer than three black cards

(b) fewer than six spades

(c) fewer than four face cards

(d) fewer than two kings

69. *Student Course Schedules* A student plans to take three courses next term. If he selects them randomly from a list of twelve courses, five of which are science courses, what is the probability that all three courses selected will be science courses?

70. *Symphony Performances* Rhonda randomly selects three symphony performances to attend this season from a schedule of ten performances, three of which feature works by Beethoven. Find the probability that she will select all of the Beethoven programs.

71. *Racing Bets* A "trifecta" is a particular horse race in which you win by picking the "win," "place," and "show" horses (the first-, second-, and third-place winners), in their proper order. If five horses of equal ability are entered in a trifecta race, and Tracy selects an entry, what is the probability that she will be a winner?

72. *Random Selection of Prime Numbers* If two distinct prime numbers are randomly selected from among the first eight prime numbers, what is the probability that their sum will be 24?

73. *Random Sums* Two integers are randomly selected from the set $\{1, 2, 3, 4, 5, 6, 7, 8, 9\}$ and are added together. Find the probability that their sum is 11 if they are selected as described.

(a) with replacement

(b) without replacement

74. *Numbers from Sets of Digits* The digits 1, 2, 3, 4, and 5 are randomly arranged to form a five-digit number. Find the probability of each event.

(a) The number is even.

(b) The first and last digits of the number both are even.

75. *Divisibility of Random Products* When a fair six-sided die is tossed on a tabletop, the bottom face cannot be seen. What is the probability that the product of the numbers on the five faces that can be seen is divisible by 6? (*Mathematics Teacher* calendar problem)

76. *Random Sums and Products* Tamika selects two different numbers at random from the set $\{8, 9, 10\}$ and adds them. Carlos takes two different numbers at random from the set $\{3, 5, 6\}$ and multiplies them. What is the probability that Tamika's result is greater than Carlos's result? (*Mathematics Teacher* calendar problem)

77. *Classroom Demographics* A high school class consists of 6 seniors, 10 juniors, 12 sophomores, and 4 freshmen. Exactly 2 of the juniors are female, and exactly 2 of the sophomores are males. If two students are randomly selected from this class, what is the probability that the pair consists of a male junior and a female sophomore? (*Mathematics Teacher* calendar problem)

78. *Fractions from Dice Rolls* Lisa has one red die and one green die, which she rolls to make up fractions. The green die is the numerator, and the red die is the denominator. Some of the fractions have terminating decimal representations. How many different terminating decimal results can these two dice represent? What is the probability of rolling a fraction with a terminating decimal representation? (*Mathematics Teacher* calendar problem)

Palindromic Numbers   *Numbers that are **palindromes** read the same forward and backward.*

30203 is a five-digit palindrome.

If a single number is chosen randomly from each set, find the probability that it will be palindromic.

79. the set of all two-digit numbers

80. the set of all three-digit numbers

Six people, call them

A, B, C, D, E, and F,

are randomly divided into three groups of two. Find the probability of each event. (Do not impose unwanted ordering among groups.)

81. *A and B are in the same group, as are C and D.*

82. *E and F are in the same group.*

11.2   EVENTS INVOLVING "NOT" AND "OR"

Properties of Probability

Recall that an empirical probability, based upon experimental observation, may be the best value available but still is only an approximation to the ("true") theoretical probability. For example, no human has ever been known to jump higher than 8.5 feet vertically, so the empirical probability of such an event is zero. Observing the rate at which high-jump records have been broken, we suspect that the event is, in fact, possible and may one day occur. Hence it must have some nonzero theoretical probability, even though we have no way of assessing its exact value.

Recall also that the theoretical probability formula,

$$P(E) = \frac{n(E)}{n(S)},$$

is valid only when all outcomes in the sample space S are equally likely. For the experiment of tossing two fair coins, we can write $S = \{\text{hh, ht, th, tt}\}$ and compute

$$P(\text{both heads}) = \frac{1}{4}. \quad \text{Correct}$$

However, if we define the sample space with non-equally likely outcomes as $S = \{\text{both heads}, \text{both tails}, \text{one of each}\}$, we are led to

$$P(\text{both heads}) = \frac{1}{3}. \quad \text{Incorrect}$$

To convince yourself that $\frac{1}{4}$ is a better value than $\frac{1}{3}$, toss two fair coins 100 times or so, to see what the empirical fraction seems to approach.

For any event E within a sample space S, we know that $0 \le n(E) \le n(S)$. Dividing all members of this inequality by $n(S)$ gives

$$\frac{0}{n(S)} \le \frac{n(E)}{n(S)} \le \frac{n(S)}{n(S)}, \quad \text{or} \quad \mathbf{0 \le P(E) \le 1.}$$

In words, the probability of any event is a number from 0 through 1, inclusive.

If event E is *impossible* (cannot happen), then $n(E)$ must be 0 (E is the empty set), so

$$P(E) = 0. \quad \text{\textit{E} is impossible.}$$

If event E is *certain* (cannot help but happen), then $n(E) = n(S)$, so

$$P(E) = \frac{n(E)}{n(S)} = \frac{n(S)}{n(S)} = 1. \quad \text{\textit{E} is certain.}$$

More on the Birth of Probability

The modern mathematical theory of probability came mainly from the Russian scholars **P. L. Chebyshev** (1821–1922), **A. A. Markov** (1856–1922), and **Andrei Nikolaevich Kolmogorov** (1903–1987). The Dutch mathematician and scientist **Christiaan Huygens** (1629–1695) wrote a formal treatise on probability. It appeared in 1657 and was based on the Pascal–Fermat correspondence. One of the first to apply probability to matters other than gambling was the French mathematician **Pierre Simon de Laplace** (1749–1827), who is usually credited with being the "father" of probability theory.

Pierre Simon de Laplace (1749–1827) began in 1773 to solve the problem of why Jupiter's orbit seems to shrink and Saturn's orbit seems to expand. Eventually Laplace worked out a complete theory of the solar system. *Celestial Mechanics* resulted from almost a lifetime of work. In five volumes, it was published between 1799 and 1825 and gained for Laplace the reputation "Newton of France."

Laplace's work on probability was actually an adjunct to his celestial mechanics. He needed to demonstrate that probability is useful in interpreting scientific data.

PROPERTIES OF PROBABILITY

Let E be an event within the sample space S. That is, E is a subset of S. Then the following properties hold.

1. $0 \leq P(E) \leq 1$ The probability of an event is a number from 0 through 1, inclusive.

2. $P(\varnothing) = 0$ The probability of an impossible event is 0.

3. $P(S) = 1$ The probability of a certain event is 1.

Probabilities are often expressed in terms of percents in the media. We will, however, give them in terms of fractions or decimals.

EXAMPLE 1 Finding Probability When Rolling a Die

When a single fair die is rolled, find the probability of each event.

(a) The number 2 is rolled.   **(b)** A number other than 2 is rolled.

(c) The number 7 is rolled.   **(d)** A number less than 7 is rolled.

Solution

(a) Since one of the six possibilities is a 2, $P(2) = \frac{1}{6}$.

(b) There are five such numbers, 1, 3, 4, 5, and 6, so $P(\text{a number other than } 2) = \frac{5}{6}$.

(c) None of the possible outcomes is 7. Thus, $P(7) = \frac{0}{6} = 0$.

(d) Since all six of the possible outcomes are less than 7,

$$P(\text{a number less than } 7) = \frac{6}{6} = 1. \qquad \blacksquare$$

Refer to the box preceding **Example 1.** No probability in that example was less than 0 or greater than 1, which illustrates Property 1. The "impossible" event of part (c) had probability 0, illustrating Property 2. The "certain" event of part (d) had probability 1, illustrating Property 3.

Events Involving "Not"

Table 4 repeats the information of **Table 8** of **Section 10.5,** with a third correspondence added in row 3. The correspondences shown in **Table 4** are the basis for the probability rules. For example, the probability of an event *not* happening involves the *complement* and *subtraction*, according to row 1 of the table.

Table 4 Set Theory/Logic/Arithmetic Correspondences

	Set Theory	**Logic**	**Arithmetic**
1. Operation or Connective (Symbol)	Complement ($'$)	Not ($\sim$)	Subtraction ($-$)
2. Operation or Connective (Symbol)	Union ($\cup$)	Or ($\vee$)	Addition ($+$)
3. Operation or Connective (Symbol)	Intersection ($\cap$)	And ($\wedge$)	Multiplication ($\cdot$)

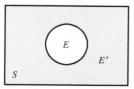

The logical connective "not" corresponds to "complement" in set theory.

$$P(not\ E) = P(S) - P(E)$$
$$= 1 - P(E)$$

Figure 5

The rule for the probability of a complement follows and is illustrated in **Figure 5**.

PROBABILITY OF A COMPLEMENT (FOR THE EVENT "NOT E")

The probability that an event E will *not* occur is equal to 1 minus the probability that it *will* occur.

$$P(\text{not } E) = 1 - P(E)$$

Notice that the events of **Examples 1(a) and (b),** namely "2" and "not 2," are complements of one another, and that their probabilities add up to 1. This illustrates the above probability rule. The equation

$$P(E) + P(E') = 1$$

is a rearrangement of the formula for the probability of a complement. Another form of the equation that is also useful at times follows.

$$P(E) = 1 - P(E')$$

EXAMPLE 2 Finding the Probability of a Complement

When a single card is drawn from a standard 52-card deck, what is the probability that it will not be a king?

Solution

$$P(\text{not a king}) = 1 - P(\text{king}) = 1 - \frac{4}{52} = \frac{48}{52} = \frac{12}{13}$$

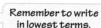
Remember to write in lowest terms.

EXAMPLE 3 Finding the Probability of a Complement

If five fair coins are tossed, find the probability of obtaining at least two heads.

Solution

A tree diagram will show that there are $2^5 = 32$ possible outcomes for the experiment of tossing five fair coins. Most include at least two heads. In fact, only the outcomes

ttttt, htttt, thttt, tthtt, tttht, and tttth   6 of these

do *not* include at least two heads. If E denotes the event "at least two heads," then E' is the event "not at least two heads,"

$$P(E) = 1 - P(E') = 1 - \frac{6}{32} = \frac{26}{32} = \frac{13}{16}$$

Events Involving "Or"

Examples 2 and 3 showed how the probability of an event can be approached *indirectly,* by first considering the complement of the event. Another indirect approach is to break the event into simpler component events. Row 2 of **Table 4** indicates that the probability of one event *or* another should involve the *union* and *addition*.

Mary Somerville (1780–1872) is associated with Laplace because of her brilliant exposition of his *Celestial Mechanics.*

Somerville studied Euclid thoroughly and perfected her Latin so she could read Newton's *Principia.* In about 1816 she went to London and soon became part of its literary and scientific circles.

Somerville's book on Laplace's theories came out in 1831 to great acclaim. Then followed a panoramic book, *Connection of the Physical Sciences* (1834). A statement in one of its editions suggested that irregularities in the orbit of Uranus might indicate that a more remote planet, not yet seen, existed. This caught the eye of the scientists who worked out the calculations for Neptune's orbit.

EXAMPLE 4 Selecting from a Set of Numbers

If one number is selected randomly from the set $\{1, 2, 3, 4, 5, 6, 7, 8, 9, 10\}$, find the probability of each of the following events.

(a) The number is odd or a multiple of 4.

(b) The number is odd or a multiple of 3.

Solution

Define the following events.

$$S = \{1, 2, 3, 4, 5, 6, 7, 8, 9, 10\} \quad \text{Sample space}$$

$$A = \{1, 3, 5, 7, 9\} \quad \text{Odd outcomes; } P(A) = \frac{5}{10}$$

$$B = \{4, 8\} \quad \text{Multiples of 4; } P(B) = \frac{2}{10}$$

$$C = \{3, 6, 9\} \quad \text{Multiples of 3; } P(C) = \frac{3}{10}$$

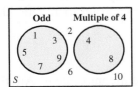

Figure 6

(a) **Figure 6** shows the positioning of the 10 integers within the sample space and within the pertinent sets A and B. The composite event "A or B" corresponds to the set $A \cup B = \{1,3,4,5,7,8,9\}$. $A \cup B$ has **seven** elements. By the theoretical probability formula,

$$P(A \text{ or } B) = \frac{7}{10}. \quad \text{Of 10 total outcomes, seven are favorable.}$$

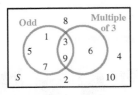

Figure 7

(b) **Figure 7** shows the situation.

Of 10 total outcomes, six are favorable.

$$P(A \text{ or } C) = \frac{6}{10} = \frac{3}{5} \quad ■$$

Would an addition formula have worked in **Example 4?** Let's check.

Part (a): $P(A \text{ or } B) = P(A) + P(B) = \dfrac{5}{10} + \dfrac{2}{10} = \dfrac{7}{10}$ Correct

Part (b): $P(A \text{ or } C) = P(A) + P(C) = \dfrac{5}{10} + \dfrac{3}{10} = \dfrac{8}{10} = \dfrac{4}{5}$ Incorrect

The trouble in part (b) is that A and C are not disjoint sets. They have outcomes in common. Just as with the additive counting principle in **Chapter 10,** an adjustment must be made here to compensate for counting the common outcomes twice.

$$P(A \text{ or } C) = P(A) + P(C) - P(A \text{ and } C)$$

$$= \frac{5}{10} + \frac{3}{10} - \frac{2}{10} = \frac{6}{10} = \frac{3}{5} \quad \text{Correct}$$

In probability theory, events that are disjoint sets are called *mutually exclusive events.*

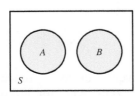

The logical connective "or" corresponds to "union" in set theory.

$P(A \text{ or } B)$
$= P(A) + P(B) - P(A \text{ and } B)$

Figure 8

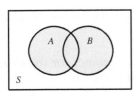

When A and B are mutually exclusive,
$P(A \text{ or } B) = P(A) + P(B).$

Figure 9

MUTUALLY EXCLUSIVE EVENTS

Two events A and B are **mutually exclusive events** if they have no outcomes in common. Mutually exclusive events cannot occur simultaneously.

The results observed in **Example 4** are generalized as follows. The two possibilities are illustrated in **Figures 8 and 9.**

> **ADDITION RULE OF PROBABILITY (FOR THE EVENT "A OR B")**
>
> If A and B are any two events, then the following holds.
>
> $$P(A \text{ or } B) = P(A) + P(B) - P(A \text{ and } B)$$
>
> If A and B are mutually exclusive, then the following holds.
>
> $$P(A \text{ or } B) = P(A) + P(B)$$

Actually, the first formula in the addition rule applies in all cases. The third term on the right drops out when A and B are mutually exclusive, because $P(A \text{ and } B) = 0$. Still, it is good to remember the second formula in the preceding box for the many cases where the component events are mutually exclusive. In this section, we consider only cases where the event "A and B" is simple. We deal with more involved composites involving "and" in the next section.

EXAMPLE 5 Finding the Probability of an Event Involving "Or"

If a single card is drawn from a standard 52-card deck, what is the probability that it will be a spade or a red card?

Solution

Two examples of "success" in Example 5

First note that "spade" and "red" cannot both occur, because there are no red spades. All spades are black. Therefore, we can use the formula for mutually exclusive events. There are 13 spades and 26 red cards in the deck.

$$P(\text{spade or red}) = P(\text{spade}) + P(\text{red}) = \frac{13}{52} + \frac{26}{52} = \frac{39}{52} = \frac{3}{4} \quad \blacksquare$$

We often need to consider composites of more than two events. When each event involved is mutually exclusive of all the others, we extend the addition rule to the appropriate number of components.

EXAMPLE 6 Treating Unions of Several Components

Table 5

x	$P(x)$
1	0.05
2	0.10
3	0.20
4	0.40
5	0.10
6	0.15

Amy plans to spend from 1 to 6 hours on her homework. If x represents the number of hours to be spent on a given night, then the probabilities of the various values of x, rounded to the nearest hour, are as shown in **Table 5**. Find the probabilities that Amy will spend each of the following amounts of time.

(a) fewer than 3 hours

(b) more than 2 hours

(c) more than 1 but no more than 5 hours

(d) fewer than 5 hours

Solution

Because the time periods in **Table 5** are mutually exclusive of one another, we can simply add the appropriate component probabilities.

(a) $P(\text{fewer than 3}) = P(1 \text{ or } 2)$ Fewer than 3 means 1 or 2.

$\qquad\qquad\qquad\quad = P(1) + P(2)$ Addition rule

$\qquad\qquad\qquad\quad = 0.05 + 0.10$ Substitute values from **Table 5**.

$\qquad\qquad\qquad\quad = 0.15$ Add.

(b) $P(\text{more than } 2) = P(3 \text{ or } 4 \text{ or } 5 \text{ or } 6)$ More than 2 means 3, 4, 5, or 6.

$\qquad\qquad\qquad\qquad = P(3) + P(4) + P(5) + P(6)$ Addition rule

$\qquad\qquad\qquad\qquad = 0.20 + 0.40 + 0.10 + 0.15$ Substitute values from **Table 5**.

$\qquad\qquad\qquad\qquad = 0.85$ Add.

(c) $P(\text{more than 1 but no more than 5})$

$\qquad\qquad = P(2 \text{ or } 3 \text{ or } 4 \text{ or } 5)$ 2, 3, 4, and 5 are more than 1 and no more than 5.

$\qquad\qquad = P(2) + P(3) + P(4) + P(5)$ Addition rule

$\qquad\qquad = 0.10 + 0.20 + 0.40 + 0.10$ Substitute values from **Table 5**.

$\qquad\qquad = 0.80$ Add.

(d) Although we could take a direct approach here, as in parts (a), (b), and (c), we will combine the complement rule with the addition rule.

$\qquad P(\text{fewer than 5}) = 1 - P(\text{not fewer than 5})$ Complement rule

$\qquad\qquad\qquad\qquad = 1 - P(5 \text{ or more})$ 5 or more is equivalent to not fewer than 5.

$\qquad\qquad\qquad\qquad = 1 - P(5 \text{ or } 6)$ 5 or more means 5 or 6.

$\qquad\qquad\qquad\qquad = 1 - [P(5) + P(6)]$ Addition rule

$\qquad\qquad\qquad\qquad = 1 - (0.10 + 0.15)$ Substitute values from **Table 5**.

$\qquad\qquad\qquad\qquad = 1 - 0.25$ Add inside the parentheses first.

$\qquad\qquad\qquad\qquad = 0.75$ ∎

Table 5 in **Example 6** lists all possible time intervals so the corresponding probabilities add up to 1, a necessary condition for the way part (d) was done. The time spent on homework here is an example of a **random variable.** It is "random" because we cannot predict which of its possible values will occur.

A listing like **Table 5,** which shows all possible values of a random variable, along with the probabilities that those values will occur, is a **probability distribution** for that random variable. *All* possible values are listed, so they make up the entire sample space, and thus the listed probabilities must add up to 1 (by probability Property 3). Probability distributions will be discussed in later sections.

EXAMPLE 7 Finding the Probability of an Event Involving "Or"

Find the probability that a single card drawn from a standard 52-card deck will be a diamond or a face card.

Solution

One example of a card that is both a diamond and a face card

The component events "diamond" and "face card" can occur simultaneously. (The jack, queen, and king of diamonds belong to both events.) So, we must use the first formula of the addition rule. We let D denote "diamond" and F denote "face card."

$\qquad P(D \text{ or } F) = P(D) + P(F) - P(D \text{ and } F)$ Addition rule

$\qquad\qquad\qquad = \dfrac{13}{52} + \dfrac{12}{52} - \dfrac{3}{52}$ There are 13 diamonds, 12 face cards, and 3 that are both.

$\qquad\qquad\qquad = \dfrac{22}{52}$ Add and subtract.

$\qquad\qquad\qquad = \dfrac{11}{26}$ Write in lowest terms. ∎

EXAMPLE 8 Finding the Probability of an Event Involving "Or"

Of 20 elective courses, Emily plans to enroll in one, which she will choose by throwing a dart at the schedule of courses. If 8 of the courses are recreational, 9 are interesting, and 3 are both recreational and interesting, find the probability that the course she chooses will have at least one of these two attributes.

Solution

If R denotes "recreational" and I denotes "interesting," then

$$P(R) = \frac{8}{20}, \quad P(I) = \frac{9}{20}, \quad \text{and} \quad P(R \text{ and } I) = \frac{3}{20}.$$

R and I are not mutually exclusive.

$$P(R \text{ or } I) = \frac{8}{20} + \frac{9}{20} - \frac{3}{20}$$

$$= \frac{14}{20} \qquad \text{Addition rule}$$

$$= \frac{7}{10} \qquad \text{Write in lowest terms.} \qquad \blacksquare$$

11.2 EXERCISES

Probabilities for Rolling a Die *For the experiment of rolling a single fair die, find the probability of each event. (Hint: Recall that 1 is neither prime nor composite.)*

1. not prime

2. not less than 2

3. even or prime

4. odd or less than 5

5. less than 3 or greater than 4

6. odd or even

Probability and Odds for Drawing a Card *For the experiment of drawing a single card from a standard 52-card deck, find* **(a)** *the probability of each event, and* **(b)** *the odds in favor of each event.*

7. king or queen

8. not an ace

9. spade or face card

10. club or heart

11. neither a heart nor a 7

12. not a heart, or a 7

Number Sums for Rolling a Pair of Dice *For the experiment of rolling an ordinary pair of dice, find the probability that the sum will be each of the following. (You may want to use a table showing the sum for each of the 36 equally likely outcomes.)*

13. even or a multiple of 3   **14.** 11 or 12

15. less than 3 or greater than 9

16. odd or greater than 9

Prime Results *Find the probability of getting a prime number in each case.*

17. A number is chosen randomly from the set $\{1, 2, 3, 4, \ldots, 12\}$.

18. Two dice are rolled and the sum is observed.

19. A single digit is randomly chosen from the number 578.

20. A single digit is randomly chosen from the number 1234.

21. *Determining Whether Events Are Mutually Exclusive* Amanda has three office assistants. If A is the event that at least two of them are men and B is the event that at least two of them are women, are A and B mutually exclusive?

22. *Determining Whether Events Are Mutually Exclusive* Jeanne earned her college degree several years ago. Consider the following four events.

Her alma mater is in the East.

Her alma mater is a private college.

Her alma mater is in the Northwest.

Her alma mater is in the South.

Are these events all mutually exclusive of one another?

Probabilities of Poker Hands *If you are dealt a 5-card hand (this implies without replacement) from a standard 52-card deck, find the probability of getting each of the following. Refer to* **Table 1** *of* **Section 11.1,** *and give answers to six decimal places.*

23. a full house or a straight

24. a black flush or two pairs

25. nothing any better than two pairs

26. a flush or three of a kind

Probabilities in Golf Scoring *The table gives Josh's probabilities of scoring in various ranges on a par-70 course. In a given round, find the probability of each event in Exercises 27–31.*

x	$P(x)$
Below 60	0.04
60–64	0.06
65–69	0.14
70–74	0.30
75–79	0.23
80–84	0.09
85–89	0.06
90–94	0.04
95–99	0.03
100 or above	0.01

27. par or above   **28.** in the 80s

29. less than 90   **30.** not in the 70s, 80s, or 90s

31. 95 or higher

32. What are the odds of Josh's scoring below par?

33. ***Probability Distribution*** Let x denote the sum of two distinct numbers selected randomly from the set of numbers $\{1, 2, 3, 4, 5\}$. Construct the probability distribution for the random variable x.

34. ***Probability Distribution*** Anne Kelly randomly chooses a single ball from the urn shown here, and x represents the color of the ball chosen. Construct a complete probability distribution for the random variable x.

Comparing Empirical and Theoretical Probabilities for Rolling Dice *Roll a pair of dice* 50 *times, keeping track of the number of times the sum is "less than 3 or greater than 9" (that is 2, 10, 11, or 12).*

35. From your results, calculate an empirical probability for the event "less than 3 or greater than 9."

36. By how much does your answer differ from the *theoretical* probability of **Exercise 15?**

37. Explain the difference between the two formulas in the addition rule of probability, illustrating each one with an appropriate example.

38. Suppose, for a given experiment, A, B, C, and D are events, all mutually exclusive of one another, such that

$$A \cup B \cup C \cup D = S \text{ (the sample space)}.$$

By extending the addition rule of probability to this case and utilizing probability Property 3, what statement can you make?

Complemental Probability *For Exercises 39–41, let A be an event within the sample space S, and let*

$$n(A) = a \quad and \quad n(S) = s.$$

39. Use the complements principle of counting to find an expression for $n(A')$.

40. Use the theoretical probability formula to express $P(A)$ and $P(A')$.

41. Evaluate and simplify $P(A) + P(A')$.

42. What rule have you proved?

The remaining exercises require careful thought for the determination of n(E) and n(S). (In some cases, you may want to employ counting methods from Chapter 10, such as the fundamental counting principle, permutations, or combinations.)

Building Numbers from Sets of Digits *Suppose we want to form three-digit numbers using the set of digits*

$$\{0, 1, 2, 3, 4, 5\}.$$

For example, 501 *and* 224 *are such numbers, but* 035 *is not.*

43. How many such numbers are possible?

44. How many of these numbers are multiples of 10?

45. How many of these numbers are multiples of 5?

46. If one three-digit number is chosen at random from all those that can be made from the above set of digits, find the probability that the one chosen is not a multiple of 5.

47. ***Drawing Colored Marbles from Boxes*** A bag contains fifty blue and fifty green marbles. Two marbles at a time are randomly selected. If both are green, they are placed in box A; if both are blue, in box B; if one is green and the other is blue, in box C. After all marbles are drawn, what is the probability that the numbers of marbles in box A and box B are the same? (*Mathematics Teacher* calendar problem)

48. ***Multiplying Numbers Generated by Spinners*** An experiment consists of spinning both spinners shown here and multiplying the resulting numbers together. Find the probability that the resulting product will be even.

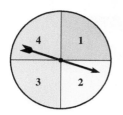 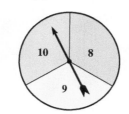

49. Luka and Janie are playing a coin toss game. If the coin lands heads up, Luka earns a point; otherwise, Janie earns a point. The first player to reach 20 points wins the game. If 19 of the first 37 tosses have been heads, what is the probability that Janie wins the game? (*Mathematics Teacher* calendar problem)

50. ***Random Births on the Same Day of the Week*** What is the probability that, of three people selected at random, at least two were born on the same day of the week? (*Mathematics Teacher* calendar problem)

OBJECTIVES

1 Apply the conditional probability formula.

2 Determine whether two events are independent.

3 Apply the multiplication rule for the event "A and B."

Conditional Probability

Sometimes the probability of an event must be computed using the knowledge that some other event has happened (or is happening, or will happen—the timing is not important). This type of probability is called *conditional probability*.

> **CONDITIONAL PROBABILITY**
>
> The probability of event B, computed on the assumption that event A has happened, is called the **conditional probability of B given A** and is denoted
>
> $$P(B|A).$$

EXAMPLE 1 Selecting from a Set of Numbers

From the sample space

$$S = \{1, 2, 3, 4, 5, 6, 7, 8, 9, 10\},$$

a single number is to be selected randomly. Find each probability given the events

A: The selected number is odd, and B: The selected number is a multiple of 3.

(a) $P(B)$ **(b)** $P(A \text{ and } B)$ **(c)** $P(B|A)$

Solution

(a) $B = \{3, 6, 9\}$, so

$$P(B) = \frac{n(B)}{n(S)} = \frac{3}{10}.$$

(b) A and B is the set $A \cap B = \{1, 3, 5, 7, 9\} \cap \{3, 6, 9\} = \{3, 9\}$.

$$P(A \text{ and } B) = \frac{n(A \cap B)}{n(S)} = \frac{2}{10} = \frac{1}{5}$$

Two elements

(c) The given condition, that A occurs, effectively reduces the sample space from S to A, and the elements of the new sample space A that are also in B are the elements of $A \cap B$.

$$P(B|A) = \frac{n(A \cap B)}{n(A)} = \frac{2}{5}$$

WHEN Will I Ever USE This ?

Monty Hall

The probability is low that anyone reading this will ever be on a televised game show. But who knows? A former popular game show host, Monty Hall, has a rather famous problem named after him, and knowing the solution to the problem might help a contestant win a car instead of a goat.

Suppose that there are three doors, and you are asked to choose one of them. One of the doors hides a new car, and behind the two other doors are goats. You pick a door, say Door A. Then the host, who knows what's behind all three doors, opens another door, say Door C, and a goat appears. The host asks you whether you want to change your choice to Door B. *Is it to your advantage to do so?*

One way to look at the problem, given that the car is *not* behind Door C, is that Doors A and B are now equally likely to contain the car. Thus, switching doors will neither help nor hurt your chances of winning the car.

However, there is another way to look at the problem. When you picked Door A, the probability was $\frac{1}{3}$ that it contained the car. Being shown the goat behind Door C doesn't really give you any new information; after all, you knew that there was a goat behind at least one of the other doors. So seeing the goat behind Door C does nothing to change your assessment of the probability that Door A has the car. It remains $\frac{1}{3}$. But because Door C has been ruled out, the probability that Door B has the car is now $\frac{2}{3}$. Thus, you should switch.

Analysis of this problem depends on the psychology of the host. If we suppose that the host must *always* show you a losing door and then give you an option to switch, then you should switch. This was not specifically stated in the problem but has been pointed out by many mathematicians.

There are several Web sites that simulate the Monty Hall problem. One of them is http://stayorswitch.com/

(The authors wish to thank David Berman of the University of New Orleans for his assistance with this explanation.)

A **cosmic impact,** the collision of a meteor, comet, or asteroid with Earth could be as catastrophic as full-scale nuclear war, killing a billion or more people.

The Spaceguard Survey has discovered more than half of the estimated number of near-Earth asteroids (NEAs) 1 kilometer or more in diameter and hopes to locate 90% of them in the next decade. Although the risk of finding one on a collision course with the Earth is slight, it is anticipated that, if we did, we would be able to deflect it before impact.

The photo above shows a crater in Arizona, 4000 feet in diameter and 570 feet deep. It is thought to have been formed 20,000 to 50,000 years ago by a meteorite about 50 meters across, hitting the ground at several kilometers per second. (See http://en.wikipedia.org/wiki/Meteor_Crater.)

Example 1 illustrates some important points. First, because

$$\frac{n(A \cap B)}{n(A)} = \frac{\frac{n(A \cap B)}{n(S)}}{\frac{n(A)}{n(S)}} \qquad \text{Multiply numerator and denominator by } \frac{1}{n(S)}.$$

$$= \frac{P(A \cap B)}{P(A)}, \qquad \text{Theoretical probability formula}$$

the final line of the example gives the following convenient formula.

CONDITIONAL PROBABILITY FORMULA

The **conditional probability of B given A** is calculated as follows.

$$P(B|A) = \frac{P(A \cap B)}{P(A)} = \frac{P(A \text{ and } B)}{P(A)}$$

A second observation from **Example 1** is that the conditional probability of B given A was $\frac{2}{5}$, whereas the "unconditional" probability of B (with no condition given) was $\frac{3}{10}$, so the condition *did* make a difference.

EXAMPLE 2 **Finding Probabilities of Boys and Girls in a Family**

Given a family with two children, find the probability of each event.

(a) Both are girls, given that at least one is a girl.

(b) Both are girls, given that the older child is a girl.

(Assume boys and girls are equally likely.)

Solution

We define the following events. (The older child's gender appears first.)

$$S = \{gg, gb, bg, bb\} \qquad \text{Sample space } S; \ n(S) = 4$$
$$A = \{gg\} \qquad \text{Both are girls. } P(A) = \frac{1}{4}$$
$$B = \{gg, gb, bg\} \qquad \text{At least one is a girl. } P(B) = \frac{3}{4}$$
$$C = \{gg, gb\} \qquad \text{The older one is a girl. } P(C) = \frac{2}{4}$$

Note that $A \cap B = \{gg\}$, and $A \cap C = \{gg\}$ as well. Thus

$$P(A \cap B) = P(A \cap C) = \frac{1}{4}.$$

(a) $P(A|B) = \dfrac{P(A \text{ and } B)}{P(B)} = \dfrac{\frac{1}{4}}{\frac{3}{4}} = \dfrac{1}{4} \div \dfrac{3}{4} = \dfrac{1}{4} \cdot \dfrac{4}{3} = \dfrac{1}{3}$

(b) $P(A|C) = \dfrac{P(A \text{ and } C)}{P(C)} = \dfrac{\frac{1}{4}}{\frac{2}{4}} = \dfrac{1}{4} \div \dfrac{2}{4} = \dfrac{1}{4} \cdot \dfrac{4}{2} = \dfrac{1}{2}$

Independent Events

Sometimes a conditional probability is no different from the corresponding unconditional probability, in which case we call the two events *independent*.

INDEPENDENT EVENTS

Two events A and B are **independent events** if knowledge about the occurrence of one of them has no effect on the probability of the other one occurring. A and B are independent if

$$P(B|A) = P(B), \quad \text{or, equivalently,} \quad P(A|B) = P(A).$$

EXAMPLE 3 Checking Events for Independence

A single card is to be drawn from a standard 52-card deck. (The sample space S has 52 elements.) Find each of the following, given the events

A: The selected card is a face card, and B: The selected card is black.

(a) $P(B)$ **(b)** $P(B|A)$

(c) Use the results of parts (a) and (b) to determine whether events A and B are independent.

Solution

(a) There are 26 black cards in the 52-card deck.

$$P(B) = \frac{26}{52} = \frac{1}{2} \quad \text{Theoretical probability formula}$$

(b) $P(B|A) = \dfrac{P(B \text{ and } A)}{P(A)}$ Conditional probability formula

$$= \frac{\frac{6}{52}}{\frac{12}{52}} \quad \text{Of 52 cards, 12 are face cards and 6 are black face cards.}$$

$$= \frac{6}{52} \cdot \frac{52}{12} \quad \text{To divide, multiply by the reciprocal of the divisor.}$$

$$= \frac{1}{2} \quad \text{Calculate and write in lowest terms.}$$

(c) Because $P(B|A) = P(B)$, events A and B are independent. ∎

Events Involving "And"

If we multiply both sides of the conditional probability formula by $P(A)$, we obtain an expression for $P(A \cap B)$, which applies to events of the form "A and B." The resulting formula is related to the fundamental counting principle of **Chapter 10.** It is illustrated in **Figure 10.**

Just as the calculation of $P(A \text{ or } B)$ is simpler when A and B are mutually exclusive, the calculation of $P(A \text{ and } B)$ is simpler when A and B are independent.

One example of a card that is both a face card and black

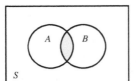

The logical connective "and" corresponds to "intersection" in set theory.

$$P(A \text{ and } B) = P(A) \cdot P(B|A)$$

Figure 10

MULTIPLICATION RULE OF PROBABILITY (FOR THE EVENT "A AND B")

If A and B are *any two events*, then

$$P(A \text{ and } B) = P(A) \cdot P(B|A).$$

If A and B are *independent*, then

$$P(A \text{ and } B) = P(A) \cdot P(B).$$

Even **a rare occurrence** can sometimes cause widespread controversy. When Mattel Toys marketed a new talking Barbie doll a few years ago, some of the Barbies were programmed to say "Math class is tough." The National Council of Teachers of Mathematics (NCTM), the American Association of University Women (AAUW), and numerous consumers voiced complaints about the damage such a message could do to the self-confidence of children and to their attitudes toward school and mathematics. Mattel subsequently agreed to erase the phrase from the microchip to be used in future doll production.

Originally, each Barbie was programmed to say four different statements, randomly selected from a pool of 270 prerecorded statements. Therefore, the probability of getting a Barbie that said "Math class is tough" was only

$$\frac{1 \cdot {}_{269}C_3}{{}_{270}C_4} \approx 0.015 = 1.5\%.$$

Other messages included in the pool were "I love school, don't you?," "I'm studying to be a doctor," and "Let's study for the quiz."

The first formula in the multiplication rule actually applies in all cases, because $P(B\,|\,A) = P(B)$ when A and B are independent. The independence of the component events is clear in many cases, so it is good to remember the second formula.

EXAMPLE 4   Selecting from a Set of Books

Each year, Jacqui adds to her book collection a number of new publications that she believes will be of lasting value and interest. She has categorized each of her twenty acquisitions for 2015 as hardcover or paperback and as fiction or nonfiction. The numbers of books in the various categories are shown in **Table 6.**

Table 6 Year 2015 Books

	Fiction (F)	Nonfiction (N)	Totals
Hardcover (H)	3	5	8
Paperback (P)	8	4	12
Totals	11	9	20

Reduced sample space in part (b)

If Jacqui randomly chooses one of these 20 books, find the probability that it will be each of the following.

(a) hardcover   **(b)** fiction, given it is hardcover   **(c)** hardcover and fiction

Solution

(a) **Eight** of the **20** books are hardcover, so $P(H) = \frac{8}{20} = \frac{2}{5}$.

(b) The given condition that the book is hardcover reduces the sample space to **eight** books. Of those eight, just three are fiction, so $P(F\,|\,H) = \frac{3}{8}$.

(c) $P(H \text{ and } F) = P(H) \cdot P(F\,|\,H) = \frac{2}{5} \cdot \frac{3}{8} = \frac{3}{20}$ Multiplication rule

It is easier here if we simply notice, directly from **Table 6,** that 3 of the 20 books are "hardcover and fiction." This verifies that the general multiplication rule of probability did give us the correct answer.   ∎

EXAMPLE 5   Selecting from a Set of Planets

Table 7 Mean Distance of Planets from the Sun

Mercury	58
Venus	108
Earth	150
Mars	228
Jupiter	778
Saturn	1430
Uranus	2870
Neptune	4500

Table 7 lists the eight planets of our solar system, together with their mean distances from the sun, in millions of kilometers. (Data is from *The World Almanac and Book of Facts*.) Carrie must choose two distinct planets to cover in her astronomy report. If she selects randomly, find the probability that the first one selected is closer to the sun than Mars and the second is closer to the sun than Saturn.

Solution

We define the following events.

   A: The first is closer than Mars. B: The second is closer than Saturn.

Then $P(A) = \frac{3}{8}$ because three of the original eight choices are favorable to event A. If the planet selected first is closer than Mars, it is also closer than Saturn, and since that planet is no longer available, four of the remaining seven are favorable to event B. Thus $P(B\,|\,A) = \frac{4}{7}$. Now apply the multiplication rule.

$$P(A \text{ and } B) = P(A) \cdot P(B\,|\,A) = \frac{3}{8} \cdot \frac{4}{7} = \frac{3}{14} \approx 0.214$$ Multiplication rule   ∎

In **Example 5,** the condition that A had occurred changed the probability of B, since the selection was done, in effect, without replacement. (Repetitions were not allowed.) Events A and B were not independent. On the other hand, in the next example the same events, A and B, are independent.

EXAMPLE 6 Selecting from a Set of Planets

Carrie must again select two planets, but this time one is for an oral report, the other is for a written report, and they need not be distinct. Here, the same planet may be selected for both reports. Again, find the probability that if she selects randomly, the first is closer than Mars and the second is closer than Saturn.

Solution

Defining events A and B as in **Example 5,** we have $P(A) = \frac{3}{8}$, just as before. But the selection is now done *with* replacement because repetitions *are* allowed. Event B is independent of event A, so we can use the second form of the multiplication rule.

$$P(A \text{ and } B) = P(A) \cdot P(B) = \frac{3}{8} \cdot \frac{5}{8} = \frac{15}{64} \approx 0.234$$

Answer is different than in **Example 5.** ∎

EXAMPLE 7 Selecting from a Deck of Cards

One example of a card that is black and one example of a card that is a diamond

(No single card is both black and a diamond.)

A single card is drawn from a standard 52-card deck. Let B denote the event that the card is black, and let D denote the event that it is a diamond. Are events B and D

(a) independent?   **(b)** mutually exclusive?

Solution

(a) For the unconditional probability of D, we get $P(D) = \frac{13}{52} = \frac{1}{4}$ because 13 of the 52 cards are diamonds. But for the conditional probability of D given B, we have $P(D|B) = \frac{0}{26} = 0$. None of the 26 black cards are diamonds. Since the conditional probability $P(D|B)$ is different from the unconditional probability $P(D)$, **B and D are not independent.**

(b) Mutually exclusive events are events that cannot both occur for a given performance of an experiment. Since no card in the deck is both black and a diamond, **B and D are mutually exclusive.** ∎

EXAMPLE 8 Selecting from an Urn of Balls

Anne is still drawing balls from the same urn, as shown at the side. This time she draws three balls, without replacement. Find the probability that she gets red, yellow, and blue balls, in that order.

Solution

Using appropriate letters to denote the colors, and subscripts to indicate first, second, and third draws, the event can be symbolized "R_1 and Y_2 and B_3."

$$P(R_1 \text{ and } Y_2 \text{ and } B_3) = P(R_1) \cdot P(Y_2|R_1) \cdot P(B_3|R_1 \text{ and } Y_2)$$

$$= \frac{4}{11} \cdot \frac{5}{10} \cdot \frac{2}{9} = \frac{4}{99} \approx 0.0404$$

∎

One example of five cards that are all hearts

EXAMPLE 9 Selecting from a Deck of Cards

If five cards are drawn without replacement from a standard 52-card deck, find the probability that they all are hearts.

Solution

Each time a heart is drawn, the number of available cards decreases by one and the number of hearts decreases by one.

$$P(\text{all hearts}) = \frac{13}{52} \cdot \frac{12}{51} \cdot \frac{11}{50} \cdot \frac{10}{49} \cdot \frac{9}{48} = \frac{33}{66{,}640} \approx 0.000495$$

We saw in **Chapter 10** that the problem of **Example 9** can also be solved by using the theoretical probability formula and combinations. The total possible number of 5-card hands, drawn without replacement, is $_{52}C_5$, and the number of those containing only hearts is $_{13}C_5$.

$$P(\text{all hearts}) = \frac{_{13}C_5}{_{52}C_5} = \frac{\dfrac{13!}{5! \cdot 8!}}{\dfrac{52!}{5! \cdot 47!}} \approx 0.000495 \quad \text{Use a calculator.}$$

The **search for extraterrestrial intelligence (SETI)** may have begun in earnest as early as 1961, when Dr. Frank Drake presented an equation for estimating the number of possible civilizations in the Milky Way galaxy whose communications we might detect. Over the years, the effort has been advanced by many scientists, including the late astronomer and exobiologist Carl Sagan, who popularized the issue in TV appearances and in his book *The Cosmic Connection: An Extraterrestrial Perspective* (Dell Paperback). "There must be other starfolk," said Sagan. In fact, some astronomers have estimated the odds against life on Earth being the only life in the universe at one hundred billion billion to one.

Other experts disagree. Freeman Dyson, a noted mathematical physicist and astronomer, says (in his book *Disturbing the Universe*) that after considering the same evidence and arguments, he believes it is just as likely as not (even odds) that there never was any other intelligent life out there.

EXAMPLE 10 Using Both Addition and Multiplication Rules

The local garage employs two mechanics, Ray and Tom. Your consumer club has found that Ray does twice as many jobs as Tom, Ray does a good job three out of four times, and Tom does a good job only two out of five times. If you plan to take your car in for repairs, find the probability that a good job will be done.

Solution

We define the following events.

R: work done by Ray T: work done by Tom G: good job done

Since Ray does twice as many jobs as Tom, the unconditional probabilities of events R and T are, respectively, $\frac{2}{3}$ and $\frac{1}{3}$. Because Ray does a good job three out of four times, the probability of a good job, given that Ray did the work, is $\frac{3}{4}$. And because Tom does well two out of five times, the probability of a good job, given that Tom did the work, is $\frac{2}{5}$. (These last two probabilities are conditional.) These four values can be summarized.

$$P(R) = \frac{2}{3}, \quad P(T) = \frac{1}{3} \quad P(G\,|\,R) = \frac{3}{4}, \quad \text{and} \quad P(G\,|\,T) = \frac{2}{5}$$

Event G can occur in two mutually exclusive ways: Ray could do the work and do a good job ($R \cap G$), or Tom could do the work and do a good job ($T \cap G$).

$$
\begin{aligned}
P(G) &= P(R \cap G) + P(T \cap G) & \text{Addition rule} \\
&= P(R) \cdot P(G\,|\,R) + P(T) \cdot P(G\,|\,T) & \text{Multiplication rule} \\
&= \frac{2}{3} \cdot \frac{3}{4} + \frac{1}{3} \cdot \frac{2}{5} & \text{Substitute the values.} \\
&= \frac{1}{2} + \frac{2}{15} = \frac{19}{30} \approx 0.633
\end{aligned}
$$

> Multiply first, then add.

The tree diagram in **Figure 11** shows a graphical way to organize the work of **Example 10.** Use the given information to draw the tree diagram; then find the probability of a good job by adding the probabilities from the two indicated branches of the tree.

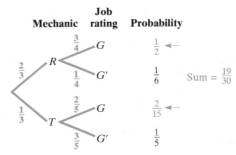

Garage mechanics experiment

Figure 11

FOR FURTHER THOUGHT

The Birthday Problem

A classic problem (with a surprising result) involves the probability that a given group of people will include at least one pair of people with the same birthday (the same day of the year, not necessarily the same year). This problem can be analyzed using the probability of a complement formula (**Section 11.2**) and the multiplication rule of probability from this section. Suppose there are three people in the group.

P (at least one duplication of birthdays)

= 1 − P(no duplications)   Complement formula

= 1 − P(2nd is different than 1st, and 3rd is different than 1st and 2nd)

= 1 − $\dfrac{364}{365} \cdot \dfrac{363}{365}$ Multiplication rule

≈ 1 − 0.992

= 0.008

(To simplify the calculations, we have assumed 365 possible birth dates, ignoring February 29.)

By doing more calculations like the one above, we find that the smaller the group, the smaller the probability of a duplication. The larger the group, the larger the probability of a duplication. The table below shows the probability of at least one duplication for numbers of people from 2 through 52.

For Group or Individual Investigation

1. Based on the data shown in the table, what are the odds in favor of a duplication in a group of 30 people?

2. Estimate from the table the least number of people for which the probability of duplication is at least $\frac{1}{2}$.

3. How small a group is required for the probability of a duplication to be *exactly* 0?

4. How large a group is required for the probability of a duplication to be *exactly* 1?

The answers are on **page 613.**

Number of People	Probability of at Least One Duplication	Number of People	Probability of at Least One Duplication	Number of People	Probability of at Least One Duplication
2	0.003	19	0.379	36	0.832
3	0.008	20	0.411	37	0.849
4	0.016	21	0.444	38	0.864
5	0.027	22	0.476	39	0.878
6	0.040	23	0.507	40	0.891
7	0.056	24	0.538	41	0.903
8	0.074	25	0.569	42	0.914
9	0.095	26	0.598	43	0.924
10	0.117	27	0.627	44	0.933
11	0.141	28	0.654	45	0.941
12	0.167	29	0.681	46	0.948
13	0.194	30	0.706	47	0.955
14	0.223	31	0.730	48	0.961
15	0.253	32	0.753	49	0.966
16	0.284	33	0.775	50	0.970
17	0.315	34	0.795	51	0.974
18	0.347	35	0.814	52	0.978

The **search for extraterrestrial intelligence (SETI)** has been mainly accomplished in recent years through **SETI@HOME,** a very large distributed computing program. Most of the data are collected by the world's largest radio telescope, built into a 20-acre natural bowl in Aricebo, Puerto Rico (pictured above), and processed by millions of personal computers around the world.

To learn more, or for a chance to be the first to "contact" an extraterrestrial civilization, check out
www.setiathome.ssl.berkeley.edu.

EXAMPLE 11 Selecting Door Prizes

Rob is among five door prize winners at a Christmas party. The five winners are asked to choose, without looking, from a bag that, they are told, contains five tokens, four of them redeemable for candy canes and one specific token redeemable for a $100 gift certificate. Can Rob improve his chance of getting the gift certificate by drawing first among the five people?

Solution

We denote candy cane by C, gift certificate by G, and first draw, second draw, and so on by subscripts $1, 2, \ldots$. If Rob draws first, his probability of getting the gift certificate is

$$P(G_1) = \frac{1}{5}.$$

If he draws second, his probability of getting the gift certificate is

$$\begin{aligned} P(G_2) &= P(C_1 \text{ and } G_2) \\ &= P(C_1) \cdot P(G_2 \mid C_1) \\ &= \frac{4}{5} \cdot \frac{1}{4} = \frac{1}{5}. \quad \text{Same result as above} \end{aligned}$$

For the third draw,

$$\begin{aligned} P(G_3) &= P(C_1 \text{ and } C_2 \text{ and } G_3) \\ &= P(C_1) \cdot P(C_2 \mid C_1) \cdot P(G_3 \mid C_1 \text{ and } C_2) \\ &= \frac{4}{5} \cdot \frac{3}{4} \cdot \frac{1}{3} = \frac{1}{5}. \quad \text{Same result as above} \end{aligned}$$

The probability of getting the gift certificate is also $\frac{1}{5}$ when drawing fourth or fifth. The order in which the five winners draw does not affect Rob's chances. ∎

11.3 EXERCISES

From the sample space

$$S = \{1, 2, 3, 4, \ldots, 15\},$$

a single number is to be selected at random. Given the events

A: *The selected number is even,*

B: *The selected number is a multiple of 4,*

C: *The selected number is a prime number,*

find each probability in Exercises 1–10.

1. $P(A)$

2. $P(B)$

3. $P(C)$

4. $P(A \text{ and } B)$

5. $P(A \text{ and } C)$

6. $P(B \text{ and } C)$

7. $P(A \mid B)$

8. $P(B \mid A)$

9. $P(C \mid A)$

10. $P(A \mid C)$

Given a family with three children, find the probability of each event.

11. All are girls.

12. All are boys.

13. The oldest two are boys, given that there are at least two boys.

14. The youngest is a girl, given that there are at least two girls.

15. The oldest is a boy and the youngest is a girl, given that there are at least one boy and at least one girl.

16. The youngest two are girls, given that there are at least two girls.

17. The oldest two are boys, given that the oldest is a boy.

18. The oldest is a boy, given that there is at least one boy.

19. The youngest is a boy, given that the birth order alternates between girls and boys.

20. The oldest is a girl, given that the middle child is a girl.

For each experiment, determine whether the two given events are independent.

21. **Coin Tosses** A fair coin is tossed twice. The events are "head on the first" and "head on the second."

22. **Dice Rolls** A pair of dice are rolled. The events are "even on the first" and "odd on the second."

23. **Planets' Mean Distances from the Sun** Two planets are selected, without replacement, from the list in **Table 7**. The events are "the first selected planet is closer than Jupiter" and "the second selected planet is farther than Mars."

24. **Mean Distances from the Sun** Two planets are selected, with replacement, from the list in **Table 7**. The events are "the first selected planet is closer than Earth" and "the second selected planet is farther than Uranus."

25. **Answers on a Multiple-choice Test** The answers are all guessed on a twenty-question multiple-choice test. The events are "the first answer is correct" and "the last answer is correct."

26. **Committees of U.S. Senators** A committee of five is randomly selected from the 100 U.S. senators. The events are "the first member selected is a Republican" and "the second member selected is a Republican." (Assume that there are both Republicans and non-Republicans in the Senate.)

Gender and Career Motivation of College Students One hundred college seniors attending a career fair at a university were categorized according to gender and according to primary career motivation. See the table for the results.

	Primary Career Motivation			
	Money	**Allowed to be Creative**	**Sense of Giving to Society**	**Total**
Male	19	15	14	48
Female	12	23	17	52
Total	31	38	31	100

If one of these students is to be selected at random, find the probability that the student selected will satisfy each condition in Exercises 27–32.

27. female

28. motivated primarily by creativity

29. not motivated primarily by money

30. male and motivated primarily by money

31. male, given that primary motivation is a sense of giving to society

32. motivated primarily by money or creativity, given that the student is female

Pet Selection *A pet store has seven puppies, including four huskies, two terriers, and one retriever. If Rebecka and Aaron, in that order, each select one puppy at random, with replacement (they may both select the same one), find the probability of each event in Exercises 33–36.*

33. Both select a husky.

34. Rebecka selects a retriever; Aaron selects a terrier.

35. Rebecka selects a terrier; Aaron selects a retriever.

36. Both select a retriever.

Pet Selection *Suppose two puppies are selected as earlier, but this time without replacement (Rebecka and Aaron cannot both select the same puppy). Find the probability of each event in Exercises 37–42.*

37. Both select a husky.

38. Aaron selects a terrier, given that Rebecka selects a husky.

39. Aaron selects a retriever, given that Rebecka selects a husky.

40. Rebecka selects a retriever.

41. Aaron selects a retriever, given that Rebecka selects a retriever.

42. Both select a retriever.

Card Dealing *Let two cards be dealt successively, without replacement, from a standard 52-card deck. Find the probability of each event in Exercises 43–49.*

43. spade dealt second, given a spade dealt first

44. club dealt second, given a diamond dealt first

45. two face cards   46. no face cards

47. The first card is a jack and the second is a face card.

48. The first card is the ace of hearts and the second is black.

49. The first card is black and the second is red.

50. **Proof of Formulas** Given events *A* and *B* within the sample space *S*, the following sequence of steps establishes formulas that can be used to compute conditional probabilities. Justify each statement.

(a) $P(A \text{ and } B) = P(A) \cdot P(B \mid A)$

(b) Therefore, $P(B \mid A) = \dfrac{P(A \text{ and } B)}{P(A)}$.

(c) Therefore, $P(B \mid A) = \dfrac{n(A \text{ and } B)/n(S)}{n(A)/n(S)}$.

(d) Therefore, $P(B \mid A) = \dfrac{n(A \text{ and } B)}{n(A)}$.

Conditions in Card Drawing *Use the results of* **Exercise 50** *to find each probability when a single card is drawn from a standard 52-card deck.*

51. $P(\text{queen} \mid \text{face card})$ 52. $P(\text{face card} \mid \text{queen})$

53. $P(\text{red} \mid \text{diamond})$ 54. $P(\text{diamond} \mid \text{red})$

Property of P(A and B) *Complete Exercises 55 and 56 to discover a general property of the probability of an event of the form "A and B."*

55. If one number is chosen randomly from the integers 1 through 10, the probability of getting a number that is *odd and prime,* by the multiplication rule, is

$$P(\text{odd}) \cdot P(\text{prime} \mid \text{odd}) = \frac{5}{10} \cdot \frac{3}{5} = \frac{3}{10}.$$

Compute the product $P(\text{prime}) \cdot P(\text{odd} \mid \text{prime})$, and compare to the product above.

56. What does **Exercise 55** imply, in general, about the probability of an event of the form "A and B"?

57. **Gender in Sequences of Babies** Two authors of this book each have three sons and no daughters. Assuming boy and girl babies are equally likely, what is the probability of this event?

58. **Dice Rolls** Three dice are rolled. What is the probability that the numbers shown will all be different? (*Mathematics Teacher* calendar problem)

The remaining exercises, and groups of exercises, may require concepts from earlier sections, such as the complements principle of counting and addition rules, as well as the multiplication rule of this section.

Warehouse Grocery Shopping *Therese manages a grocery warehouse that encourages volume shopping on the part of its customers. Therese has discovered that on any given weekday, 70% of the customer sales amount to*  *more than $100. That is, any given sale on such a day has a probability of 0.70 of being for more than $100. (Actually, the conditional probabilities throughout the day would change slightly, depending on earlier sales, but this effect would be negligible for the first several sales of the day, so we can treat them as independent.)*

Find the probability of each event in Exercises 59–62. (Give answers to three decimal places.)

59. The first two sales on Wednesday are both for more than $100.

60. The first three sales on Wednesday are all for more than $100.

61. None of the first three sales on Wednesday is for more than $100.

62. Exactly one of the first three sales on Wednesday is for more than $100.

Pollution from the Space Shuttle Launch Site *One problem encountered by developers of the space shuttle program was air pollution in the area surrounding the launch site. A certain direction from the launch site was considered critical in terms of hydrogen chloride pollution from the exhaust cloud. It has been determined that weather conditions would cause emission cloud movement in the critical direction only 5% of the time.*

In Exercises 63–66, find the probability for each event. Assume that probabilities for a particular launch in no way depend on the probabilities for other launches. (Give answers to two decimal places.)

63. A given launch will not result in cloud movement in the critical direction.

64. No cloud movement in the critical direction will occur during any of 5 launches.

65. Any 5 launches will result in at least one cloud movement in the critical direction.

66. Any 10 launches will result in at least one cloud movement in the critical direction.

Job Interviews *Three men and three women are waiting to be interviewed for jobs. If they are all selected in random order, find the probability of each event in Exercises 67–70.*

67. All the women will be interviewed first.

68. The first interviewee will be a man, and the remaining ones will alternate gender.

69. The first three chosen will all be the same gender.

70. No man will be interviewed until at least two women have been interviewed.

Garage Door Opener *Kevin installed a certain brand of automatic garage door opener that utilizes a transmitter control with six independent switches, each one set on or off. The receiver (wired to the door) must be set with the same pattern as the transmitter. (Exercises 71–74 are based on ideas similar to those of the "birthday problem" in the* **For Further Thought** *feature in this section.)*

71. How many different ways can Kevin set the switches?

72. If one of Kevin's neighbors also has this same brand of opener, and both of them set the switches randomly, what is the probability, to four decimal places, that they will use the same settings?

73. If five neighbors with the same type of opener set their switches independently, what is the probability of at least one pair of neighbors using the same settings? (Give your answer to four decimal places.)

74. What is the minimum number of neighbors who must use this brand of opener before the probability of at least one duplication of settings is greater than $\frac{1}{2}$?

Weather Conditions on Successive Days *In November, the rain in a certain valley tends to fall in storms of several days' duration. The unconditional probability of rain on any given day of the month is 0.500. But the probability of rain on a day that follows a rainy day is 0.800, and the probability of rain on a day following a nonrainy day is 0.300. Find the probability of each event in Exercises 75–78. Give answers to three decimal places.*

75. rain on two randomly selected consecutive days in November

76. rain on three randomly selected consecutive days in November

77. rain on November 1 and 2, but not on November 3 (The October 31 weather is unknown.)

78. rain on the first four days of November, given that October 31 was clear all day

Engine Failures in a Vintage Aircraft *In a certain four-engine vintage aircraft, now quite unreliable, each engine has a 10% chance of failure on any flight, as long as it is carrying its one-fourth share of the load. But if one engine fails, then the chance of failure increases to 20% for each of the other three engines. And if a second engine fails, each of the remaining two has a 30% chance of failure.*

Assuming that no two engines ever fail simultaneously, and that the aircraft can continue flying with as few as two operating engines, find each probability for a given flight of this aircraft. (Give answers to four decimal places.)

79. no engine failures

80. exactly one engine failure (any one of four engines)

81. exactly two engine failures (any two of four engines)

82. a failed flight

Fair Decisions from Biased Coins *Many everyday decisions, like who will drive to lunch or who will pay for the coffee, are made by the toss of a (presumably fair) coin and using the criterion "heads, you will; tails, I will." This criterion is not quite fair, however, if the coin is biased (perhaps due to slightly irregular construction or wear). John von Neumann suggested a way to make perfectly fair decisions, even with a possibly biased coin. If a coin, biased so that*

$$P(h) = 0.5200 \quad \text{and} \quad P(t) = 0.4800,$$

is tossed twice, find each probability. Give answers to four decimal places.

83. $P(hh)$ **84.** $P(ht)$

85. $P(th)$ **86.** $P(tt)$

87. Having completed **Exercises 83–86**, can you suggest what von Neumann's scheme may have been?

One-and-one Free Throw Shooting in Basketball *In basketball, "one-and-one" free throw shooting (commonly called foul shooting) is done as follows: If the player makes the first shot (1 point), she is given a second shot. If she misses the first shot, she is not given a second shot (see the tree diagram).*

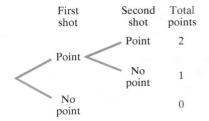

Christine, a basketball player, has a 70% free throw record. (She makes 70% of her free throws.) Find the probability that, on a given one-and-one free throw shooting opportunity, Christine will score each number of points.

88. no points   **89.** one point   **90.** two points

91. *Gender in Sequences of Babies*   Assuming boy and girl babies are equally likely, find the probability that it would take

(a) at least three births to obtain two girls

(b) at least four births to obtain two girls

(c) at least five births to obtain two girls.

92. *Card Choices*   Cards are drawn, without replacement, from an ordinary 52-card deck.

(a) How many must be drawn before the probability of obtaining at least one face card is greater than $\frac{1}{2}$?

(b) How many must be drawn before the probability of obtaining at least one king is greater than $\frac{1}{2}$?

93. *A Two-Headed Coin?*   A gambler has two coins in his pocket—one fair coin and one two-headed coin. He selects a coin at random and flips it twice. If he gets two heads, what is the probability that he selected the fair coin? (*Mathematics Teacher* calendar problem)

94. *Cube Cuts*   A $4'' \times 4'' \times 4''$ cube is painted and then cut into sixty-four $1'' \times 1'' \times 1''$ cubes. A unit cube is then randomly selected and rolled. What is the probability that the top face of the rolled cube is painted? Express your answer as a common fraction. (*Mathematics Teacher* calendar problem)

95. *Anne Continues*   In **Example 8,** where Anne draws three balls without replacement, what would be her probability of getting one of each color, where the order does not matter?

96. *Card Choices*   There are three cards, one that is green on both sides, one that is red on both sides, and one that is green on one side and red on the other. One of the three cards is selected randomly and laid on the table. If it happens that the card on the table has a red side up, what is the probability that it is also red on the other side?

97. *Empirical and Theoretical Probabilities in Dice Rolling*   Roll a pair of dice until a sum of seven appears, keeping track of how many rolls it took. Repeat the process a total of 50 times, each time recording the number of rolls it took to get a sum of seven.

(a) Use your experimental data to compute an empirical probability to two decimal places that it would take at least three rolls to get a sum of seven.

(b) Find the theoretical probability to two decimal places that it would take at least three rolls to obtain a sum of seven.

98. Go to the Web site http://www.planetary.org/explore/space-topics/ and select the topic *Asteroids and Comets*. Write a report on the threat to humanity of cosmic impacts. Include an explanation of the acronym *NEO*.

11.4   BINOMIAL PROBABILITY

OBJECTIVES

1 Construct a simple binomial probability distribution.

2 Apply the binomial probability formula for an experiment involving Bernoulli trials.

Binomial Probability Distribution

Suppose the spinner in **Figure 12** on the next page is spun twice. We are interested in the number of times a 2 is obtained. (Assume that 1, 2, and 3 all are equally likely on a given spin.) We can think of the outcome 2 as a "success," while a 1 or a 3 would be a "failure."

When the outcomes of an experiment are divided into just two categories, success and failure, the associated probabilities are called "binomial." (The prefix *bi* means *two*.) Repeated performances of such an experiment, where the probability of success remains constant throughout all repetitions, are also known as repeated **Bernoulli trials** (after James Bernoulli). If we use an ordered pair to represent the result of each pair of spins, then the sample space for this experiment is

$$S = \{(1,1), (1,2), (1,3), (2,1), (2,2), (2,3), (3,1), (3,2), (3,3)\}.$$

The nine outcomes in S are all equally likely. This follows from the numbers 1, 2, and 3 being equally likely on a particular spin.

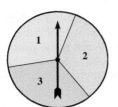

Figure 12

Table 8 Probability Distribution for the Number of 2s in Two Spins

x	$P(x)$
0	$\frac{4}{9}$
1	$\frac{4}{9}$
2	$\frac{1}{9}$
Sum:	$\frac{9}{9} = 1$

If x denotes the number of 2s occurring on each pair of spins, then x is an example of a *random variable*. Although we cannot predict the result of any particular pair of spins, we can find the probabilities of various events from the sample space listing. In S, the number of 2s is 0 in four cases, 1 in four cases, and 2 in one case, as reflected in **Table 8**. Because the table includes all possible values of x, together with their probabilities, it is an example of a *probability distribution*. In this case, we have a **binomial probability distribution**. The probability column in **Table 8** has a sum of 1, in agreement with probability Property 3 in **Section 11.2**.

In order to develop a general formula for binomial probabilities, we can consider another way to obtain the probability values in **Table 8**. The various spins of the spinner are independent of one another, and on each spin the probability of success (S) is $\frac{1}{3}$ and the probability of failure (F) is $\frac{2}{3}$. We will denote success on the first spin by S_1, failure on the second by F_2, and so on.

$$P(x = 0) = P(F_1 \text{ and } F_2)$$

$$= P(F_1) \cdot P(F_2) \qquad \text{Multiplication rule}$$

$$= \frac{2}{3} \cdot \frac{2}{3} \qquad \text{Substitute values.}$$

$$= \frac{4}{9} \qquad \text{Multiply.}$$

$$P(x = 1) = P[\,(S_1 \text{ and } F_2) \text{ or } (F_1 \text{ and } S_2)\,] \qquad \text{2 ways to get } x = 1$$

$$= P(S_1 \text{ and } F_2) + P(F_1 \text{ and } S_2) \qquad \text{Addition rule}$$

$$= P(S_1) \cdot P(F_2) + P(F_1) \cdot P(S_2) \qquad \text{Multiplication rule}$$

$$= \frac{1}{3} \cdot \frac{2}{3} + \frac{2}{3} \cdot \frac{1}{3} \qquad \text{Substitute values.}$$

$$= \frac{2}{9} + \frac{2}{9} \qquad \text{Multiply.}$$

$$= \frac{4}{9} \qquad \text{Add.}$$

$$P(x = 2) = P(S_1 \text{ and } S_2)$$

$$= P(S_1) \cdot P(S_2) \qquad \text{Multiplication rule}$$

$$= \frac{1}{3} \cdot \frac{1}{3} \qquad \text{Substitute values.}$$

$$= \frac{1}{9} \qquad \text{Multiply.}$$

James Bernoulli (1654–1705) is also known as Jacob or Jacques. He was charmed away from theology by the writings of Leibniz, became his pupil, and later headed the mathematics faculty at the University of Basel. His results in probability are contained in the *Art of Conjecture,* which was published in 1713, after his death, and which also included a reprint of the earlier Huygens paper. Bernoulli also made many contributions to calculus and analytic geometry.

Notice the following pattern in the above calculations. There is only one way to get $x = 0$ (namely, F_1 and F_2). And there is only one way to get $x = 2$ (namely, S_1 and S_2). But there are two ways to get $x = 1$. One way is S_1 and F_2; the other is F_1 and S_2. There are two ways because the one success required can occur on the first spin or on the second spin. How many ways can exactly one success occur in two repeated trials? This question is equivalent to

How many size-one subsets are there of the set of two trials?

The answer is $_2C_1 = 2$. The expression $_2C_1$ denotes "combinations of 2 things taken 1 at a time." Each of the two ways to get exactly one success has a probability equal to $\frac{1}{3} \cdot \frac{2}{3}$, the probability of success times the probability of failure.

EXAMPLE 1 **Constructing a Probability Distribution**

Use a tree diagram to construct a probability distribution for the number of 2s in three spins of the spinner in **Figure 12.**

Solution

If the spinner is spun three times rather than two, then x, the number of successes (2s) could have values of 0, 1, 2, or 3. Then the number of ways to get exactly 1 success is $_3C_1 = 3$. They are

$$S_1 \text{ and } F_2 \text{ and } F_3, \quad F_1 \text{ and } S_2 \text{ and } F_3, \quad F_1 \text{ and } F_2 \text{ and } S_3.$$

The probability of each of these three ways is $\frac{1}{3} \cdot \frac{2}{3} \cdot \frac{2}{3} = \frac{4}{27}$.

$$P(x = 1) = 3 \cdot \frac{4}{27} = \frac{12}{27} = \frac{4}{9}$$

Figure 13 shows all possibilities for three spins, and **Table 9** gives the associated probability distribution. In the tree diagram, the number of ways of getting two successes in three trials is 3, in agreement with the fact that $_3C_2 = 3$. Also the sum of the $P(x)$ column in **Table 9** is again 1.

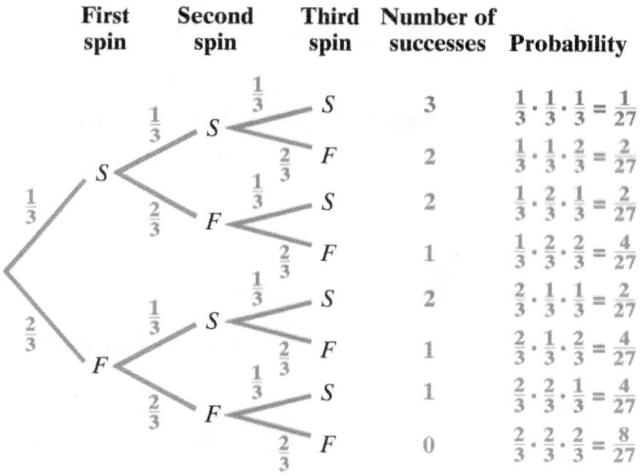

Table 9 Probability Distribution for the Number of 2s in Three Spins

x	$P(x)$
0	$\frac{8}{27}$
1	$\frac{12}{27}$
2	$\frac{6}{27}$
3	$\frac{1}{27}$
	Sum: $\frac{27}{27} = 1$

Tree diagram for three spins

Figure 13

Problem-Solving Strategy

One of the various problem-solving strategies from **Chapter 1** was "Look for a pattern." Having constructed complete probability distributions for binomial experiments with 2 and 3 repeated trials (and probability of success $\frac{1}{3}$), we can now generalize the observed pattern to any binomial experiment, as shown next.

Binomial Probability Formula

Define the following quantities.

$n = $ the number of repeated trials

$p = $ the probability of success on any given trial

$q = 1 - p = $ the probability of failure on any given trial

$x = $ the number of successes that occur

Note that p remains fixed throughout all n trials. This means that all trials are independent of one another. The random variable x representing the number of successes can have any integer value from 0 through n. In general, x successes can be assigned among n repeated trials in $_nC_x$ different ways, because this is the number of different subsets of x positions among a set of n positions. Also, regardless of which x of the trials result in successes, there will always be x successes and $n - x$ failures, so we multiply x factors of p and $n - x$ factors of q together.

BINOMIAL PROBABILITY FORMULA

When n independent repeated trials occur, where

$$p = \text{probability of success} \quad \text{and} \quad q = \text{probability of failure}$$

with p and q (where $q = 1 - p$) remaining constant throughout all n trials, the probability of exactly x successes is calculated as follows.

$$P(x) = {}_nC_x\, p^x q^{n-x} = \frac{n!}{x!(n-x)!}\, p^x q^{n-x}$$

Binomial probabilities for particular values of n, p, and x can be found directly using tables, statistical software, and some handheld calculators. In the following examples, we use the formula derived above.

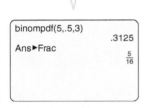

From the DISTR menu

binompdf(5,.5,3)
      .3125
Ans▶Frac
      $\frac{5}{16}$

The TI-83/84 Plus calculator will find the probability discussed in **Example 2.**

EXAMPLE 2 Finding Probability in Coin Tossing

Find the probability of obtaining exactly three heads in five tosses of a fair coin.

Solution

Let heads be "success." Then this is a binomial experiment with

$$n = 5, \quad p = \frac{1}{2}, \quad q = \frac{1}{2}, \quad \text{and} \quad x = 3.$$

$$P(x = 3) = {}_5C_3\left(\frac{1}{2}\right)^3\left(\frac{1}{2}\right)^{5-3} = 10 \cdot \frac{1}{8} \cdot \frac{1}{4} = \frac{5}{16} \qquad \text{Binomial probability formula} \quad ■$$

binompdf(6,1/6,2)
      .200938786

This screen supports the answer in **Example 3.**

EXAMPLE 3 Finding Probability in Dice Rolling

Find the probability of obtaining exactly two 5s in six rolls of a fair die.

Solution

Let 5 be "success." Then $n = 6$, $p = \frac{1}{6}$, $q = \frac{5}{6}$, and $x = 2$.

$$P(x = 2) = {}_6C_2\left(\frac{1}{6}\right)^2\left(\frac{5}{6}\right)^4 = 15 \cdot \frac{1}{36} \cdot \frac{625}{1296} = \frac{3125}{15{,}552} \approx 0.201 \qquad ■$$

In the case of repeated independent trials, when an event involves more than one specific number of successes, we can employ the binomial probability formula along with the complement and/or addition rules.

EXAMPLE 4 Finding the Probability of Female Children

A couple plans to have 5 children. Find the probability that they will have more than 3 girls. (Assume girl and boy babies are equally likely.)

Solution

Let a girl be "success." Then $n = 5$, $p = q = \frac{1}{2}$, and $x > 3$.

$$P(x > 3) = P(x = 4 \text{ or } 5) \qquad \text{More than 3 means 4 or 5.}$$

$$= P(4) + P(5) \qquad \text{Addition rule}$$

$$= {}_5C_4\left(\frac{1}{2}\right)^4\left(\frac{1}{2}\right)^1 + {}_5C_5\left(\frac{1}{2}\right)^5\left(\frac{1}{2}\right)^0 \qquad \text{Binomial probability formula}$$

$$= 5 \cdot \frac{1}{16} \cdot \frac{1}{2} + 1 \cdot \frac{1}{32} \cdot 1 \qquad \text{Simplify.}$$

$$= \frac{5}{32} + \frac{1}{32} = \frac{6}{32} = \frac{3}{16} = 0.1875$$

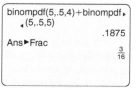

This screen supports the answer in **Example 4.**

EXAMPLE 5 Finding the Probability of Hits in Baseball

Gary Bell, a pitcher who is also an excellent hitter, has a well-established career batting average of .300. Suppose that he bats ten times. Find the probability that he will get more than two hits in the ten at-bats.

Solution

This "experiment" involves $n = 10$ repeated Bernoulli trials, with probability of success (a hit) given by $p = 0.3$ (which implies $q = 1 - 0.3 = 0.7$). Since, in this case, "more than 2" means

"3 or 4 or 5 or 6 or 7 or 8 or 9 or 10"   (eight different possibilities),

it will be less work to apply the complement rule.

$$P(x > 2) = 1 - P(x \le 2) \qquad \text{Complement rule}$$

$$= 1 - P(x = 0 \text{ or } 1 \text{ or } 2) \qquad \text{Only three different possibilities}$$

$$= 1 - [P(0) + P(1) + P(2)] \qquad \text{Addition rule}$$

$$= 1 - [{}_{10}C_0(0.3)^0(0.7)^{10} \qquad \text{Binomial probability formula}$$

$$+ {}_{10}C_1(0.3)^1(0.7)^9 + {}_{10}C_2(0.3)^2(0.7)^8]$$

$$\approx 1 - [0.0282 + 0.1211 + 0.2335] \qquad \text{Simplify.}$$

$$= 1 - 0.3828 = 0.6172$$

This screen supports the answer in **Example 5.**

11.4 EXERCISES

For Exercises 1–22, give all numerical answers as common fractions reduced to lowest terms. For Exercises 23–56, give all numerical answers to three decimal places.

Coin Tossing *If three fair coins are tossed, find the probability of each number of heads.*

1. 0

2. 1

3. 2

4. 3

5. 1 or 2

6. at least 1

7. no more than 1

8. fewer than 3

9. ***Relating Pascal's Triangle to Coin Tossing*** Pascal's triangle was shown in **Table 5** of **Section 10.4.** Explain how the probabilities in **Exercises 1–4** here relate to row 3 of the "triangle." (We will refer to the topmost row of the triangle as "row number 0" and to the leftmost entry of each row as "entry number 0.")

10. Generalize the pattern in **Exercise 9** to complete the following statement. If n fair coins are tossed, the probability of exactly x heads is the fraction whose numerator is entry number _____ of row number _____ in Pascal's triangle, and whose denominator is the sum of the entries in row number _____.

Binomial Probability Applied to Tossing Coins *Use the pattern noted in* **Exercises 9 and 10** *to find the probabilities of each number of heads when seven fair coins are tossed.*

11. 0   **12.** 1   **13.** 2   **14.** 3

15. 4   **16.** 5   **17.** 6   **18.** 7

Binomial Probability Applied to Rolling Dice *A fair die is rolled three times. A 4 is considered "success," while all other outcomes are "failures." Find the probability of each number of successes.*

19. 0   **20.** 1   **21.** 2   **22.** 3

For n repeated independent trials, with constant probability of success p for all trials, find the probability of exactly x successes in each of Exercises 23–26.

23. $n = 5$, $p = \frac{1}{3}$, $x = 4$ **24.** $n = 10$, $p = \frac{7}{10}$, $x = 5$

25. $n = 20$, $p = 0.125$, $x = 2$

26. $n = 30$, $p = 0.6$, $x = 22$

For Exercises 27–30, refer to **Example 5.**

27. Batting Averages in Baseball If Gary's batting average is exactly .300 going into the series based on exactly 1200 career hits out of 4000 previous times at bat, what is the greatest his average could possibly be when he goes up to bat the tenth time of the series?

28. Batting Averages in Baseball Refer to **Exercise 27.** What is the least his average could possibly be when he goes up to bat the tenth time of the series?

29. Batting Averages in Baseball Does Gary's probability of a hit really remain constant at exactly 0.300 through all ten times at bat? Explain your reasoning.

30. Do you think the use of the binomial probability formula was justified in **Example 5,** even though p is not strictly constant? Explain your reasoning.

Random Selection of Answers on a Multiple-choice Test *Beth is taking a ten-question multiple-choice test for which each question has three answer choices, only one of which is correct. Beth decides on answers by rolling a fair die and marking the first answer choice if the die shows 1 or 2, the second if it shows 3 or 4, and the third if it shows 5 or 6. Find the probability of each event in Exercises 31–34.*

31. exactly four correct answers

32. exactly seven correct answers

33. fewer than three correct answers

34. at least seven correct answers

Side Effects of Prescription Drugs *It is known that a certain prescription drug produces undesirable side effects in 35% of all patients who use it. Among a random sample of eight patients using the drug, find the probability of each event in Exercises 35–38.*

35. None have undesirable side effects.

36. Exactly one has undesirable side effects.

37. Exactly two have undesirable side effects.

38. More than two have undesirable side effects.

Likelihood of Capable Students Attending College *It has been shown that 60% of the high school graduates who are capable of college work actually enroll in colleges. Find the probability that, among nine capable high school graduates in a state, each number will enroll in college.*

39. exactly 4   **40.** from 4 through 6

41. all 9   **42.** at least 3

43. Ball Choices A bag contains only white balls and black balls. Let p be the probability that a ball selected at random is black. Each time a ball is selected, it is placed back in the bag before the next ball is selected. Four balls are selected at random. What is the probability that two of the four balls are black and two are white? (*Mathematics Teacher* calendar problem) (*Hint:* Use the binomial probability formula to express the probability in terms of p.)

44. Ball Choices Evaluate the probability of **Exercise 43** in the case where the bag actually contains 15 black balls and 25 white balls.

45. Frost Survival among Orange Trees If it is known that 65% of all orange trees will survive a hard frost, then what is the probability that at least half of a group of six trees will survive such a frost?

46. Rate of Favorable Media Coverage of an Incumbent President During a presidential campaign, 64% of the political columns in a certain group of major newspapers were favorable to the incumbent president. If a sample of fifteen of these columns is selected at random, what is the probability that exactly ten of them will be favorable?

47. ***Student Ownership of Personal Computers*** At a large midwestern university, 90% of all students have their own personal computers. If five students at that university are selected at random, find the probability that exactly three of them have their own computers.

Taking a Random Walk *Abby is parked at a mile marker on an east-west country road. She decides to toss a fair coin 10 times, each time driving 1 mile east if it lands heads up and 1 mile west if it lands tails up. The term "random walk" applies to this process, even though she drives rather than walks. It is a simplified model of Brownian motion, which is mentioned in a margin note in* ***Section 11.1.***

In each of Exercises 48–55, find the probability that Abby's "walk" will end as described.

48. 6 miles east of the start

49. 10 miles east of the start

50. 5 miles west of the start

51. 6 miles west of the start

52. at least 2 miles east of the start

53. 2 miles east of the start

54. exactly at the start

55. at least 2 miles from the start

11.5 EXPECTED VALUE AND SIMULATION

OBJECTIVES

1 Determine expected value of a random variable and expected net winnings in a game of chance.

2 Determine if a game of chance is a fair game.

3 Use expected value to make business and insurance decisions.

4 Use simulation in genetic processes such as flower color and birth gender.

Expected Value

We repeat the beginning of **Example 6** in **Section 11.2**.

> *Amy plans to spend from 1 to 6 hours on her homework. If x represents the number of hours to be spent on a given night, then the probabilities of the various values of x, rounded to the nearest hour, are as shown in* **Table 10**.

If Amy's friend Tara asks her how many hours her studies will take, what would be her best guess? Six different time values are possible, with some more likely than others. One thing Amy could do is calculate a "weighted average" by multiplying each possible time value by its probability and then adding the six products.

$$1(0.05) + 2(0.10) + 3(0.20) + 4(0.40) + 5(0.10) + 6(0.15)$$

$$= 0.05 + 0.20 + 0.60 + 1.60 + 0.50 + 0.90$$

$$= 3.85$$

Thus 3.85 hours is the **expected value** (or the **mathematical expectation**) of the quantity of time to be spent.

Table 10

x	$P(x)$
1	0.05
2	0.10
3	0.20
4	0.40
5	0.10
6	0.15

EXPECTED VALUE

If a random variable x can have any of the values $x_1, x_2, x_3, \ldots, x_n$, and the corresponding probabilities of these values occurring are $P(x_1)$, $P(x_2)$, $P(x_3), \ldots, P(x_n)$, then $E(x)$, the **expected value of x,** is calculated as follows.

$$E(x) = x_1 \cdot P(x_1) + x_2 \cdot P(x_2) + x_3 \cdot P(x_3) + \cdots + x_n \cdot P(x_n)$$

EXAMPLE 1 Finding the Expected Number of Boys

Find the expected number of boys for a three-child family—that is, the expected value of the number of boys. Assume girls and boys are equally likely.

Solution

The sample space for this experiment is

$$S = \{ggg, ggb, gbg, bgg, gbb, bgb, bbg, bbb\}.$$

The probability distribution is shown in **Table 11,** along with the products and their sum, which gives the expected value.

Table 11

Number of Boys x	Probability $P(x)$	Product $x \cdot P(x)$
0	$\frac{1}{8}$	0
1	$\frac{3}{8}$	$\frac{3}{8}$
2	$\frac{3}{8}$	$\frac{6}{8}$
3	$\frac{1}{8}$	$\frac{3}{8}$
		Expected value: $E(x) = \frac{12}{8} = \frac{3}{2}$

The expected number of boys is $\frac{3}{2}$, or 1.5. This result seems reasonable. Boys and girls are equally likely, so "half" the children are expected to be boys. ■

The expected value for the number of boys in the family could never actually occur. It is only a kind of long-run average of the various values that *could* occur. If we record the number of boys in many different three-child families, then by the law of large numbers, or law of averages, as the number of observed families increases, the observed average number of boys should approach the expected value.

Games and Gambling

EXAMPLE 2 Finding Expected Winnings

A player pays $3 to play the following game: He tosses three fair coins and receives back "payoffs" of $1 if he tosses no heads, $2 for one head, $3 for two heads, and $4 for three heads. Find the player's expected net winnings for this game.

Solution

See **Table 12.** For each possible event, "net winnings" are "gross winnings" (payoff) minus cost to play. Probabilities are derived from the sample space.

$$S = \{\text{ttt, htt, tht, tth, hht, hth, thh, hhh}\}$$

The expected net loss of 50 cents is a long-run average only. On any particular play of this game, the player would lose $2 or lose $1 or break even or win $1. Over a long series of plays, say 100, there would be some wins and some losses, but the total net result would likely be around a $100 \cdot (\$0.50) = \$50$ *loss*.

Eisenhower Dollar Coins

Table 12

Number of Heads	Payoff	Net Winnings x	Probability $P(x)$	Product $x \cdot P(x)$
0	$1	−$2	$\frac{1}{8}$	−$\frac{2}{8}$
1	2	−1	$\frac{3}{8}$	−$\frac{3}{8}$
2	3	0	$\frac{3}{8}$	0
3	4	1	$\frac{1}{8}$	$\frac{1}{8}$
			Expected value: $E(x) = -\$\frac{1}{2} = -\$0.50$	

■

A game in which the expected net winnings are zero is called a **fair game.** The game in **Example 2** has negative expected net winnings, so it is unfair against the player. A game with positive expected net winnings is unfair in favor of the player.

EXAMPLE 3 Finding the Fair Cost to Play a Game

The $3 cost to play the game of **Example 2** makes the game unfair against the player (since the player's expected net winnings are negative). What cost would make this a fair game?

Solution

We already computed, in **Example 2,** that the $3 cost to play resulted in an expected net loss of $0.50. Therefore, we can conclude that the $3 cost was 50 cents too high. A fair cost to play the game would then be $3 − $0.50 = $2.50. ■

The result in **Example 3** can be verified. Disregard the cost to play, and find the expected *gross* winnings by summing the products of payoff times probability.

$$E(\text{gross winnings}) = \$1 \cdot \frac{1}{8} + \$2 \cdot \frac{3}{8} + \$3 \cdot \frac{3}{8} + \$4 \cdot \frac{1}{8} = \frac{\$20}{8} = \$2.50$$

Expected gross winnings (payoff) are $2.50, so this amount is a fair cost to play.

Roulette ("little wheel") was invented in France in the seventeenth or early eighteenth century. It has been a featured game of chance in the gambling casino of Monte Carlo.

The disk is divided into red and black alternating compartments numbered 1 to 36 (but not in that order). There is a compartment also for 0 (and for 00 in the United States). In roulette, the wheel is set in motion, and an ivory ball is thrown into the bowl opposite to the direction of the wheel. When the wheel stops, the ball comes to rest in one of the compartments—the number and color determine who wins.

The players bet against the banker (person in charge of the pool of money) by placing money or equivalent chips in spaces on the roulette table corresponding to the wheel's colors or numbers. Bets can be made on one number or several, on odd or even, on red or black, or on combinations. The banker pays off according to the odds against the particular bet(s). For example, the classic payoff for a winning single number is $36 for each $1 bet.

EXAMPLE 4 Finding the Fair Cost to Play a Game

In a certain state lottery, a player chooses three digits, in a specific order. Leading digits may be 0, so numbers such as 028 and 003 are legitimate entries. The lottery operators randomly select a three-digit sequence, and any player matching that selection receives a payoff of $600. What is a fair cost to play this game?

Solution

In this case, no cost has been proposed, so we have no choice but to compute expected *gross* winnings. The probability of selecting all three digits correctly is $\frac{1}{10} \cdot \frac{1}{10} \cdot \frac{1}{10} = \frac{1}{1000}$, and the probability of not selecting all three correctly is $1 - \frac{1}{1000} = \frac{999}{1000}$. The expected gross winnings are

$$E(\text{gross winnings}) = \$600 \cdot \frac{1}{1000} + \$0 \cdot \frac{999}{1000} = \$0.60.$$

Thus the fair cost to play this game is 60 cents. (In fact, the lottery charges $1 to play, so players should expect to lose 40 cents per play *on the average.*) ■

State lotteries must be unfair against players because they are designed to help fund benefits (such as the state's school system), as well as to cover administrative costs and certain other expenses. Among people's reasons for playing may be a willingness to support such causes, but most people undoubtedly play for the chance to "beat the odds" and be one of the few net winners.

Gaming casinos are major business enterprises, by no means designed to break even. The games they offer are always unfair in favor of the house. The bias does not need to be great, however, because even relatively small average losses per player, multiplied by large numbers of players, can result in huge profits for the house.

EXAMPLE 5 Finding Expected Winnings in Roulette

One simple type of *roulette* is played with an ivory ball and a wheel set in motion. The wheel contains thirty-eight compartments. Eighteen of the compartments are black, eighteen are red, one is labeled "zero," and one is labeled "double zero." (These last two are neither black nor red.) In this case, assume the player places $1 on either red or black. If the player picks the correct color of the compartment in which the ball finally lands, the payoff is $2. Otherwise, the payoff is zero. Find the expected net winnings.

Solution

By the expected value formula, expected net winnings are

$$E(\text{net winnings}) = (\$1)\frac{18}{38} + (-\$1)\frac{20}{38} = -\$\frac{1}{19}.$$

The expected net *loss* here is $\$\frac{1}{19}$, or about 5.3¢, per play.

FOR FURTHER THOUGHT

Expected Value of Games of Chance

Slot machines are a popular game for those who want to lose their money with very little mental effort. We cannot calculate an expected value applicable to all slot machines since payoffs vary from machine to machine. But we can calculate the "typical expected value."

A player operates a classic slot machine by pulling a handle after inserting a coin or coins. (We assume one coin in this discussion.) Reels inside the machine then rotate, and come to rest in some random order. (Most *modern* machines employ an electronic equivalent rather than actual rotating reels.) Assume that three reels show the pictures listed in **Table 13.** For example, of the 20 pictures on the first reel, 2 are cherries, 5 are oranges, 5 are plums, 2 are bells, 2 are melons, 3 are bars, and 1 is the number 7.

Table 13 Pictures on Reels

Pictures	Reels		
	1	**2**	**3**
Cherries	2	5	4
Oranges	5	4	5
Plums	5	3	3
Bells	2	4	4
Melons	2	1	2
Bars	3	2	1
7s	1	1	1
Totals	20	20	20

This Cleveland Indians fan hit four 7s in a row on a progressive nickel slot machine at the Sands Casino in Las Vegas in 1988.

A picture of cherries on the first reel, but not on the second, leads to a payoff of 3 coins (*net* winnings: 2 coins); a picture of cherries on the first two reels, but not the third, leads to a payoff of 5 coins (*net* winnings: 4 coins). These and all other winning combinations are listed in **Table 14.**

Since, according to **Table 13,** there are 2 ways of getting cherries on the first reel, 15 ways of *not* getting cherries on the second reel, and 20 ways of getting anything on the third reel, we have a total of 2 · 15 · 20 = 600 ways of getting a net payoff of 2. Since there are 20 pictures per reel, there are a total of 20 · 20 · 20 = 8000 possible outcomes. Hence, the probability of receiving a net payoff of 2 coins is $\frac{600}{8000}$.

Table 14 takes into account all *winning* outcomes, with the necessary products for finding expectation added in the last column. However, since a *nonwinning* outcome can occur in

8000 − 988 = 7012 ways (with winnings of −1 coin),

the product (−1) · 7012/8000 must also be included. Hence, the expected value of this particular slot machine is

$$\frac{6318}{8000} + (-1) \cdot \frac{7012}{8000} \approx -0.087 \text{ coin.}$$

Table 14 Calculating Expected Loss on a Three-Reel Slot Machine

Winning Combinations	Number of Ways	Probability	Number of Coins Received	Net Winnings (in coins)	Probability Times Net Winnings
1 cherry (on first reel)	$2 \cdot 15 \cdot 20 = 600$	600/8000	3	2	1200/8000
2 cherries (on first two reels)	$2 \cdot 5 \cdot 16 = 160$	160/8000	5	4	640/8000
3 cherries	$2 \cdot 5 \cdot 4 = 40$	40/8000	10	9	360/8000
3 oranges	$5 \cdot 4 \cdot 5 = 100$	100/8000	10	9	900/8000
3 plums	$5 \cdot 3 \cdot 3 = 45$	45/8000	14	13	585/8000
3 bells	$\_ \cdot \_ \cdot \_ = \_$	___/8000	18	___	___/8000
3 melons (jackpot)	$\_ \cdot \_ \cdot \_ = \_$	___/8000	100	___	___/8000
3 bars (jackpot)	$\_ \cdot \_ \cdot \_ = \_$	___/8000	200	___	___/8000
3 7s (jackpot)	$\_ \cdot \_ \cdot \_ = \_$	___/8000	500	___	___/8000
Totals	___				6318/8000

On a machine costing one dollar per play, the expected *loss* (per play) is about

$$(0.087)(1 \text{ dollar}) = 8.7 \text{ cents}.$$

Actual slot machines vary in expected loss per dollar of play. But author Hornsby was able to beat a Las Vegas slot machine in 1988.

Table 15 comes from an article by Andrew Sterrett in *The Mathematics Teacher* (March 1967), in which he discusses rules for various games of chance and calculates their expected values. He uses expected values to find expected times it would take to lose $1000 if you played continually at the rate of $1 per play and one play per minute.

For Group or Individual Investigation

1. Explain why the entries of the "Net Winnings" column of **Table 14** are all one fewer than the corresponding entries of the "Number of Coins Received" column.

2. Find the 29 missing values in **Table 14** and verify that the final result, 6318/8000, is correct. (Refer to **Table 13** for the values in the "Number of Ways" column.)

3. In order to make your money last as long as possible in a casino, which game should you play? (Refer to **Table 15**.)

Table 15 Expected Time to Lose $1000

Game	Expected Value	Days	Hours	Minutes
Roulette (with one 0)	−$0.027	25	16	40
Roulette (with 0 and 00)	−$0.053	13	4	40
Chuck-a-luck	−$0.079	8	19	46
Keno (one number)	−$0.200	3	11	20
Numbers	−$0.300	2	7	33
Football pool (4 winners)	−$0.375	1	20	27
Football pool (10 winners)	−$0.658	1	1	19

Investments

EXAMPLE 6 Finding Expected Investment Profits

Nick has $5000 to invest and will commit the whole amount, for six months, to one of three technology stocks. A number of uncertainties could affect the prices of these stocks, but Nick is confident, based on his research, that one of only several possible profit scenarios will prove true of each one at the end of the six-month period. His complete analysis is shown in **Table 16**. For example, stock ABC could lose $400, gain $800, or gain $1500. Find the expected profit (or loss) for each of the three stocks, and select Nick's optimum choice based on these calculations.

Table 16

Company ABC		Company RST		Company XYZ	
Profit or Loss x	Probability $P(x)$	Profit or Loss x	Probability $P(x)$	Profit or Loss x	Probability $P(x)$
−$400	0.2	$500	0.8	$0	0.4
800	0.5	1000	0.2	700	0.3
1500	0.3			1200	0.1
				2000	0.2

Solution

Apply the expected value formula.

ABC: −$400 \cdot (0.2) + $800 \cdot (0.5) + $1500 \cdot (0.3) = 770 ← Largest

RST: $500 \cdot (0.8) + $1000 \cdot (0.2) = 600

XYZ: $0 \cdot (0.4) + $700 \cdot (0.3) + $1200 \cdot (0.1) + $2000 \cdot (0.2) = 730

The largest expected profit is $770. Nick should invest in stock ABC. ■

Of course, by investing in stock ABC, Nick may in fact *lose* $400 over the six months. The "expected" return of $770 is only a long-run average over many identical situations. Because this particular investment situation may never occur again, you may argue that using expected values is not the best approach for Nick to use.

An optimist would ignore most possibilities and focus on the *best* that each investment could do, while a pessimist would focus on the *worst* possibility.

The first **Silver Dollar Slot Machine** was fashioned in 1929 by the Fey Manufacturing Company, San Francisco, inventors of the 3-reel, automatic payout machine (1895).

EXAMPLE 7 Choosing Stock Investments

Decide which stock of **Example 6** Nick would pick in each case.

(a) He is an optimist.   **(b)** He is a pessimist.

Solution

(a) Disregarding the probabilities, he would focus on the best case for each stock. Since ABC could return as much as $1500, RST as much as $1000, and XYZ as much as $2000, the optimum is $2000. He would buy stock XYZ (the best of the three *best* cases).

(b) In this situation, he would focus on the worst possible cases. Since ABC might return as little as −$400 (a $400 loss), RST as little as $500, and XYZ as little as $0, he would buy stock RST (the best of the three *worst* cases). ■

Business and Insurance

EXAMPLE 8 Finding Expected Lumber Revenue

Mike, a lumber wholesaler, is considering the purchase of a (railroad) carload of varied dimensional lumber. He calculates that the probabilities of reselling the load for $10,000, for $9000, and for $8000 are 0.22, 0.33, and 0.45, respectively. In order to ensure an *expected* profit of at least $3000, how much can Mike pay for the load?

Solution

The expected revenue (or income) from resales can be found as in **Table 17.**

Table 17 Expected Lumber Revenue

Income x	Probability $P(x)$	Product $x \cdot P(x)$
$10,000	0.22	$2200
9000	0.33	2970
8000	0.45	3600
		Expected revenue: $8770

In general, we have the relationship

$$\text{profit} = \text{revenue} - \text{cost}.$$

Therefore, in terms of expectations,

$$\text{expected profit} = \text{expected revenue} - \text{cost}.$$

So
$$\$3000 = \$8770 - \text{cost}$$
$$\text{cost} = \$8770 - \$3000 \quad \text{Add cost and subtract \$3000.}$$
$$\text{cost} = \$5770. \quad \text{Subtract.}$$

Mike can pay up to $5770 and still maintain an expected profit of at least $3000. ■

EXAMPLE 9 Analyzing an Insurance Decision

Jeff, a farmer, will realize a profit of $150,000 on his wheat crop, unless there is rain before harvest, in which case he will realize only $40,000. The long-term weather forecast assigns rain a probability of 0.16. (The probability of no rain is $1 - 0.16 = 0.84$.) An insurance company offers crop insurance of $150,000 against rain for a premium of $20,000. Should he buy the insurance?

Solution

In order to make a wise decision, Jeff computes his expected profit under both options: to insure and not to insure. The complete calculations are summarized in the two "expectation" **Tables 18 and 19** on the next page.

For example, if insurance is purchased and it rains, Jeff's net profit is

$$\begin{bmatrix} \text{Insurance} \\ \text{proceeds} \end{bmatrix} + \begin{bmatrix} \text{Reduced} \\ \text{crop profit} \end{bmatrix} - \begin{bmatrix} \text{Insurance} \\ \text{premium} \end{bmatrix} \quad \text{Net profit}$$

$$\$150,000 + \$40,000 - \$20,000 = \$170,000.$$

Pilots, astronauts, race car drivers, and others train in **simulators.** Some of these devices, which may be viewed as very technical, high-cost versions of video games, imitate conditions to be encountered later in the "real world." A simulator session allows estimation of the likelihood, or probability, of different responses that the learner would display under actual conditions. Repeated sessions help the learner to develop more successful responses before actual lives and equipment are put at risk.

Table 18 Expectation When Insuring

	Net Profit x	Probability $P(x)$	Product $x \cdot P(x)$
Rain	$170,000	0.16	$27,200
No rain	130,000	0.84	109,200
		Expected profit:	$136,400

Table 19 Expectation When Not Insuring

	Net Profit x	Probability $P(x)$	Product $x \cdot P(x)$
Rain	$40,000	0.16	$6400
No rain	150,000	0.84	126,000
		Expected profit:	$132,400

By comparing expected profits ($136,400 > 132,400$), we conclude that Jeff is better off buying the insurance. ∎

Simulation

An important area within probability theory is the process called **simulation.** It is possible to study a complicated, or unclear, phenomenon by *simulating*, or imitating, it with a simpler phenomenon involving the same basic probabilities. **Simulation methods** (also called **Monte Carlo methods**) require huge numbers of random digits, so computers are used to produce them. A com-

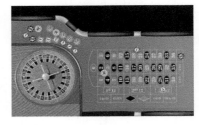

puter, however, cannot toss coins. It must use an algorithmic process, programmed into the computer, that is called a *random number generator.* It is very difficult to avoid all nonrandom patterns in the results, so the digits produced are called "pseudorandom" numbers. They must pass a battery of tests of randomness before being "approved for use."

Computer scientists and physicists have been encountering unexpected difficulties with even the most sophisticated random number generators. Therefore, these must be carefully checked along with each new simulation application proposed.

Simulating Genetic Traits

		Second Parent	
		R	**r**
First Parent	**R**	RR	Rr
	r	rR	rr

Recall from **Section 11.1** Mendel's discovery that when two Rr pea plants (red-flowered but carrying genes for both red and white flowers) are crossed, the offspring will have red flowers if an R gene is received from either parent or from both. This is because red is dominant and white is recessive. **Table 3,** reproduced here in the margin, shows that three of the four equally likely possibilities result in red-flowered offspring.

Now suppose we want to estimate the probability that three offspring in a row will have red flowers. It is much easier (and quicker) to toss coins than to cross pea plants. And the equally likely outcomes, heads and tails, can be used to simulate the transfer of the equally likely genes, R and r. If we toss two coins (say a nickel and a penny), then we can interpret the results as follows.

A:

B:

Two **possible sequences** of outcomes, when a fair die is rolled ten times in succession, are

> A: 1–1–1–1–1–1–1–1–1–1   and
> B: 6–1–2–5–5–6–3–1–5–2.

Which of the following options would you choose?

(a) Result A is more likely.
(b) Result B is more likely.
(c) They are equally likely.

Even though the specific sequences A and B are, in fact, equally likely (choice (c)), 67% (rounded) of the students in a class of college freshman business majors, not previously trained in probability theory, initially selected choice (b), as shown here.

Answer Choice	Pre-activity Survey	Post-activity Survey
(a)	4%	0%
(b)	67%	42%
(c)	29%	58%

Note that, even after a classroom session of hands-on simulation activities, 42% of the students persisted in their faulty reasoning.

(*Source: Mathematics Teacher*, September 2014, page 126.)

hh $\Rightarrow$ RR $\Rightarrow$ red gene from first parent and red gene from second parent
$\Rightarrow$ red flowers

ht $\Rightarrow$ Rr $\Rightarrow$ red gene from first parent and white gene from second parent
$\Rightarrow$ red flowers

th $\Rightarrow$ rR $\Rightarrow$ white gene from first parent and red gene from second parent
$\Rightarrow$ red flowers

tt $\Rightarrow$ rr $\Rightarrow$ white gene from first parent and white gene from second parent
$\Rightarrow$ white flowers

Although nothing is certain for a few tosses, the law of large numbers indicates that larger and larger numbers of tosses should become better and better indicators of general trends in the genetic process.

EXAMPLE 10   Simulating Genetic Processes

Toss two coins 50 times and use the results to approximate the probability that the crossing of Rr pea plants will produce three successive red-flowered offspring.

Solution

We actually tossed two coins 50 times and got the following sequence.

> th, hh, th, tt, th, hh, ht, th, ht, th, hh, hh, tt, th, hh,
> ht, ht, ht, ht, th, hh, hh, hh, tt, ht, tt, hh, ht, ht, hh, tt,
> tt, tt, th, tt, tt, hh, ht, ht, ht, hh, tt, th, hh, tt, hh, ht,
> tt, tt, tt

By the color interpretation described above, this gives the following sequence of flower colors in the offspring. (Only "both tails" gives white.)

> red–red–red–white–red–red–red–red–red–red–red–red–white–
>
> red–red–red–red–red–red–red–red–red–red–white–red–white–
>
> red–red–red–red–white–white–white–red–white–white–red–red–
>
> red–red–red–white–red–red–white–red–red–white–white–white

We now have an experimental list of 48 sets of three successive plants, the 1st, 2nd, and 3rd entries, then the 2nd, 3rd, and 4th entries, and so on. Do you see why there are 48 in all?

Now we just count up the number of these sets of three that are "red-red-red." Since there are 20 of those, our empirical probability of three successive red offspring, obtained through simulation, is $\frac{20}{48} = \frac{5}{12}$, or about 0.417. By applying the multiplication rule of probability (with all outcomes independent of one another), we find that the theoretical value is $\left(\frac{3}{4}\right)^3 = \frac{27}{64}$, or about 0.422, so our approximation obtained by simulation is very close. ∎

Simulating Other Phenomena

In human births, boys and girls are (essentially) equally likely. Therefore, an individual birth can be simulated by tossing a fair coin, letting a head correspond to a girl and a tail to a boy.

Table 20

→ 51592
77876
36500
40571
04822

→ 53033
92080
01587
36006
63698

→ 17297
22841
→ 91979
96480
74949

76896
47588
45521
02472
55184

40177
84861
86937
20931
22454

→ 73219
→ 55707
48007
→ 65191
06772

94928
→ 15709
39922
96365
14655

65587
76905
12369
54219
89329

90060
06975
05050
69774
→ 78351

11464
84086
→ 51497
12307
68009

EXAMPLE 11 Simulating Births with Coin Tossing

A sequence of 40 actual coin tosses produced the results below.

bbggb, gbbbg, gbgbb, bggbg, bbbbg, gbbgg, gbbgg, bgbbg

(For every head we have written g, for girl. For every tail, b, for boy.)

(a) How many pairs of two successive births are represented by the sequence?

(b) How many of those pairs consist of both boys?

(c) Find the empirical probability, based on this simulation, that two successive births both will be boys. Give your answer to three decimal places.

Solution

(a) Beginning with the 1st–2nd pair and ending with the 39th–40th pair, there are 39 pairs.

(b) Observing the above sequence, we count 11 pairs of two consecutive boys.

(c) Utilizing parts (a) and (b), we have $\frac{11}{39} \approx 0.282$. ∎

Another way to simulate births, and other phenomena, is with random numbers. The spinner in **Figure 14** can be used to obtain a table of random digits, as in **Table 20.** The 250 random digits generated have been grouped conveniently so that we can easily follow down a column or across a row to carry out a simulation.

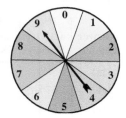

Figure 14

EXAMPLE 12 Simulating Births with Random Numbers

A couple plans to have five children. Use random number simulation to estimate the probability that they will have more than three boys.

Solution

Let each sequence of five digits, as they appear in **Table 20,** represent a family with five children, and (arbitrarily) associate odd digits with boys, even digits with girls. (Recall that 0 is even.) Verify that, of the fifty families simulated, only the ten marked with arrows have more than 3 boys (4 boys or 5 boys).

$$P(\text{more than 3 boys}) = \frac{10}{50} = 0.20 \quad \text{Estimated (empirical) probability} \quad ∎$$

The theoretical value for the probability in **Example 12** above would be the same as that obtained in **Example 4** of **Section 11.4.** It was 0.1875. Our estimate above was fairly close. In light of the law of large numbers, a larger sampling of random digits (more than 50 simulated families) would likely yield a closer approximation.

EXAMPLE 13 Simulating Card Drawing with Random Numbers

Use random number simulation to estimate the probability that two cards drawn from a standard deck, with replacement, both will be of the same suit.

Solution

Use this correspondence: 0 and 1 mean clubs, 2 and 3 mean diamonds, 4 and 5 mean hearts, 6 and 7 mean spades, 8 and 9 are disregarded. Now refer to **Table 20.**

If we (arbitrarily) use the first digit of each five-digit group, omitting 8s and 9s, we obtain the sequence

$$5-7-3-4-0-5-0-3-6-1-2-7-7-4-4-0-5-4-2-2-$$
$$7-5-4-6-0-1-3-1-6-7-1-5-0-0-6-7-1-5-1-6.$$

First digits of all groups

This 40-digit sequence of digits yields the sequence of suits shown next.

> 5 gives hearts, 7 gives spades, 3 gives diamonds, and so on.

hearts–spades–diamonds–hearts–clubs–hearts–clubs–diamonds–spades–

clubs–diamonds–spades–spades–hearts–hearts–clubs–hearts–hearts–

diamonds–diamonds–spades–hearts–hearts–spades–clubs–clubs–

diamonds–clubs–spades–spades–clubs–hearts–clubs–clubs–spades–

spades–clubs–hearts–clubs–spades

Verify that of the 39 successive pairs of suits (hearts–spades, spades–diamonds, diamonds–hearts, etc.), 9 of them are pairs of the same suit. This makes the estimated probability $\frac{9}{39} \approx 0.23$. (For comparison, the theoretical value is 0.25.) ■

FOR FURTHER THOUGHT

Assessing Randomness

Observe the two listings that follow, each of which simulates 200 tosses of a coin. Read from left to right across the top row, then from left to right across the second row, and so on, to the bottom row. One of the listings was obtained by actual tossing, and the other was made up by a student.

Make an educated guess about which is which, before reading the paragraph that follows the listings.

A

thhtt	thhtt	hthhh	tthth	httth
hthht	thttt	thhth	tthht	hthhh
thhht	thttt	thhht	hthth	htthh
htthh	htthh	thttt	hhtht	thhht
thttt	hthhh	htthh	hhtth	hthth
httth	hthhh	httht	hhttt	thhth
htthh	hthtt	tttht	hhtth	hhtth
thhtt	thhth	hthth	thhtt	htthh

B

thhth	hthhh	thttt	ttttt	thhth
hhhtt	thtth	tthth	ttttt	hhtth
hthhh	tthth	thhtt	tttth	thhth
thhht	hthhh	tttht	thhtt	hthht
hthht	hhhth	ththh	hthtt	tthht
htttt	thhhh	thhhh	hhthh	ththh
htthh	thhtt	tthth	ttttt	hthtt
tthht	ththh	hthhh	hthth	hthth

Consider the following fact of probability. When a fair coin is tossed 200 times, there is a 97% chance that there will be a run of six consecutive heads or six consecutive tails. Now look at the listings again, and based on this *almost* certain outcome, decide whether your earlier choice is correct. The answer is in the margin above. (The authors thank Marty Triola for his input into this For Further Thought feature.)

11.5 EXERCISES

1. ***Coin Tosses*** Five fair coins are tossed. Find the expected number of heads.

2. ***Card Choices*** Two cards are drawn, with replacement, from a standard 52-card deck. Find the expected number of diamonds.

Expected Winnings in a Die-rolling Game *A game consists of rolling a single fair die and pays off as follows: $3 for a 6, $2 for a 5, $1 for a 4, and no payoff otherwise.*

3. Find the expected winnings for this game.

4. What is a fair price to pay to play this game?

Expected Winnings in a Die-rolling Game *For Exercises 5 and 6, consider a game consisting of rolling a single fair die, with payoffs as follows. If an even number of spots turns up, you receive as many dollars as there are spots up. But if an odd number of spots turns up, you must pay as many dollars as there are spots up.*

5. Find the expected net winnings of this game.

6. Is this game fair, or unfair against the player, or unfair in favor of the player?

7. ***Expected Winnings in a Coin-tossing Game*** A certain game involves tossing 3 fair coins, and it pays 10¢ for 3 heads, 5¢ for 2 heads, and 3¢ for 1 head. Is 5¢ a fair price to pay to play this game? That is, does the 5¢ cost to play make the game fair?

8. ***Expected Winnings in Roulette*** In a form of roulette slightly different from that in **Example 5,** a more generous management supplies a wheel having only thirty-seven compartments, with eighteen red, eighteen black, and one zero. Find the expected net winnings if you bet $1 on red in this game.

9. ***Expected Number of Absences in a Math Class*** In a certain mathematics class, the probabilities have been empirically determined for various numbers of absentees on any given day. These values are shown in the table below. Find the expected number of absentees on a given day. Give the answer to two decimal places.

Number absent	0	1	2	3	4
Probability	0.18	0.26	0.29	0.23	0.04

10. ***Expected Profit of an Insurance Company*** An insurance company will insure a $200,000 home for its total value for an annual premium of $650. If the company spends $25 per year to service such a policy, the probability of total loss for such a home in a given year is 0.002, and you assume that either total loss or no loss will occur, what is the company's expected annual gain (or profit) on each such policy?

Profits from a College Foundation Raffle *A college foundation raises funds by selling raffle tickets for a new car worth $36,000.*

11. If 600 tickets are sold for $120 each, determine each of the following.

    (a) The expected *net* winnings of a person buying one of the tickets

    (b) The total profit for the foundation, assuming that it had to purchase the car

    (c) The total profit for the foundation, assuming that the car was donated

12. For the raffle described in **Exercise 11,** if 720 tickets are sold for $120 each, determine each of the following.

    (a) The expected *net* winnings of a person buying one of the tickets

    (b) The total profit for the foundation, assuming that it had to purchase the car

    (c) The total profit for the foundation, assuming that the car was donated

Winnings and Profits of a Raffle *Five thousand raffle tickets are sold. One first prize of $1000, two second prizes of $500 each, and three third prizes of $100 each will be awarded, with all winners selected randomly.*

13. If you purchased one ticket, what are your expected gross winnings?

14. If you purchased ten tickets, what are your expected gross winnings?

15. If the tickets were sold for $1 each, how much profit goes to the raffle sponsor?

16. ***Expected Sales at a Theater Snack Bar*** A children's theater found in a random survey that 58 customers bought one snack bar item, 49 bought two items, 31 bought three items, 4 bought four items, and 8 avoided the snack bar altogether. Use this information to find the expected number of snack bar items per customer. Round your answer to the nearest tenth.

17. ***Expected Number of Children to Attend an Amusement Park*** An amusement park, considering adding some new attractions, conducted a study over several typical days and found that, of 10,000 families entering the park, 1020 brought just one child (defined as younger than age twelve), 3370 brought two children, 3510 brought three children, 1340 brought four children, 510 brought five children, 80 brought six children, and 170 brought no children at all. Find the expected number of children per family attending this park. Round your answer to the nearest tenth.

18. ***Expected Sums of Randomly Selected Numbers*** Four cards are numbered 1 through 4. Two of these cards are chosen randomly without replacement, and the numbers on them are added. Find the expected value of this sum.

19. ***Prospects for Electronics Jobs in a City*** In a certain California city, projections for the next year are that there is a 20% chance that electronics jobs will increase by 200, a 50% chance that they will increase by 300, and a 30% chance that they will decrease by 800. What is the expected change in the number of electronics jobs in that city in the next year?

20. ***Expected Winnings in Keno*** In one version of the game *keno,* the house has a pot containing 80 balls, numbered 1 through 80. A player buys a ticket for $1 and marks on it one number from 1 to 80. The house then selects 20 of the 80 numbers at random. If the number selected by the player is among the 20 selected by the management, the player is paid $3.20. Find the expected net winnings for this game.

Contractor Decisions Based on Expected Profits *Lori, a commercial building contractor, will commit her company to one of three projects, depending on her analysis of potential profits or losses as shown here.*

Project A		Project B		Project C	
Profit or Loss x	**Probability** $P(x)$	**Profit or Loss** x	**Probability** $P(x)$	**Profit or Loss** x	**Probability** $P(x)$
$60,000	0.10	$0	0.20	$40,000	0.65
180,000	0.60	210,000	0.35	340,000	0.35
250,000	0.30	290,000	0.45		

In Exercises 21–23, determine which project Lori should choose according to each approach.

21. expected values

22. the optimist viewpoint

23. the pessimist viewpoint

24. Refer to **Examples 6 and 7.** Considering the three different approaches (expected values, optimist, and pessimist), which one seems most reasonable to you, and why?

Expected Winnings in a Game Show *A game show contestant is offered the option of receiving a computer system worth $2300 or accepting a chance to win either a luxury vacation worth $5000 or a boat worth $8000. If the second option is chosen the contestant's probabilities of winning the vacation and of winning the boat are 0.20 and 0.15, respectively.*

25. If the contestant were to turn down the computer system and go for one of the other prizes, what would be the expected winnings?

26. Purely in terms of monetary value, what is the contestant's wiser choice?

Insurance Purchase *David, the promoter of an outdoor concert, expects a gate profit of $100,000 unless it rains, which would reduce the gate profit to $30,000. The probability of rain is 0.20. For a premium of $25,000 David can purchase insurance coverage that would pay him $100,000 in case of rain.*

Use this information for Exercises 27–30.

27. Find the expected net profit when the insurance is purchased.

28. Find the expected net profit when the insurance is not purchased.

29. Based on expected values, which is David's wiser choice in this situation?

30. If you were the promoter, would you base your decision on expected values? Explain your reasoning.

Expected Values in Book Sales *Jessica, an educational publisher representative, presently has five accounts, and her manager is considering assigning her three additional accounts. The new accounts would bring potential volume to her business, and some of her present accounts have potential for growth as well. See the accompanying table.*

1	2	3	4	5	6
Account Number	**Existing Volume**	**Potential Additional Volume**	**Probability of Getting Additional Volume**	**Expected Value of Additional Volume**	**Existing Volume plus Expected Value of Additional Volume**
1	$10,000	$10,000	0.40	$4000	$14,000
2	30,000	0	—	—	30,000
3	25,000	15,000	0.20	3000	
4	35,000	0	—	—	
5	15,000	5,000	0.30		
6	0	30,000	0.10		
7	0	25,000	0.70		
8	0	45,000	0.60		

Use the preceding table to work Exercises 31–35.

31. Compute the four missing expected values in column 5.

32. Compute the six missing amounts in column 6.

33. What is Jessica's total "expected" additional volume?

34. If Jessica achieved her expected additional volume in all accounts, what would be the total volume of all her accounts?

35. If Jessica achieved her expected additional volume in all accounts, by what percentage (to the nearest tenth of a percent) would she increase her total volume?

36. *Expected Winnings in Keno* Recall that in the game keno of **Exercise 20,** the house randomly selects 20 numbers from the counting numbers 1–80. In the variation called 6-spot keno, the player pays 60¢ for his ticket and marks 6 numbers of his choice. If the 20 numbers selected by the house contain at least 3 of those chosen by the player, he gets a payoff according to this scheme.

3 of the player's numbers among the 20	$0.35
4 of the player's numbers among the 20	2.00
5 of the player's numbers among the 20	60.00
6 of the player's numbers among the 20	1250.00

Find the player's expected net winnings in this game.

[*Hint:* The four probabilities required here can be found using combinations **(Section 10.3),** the fundamental counting principle **(Section 10.2),** and the theoretical probability formula **(Section 11.1).**]

37. *Pea Plant Reproduction Simulation with Coin Tossing* Use the sequence of flower colors of **Example 10** to approximate the probability that *four* successive offspring all will have red flowers.

38. *Pea Plant Reproduction Simulation with Coin Tossing* Explain why, in **Example 10,** fifty tosses of the coins produced only 48 sets of three successive offspring.

39. *Boy and Girl Simulation with Random Numbers* Use **Table 20** to simulate fifty families with three children. Let 0–4 correspond to boys and 5–9 to girls, and use the middle three digits of the 5-digit groupings (159, 787, 650, and so on). Estimate the probability of exactly two boys in a family of three children. Compare with the theoretical probability, which is $\frac{3}{8} = 0.375$.

40. *Empirical Probability of Successive Girls* Simulate 40 births by tossing coins yourself, and obtain an empirical probability for two successive girls.

41. *Likelihoods of Girl and Boy Births* Should the probability of two successive girl births be any different from that of two successive boy births?

One-and-One Free Throw Shooting *In Exercises 88–90 of Section 11.3, Christine, who had a 70% foul-shooting record, had probabilities of scoring 0, 1, or 2 points of 0.30, 0.21, and 0.49, respectively.*

Use **Table 20** *(with digits 0–6 representing hit and 7–9 representing miss) to simulate 50 one-and-one shooting opportunities for Christine. Begin at the top left (5, 7, 3, etc., to the bottom), then move to the second column (1, 7, 6, etc.), going until 50 one-and-one opportunities are obtained. (Some "opportunities" involve one shot and one random digit, while others involve two shots and two random digits.) Keep a tally of the numbers of times 0, 1, and 2 points are scored.*

Number of Points	**Tally**
0	
1	
2	

From the tally, find the empirical probability (to two decimal places) of each event.

42. no points   **43.** 1 point

44. 2 points

Simulation with Coin Tossing *A coin was actually tossed 200 times, producing the following sequence of outcomes. Read from left to right across the top row, then from left to right across the second row, and so on, to the bottom row.*

```
hhtht   ththh   ttttt   tthtt   hthhh
thtth   hhhhh   htthh   hthht   hhtth
ththt   hhttt   hhhhh   tthth   ththh
thhhh   hhhht   thtth   thhth   thhtt
thhtt   thttt   hthht   thhht   htttt
htthh   htttt   tttht   tttth   ththh
hhhhh   tthht   tthht   hthtt   hhhht
hthtt   htttt   hhtth   ttthh   thtth
```

Find the empirical probability of each of the following. Round to three decimal places.

45. two consecutive heads

46. two consecutive tails

47. three consecutive tosses of the same outcome

48. six consecutive tosses of the same outcome

Path of a Random Walk Using a Die and a Coin *Exercises 49–56 of Section 11.4 illustrated a simple version of the idea of a "random walk." Atomic particles released in nuclear fission also move in a random fashion. During World War II, John von Neumann and Stanislaw Ulam used simulation with random numbers to study particle motion in nuclear reactions. Von Neumann coined the name "Monte Carlo" for the methods used.*

The figure suggests a model for random motion in two dimensions. Assume that a particle moves in a series of 1-unit "jumps," each one in a random direction, any one of 12 equally likely possibilities. One way to choose directions is to roll a fair die and toss a fair coin. The die determines one of the directions 1–6, coupled with heads on the coin. Tails on the coin reverses the direction of the die, so that the die coupled with tails gives directions 7–12. So 3h (meaning 3 with the die and heads with the coin) gives direction 3; 3t gives direction 9 (opposite to 3); and so on.

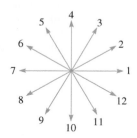

49. Simulate the motion described above with 10 rolls of a die and tosses of a coin. Draw the 10-jump path you get. Make your drawing accurate enough so you can estimate (by measuring) how far from its starting point the particle ends up.

50. Repeat the experiment of **Exercise 49** four more times. Measure distance from start to finish for each of the 5 "random trips." Add these 5 distances and divide the sum by 5, to arrive at an "expected net distance" for such a trip.

In Exercises 51 and 52, consider another two-dimensional random walk governed by the following conditions.

- *Start out from a given street corner, and travel one block north. At each intersection:*

- *Turn left with probability $\frac{1}{6}$.*

- *Go straight with probability $\frac{2}{6}\left(=\frac{1}{3}\right)$.*

- *Turn right with probability $\frac{3}{6}\left(=\frac{1}{2}\right)$.*

   (Never turn around.)

51. *A Random Walk Using a Random Number Table* Use **Table 20** to simulate this random walk. For every 1 encountered in the table, turn left and proceed for another block. For every 2 or 3, go straight and proceed for another block. For every 4, 5, or 6, turn right and proceed for another block. Disregard all other digits—that is, 0s, 7s, 8s, and 9s. (Do you see how this scheme satisfies the probabilities given above?) This time, begin at the upper right corner of the table, running down the column 2, 6, 0, and so on, to the bottom. When this column of digits is used up, stop the "walk." Describe, in terms of distance and direction, where you have ended up relative to your starting point.

52. *A Random Walk Using a Fair Die* Explain how a fair die could be used to simulate this random walk.

Buffon's Needle Problem *The following problem was posed by Georges Louis Leclerc, Comte de Buffon (1707–1788) in his* Histoire Naturelle *in 1777. A large plane area is ruled with equidistant parallel lines, the distance between two consecutive lines of the series being "a". A thin needle of length*

$$\ell < a$$

is tossed randomly onto the plane. What is the probability that the needle will intersect one of these lines?

The answer to this problem is found using integral calculus, and the probability p is shown to be $p = \frac{2\ell}{\pi a}$. Solving for π gives the formula

$$\pi = \frac{2\ell}{pa},$$

which can be used to approximate the value of π experimentally. This was first observed by Pierre Simon de Laplace, and such an experiment was carried out by Johann Wolf, a professor of astronomy at Bern, in about 1850. (Source: Burton, David M. History of Mathematics: An Introduction. *Wm. C. Brown, 1995.)*

53. On a sheet of paper, draw a series of parallel lines evenly spaced across it. Then find a thin needle, or needlelike object, with a length less than the distance between adjacent parallel lines on the paper.

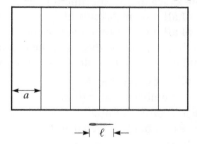

Carry out the following steps in order.

   (a) Measure and record the distance between lines (a) and the length of the needle (ℓ), using the same units for both.

   (b) Drop the needle onto the paper 100 times. Determine whether the needle "hits" a line or not, and keep a tally of hits and misses.

   (c) Now calculate $p = (\text{number of hits})/100$. Is this probability value theoretical or empirical?

   (d) Enter the calculated value of p and the measured values of a and ℓ into the formula to obtain an approximation for π. Round this value to four decimal places.

   (e) The correct value of π, to four decimal places, is 3.1416. What value did your simulation give? How far off is it?

54. *Dynamic Simulation* See www.metablake.com/pi.swf for a dynamic illustration of the Buffon Needle Problem. (One of the authors of this text used 21,734 iterations, to get 13,805 intersections, for an empirical value of π to be 3.148569358927.)

CHAPTER 11 | SUMMARY

KEY TERMS

11.1
deterministic phenomenon
random phenomenon
probability
experiment
outcome
sample space
event
theoretical probability

empirical probability
law of large numbers
  (law of averages)
odds in favor
odds against

11.2
mutually exclusive events
random variable
probability distribution

11.3
conditional probability of
  B given A
independent events

11.4
Bernoulli trials
binomial probability
  distribution

11.5
expected value
  (mathematical expectation)
simulation
simulation methods
  (Monte Carlo methods)
random number generator

NEW SYMBOLS

$P(E)$ probability of event E

$P(B|A)$ probability of event B, given that event A has occurred

$E(x)$ expected value of random variable x

TEST YOUR WORD POWER

See how well you have learned the vocabulary in this chapter.

1. The **sample space** of an experiment is
   A. the set of all possible events of the experiment.
   B. the set of all possible outcomes of the experiment.
   C. the number of possible events of the experiment.
   D. the number of possible outcomes of the experiment.

2. The **probability of an event** E
   A. must be a number greater than 1.
   B. may be a negative number.
   C. must be a number between 0 and 1, inclusive of both.
   D. cannot be 0.

3. If E is an event, the **probability of "not E"** must be
   A. 0.
   B. equal to 1 plus the probability of E.
   C. equal to 1 minus the probability of E.
   D. less than the probability of E.

4. A **probability distribution**
   A. shows all possible values of a random variable, along with the probabilities that those values will occur.
   B. is a listing of empirical values of an experiment.
   C. is a number between 0 and 1, inclusive of both.
   D. is an application of the distributive property to probability.

ANSWERS
1. B **2.** C **3.** C **4.** A

QUICK REVIEW

Concepts	Examples

11.1 Basic Concepts

Theoretical Probability Formula

If all outcomes in a sample space S are equally likely, and E is an event within that sample space, then the **theoretical probability** of event E is given by the following formula.

$$P(E) = \frac{\text{number of favorable outcomes}}{\text{total number of outcomes}} = \frac{n(E)}{n(S)}$$

The spinner shown here is spun twice. Find the probability that both spins yield the same number.

The sample space S is $\{(1,1), (1,2),$ $(1,3), (2,1), (2,2), (2,3), (3,1),$ $(3,2)(3,3)\}$. Of these, three indicate the same number: $E = \{(1,1), (2,2), (3,3)\}$. Therefore,

$$P(E) = \frac{n(E)}{n(S)} = \frac{3}{9} = \frac{1}{3}.$$

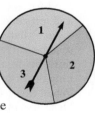

Concepts	Examples
Empirical Probability Formula If E is an event that may happen when an experiment is performed, then an **empirical probability** of event E is given by the following formula. $$P(E) = \frac{\text{number of times event } E \text{ occurred}}{\text{number of times the experiment was performed}}$$	A coin was actually tossed 100 times, producing the following sequence of outcomes. If E represents two consecutive tosses of heads (h), what is the empirical probability of E? thhht thhht hthth thhhh thttt ttttt tthht htthh tttth tttth hhthh thttt thttt thtth thhht hthhh ttthh hhhht ththt hhhht
Law of Large Numbers (Law of Averages) As an experiment is repeated more and more times, the proportion of outcomes favorable to any particular event will tend to come closer and closer to the theoretical probability of that event.	There are 99 cases of two consecutive tosses, and 24 of them show both heads, so $$P(E) = \frac{24}{99} \approx 0.242. \quad \text{Empirical probability}$$ In the experiment above, what is the theoretical probability that two consecutive heads will occur? How does the empirical result compare? The theoretical probability is $\frac{1}{4} = 0.25$. This is very close to 0.242, the empirical value obtained above.
Odds If all outcomes in a sample space are equally likely, a of them are favorable to the event E, and the remaining b outcomes are unfavorable to E, then the **odds in favor** of E are a to b, and the **odds against** E are b to a.	A single card is drawn from a standard deck of 52 cards. **(a)** What is the probability that the card is a queen? There are 4 queens (and thus 48 non-queens). $$P(\text{queen}) = \frac{4}{52} = \frac{1}{13} \quad \text{Probability of a queen}$$
Converting between Probability and Odds Let E be an event. • If $P(E) = \frac{a}{b}$, then the odds in favor of E are a to $(b - a)$. • If the odds in favor of E are a to b, then $P(E) = \frac{a}{a+b}$.	**(b)** What are the odds in favor of drawing a queen? 4 to 48, or 1 to 12 Odds in favor of a queen **(c)** What are the odds against drawing a queen? 48 to 4, or 12 to 1 Odds against a queen

11.2 Events Involving "Not" and "Or"

Properties of Probability Let E be an event within the sample space S. That is, E is a subset of S. Then the following properties hold. **1. $0 \le P(E) \le 1$** (The probability of an event is a number from 0 through 1, inclusive.) **2. $P(\varnothing) = 0$** (The probability of an impossible event is 0.) **3. $P(S) = 1$** (The probability of a certain event is 1.)	If 6 fair coins are tossed, what is the probability that at most 5 will show tails? There are $2^6 = 64$ possible outcomes. Only one of them, tttttt, does not show at most 5 tails, so there are $64 - 1 = 63$ favorable outcomes. $$P(\text{at most 5 tails}) = \frac{64 - 1}{64} = \frac{63}{64}$$

Concepts	Examples
Probability of a Complement (for the Event "Not E")	If a single card is drawn from a standard 52-card deck, find the probability that it is the following.
The probability that an event E will *not* occur is equal to 1 minus the probability that it will occur.	**(a)** a heart or a black card **(b)** a heart or a 6
$$P(\text{not } E) = 1 - P(E)$$	$P(\text{heart or black}) = P(\text{heart}) + P(\text{black})$ These are mutually exclusive.

Mutually Exclusive Events

Two events A and B are **mutually exclusive events** if they have no outcomes in common. Mutually exclusive events cannot occur simultaneously.

$$= \frac{13}{52} + \frac{26}{52}$$

$$= \frac{39}{52}$$

Addition Rule of Probability (for the Event "A or B")

If A and B are any two events, then the following holds.

$$= \frac{3}{4}$$

$$P(A \text{ or } B) = P(A) + P(B) - P(A \text{ and } B)$$

$P(\text{heart or a 6}) = P(\text{heart}) + P(6) - P(6 \text{ of hearts})$ These are not mutually exclusive.

If A and B are mutually exclusive, then the following holds.

$$= \frac{13}{52} + \frac{4}{52} - \frac{1}{52}$$

$$P(A \text{ or } B) = P(A) + P(B)$$

$$= \frac{16}{52}$$

$$= \frac{4}{13}$$

11.3 Conditional Probability and Events Involving "And"

From the sample space

$$S = \{1, 2, 3, 4, 5, 6, 7, 8, 9, 10, 11, 12\},$$

a single number is to be selected randomly. Find each probability given the events

Conditional Probability

The probability of event B, computed on the assumption that event A has happened, is the **conditional probability of B given A** and is denoted $P(B|A)$.

A: The selected number is even.

B: The selected number is a multiple of 3.

Conditional Probability Formula

The **conditional probability of B given A** is calculated as

(a) $P(B)$

$B = \{3, 6, 9, 12\}$, so

$$P(B|A) = \frac{P(A \cap B)}{P(A)} = \frac{P(A \text{ and } B)}{P(A)}.$$

$$P(B) = \frac{n(B)}{n(S)} = \frac{4}{12} = \frac{1}{3}.$$

(b) $P(A \text{ and } B)$

$A = \{2, 4, 6, 8, 10, 12\}$, so $A \cap B = \{6, 12\}$.

Independent Events

Two events A and B are **independent events** if knowledge about the occurrence of one of them has no effect on the probability of the other one occurring. A and B are independent if

$$P(A \text{ and } B) = P(A \cap B) = \frac{2}{12} = \frac{1}{6}$$

(c) $P(B|A)$ Are A and B independent?

$$P(B|A) = P(B), \quad \text{or, equivalently,} \quad P(A|B) = P(A).$$

In the reduced sample space of A, 2 of the 6 outcomes belong to B.

$$P(B|A) = \frac{2}{6} = \frac{1}{3}$$

Multiplication Rule of Probability (for the Event "A and B")

If A and B are *any two events*, then

$$P(A \text{ and } B) = P(A) \cdot P(B|A).$$

Equivalently, $P(B|A) = \dfrac{P(A \cap B)}{P(A)} = \dfrac{\frac{1}{6}}{\frac{1}{2}} = \dfrac{1}{6} \cdot \dfrac{2}{1} = \dfrac{1}{3}$.

If A and B are *independent*, then

$$P(A \text{ and } B) = P(A) \cdot P(B).$$

Because $P(B) = P(B|A)$, A and B are independent.

Concepts	Examples

11.4 Binomial Probability

Binomial Probability Formula

When n independent repeated trials occur, where

p = probability of success and q = probability of failure

with p and q (where $q = 1 - p$) remaining constant throughout all n trials, the probability of exactly x successes is calculated as follows.

$$P(x) = {}_nC_x p^x q^{n-x} = \frac{n!}{x!(n-x)!} p^x q^{n-x}$$

A die is rolled ten times. Find the probability that exactly four of the tosses result in a 3.

The probability of rolling a 3 on one roll is $p = \frac{1}{6}$, so the probability of not rolling a 3 is

$$q = 1 - \frac{1}{6} = \frac{5}{6}.$$

Here $n = 10$ and $x = 4$.

$$P(\text{exactly four 3s}) = {}_{10}C_4 \left(\frac{1}{6}\right)^4 \left(\frac{5}{6}\right)^{10-4}$$

$$= 210\left(\frac{1}{1296}\right)\left(\frac{15,625}{46,656}\right)$$

$$\approx 0.054$$

11.5 Expected Value and Simulation

Expected Value

If a random variable x can have any of the values $x_1, x_2, x_3, \ldots, x_n$, and the corresponding probabilities of these values occurring are $P(x_1), P(x_2), P(x_3), \ldots, P(x_n)$, then $E(x)$, the **expected value of x,** is calculated as follows.

$$E(x) = x_1 \cdot P(x_1) + x_2 \cdot P(x_2) + x_3 \cdot P(x_3)$$
$$+ \cdots + x_n \cdot P(x_n)$$

In a certain lottery, a player chooses four digits in a specific order. The leading digit may be 0, so a number such as 0460 is legitimate. A four-digit sequence is randomly chosen, and any player matching that selection receives a payoff of $10,000. Find the expected gross winnings.

The probability of selecting the correct four digits is $\left(\frac{1}{10}\right)^4 = \frac{1}{10,000}$, and the probability of not selecting them is $1 - \left(\frac{1}{10}\right)^4 = \frac{9999}{10,000}$. The expected gross winnings are

$$E(\text{gross winnings}) = \$10,000 \cdot \frac{1}{10,000} + \$0 \cdot \frac{9999}{10,000}$$

$$= \$1.00. \quad \text{A fair cost to play this game}$$

CHAPTER 11   TEST

Numbers from Sets of Digits   *Two numbers are randomly selected without replacement from the set*

$$\{1, 2, 3, 4, 5\}.$$

Find the probability of each event.

1. Both numbers are even.

2. Both numbers are prime.

3. The sum of the two numbers is odd.

4. The product of the two numbers is odd.

Days Off for Pizza Parlor Workers   *The manager of a pizza parlor (which operates seven days a week) allows each of three employees to select one day off next week. Assuming the selection is done randomly and independently, find the probability of each event.*

5. All three select different days.

6. All three select the same day, given that all three select a day beginning with the same letter.

7. Exactly two of them select the same day.

Genetics of Cystic Fibrosis *The chart represents genetic transmission of cystic fibrosis. C denotes a normal gene, and c denotes a cystic fibrosis gene. (Normal is dominant.) Both parents in this case are Cc, which means that they inherited one of each gene. Therefore, they are both carriers but do not have the disease.*

		Second Parent	
		C	**c**
First	**C**		Cc
Parent	**c**		

8. Complete the chart, showing all four equally likely gene arrangements.

9. Find the probability that a child of these parents will also be a carrier without the disease.

10. What are the odds that a child of these parents actually will have cystic fibrosis?

Drawing Cards *A single card is chosen at random from a standard 52-card deck. Find the odds against its being each of the following.*

11. a heart   **12.** a red queen

13. a king or a black face card

Selecting Committees *A three-member committee is selected randomly from a group consisting of three men and two women.*

14. Let *x* denote the number of men on the committee, and complete the probability distribution table.

x	*P(x)*
0	0
1	
2	
3	

15. Find the probability that the committee members are not all men.

16. Find the expected number of men on the committee.

Rolling Dice *A pair of dice are rolled. Find the following.*

17. the probability of "doubles" (the same number on both dice)

18. the odds in favor of a sum greater than 2

19. the odds against a sum of "7 or 11"

20. the probability of a sum that is even and less than 5

Making Par in Golf *Ted has a 0.78 chance of making par on each hole of golf that he plays. Today he plans to play just three holes. Find the probability of each event. Round answers to three decimal places.*

21. He makes par on all three holes.

22. He makes par on exactly two of the three holes.

23. He makes par on at least one of the three holes.

24. He makes par on the first and third holes but not on the second.

Card Choices *Two cards are drawn, without replacement, from a standard 52-card deck. Find the probability of each event.*

25. Both cards are red.

26. Both cards are the same color.

27. The second card is a queen, given that the first card is an ace.

28. The first card is a face card and the second is black.

29. **Gender in Sequences of Babies** Assuming boy and girl babies are equally likely, find the probability that a family with three children will have exactly two boys.

30. **Simulation of Pea Plant Reproduction with Coin Tossing** Use the sequence of flower colors in **Example 10** of **Section 11.5** to approximate, to three decimal places, the probability that three successive offspring will all have white flowers.

Simulation with Coin Tossing *A coin was actually tossed 100 times, producing the following sequence of outcomes. Read from left to right across the top row, then from left to right across the second row, and so on, to the bottom row.*

tttth	ththh	htttt	hhhth	ththh
hhhth	httht	hhhht	thttt	thtth
htttth	hhhhh	hhhhh	tttht	ttttt
htthh	tttth	htttth	tthhh	tthhh

Find, to three decimal places, the empirical probability of each event.

31. Two consecutive tails (tt) occur.

32. Three consecutive heads (hhh) occur.

ANSWERS TO SELECTED EXERCISES

CHAPTER 1 THE ART OF PROBLEM SOLVING

1.1 Exercises (pages 6–8)

1. inductive **3.** deductive **5.** deductive **7.** inductive
9. deductive **11.** deductive **13.** inductive
15. inductive **17.** Answers will vary. **19.** 21 **21.** 3072
23. 63 **25.** $\frac{11}{12}$ **27.** 216 **29.** 52 **31.** 5
33. One such list is 10, 20, 30, 40, 50, ...
35. $(98{,}765 \times 9) + 3 = 888{,}888$
37. $3367 \times 15 = 50{,}505$
39. $33{,}334 \times 33{,}334 = 1{,}111{,}155{,}556$
41. $3 + 6 + 9 + 12 + 15 = \frac{15(6)}{2}$
43. $5(6) + 5(36) + 5(216) + 5(1296) + 5(7776)$
$= 6(7776 - 1)$
45. $\frac{1}{2} + \frac{1}{4} + \frac{1}{8} + \frac{1}{16} + \frac{1}{32} = 1 - \frac{1}{32}$ **47.** 20,100 **49.** 320,400
51. 15,400 **53.** 2550 **55.** 1 (These are the numbers of
chimes a clock rings, starting with 12 o'clock, if it rings the
number of hours on the hour, and 1 chime on the half-hour.)
57. (a) Answers will vary. **(b)** The middle digit is
always 9, and the sum of the first and third digits is always
9 (considering 0 as the first digit if the difference has only
two digits). **(c)** Answers will vary.
59. 142,857; 285,714; 428,571; 571,428; 714,285; 857,142.
Each result consists of the same six digits, but in a different
order. $142{,}857 \times 7 = 999{,}999$

1.2 Exercises (pages 15–19)

1. arithmetic; 56 **3.** geometric; 1215 **5.** neither
7. geometric; 8 **9.** neither **11.** arithmetic; 22
13. 79 **15.** 450 **17.** 4032 **19.** 32,758 **21.** 57; 99
23. $(4321 \times 9) - 1 = 38{,}888$ **25.** $999{,}999 \times 4 = 3{,}999{,}996$
27. $21^2 - 15^2 = 6^3$ **29.** $5^2 - 4^2 = 5 + 4$
31. $1 + 5 + 9 + 13 = 4 \times 7$ **33.** 45,150 **35.** 228,150
37. 2601 **39.** 250,000 **41.** $S = n(n + 1)$
43. Answers will vary. **45.** *row 1:* 28, 36; *row 2:* 36,
49, 64; *row 3:* 35, 51, 70, 92; *row 4:* 28, 45, 66, 91, 120;
row 5: 18, 34, 55, 81, 112, 148; *row 6:* 8, 21, 40, 65, 96,
133, 176
47. $8(1) + 1 = 9 = 3^2; 8(3) + 1 = 25 = 5^2;$
$8(6) + 1 = 49 = 7^2; 8(10) + 1 = 81 = 9^2$
49. The pattern is 1, 0, 1, 0, 1, 0, ...

51.

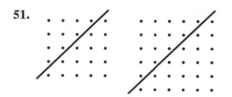

53. 256 **55.** 117 **57.** 235 **59.** $N_n = \frac{n(7n - 5)}{2}$
61. a square number **63.** a perfect cube **65.** 42
67. 419 **69.** $\frac{101}{2}$ **71.** 2048 **73.** $\frac{1}{2048}$ **75.** $\frac{5}{2048}$ **77.** 495
79. To find any entry within the body of the triangle, add
the two entries immediately to the left and to the right in the
row above it. For example, in the sixth row, $10 = 4 + 6$.
The next three rows of Pascal's triangle are as follows.

$$\begin{array}{ccccccccccccc} & & 1 & & 6 & & 15 & & 20 & & 15 & & 6 & & 1 \\ & 1 & & 7 & & 21 & & 35 & & 35 & & 21 & & 7 & & 1 \\ 1 & & 8 & & 28 & & 56 & & 70 & & 56 & & 28 & & 8 & & 1 \end{array}$$

81. The sums along the diagonals are 1, 1, 2, 3, 5, 8. These
are the first six terms of the Fibonacci sequence.

1.3 Exercises (pages 25–30)

1. 50 **3.** 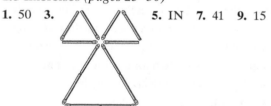 **5.** IN **7.** 41 **9.** 15

11. 32 **13.** 0 (The product of the first and last digits is
the two-digit number between them.) **15.** 11
17. infinitely many (Any line through the center of the
square will do this.) **19.** 48.5 in. **21.** 42 **23.** 6
25. If you multiply the two digits in the numbers in the
first row, you will get the second row of numbers. The
second row of numbers is a pattern of two numbers
(8 and 24) repeating. **27.** 59 **29.** A **31.** You should
choose a sock from the box labeled *red and green socks*.
Because it is mislabeled, it contains only red socks or only
green socks, determined by the sock you choose. If the
sock is green, relabel this box *green socks*. Since the other
two boxes were mislabeled, switch the remaining label to
the other box and place the label that says *red and green
socks* on the unlabeled box. No other choice guarantees
a correct relabeling because you can remove only one
sock. **33.** D

35. One example of a solution follows.

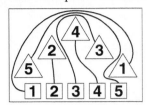

37. Here is one solution.   **39.** D   **41.** $\frac{1}{3}$

43. 90   **45.** 55 mph   **47.** 07   **49.** 437   **51.** 3
53. 21 stamps (5 five-cent stamps and 16 eight-cent stamps)   **55.** 3 socks   **57.** 6   **59.** the nineteenth day
61. 1967   **63.** Eve has $5, and Adam has $7.

65.
$$\begin{array}{r} 4\ 0\ 2 \\ \times\ \ \ \ \ 3\ 9 \\ \hline 1\ 5,\ 6\ 7\ 8 \end{array}$$

67.

6	12	7	9
1	15	4	14
11	5	10	8
16	2	13	3

69. 25 pitches (The visiting team's pitcher retires 24 consecutive batters through the first eight innings, using only one pitch per batter. His team does not score either. Going into the bottom of the ninth tied 0–0, the first batter for the home team hits his first pitch for a home run. The pitcher threw 25 pitches and loses the game by a score of 1–0.)   **71.** Q   **73.** Here is one solution.

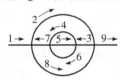

75. 6 ways   **77.** 86 cm   **79.** Dan (36) is married to Jessica (29); James (30) is married to Cathy (31).

81. 6

	X	X
X		X
X	X	

One of the
possibilities

1.4 Exercises *(pages 39–41)*
1. 43.8   **3.** 2.3589   **5.** 7.48   **7.** 7.1289   **9.** 6340.338097
11. 1   **13.** 1.061858759   **15.** 2.221441469
17. 3.141592653   **19.** 0.7782717162   **21.** yes
23. positive   **25.** 1   **27.** the same as   **29.** 0
31. negative   **33.** Answers will vary.

35. Answers will vary.   **37.** 63   **39.** 14   **41.** B   **43.** A
45. D   **47.** 6%   **49.** about 4.5 million
51. 2007, 2008, 2009, 2010   **53.** 2004: about 171 billion lb; 2010: about 193 billion lb   **55.** 2009 to 2010; about 1.5 million   **57.** The number of cars imported each year was decreasing.

Chapter 1 Test *(pages 45–46)*
1. inductive   **2.** deductive   **3.** 31
4. $65,359,477,124,183 \times 68 = 4,444,444,444,444,444$
5. 351   **6.** 31,375   **7.** 65; $65 = 1 + 7 + 13 + 19 + 25$
8. 1, 8, 21, 40, 65, 96, 133, 176; The pattern is 1, 0, 1, 0, 1, 0, 1, 0, ...   **9.** The first two terms are both 1. Each term after the second is found by adding the two previous terms. The next term is 34.   **10.** $\frac{1}{4}$ **11.** 9   **12.** 35
13. Answers will vary. One possible solution is $1 + 2 + 3 - 4 + 5 + 6 + 78 + 9 + 0 = 100$.
14. 108 in., or 9 ft   **15.** 3   **16.** The sum of the digits is always 9.   **17.** 9.907572861 (Answers may vary due to the model of calculator used.)   **18.** 34.328125   **19.** B
20. (a) between 2003 and 2004, 2004 and 2005, and 2005 and 2006   **(b)** The unemployment rate was increasing.
(c) 2008: 5.8%; 2009: 9.3%; increase: 3.5%

CHAPTER 2 THE BASIC CONCEPTS OF SET THEORY

2.1 Exercises *(pages 52–54)*
1. F   **3.** E   **5.** B   **7.** H   **9.** {1, 2, 3, 4, 5, 6}
11. {0, 1, 2, 3, 4}   **13.** {6, 7, 8, 9, 10, 11, 12, 13, 14}
15. {2, 4, 8, 16, 32, 64, 128, 256}   **17.** {0, 2, 4, 6, 8, 10}
19. {220, 240, 260, . . . }   **21.** {Lake Erie, Lake Huron, Lake Michigan, Lake Ontario, Lake Superior}
23. $\left\{1, \frac{1}{2}, \frac{1}{3}, \frac{1}{4}, \frac{1}{5}, \ldots\right\}$ **25.** {(0, 5), (3, 4), (4, 3), (5, 0)}
In Exercises 27 and 29, there are other ways to describe the sets.   **27.** {$x \mid x$ is a rational number}   **29.** {$x \mid x$ is an odd natural number less than 76}   **31.** the set of single-digit integers   **33.** the set of states of the United States
35. finite   **37.** infinite   **39.** infinite   **41.** infinite   **43.** 8
45. 500   **47.** 26   **49.** 39   **51.** 28   **53.** Answers will vary.
55. well defined   **57.** not well defined   **59.** $\notin$ **61.** $\in$
63. $\in$ **65.** false   **67.** false   **69.** true   **71.** true
73. false   **75.** true   **77.** true   **79.** true
81. false   **83.** true   **85.** Answers will vary.
87. {2} and {3, 4} (Other examples are possible.)
89. {a, b} and {a, c} (Other examples are possible.)

91. (a) {Bernice, Heather, Marcy}, {Bernice, Heather, Natalie}, {Bernice, Susan, Marcy}, {Bernice, Susan, Natalie}, {Heather, Susan, Marcy}, {Heather, Susan, Natalie}
(b) {Bernice, Marcy, Natalie}, {Heather, Marcy, Natalie}, {Susan, Marcy, Natalie}   **(c)** {Bernice, Heather, Susan}

2.2 Exercises *(pages 58–60)*

1. D   **3.** B   **5.** ⊄   **7.** ⊆   **9.** ⊆   **11.** ⊄   **13.** both
15. ⊆   **17.** both   **19.** neither   **21.** true   **23.** false
25. true   **27.** false   **29.** true   **31.** false   **33.** true
35. false   **37. (a)** 64   **(b)** 63   **39. (a)** 32   **(b)** 31   **41.** ∅
43. {5, 7, 9, 10}   **45.** {Higher cost, Lower cost, Educational, More time to see the sights in California, Less time to see the sights in California, Cannot visit friends along the way, Can visit friends along the way}
47. {Higher cost, More time to see the sights in California, Cannot visit friends along the way}
49. ∅   **51.** {A, B, C, D, E} (All are present.)
53. {A, B, C}, {A, B, D}, {A, B, E}, {A, C, D}, {A, C, E}, {A, D, E}, {B, C, D}, {B, C, E}, {B, D, E}, {C, D, E}   **55.** {A}, {B}, {C}, {D}, {E}   **57.** 32
59. $2^{25} - 1 = 33{,}554{,}431$ **61. (a)** 15   **(b)** 16; It is now possible to select *no* bills.
63. (a) s **(b)** s **(c)** $2s$ **(d)** Adding one more element will always double the number of subsets, so the expression 2^n is true in general.

2.3 Exercises *(pages 69–71)*

1. B   **3.** A   **5.** E   **7.** {a, c}   **9.** {a, b, c, d, e, f}
11. {b, d, f}   **13.** {d, f}   **15.** {a, b, c, e, g}   **17.** {e, g}
19. {a}   **21.** {e, g}   **23.** {d, f}
In Exercises 25–28, there may be other acceptable descriptions.   **25.** the set of all elements that either are in A, or are not in B and not in C **27.** the set of all elements that are in C but not in B, or are in A **29.** {e, h, c, l, b}
31. {e, h, c, l, b}   **33.** the set of all tax returns filed in 2014 without itemized deductions   **35.** the set of all tax returns with itemized deductions or showing business income, but not selected for audit   **37.** always true   **39.** not always true
41. (a) {1, 3, 5, 2}   **(b)** {1, 2, 3, 5}   **(c)** For any sets X and Y, $X \cup Y = Y \cup X$.   **43. (a)** {1, 3, 5, 2, 4}
(b) {1, 3, 5, 2, 4}   **(c)** For any sets X, Y, and Z, $X \cup (Y \cup Z) = (X \cup Y) \cup Z$.   **45.** true   **47.** true
49. $A \times B = \{(d, p), (d, i), (d, g), (o, p), (o, i), (o, g), (g, p), (g, i), (g, g)\}$; $B \times A = \{(p, d), (p, o), (p, g), (i, d), (i, o), (i, g), (g, d), (g, o), (g, g)\}$
51. $n(A \times B) = 210$; $n(B \times A) = 210$ **53.** 6

55.

57.

$A' \cup B$

59.

$B \cap A'$

61.

$B' \cap B = \varnothing$

63.

$B' \cup (A' \cap B')$

65.

67.

$(A \cap B) \cap C$

69.

$(A' \cap B') \cap C$

71.

$(A \cap B') \cap C'$

73. $A' \cap B'$,   or $(A \cup B)'$
75. $(A \cup B) \cap (A \cap B)'$, or $(A \cup B) - (A \cap B)$, or $(A - B) \cup (B - A)$
77. $(A \cap B) \cup (A \cap C)$, or $A \cap (B \cup C)$

79. $A \cap B = \varnothing$ **81.** This statement is true for any set A.
83. $B \subseteq A$ **85.** always true   **87.** not always true
89. Answers will vary.

2.4 Exercises *(pages 75–78)*

1. (a) 5   **(b)** 7   **(c)** 0   **(d)** 2   **(e)** 8   **3. (a)** 1   **(b)** 3
(c) 4   **(d)** 0   **(e)** 2   **(f)** 8   **(g)** 2   **(h)** 6   **5.** 21
7. 7   **9.** 35

11.

13.

15.

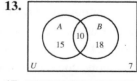

17.

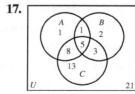

19. (a) 2 **(b)** 4 **21. (a)** 25 **(b)** 30 **(c)** 2 **(d)** 10
(e) 19 **(f)** 57 **23. (a)** 8 **(b)** 26 **(c)** 60 **25. (a)** 500
(b) 91 **27. (a)** 31 **(b)** 24 **(c)** 11 **(d)** 45 **29. (a)** 1
(b) 1, 2, 3, 4, 5, 6, 7, 8, 9, 10, 11, 12, 13, 14, 15 **(c)** 1, 2, 3, 4,
5, 9, 11 **(d)** 5, 8, 13 **31. (a)** 9 **(b)** 9 **(c)** 20 **(d)** 20
(e) 27 **(f)** 15 **33.** Answers will vary.

Chapter 2 Test *(page 82)*

1. {a, b, c, d, e} **2.** {a, b, d} **3.** {c, f, g, h} **4.** {a, c}
5. false **6.** true **7.** true **8.** true **9.** false **10.** false
11. true **12.** true **13.** 16 **14.** 15
Answers may vary in Exercises 15–18. **15.** the set of odd
integers between −4 and 10 **16.** the set of days of the week
17. $\{x \,|\, x$ is a negative integer$\}$ **18.** $\{x \,|\, x$ is a multiple of 8
between 20 and 90$\}$ **19.** ⊆ **20.** neither

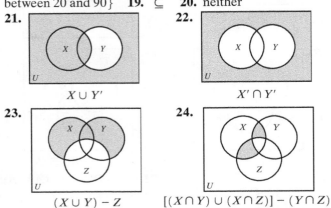

21. $X \cup Y'$
22. $X' \cap Y'$
23. $(X \cup Y) - Z$
24. $[(X \cap Y) \cup (X \cap Z)] - (Y \cap Z)$

25. Answers will vary. **26.** {Electric razor}
27. {Adding machine, Baking powder, Pendulum clock,
Thermometer} **28.** {Telegraph, Zipper} **29. (a)** 22
(b) 12 **(c)** 28 **30. (a)** 16 **(b)** 32 **(c)** 33 **(d)** 45
(e) 14 **(f)** 26

CHAPTER 3 INTRODUCTION TO LOGIC

3.1 Exercises *(pages 88–90)*

1. statement **3.** not a statement **5.** statement
7. statement **9.** statement **11.** not a statement
13. statement **15.** compound **17.** not compound
19. not compound **21.** compound **23.** Her aunt's name
is not Hermione. **25.** No book is longer than this book.
27. At least one computer repairman can play blackjack.
29. Someone does not love somebody sometime.
31. The trash does not need to be collected. **33.** $x \leq 12$
35. $x < 5$ **37.** Answers will vary. **39.** She does not have
green eyes. **41.** She has green eyes and he is 60 years old.
43. She does not have green eyes or he is 60 years old.
45. She does not have green eyes or he is not 60 years old.

47. It is not the case that she does not have green eyes and
he is 60 years old. **49.** $p \wedge {\sim}q$ **51.** ${\sim}p \vee q$
53. ${\sim}(p \vee q)$ or, equivalently, ${\sim}p \wedge {\sim}q$
55. Answers will vary. **57.** C **59.** A, B **61.** A, C
63. B **65.** true **67.** false **69.** true **71.** true
73. false **75.** Answers will vary. **77.** Every person here
has made mistakes before. **79.** $(\forall c)({\sim}f)$

3.2 Exercises *(pages 100–101)*

1. false **3.** true **5.** true **7.** They must both be false.
9. T **11.** T **13.** F **15.** T **17.** T **19.** T **21.** It is a
disjunction, because it means "6 > 2 or 6 = 2." **23.** T
25. F **27.** T **29.** T **31.** F **33.** F **35.** T **37.** T
39. T **41.** 4 **43.** 16 **45.** 128 **47.** six **49.** FFTF
51. FTTT **53.** TTTT **55.** TFFF **57.** FFFFTFFF
59. FTFTTTTT **61.** TTTTTTTTTTTFTTT
63. You can't pay me now and you can't pay me later.
65. It is not summer or there is snow. **67.** I did not say
yes or she did not say no. **69.** $6 - 1 \neq 5$ or $9 + 13 = 7$
71. Neither Prancer nor Vixen will lead Santa's reindeer
sleigh next Christmas. **73.** T **75.** F

p	q	$p \veebar q$
T	T	F
T	F	T
F	T	T
F	F	F

77. (see table) **79.** F **81.** T

83. The lady is behind Door 2. *Reasoning:* Suppose that the
sign on Door 1 is true. Then the sign on Door 2 would also
be true, but this is impossible. So the sign on Door 2 must be
true, and the sign on Door 1 must be false. Because the sign
on Door 1 says the lady is in Room 1, and this is false, the
lady must be behind Door 2. **85.** The negation of a conjuc-
tion is equivalent to the disjunction of the negations.

3.3 Exercises *(pages 109–111)*

1. If you just believe, then you can do it. **3.** If it is an even
integer divisible by 5, then it is divisible by 10. **5.** If it is a
grizzly bear, then it does not live in California. **7.** If they
are surfers, then they can't stay away from the beach.
9. true **11.** true **13.** false **15.** true **17.** Answers will
vary. **19.** F **21.** T **23.** T **25.** If they do not collect
classics, then he fixes cars. **27.** If she sings for a living,
then they collect classics and he fixes cars. **29.** If he does
not fix cars, then they do not collect classics or she sings
for a living. **31.** $b \to p$ **33.** $p \wedge (s \to {\sim}b)$ **35.** $p \to s$
37. T **39.** T **41.** F **43.** T **45.** T **47.** Answers will
vary. **49.** TTTF **51.** TTFT **53.** TTTT; tautology
55. TTTTTTFT **57.** TTTFTTTTTTTTTTTT **59.** one

61. That is an authentic Coach bag and I am not surprised.
63. The bullfighter doesn't get going and doesn't get gored.
65. You want to be happy for the rest of your life and you make a pretty woman your wife.   **67.** You do not give your plants tender, loving care or they flourish.   **69.** She does or he will.   **71.** The person is not a resident of Pensacola or is a resident of Florida.   **73.** equivalent   **75.** equivalent
77. equivalent   **79.** equivalent   **81.** $(p \wedge q) \vee (p \wedge \sim q)$; The statement simplifies to p.   **83.** $p \vee (\sim q \wedge r)$
85. $\sim p \vee (p \vee q)$; The statement simplifies to T.

87. The statement simplifies to $p \wedge q$.

89. The statement simplifies to F.

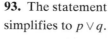

91. The statement simplifies to $(r \wedge \sim p) \wedge q$.

93. The statement simplifies to $p \vee q$.

95. $525.60   **97.** The circuit is equivalent to
$\sim (A \wedge A) \vee B \equiv \sim A \vee B \equiv A \rightarrow B$.

3.4 Exercises *(pages 116–117)*

1. (a) If you were an hour, then beauty would be a minute.
(b) If beauty were not a minute, then you would not be an hour.   **(c)** If you were not an hour, then beauty would not be a minute.
3. (a) If you don't fix it, then it ain't broke.
(b) If it's broke, then fix it.   **(c)** If you fix it, then it's broke.   **5. (a)** If it is dangerous to your health, then you walk in front of a moving car.   **(b)** If you do not walk in front of a moving car, then it is not dangerous to your health.   **(c)** If it is not dangerous to your health, then you do not walk in front of a moving car.   **7. (a)** If they flock together, then they are birds of a feather.   **(b)** If they are not birds of a feather, then they do not flock together.
(c) If they do not flock together, then they are not birds of a feather.   **9. (a)** If he comes, then you built it.   **(b)** If you don't build it, then he won't come.   **(c)** If he doesn't come, then you didn't build it.
11. (a) $\sim q \rightarrow p$ **(b)** $\sim p \rightarrow q$ **(c)** $q \rightarrow \sim p$
13. (a) $\sim q \rightarrow \sim p$ **(b)** $p \rightarrow q$ **(c)** $q \rightarrow p$
15. (a) $(q \vee r) \rightarrow p$ **(b)** $\sim p \rightarrow (\sim q \wedge \sim r)$
(c) $(\sim q \wedge \sim r) \rightarrow \sim p$ **17.** Answers will vary.
19. If the Kings go to the playoffs, then pigs will fly.
21. If it has legs of 3 and 4, then it has a hypotenuse of 5.
23. If a number is a whole number, then it is a rational number.

25. If I do logic puzzles, then I am driven crazy.
27. If the graffiti are to be covered, then two coats of paint must be used.   **29.** If employment improves, then the economy recovers.   **31.** If a number is a whole number, then it is an integer.   **33.** If their pitching improves, then the Phillies will win the pennant.   **35.** If the figure is a rectangle, then it is a parallelogram with perpendicular adjacent sides.   **37.** If a triangle has two perpendicular sides, then it is a right triangle.   **39.** If a three-digit number whose units digit is 5 is squared, then the square will end in 25.   **41.** D   **43.** Answers will vary.   **45.** true   **47.** false
49. false   **51.** contrary   **53.** contrary   **55.** consistent
57. (1) $p \rightarrow (p \rightarrow q)$ **(2)** $(p \rightarrow q) \rightarrow p$

3.5 Exercises *(pages 121–122)*

1. valid   **3.** invalid   **5.** valid   **7.** invalid   **9.** invalid
11. invalid   **13.** yes
15. All people with blue eyes have blond hair.
   Erin does not have blond hair.
   _____
   Erin does not have blue eyes.
17. invalid   **19.** valid   **21.** invalid   **23.** valid   **25.** invalid
27. invalid   **29.** valid

3.6 Exercises *(pages 130–132)*

1. valid by reasoning by transitivity   **3.** valid by modus ponens   **5.** fallacy by fallacy of the converse   **7.** valid by modus tollens   **9.** fallacy by fallacy of the inverse
11. valid by disjunctive syllogism   **13.** invalid   **15.** valid
17. invalid   **19.** valid   **21.** valid   **23.** invalid
25. invalid
27. Every time something squeaks, I use WD-40.
   Every time I use WD-40, I go to the hardware store.
   _____
   Every time something squeaks, I go to the hardware store.

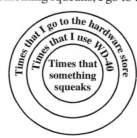

29. valid   **31.** invalid   **33.** invalid   **35.** valid   **37.** valid
39. (a) When the cable company keeps you on hold, your dad gets punched over a can of soup.   **(b)** The cable company doesn't keep you on hold.   **41.** If it is my poultry, then it is a duck.   **43.** If it is a guinea pig, then it is hopelessly ignorant of music.   **45.** If it is a teachable kitten, then it does not have green eyes.   **47.** If I can read it, then I have not filed it.   **49. (a)** $p \rightarrow \sim s$ **(b)** $r \rightarrow s$ **(c)** $q \rightarrow$

49. (d) None of my poultry are officers.   **51. (a)** $r \rightarrow \sim s$
(b) $u \rightarrow t$ **(c)** $\sim r \rightarrow p$ **(d)** $\sim u \rightarrow \sim q$ **(e)** $t \rightarrow s$
(f) All pawnbrokers are honest.   **53. (a)** $r \rightarrow w$
(b) $\sim u \rightarrow \sim t$ **(c)** $v \rightarrow \sim s$ **(d)** $x \rightarrow r$ **(e)** $\sim q \rightarrow t$
(f) $y \rightarrow p$ **(g)** $w \rightarrow s$ **(h)** $\sim x \rightarrow \sim q$ **(i)** $p \rightarrow \sim u$
(j) I can't read any of Brown's letters.

Chapter 3 Test *(pages 137– 138)*
1. $6 - 3 \neq 3$ **2.** Some men are not created equal.
3. No members of the class went on the field trip.
4. I fall in love and it will not be forever.   **5.** She did
not apply or she got a student loan.   **6.** $\sim p \rightarrow q$
7. $p \rightarrow q$ **8.** $\sim q \leftrightarrow \sim p$ **9.** You won't love me and I will
love you.   **10.** It is not the case that you will love me or
I will not love you. (Equivalently: You won't love me and
I will love you.)   **11.** T   **12.** T   **13.** T   **14.** F
15. Answers will vary.   **16. (a)** The antecedent must be true
and the consequent must be false.   **(b)** Both component
statements must be true.   **(c)** Both component statements
must be false.   **(d)** Both component statements must have
the same truth value.   **17.** TFFF   **18.** TTTT (tautology)
19. false   **20.** true
Wording may vary in the answers for Exercises 21–25.
21. If the number is an integer, then it is a rational number.
22. If a polygon is a rhombus, then it is a quadrilateral.
23. If a number is divisible by 4, then it is divisible by 2.
24. If she digs dinosaur bones, then she is a paleontologist.
25. (a) If the graph helps me understand it, then a
picture paints a thousand words.   **(b)** If a picture
doesn't paint a thousand words, then the graph won't
help me understand it.   **(c)** If the graph doesn't help me
understand it, then a picture doesn't paint a thousand
words. **26. (a)** $(q \wedge r) \rightarrow \sim p$ **(b)** $p \rightarrow (\sim q \vee \sim r)$
(c) $(\sim q \vee \sim r) \rightarrow p$ **27.** valid   **28. (a)** A   **(b)** F   **(c)** C
(d) D   **29.** valid   **30.** invalid

17. (a) $\overset{\bullet\bullet}{AB}$ **(b)**

19. (a) $\overset{\rightarrow}{CB}$ **(b)**

21. (a) $\overset{\circ\rightarrow}{BC}$ **(b)**

23. (a) $\overset{\rightarrow}{BA}$ **(b)**

25. F   **27.** D   **29.** B   **31.** E

There may be other correct forms of the answers in Exercises 33–39.   33. $\overset{\bullet\bullet}{MO}$ **35.** $\overset{\bullet\bullet}{NO}$ **37.** $\varnothing$

39. $\overset{\bullet\bullet}{OP}$ **41.** 62°   **43.** 1°   **45.** $(90 - x)°$

47. 48°   **49.** 154°   **51.** $(180 - y)°$ **53.** 40°

55. 52°   **57.** $\angle CBD$ and $\angle ABE$; $\angle CBE$ and $\angle DBA$

59. (a) 52°   **(b)** 128°   **61.** 107° and 73°   **63.** 75° and 75°

65. 139° and 139°   **67.** 35° and 55°   **69.** 49° and 49°

71. 48° and 132°   **73. (a)** 3   **(b)** 6   **(c)** 7   **(d)** 7; exterior

75. (a) 180   **(b)** 180   **(c)** 180; 180   **(d)** 0   **(e)** 0   **(f)** 3

9.2 Exercises *(pages 463–465)*

1. chord   **3.** equilateral (or equiangular)   **5.** false

7. false   **9.** true   **11.** Answers will vary.   **13.** both

15. closed   **17.** closed   **19.** neither   **21.** convex

23. convex   **25.** not convex   **27.** right, scalene

29. acute, equilateral   **31.** right, scalene   **33.** right, isosceles   **35.** obtuse, scalene   **37.** An isosceles right triangle is a triangle having a 90° angle and two perpendicular sides of equal length.

39. $A = 50°$; $B = 70°$; $C = 60°$ **41.** $A = B = C = 60°$

43. $A = B = 55°$; $C = 70°$ **45.** 155°   **47.** 360°

49. (a) O **(b)** $\overset{\bullet\bullet}{OA}$, $\overset{\bullet\bullet}{OC}$, $\overset{\bullet\bullet}{OB}$, $\overset{\bullet\bullet}{OD}$ **(c)** $\overset{\bullet\bullet}{AC}$, $\overset{\bullet\bullet}{BD}$ **(d)** $\overset{\bullet\bullet}{AC}$, $\overset{\bullet\bullet}{BD}$, $\overset{\bullet\bullet}{BC}$, $\overset{\bullet\bullet}{AB}$ **(e)** $\overset{\leftrightarrow}{BC}$, $\overset{\leftrightarrow}{AB}$ **(f)** $\overset{\rightarrow}{AE}$

51. With the radius of the compass greater than one-half the length PQ, place the point of the compass at P and swing arcs above and below line r. Then, with the same radius and the point of the compass at Q, swing two more arcs above and below line r. Locate the two points of intersection of the arcs above and below, and call them A and B. With a straightedge, join A and B. AB is the perpendicular bisector of PQ.

53. With the radius of the compass greater than the distance from P to r, place the point of the compass at P and swing an arc intersecting line r in two points. Call these points A and B. Swing arcs of equal radius to the left of line r, with the point of the compass at A and at B, intersecting at point Q. With a straightedge, join P and Q. PQ is the perpendicular from P to line r.

55. With any radius, place the point of the compass at P and swing arcs to the left and right, intersecting line r in two points. Call these points A and B. With an arc of

CHAPTER 9 GEOMETRY

9.1 Exercises *(pages 456–457)*
(The art here is not to scale with the exercise art.)

1. 90   **3.** equal   **5.** true   **7.** false   **9.** true

11. false   **13.** true   **15.** false

sufficient length, place the point of the compass first at A and then at B, and swing arcs either both above or both below line r, intersecting at point Q. With a straightedge, join P and Q. PQ is perpendicular to line r at P.

57. With any radius, place the point of the compass at A and swing an arc intersecting the sides of angle A at two points. Call the point of intersection on the horizontal side B and call the other point of intersection C. Draw a horizontal working line, and locate any point A' on this line. With the same radius used earlier, place the point of the compass at A' and swing an arc intersecting the working line at B'. Return to angle A, and set the radius of the compass equal to BC. On the working line, place the point of the compass at B' and swing an arc intersecting the first arc at C'. Now draw line $A'C'$. Angle A' is equal to angle A.

59. Answers will vary.

9.3 Exercises *(pages 472–476)*

1.

STATEMENTS	REASONS
1. $AC = BD$	1. Given
2. $AD = BC$	2. Given
3. $AB = AB$	3. Reflexive property
4. $\triangle ABD \cong \triangle BAC$	4. SSS congruence property

3.

STATEMENTS	REASONS
1. $\angle BAC = \angle DAC$	1. Given
2. $\angle BCA = \angle DCA$	2. Given
3. $AC = AC$	3. Reflexive property
4. $\triangle ABC \cong \triangle ADC$	4. ASA congruence property

5.

STATEMENTS	REASONS
1. $\overleftrightarrow{DB}$ is perpendicular to $\overleftrightarrow{AC}$.	1. Given
2. $AB = BC$	2. Given
3. $\angle ABD = \angle CBD$	3. Both are right angles by definition of perpendicularity.
4. $DB = DB$	4. Reflexive property
5. $\triangle ABD \cong \triangle CBD$	5. SAS congruence property

7. $110°$ **9.** $67°, 67°$ **11.** Answers will vary.
13. $\angle H$ and $\angle F$; $\angle K$ and $\angle E$; $\angle HGK$ and $\angle FGE$; $\overline{HK}$ and $\overline{FE}$; $\overline{GK}$ and $\overline{GE}$; $\overline{HG}$ and $\overline{FG}$
15. $\angle A$ and $\angle P$; $\angle C$ and $\angle R$; $\angle B$ and $\angle Q$; $\overleftrightarrow{AC}$ and $\overleftrightarrow{PR}$; $\overleftrightarrow{CB}$ and $\overleftrightarrow{RQ}$; $\overleftrightarrow{AB}$ and $\overleftrightarrow{PQ}$
17. $\angle P = 76°$; $\angle M = 48°$; $\angle A = \angle N = 56°$

19. $\angle T = 20°$; $\angle V = 64°$; $\angle R = \angle U = 96°$
21. $\angle T = 74°$; $\angle Y = 28°$; $\angle Z = \angle W = 78°$
23. $a = 12$; $b = 9$ **25.** $x = 6$ **27.** $a = 6$; $b = \frac{15}{2}$
29. $x = 165$ **31.** $c = 111\frac{1}{9}$ **33.** $r = \frac{108}{7}$ **35.** 60 m
37. 250 m, 350 m **39.** 112.5 ft **41.** 10 **43.** $c = 17$
45. $a = 13$ **47.** $c = 50$ m **49.** $a = 20$ in.
51. The sum of the squares of the two shorter sides of a right triangle is equal to the square of the longest side.
53. $(3, 4, 5)$ **55.** $(7, 24, 25)$ **57.** Answers will vary.
59. $(3, 4, 5)$ **61.** $(7, 24, 25)$ **63.** Answers will vary.
65. $(4, 3, 5)$ **67.** $(8, 15, 17)$ **69.** Answers will vary.
71. 24 m **73.** 18 ft **75.** 4.55 ft **77.** 19 ft, 3 in.
79. 28 ft, 10 in. **81.** (a) b (b) k (c) cj (d) ck
(e) $j + k$; $j + k$; $a^2 + b^2 = c^2$ **83.** 9 **85.** 16 **87.** $55°$
89. $360°$ **91.** Answers will vary. **93.** Answers will vary.

9.4 Exercises *(pages 484–488)*

1. 24 **3.** 10 **5.** perimeter **7.** 48 cm^2 **9.** 10 cm^2
11. 8 in.^{2} **13.** 418 mm^2 **15.** 8 cm^2 **17.** 3.14 cm^2
19. 1017 m^2 **21.** 4 m **23.** 300 ft, 400 ft, 500 ft
25. 50 ft **27.** $23{,}800.10$ ft^2 **29.** $14{,}600$ mi^2
31. 12 in., 12π in., 36π in.^{2} **33.** 5 ft, 10π ft, 25π ft^2
35. 6 cm, 12 cm, 36π cm^2 **37.** 10 in., 20 in., 20π in.
39. $\frac{20}{\pi}$ yd, $\frac{40}{\pi}$ yd, 40 yd **41.** 14.5 **43.** 7 **45.** 5.7
47. 6 **49.** 5 **51.** 1.5 **53.** (a) 20 cm^2 (b) 80 cm^2
(c) 180 cm^2 (d) 320 cm^2 (e) 4 (f) 3; 9 (g) 4; 16
(h) n^2 **55.** n^2 **57.** $\$800$ **59.** 80 **61.** 76.26
63. 132 ft^2 **65.** 5376 cm^2 **67.** 145.34 m^2
69. 16-in. pizza **71.** 16-in. pizza **73.** $\frac{1}{2}(a + b)(a + b)$
75. $\frac{1}{2}(a + b)(a + b) = \frac{1}{2}ab + \frac{1}{2}ab + \frac{1}{2}c^2$
77. 26 in. **79.** 625 ft^2 **81.** 6 cm^2 **83.** $\frac{(4 - \pi)r^2}{4}$
85. $24 + 4\sqrt{6}$ **87.** 5 in.

9.5 Exercises *(pages 493–496)*

1. true **3.** true **5.** false **7.** (a) $22\frac{1}{2}$ m^3 (b) $49\frac{1}{4}$ m^2
9. (a) $267{,}946.67$ ft^3 (b) $20{,}096$ ft^2 **11.** (a) 549.5 cm^3
(b) 376.8 cm^2 **13.** (a) 65.94 m^3 (b) 100.00 m^2
15. 168 in.^{3} **17.** 1969.10 cm^3 **19.** 427.29 cm^3
21. 508.68 cm^3 **23.** $1{,}694{,}000$ m^3 **25.** 0.52 m^3
27. 288π in.^{3}, 144π in.^{2} **29.** 2 cm, 16π cm^2
31. 1 m, $\frac{4}{3}\pi$ m^3 **33.** volume **35.** 270 ft^3
37. $\sqrt[3]{2}\,x$ **39.** $\$8100$ **41.** $\$37{,}500$ **43.** 65.7%
45. 2.5 **47.** 6 **49.** 210 in.^{3} **51.** 300 mi **53.** 2 to 1
55. 288 **57.** Answers will vary. **59.** $4, 4, 6, 2$
61. $8, 6, 12, 2$ **63.** $20, 12, 30, 2$

9.6 Exercises *(pages 505–507)*
(The answers are given in blue for this section.)

1.

3.

5.

7. The figure is its own reflection image.

9.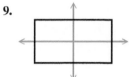

11.

13.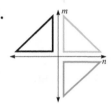

15.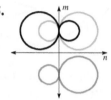

17.

19.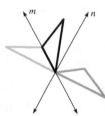

21.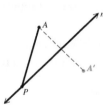

23.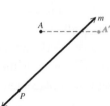

25.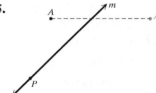

27.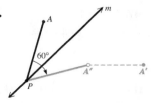

29.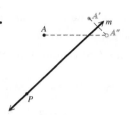

31.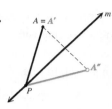

33. no

35.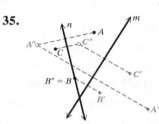

37.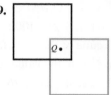

39.

41.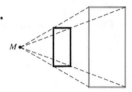

43.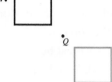

45.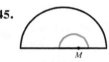

47. 6   **49.** $R_P{}^2 \cdot C_P{}^{6n+2}$

9.7 Exercises *(pages 514–516)*
1. Euclidean   **3.** Lobachevskian   **5.** greater than
7. Riemannian   **9.** Euclidean

11.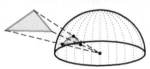

13. Yes; any two distinct lines have at least one point in common.   **15.** Yes; any two points in a plane have at least one line of the plane in common.   **17.** Yes; every point is contained by at least three lines of the plane.

19. no   **21.** yes   **23.** C   **25.** A, E   **27.** B, D
29. A, E   **31.** 1   **33.** 3   **35.** 1

37. (a)–(g)

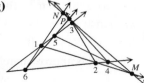

37. (h) Suppose that a hexagon is inscribed in an angle. Let each pair of opposite sides be extended so as to intersect. Then the three points of intersection thus obtained will lie in a straight line.

9.8 Exercises *(pages 520–521)*

1. 4   **2.** 4   **3.** 2   **4.** $\frac{2}{1} = 2$ **5.** $\frac{4}{1} = 4$ **6.** $\frac{3}{1} = 3; \frac{9}{1} = 9$
7. $\frac{4}{1} = 4; \frac{16}{1} = 16$ **8.** 4, 9, 16, 25, 36, 100
9. Each ratio in the bottom row is the square of the scale factor in the top row.   **10.** 4   **11.** 4, 9, 16, 25, 36, 100
12. Each ratio in the bottom row is again the square of the scale factor in the top row.   **13.** Answers will vary. Some examples are: $3^d = 9$, thus $d = 2$; $5^d = 25$, thus $d = 2$; $4^d = 16$, thus $d = 2$.   **14.** 8   **15.** $\frac{2}{1} = 2; \frac{8}{1} = 8$
16. 8, 27, 64, 125, 216, 1000   **17.** Each ratio in the bottom row is the cube of the scale factor in the top row.
18. Since $2^3 = 8$, the value of d in $2^d = 8$ must be 3.
19. $\frac{3}{1} = 3$ **20.** 4   **21.** 1.262, or $\frac{\ln 4}{\ln 3}$ **22.** $\frac{2}{1} = 2$ **23.** 3
24. It is between 1 and 2.   **25.** 1.585, or $\frac{\ln 3}{\ln 2}$
27. 0.842, 0.452, 0.842, 0.452, ... The two attractors are approximately 0.842 and 0.452.

Chapter 9 Test *(pages 529–530)*

1. (a) 48°   **(b)** 138°   **(c)** acute   **2.** 40°, 140°
3. 45°, 45°   **4.** 30°, 60°   **5.** 130°, 50°   **6.** 117°, 117°
7. Answers will vary.   **8.** C   **9.** both   **10.** neither
11. 30°, 45°, 105°   **12.** 72 cm²   **13.** 60 in.²   **14.** 68 m²
15. 180 m²   **16.** 57 cm²   **17.** 24π in.   **18.** 1978 ft
19.

STATEMENTS	REASONS
1. $\angle CAB = \angle DBA$	1. Given
2. $DB = CA$	2. Given
3. $AB = AB$	3. Reflexive property
4. $\triangle ABD \cong \triangle BAC$	4. SAS congruence property

20. 64 ft   **21.** 29 m   **22.**

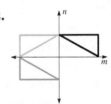

23.   **24. (a)** 904.32 in.³   **(b)** 452.16 in.²
25. (a) 864 ft³   **(b)** 552 ft²
26. (a) 1582.56 m³   **(b)** 753.60 m²
27. Answers will vary.   **28. (a)** yes
(b) no   **29.** no   **30.** The only attractor is approximately 0.524.

CHAPTER 10 COUNTING METHODS

10.1 Exercises *(pages 539–541)*

1. *AB, AC, AD, AE, BA, BC, BD, BE, CA, CB, CD, CE, DA, DB, DC, DE, EA, EB, EC, ED*; 20 ways
3. *AB, AD, BA, BD, CE, DA, DB, EC*; 8 ways
5. *ACE, AEC, BCE, BEC, DCE, DEC*; 6 ways
7. *ABC, ABD, ABE, ACD, ACE, ADE, BCD, BCE, BDE, CDE*; 10 ways   **9.** 1   **11.** 3   **13.** 5   **15.** 5
17. 3   **19.** 1   **21.** 18   **23.** 15   **25.** 27   **27.** 15   **29.** 30
31. 22, 33, 55, 77   **33.** 23, 37, 53, 73
35.

First coin	Second coin	Third coin	Result
		h	hhh
	h	t	hht
h		h	hth
	t	t	htt
		h	thh
	h	t	tht
t		h	tth
	t	t	ttt

(a) hhh, hht, hth, thh   **(b)** hhh   **(c)** hht, hth, htt, thh, tht, tth, ttt   **(d)** htt, tht, tth, ttt
37. 16   **39.** 36   **41.** 17   **43.** 72   **45.** 12   **47.** 10   **49.** 6
51. 9   **53.** 49   **55.** 21   **57.** 15   **59.** 16   **61.** 13   **63.** 4
65. (a) 1600   **(b)** $4k + 1$ for all positive integers k
(c) $4k^2$ **67.** 3

Wording may vary in the answers for Exercise 69.
69. (a) Determine the number of two-digit numbers that can be formed using only the digits 1, 2, and 3 if repetition of digits is allowed.
(b) Determine the number of two-digit numbers that can be formed using only the digits 1, 2, and 3 if the selection is done with replacement.

10.2 Exercises *(pages 549–552)*

1. 24   **3.** 72   **5.** 20   **7.** 28   **9.** 10   **11.** 1225
13. (a) 720   **(b)** 120   **15. (a)** 306   **(b)** 153
17. 3,628,800   **19.** 3,991,680   **21.** 4,151,347,200
23. 184,756   **25.** 980,179,200   **27.** 134,596   **29.** 60
31. 2,162,160   **33.** $2^3 = 8$ **35.** Answers will vary.
37. $6^3 = 216$ **39.** $2^{10} = 1024$ **41.** $5! = 120$
43. $3 \cdot 2 = 6$ **45.** $3 \cdot 3 = 9$ **47.** $3 \cdot 2 \cdot 1 = 6$
49. $5 \cdot 2 \cdot 4 = 40$ **51.** $2^6 = 64$ **53.** $2 \cdot 3 \cdot 4 \cdot 5 = 120$
55. $2 \cdot 3 \cdot 4 \cdot 3 = 72$ **57.** $2 \cdot 3 \cdot 1 \cdot 3 = 18$
59. $2 \cdot 4 \cdot 6 = 48$ **61.** $5! = 120$ **63.** 800   **65. (a)** 6
(b) 5   **(c)** 4   **(d)** 3   **(e)** 2   **(f)** 1; 720   **67. (a)** 3   **(b)** 3
(c) 2   **(d)** 2   **(e)** 1   **(f)** 1; 36   **69.** 516,243   **71.** 48

10.3 Exercises *(pages 561–565)*

1. 504 **3.** 95,040 **5.** 330 **7.** 45 **9.** 116,280

11. 43,680 **13.** 126 **15.** 792 **17.** $1.805037696 \times 10^{11}$

19. 225,792,840 **21.** permutation **23.** combination

25. permutation **27.** permutation **29.** $_8P_5 = 6720$

31. $_{12}P_2 = 132$ **33.** $_{25}P_5 = 6,375,600$ **35.** $_6P_3 = 120$

37. (a) $_6C_3 = 20$ (b) $_6C_2 = 15$ **39.** $_{18}C_5 = 8568$

41. (a) $_{13}C_5 = 1287$ (b) $_{26}C_5 = 65,780$

(c) 0 (impossible) **43.** $_9C_3 = 84$

45. $_{26}P_3 \cdot {}_{10}P_3 \cdot {}_{26}P_3 = 175,219,200,000$

47. $2 \cdot {}_{25}P_3 = 27,600$ **49.** $7 \cdot {}_{12}P_8 = 139,708,800$

51. (a) $6! = 720$ (b) $2 \cdot 4! = 48$ (c) $4! = 24$

53. $_{15}C_1 \cdot {}_{14}C_2 \cdot {}_{12}C_3 \cdot {}_9C_4 \cdot {}_5C_5 = 37,837,800$

55. $\frac{_8C_3 \cdot {}_5C_3 \cdot {}_2C_2}{2!} = 280$ **57.** (a) $_{13}C_4 \cdot 39 = 27,885$

(b) $_{12}C_2 \cdot {}_{40}C_3 = 652,080$ (c) $_{26}C_2 \cdot {}_{13}C_2 \cdot 13 = 329,550$

59. $4 \cdot {}_{13}C_5 = 5148$ **61.** (a) $_7P_2 = 42$ (b) $3 \cdot 6 = 18$

(c) $_7P_2 \cdot 5 = 210$ **63.** $_{20}C_3 = 1140$ **65.** $_8P_3 = 336$

67. $_9C_2 \cdot {}_7C_3 \cdot {}_4C_4 \cdot 2 \cdot 3 \cdot 4 = 30,240$

69. (a) $_6C_2 \cdot {}_6C_3 \cdot {}_6C_4 = 4500$

(b) $3! \cdot {}_6C_2 \cdot {}_6C_3 \cdot {}_6C_4 = 27,000$

71. (a) $6! = 720$ (b) 745,896

73. Each equals 220.

10.4 Exercises *(pages 569–570)*

1. 6 **3.** 20 **5.** 56 **7.** 36 **9.** $_7C_1 \cdot {}_3C_3 = 7$

11. $_7C_3 \cdot {}_3C_1 = 105$ **13.** $_8C_3 = 56$ **15.** $_8C_5 = 56$

17. $_9C_4 = 126$ **19.** $1 \cdot {}_8C_3 = 56$ **21.** 1 **23.** 10 **25.** 5

27. 32 **29.** the even-numbered rows

31. (a) All are multiples of the row number.

(b) The same pattern holds. (c) The same pattern

holds. Each entry is a multiple of 11. **33.** ... 8, 13, 21,

34, ...; A number in this sequence is the sum of the two

preceding terms. This is the Fibonacci sequence.

35. row 8 **37.** The sum of the squares of the entries

across the top row equals the entry at the bottom vertex.

Wording may vary in the answers for Exercises 39 and 41.

39. sum = N; Any entry in the array equals the sum of

the column of entries from its immediate left upward to

the top of the array. **41.** sum = $N - 1$; Any entry in the

array equals 1 more than the sum of all entries whose

cells make up the largest rectangle entirely to the left and

above that entry.

10.5 Exercises *(pages 575–578)*

1. $2^4 - 1 = 15$ **3.** $2^7 - 1 = 127$ **5.** $2^7 - 1 = 127$

7. 120 **9.** $36 - 6 = 30$ **11.** $6 + 6 - 1 = 11$ **13.** 51

15. 48 **17.** $90 - 9 = 81$ **19.** $29 + 9 - 2 = 36$

21. (a) $_{10}C_3 = 120$ (b) $_9C_3 = 84$ (c) $120 - 84 = 36$

23. $_7C_3 - {}_5C_3 = 25$ **25.** $_8P_4 - {}_5P_4 = 1560$

27. $_{10}P_3 - {}_7P_3 = 510$ **29.** $2 \cdot 26^2 + 2 \cdot 26^3 = 36,504$

31. $_{12}C_4 - {}_8C_4 = 425$ **33.** $13 + 4 - 1 = 16$

35. $12 + 26 - 6 = 32$ **37.** $9 + 8 - 5 = 12$

39. $11 + 5 = 16$ **41.** $2,598,960 - {}_{13}C_5 = 2,597,673$

43. $2,598,960 - {}_{40}C_5 = 1,940,952$ **45.** 56

47. $_{10}C_0 + {}_{10}C_1 + {}_{10}C_2 = 56$ **49.** $2^{10} - 56 = 968$

51. $26^2 \cdot 10^3 - {}_{26}P_2 \cdot {}_{10}P_3 = 208,000$

53. Answers will vary. **55.** $_4C_3 + {}_3C_3 + {}_5C_3 = 15$

57. $_{12}C_3 - {}_4C_1 \cdot {}_3C_1 \cdot {}_5C_1 = 160$ **59.** Answers will vary.

61. Answers will vary.

Chapter 10 Test *(pages 581–582)*

1. $6 \cdot 7 \cdot 7 = 294$ **2.** $6 \cdot 7 \cdot 3 = 126$ **3.** $6 \cdot 6 \cdot 5 = 180$

4. $6 \cdot 5 \cdot 1 = 30$ end in 0; $5 \cdot 5 \cdot 1 = 25$ end in 5;

$30 + 25 = 55$ **5.** 13

6.

First toss	Second toss	Third toss	Fourth toss	Result

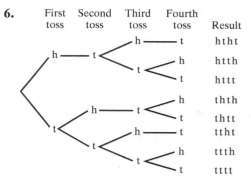

7. $4! = 24$ **8.** $2 \cdot 3 \cdot 4! = 144$ **9.** 720 **10.** 56

11. 1320 **12.** 56 **13.** $_{26}P_5 = 7,893,600$

14. $32^5 = 33,554,432$ **15.** $_7P_2 = 42$ **16.** $5! = 120$

17. $\frac{6!}{2! \cdot 3!} = 60$ **18.** $_{10}C_4 = 210$ **19.** $_{10}C_2 \cdot {}_8C_2 = 1260$

20. $_{10}C_5 \cdot {}_5C_5 = 252$ **21.** $\frac{_{10}C_4 \cdot {}_6C_4}{2!} = 1575$

22. $2^{10} - ({}_{10}C_0 + {}_{10}C_1 + {}_{10}C_2) = 968$ **23.** $2^5 = 32$

24. $2^3 = 8$ **25.** $2 \cdot 2^3 = 16$ **26.** 13 **27.** 2

28. $32 - (1 + 5) = 26$ **29.** $1 \cdot {}_6C_2 = 15$

30. $1 \cdot 1 \cdot {}_5C_1 = 5$ **31.** $2 \cdot {}_5C_2 = 20$ **32.** $1 \cdot {}_5C_1 = 5$

33. $_5C_3 + {}_5C_2 \cdot {}_2C_1 = 30$ **34.** $_{60}C_3 \cdot {}_{40}C_2 = 26,691,600$

35. $_9C_4 = 126$ **36.** the counting numbers

CHAPTER 11 PROBABILITY

11.1 Exercises *(pages 592–597)*

1. (a) $\frac{1}{3}$ (b) $\frac{1}{3}$ (c) $\frac{1}{3}$ **3.** (a) $\frac{1}{2}$ (b) $\frac{1}{3}$ (c) $\frac{1}{6}$

5. (a) $\{1, 2, 3\}$ (b) 2 (c) 1 (d) 3 (e) $\frac{2}{3}$ (f) 2 to 1

7. (a) $\{11, 12, 13, 21, 22, 23, 31, 32, 33\}$ (b) $\frac{2}{3}$ (c) $\frac{1}{3}$

(d) $\frac{1}{3}$ (e) $\frac{4}{9}$ **9.** (a) $\frac{1}{50}$ (b) $\frac{2}{50} = \frac{1}{25}$ (c) $\frac{3}{50}$ (d) $\frac{4}{50} = \frac{2}{25}$

9. (e) $\frac{5}{50} = \frac{1}{10}$ **11.** (a) $\frac{1}{36}$ (b) $\frac{2}{36} = \frac{1}{18}$ (c) $\frac{3}{36} = \frac{1}{12}$

(d) $\frac{4}{36} = \frac{1}{9}$ (e) $\frac{5}{36}$ (f) $\frac{6}{36} = \frac{1}{6}$ (g) $\frac{5}{36}$ (h) $\frac{4}{36} = \frac{1}{9}$

(i) $\frac{3}{36} = \frac{1}{12}$ (j) $\frac{2}{36} = \frac{1}{18}$ (k) $\frac{1}{36}$ **13.** $\frac{36}{2,598,960} \approx 0.00001385$

15. $\frac{624}{2,598,960} \approx 0.00024010$ **17.** $\frac{1}{4} \cdot \frac{5108}{2,598,960} \approx 0.00049135$

19. $\frac{175}{200} = 0.875$ **21.** $\frac{1}{{}_{26}P_3} \approx 0.000064$ **23.** (a) $\frac{5}{9}$

(b) $\frac{49}{144}$ (c) $\frac{5}{48}$ **25.** $\frac{1}{4}$ **27.** $\frac{1}{4}$ **29.** (a) $\frac{3}{4}$ (b) $\frac{1}{4}$

31. $\frac{1}{250,000} = 0.000004$ **33.** $\frac{1}{4}$ **35.** $\frac{1}{4}$ **37.** $\frac{2}{4} = \frac{1}{2}$

39. $\frac{1}{500} = 0.002$ **41.** 160 **43.** $\frac{2}{4} = \frac{1}{2}$ **45.** 7 to 4

47. 9 to 2 **49.** 4 to 7 **51.** 4 to 1 **53.** 2 to 3

55. 37 to 63 **57.** $\frac{12}{31}$ **59.** (a) 0 (b) no (c) yes

61. (a) $3 \cdot 1 \cdot 2 \cdot 1 \cdot 1 \cdot 1 = 6$ (b) $\frac{6}{720} = \frac{1}{120} \approx 0.0083$

63. (a) $4 \cdot 3! \cdot 3! = 144$ (b) $\frac{144}{720} = \frac{1}{5} = 0.2$ **65.** $\frac{1}{9}$

67. $\frac{2}{{}_7C_2} = \frac{2}{21} \approx 0.095$ **69.** $\frac{{}_5C_3}{{}_{12}C_3} = \frac{10}{220} \approx 0.045$

71. $\frac{1}{{}_5P_3} = \frac{1}{60} \approx 0.017$ **73.** (a) $\frac{8}{9^2} = \frac{8}{81} \approx 0.099$

(b) $\frac{4}{{}_9C_2} = \frac{1}{9} \approx 0.111$ **75.** 1 **77.** $\frac{5}{31}$ **79.** $\frac{9}{9 \cdot 10} = \frac{1}{10}$ **81.** $\frac{1}{15}$

11.2 Exercises *(pages 603–605)*

1. $\frac{1}{2}$ **3.** $\frac{5}{6}$ **5.** $\frac{2}{3}$ **7.** (a) $\frac{2}{13}$ (b) 2 to 11 **9.** (a) $\frac{11}{26}$

(b) 11 to 15 **11.** (a) $\frac{9}{13}$ (b) 9 to 4 **13.** $\frac{2}{3}$ **15.** $\frac{7}{36}$

17. $\frac{5}{12}$ **19.** $\frac{2}{3}$ **21.** yes **23.** 0.005365 **25.** 0.971285

27. 0.76 **29.** 0.92 **31.** 0.04

33.

x	P(x)
3	0.1
4	0.1
5	0.2
6	0.2
7	0.2
8	0.1
9	0.1

35. Answers will vary.
37. Answers will vary.
39. $n(A') = s - a$
41. $P(A) + P(A') = 1$
43. 180 **45.** 60
47. 1 **49.** $\frac{1}{4}$

11.3 Exercises *(pages 613–617)*

1. $\frac{7}{15}$ **3.** $\frac{2}{5}$ **5.** $\frac{1}{15}$ **7.** 1 **9.** $\frac{1}{7}$ **11.** $\frac{1}{8}$ **13.** $\frac{2}{4} = \frac{1}{2}$

15. $\frac{2}{6} = \frac{1}{3}$ **17.** $\frac{2}{4} = \frac{1}{2}$ **19.** $\frac{1}{2}$ **21.** independent

23. not independent **25.** independent **27.** $\frac{52}{100} = \frac{13}{25}$

29. $\frac{69}{100}$ **31.** $\frac{14}{31}$ **33.** $\frac{4}{7} \cdot \frac{4}{7} = \frac{16}{49}$ **35.** $\frac{2}{7} \cdot \frac{1}{7} = \frac{2}{49}$ **37.** $\frac{4}{7} \cdot \frac{3}{6} = \frac{2}{7}$

39. $\frac{1}{6}$ **41.** 0 **43.** $\frac{12}{51} = \frac{4}{17}$ **45.** $\frac{12}{52} \cdot \frac{11}{51} = \frac{11}{221}$ **47.** $\frac{4}{52} \cdot \frac{11}{51} = \frac{11}{663}$

49. $\frac{26}{52} \cdot \frac{26}{51} = \frac{13}{51}$ **51.** $\frac{1}{3}$ **53.** 1 **55.** $\frac{3}{10}$ (the same)

57. $\frac{1}{2} \cdot \frac{1}{2} \cdot \frac{1}{2} \cdot \frac{1}{2} \cdot \frac{1}{2} \cdot \frac{1}{2} = \frac{1}{64}$ **59.** 0.490 **61.** 0.027

63. 0.95 **65.** 0.23 **67.** $\frac{1}{20}$ **69.** $\frac{1}{10}$ **71.** $2^6 = 64$

73. 0.1479 **75.** 0.400 **77.** 0.080 **79.** $(0.90)^4 = 0.6561$

81. ${}_4C_2 \cdot (0.10) \cdot (0.20) \cdot (0.70)^2 = 0.0588$ **83.** 0.2704

85. 0.2496 **87.** Answers will vary. **89.** 0.21 **91.** (a) $\frac{3}{4}$

(b) $\frac{1}{2}$ (c) $\frac{5}{16}$ **93.** $\frac{1}{5}$ **95.** $\frac{8}{33}$ **97.** (a) Answers will

vary. (b) $\frac{25}{36} \approx 0.69$

11.4 Exercises *(pages 621–623)*

1. $\frac{1}{8}$ **3.** $\frac{3}{8}$ **5.** $\frac{3}{4}$ **7.** $\frac{1}{2}$ **9.** Answers will vary. **11.** $\frac{1}{128}$

13. $\frac{21}{128}$ **15.** $\frac{35}{128}$ **17.** $\frac{7}{128}$ **19.** $\frac{125}{216}$ **21.** $\frac{5}{72}$ **23.** 0.041

25. 0.268 **27.** .302 **29.** Answers will vary. **31.** 0.228

33. 0.299 **35.** 0.032 **37.** 0.259 **39.** 0.167 **41.** 0.010

43. $6p^2(1 - p)^2$ **45.** 0.883 **47.** 0.073 **49.** $\frac{1}{1024} \approx 0.001$

51. $\frac{45}{1024} \approx 0.044$ **53.** $\frac{210}{1024} = \frac{105}{512} \approx 0.205$ **55.** $\frac{772}{1024} \approx 0.754$

11.5 Exercises *(pages 633–637)*

1. $\frac{5}{2}$ **3.** \$1 **5.** \$0.50 **7.** no $\left(\text{expected net winnings:} -\frac{3}{4}¢\right)$

9. 1.69 **11.** (a) −\$60 (b) \$36,000 (c) \$72,000

13. \$0.46 **15.** \$2700 **17.** 2.7 **19.** a decrease of 50

21. Project B **23.** Project A **25.** \$2200 **27.** \$81,000

29. Do not purchase the insurance (because

\$86,000 > \$81,000). **31.** \$1500; \$3000; \$17,500; \$27,000

33. \$56,000 **35.** 48.7% **37.** $\frac{15}{47} \approx 0.319$ **39.** $\frac{18}{50} = 0.36$;

This is quite close to 0.375, the theoretical value. **41.** no

43. $\frac{6}{50} = 0.12$ **45.** $\frac{48}{199} \approx 0.241$ **47.** $\frac{48}{198} \approx 0.242$

49. Answers will vary. **51.** The walk ends 12 blocks

north of the starting point. **53.** (a) Answers will vary.

(c) The value of p will vary; empirical (d) Answers will

vary. (e) Answers will vary.

Chapter 11 Test *(pages 641–642)*

1. $\frac{{}_2C_2}{{}_5C_2} = \frac{1}{10}$ **2.** $\frac{{}_3C_2}{{}_5C_2} = \frac{3}{10}$ **3.** $\frac{6}{10} = \frac{3}{5}$ **4.** $\frac{3}{10}$

5. $\frac{7}{7} \cdot \frac{6}{7} \cdot \frac{5}{7} = \frac{30}{49}$ **6.** $\frac{7}{19}$ **7.** $1 - \left(\frac{30}{49} + \frac{1}{49}\right) = \frac{18}{49}$

8. row 1: CC; row 2: cC, cc **9.** $\frac{1}{2}$ **10.** 1 to 3 **11.** 3 to 1

12. 25 to 1 **13.** 11 to 2 **14.** $\frac{3}{10}; \frac{6}{10}; \frac{1}{10}$ **15.** $\frac{9}{10}$

16. $\frac{18}{10} = \frac{9}{5}$ **17.** $\frac{6}{36} = \frac{1}{6}$ **18.** 35 to 1 **19.** 7 to 2 **20.** $\frac{4}{36} = \frac{1}{9}$

21. $(0.78)^3 \approx 0.475$ **22.** ${}_3C_2 \cdot (0.78)^2 \cdot (0.22) \approx 0.402$

23. $1 - (0.22)^3 \approx 0.989$

24. $(0.78) \cdot (0.22) \cdot (0.78) \approx 0.134$

25. $\frac{25}{102}$ **26.** $\frac{25}{51}$ **27.** $\frac{4}{51}$ **28.** $\frac{3}{26}$ **29.** $\frac{3}{8}$ **30.** $\frac{1}{24} \approx 0.042$

31. $\frac{29}{99} \approx 0.293$ **32.** $\frac{18}{98} \approx 0.184$

CREDITS

Text Credits

CHAPTER 1: **25–30** Exercises 1–47, 49, 53, 77, 80, 82: From the monthly calendar of *Mathematics Teacher*. Copyright © by National Council of Teachers of Mathematics. Used by permission of National Council of Teachers of Mathematics. **34** Margin note: Excerpt from *Innumeracy: Mathematical Illiteracy and Its Consequences* by John Allen Paulos. Published by Macmillan & Company, © 1988.

CHAPTER 3: **101** Exercise 83: Problem from *The Lady or the Tiger and Other Logic Puzzles* by Raymond M. Smullyan. Copyright © 2009 by Dover Publications. Used by permission of Dover Publications. **130** Exercise 6: Quote by Paul Erdos; Exercise 9: Quote by Winston Churchill; Exercise 10: Quote by George Bernard Shaw. **131** Exercise 39: Excerpt from DirecTV commercial. Used by permission of DirecTV, LLC.

CHAPTER 4: **146** Margin note: Excerpt from *Ethnomathematics: A Multicultural View of Mathematical Ideas* by Marcia Ascher. Published by Brooks/Cole Publishing Company. **158** Margin note: "Napier's Abacus." Used by permission of Google Inc. and Bonaventura Novellino.

CHAPTER 6: **219** Chapter opener text: Excerpt from "Old Math or Common Core Math: Which Troubles You More?" by Jarvis DeBerry, as published in *The Times-Picayune* and NOLA.com. Used by permission of Jarvis DeBerry. **260** Example 2: Excerpt from *Mathematics for the Trades: A Guided Approach* by Robert A. Carman, Emeritus, and Hal M. Saunders. Published by Pearson Education, © 2014. **267** Exercise 63: "Move One Matchstick to Make the Equation Approximately True" from *The Joy of Pi*. Used by permission of 63p.com. **269** Margin note: Excerpt from "Computation, Calculators, and Common Sense" from National Council of Teachers of Mathematics. Copyright © 2005 by National Council of Teachers of Mathematics. Used by permission of National Council of Teachers of Mathematics. **271** Margin note: Excerpt from *Historical Topics for the Mathematics Classroom, Thirty-First Yearbook* by National Council of Teachers of Mathematics. Published by National Council of Teachers of Mathematics, © 1969.

CHAPTER 7: **300** Exercises 41–50: Formulas from *Math Skills for Allied Health Careers* by Daniel L. Timmons and Catherine W. Johnson, published by Pearson Education, © 2008, and *Mathematics for the Trades: A Guided Approach* by Robert A. Carman, Emeritus, and Hal M. Saunders, published by Pearson Education, © 2014.

CHAPTER 8: **399** Exercise 44: Problem from "A Sourcebook of Applications of School Mathematics" by National Council of Teachers of Mathematics and Mathematical Association of America. Copyright © 1980 by National Council of Teachers of Mathematics. Used by permission of National Council of Teachers of Mathematics.

CHAPTER 9: **465** Exercises 47–48: From the monthly calendar of *Mathematics Teacher* by John Grant McLoughlin. Copyright © 2002 by National Council of Teachers of Mathematics. Used by permission of National Council of Teachers of Mathematics. **476** Exercises 83–90: From the monthly calendar of *Mathematics Teacher* by John Grant McLoughlin. Copyright © 2002 by National Council of Teachers of Mathematics. Used by permission of National Council of Teachers of Mathematics. **483** Margin note: Malaysia Airlines, Flight 370 map from Google Inc. Used by permission of Google Inc. **485** Exercise 29 (map): Search area map from Google Inc. Used by permission of Google Inc. **489** Screenshot (Dice App): From Teazel.com. Used with permission of Teazel.com and Google Inc. **503–504** For Further Thought: Excerpt from the article "What is a Tesselation?" from The Math Forum @ Drexel. Used by permission of The Math Forum @ Drexel. **509** Margin note: Excerpt from *LP Songs* by Tom Lehrer. Used by permission of Tom Lehrer. **516** "Does Chaos Rule the Cosmos?" from *Discover Magazine*. Published by Kalmbach Publishing Company, © 1992. **519** Screenshot (Fractoid): Android Apps of Dave Byrne. Used by permission of Dave Byrne and Google Inc. **520–521** Exercises 1–25: From *Student Math Notes*. Used by permission of National Council of Teachers of Mathematics.

CHAPTER 10: **549** Exercise 39: From the monthly calendar of *Mathematics Teacher* by John Grant McLoughlin. Copyright © 2002 by National Council of Teachers of Mathematics. Used by permission of National Council of Teachers of Mathematics. **551** Exercises 63 and 69: From the monthly calendar of *Mathematics Teacher* by John Grant McLoughlin. Copyright © 2002 by National Council of Teachers of Mathematics. Used by permission of National Council of Teachers of Mathematics. **552** Exercises 70–72: From the monthly calendar of *Mathematics Teacher* by John Grant McLoughlin. Copyright © 2002 by National Council of Teachers of Mathematics. Used by permission of National Council of Teachers of Mathematics. **562** Exercise 43: From the monthly calendar of *Mathematics Teacher* by John Grant McLoughlin. Copyright © 2002 by National Council of Teachers of Mathematics. Used by permission of National Council of Teachers of Mathematics. **565** Exercise 72: From the monthly calendar of *Mathematics Teacher* by John Grant McLoughlin. Copyright © 2002 by National Council of Teachers of Mathematics. Used by permission of National Council of Teachers of Mathematics. **569** Exercise 30: From the monthly calendar of *Mathematics Teacher* by John Grant McLoughlin. Copyright © 2002 by National Council of Teachers of Mathematics. Used by permission of National Council of Teachers of Mathematics. **576** Exercise 29: From the monthly calendar of *Mathematics Teacher* by John Grant McLoughlin. Copyright © 2002 by National Council of Teachers of Mathematics. Used by permission of National Council of Teachers of Mathematics. **577** Exercises 32, 45, and 46: From the monthly calendar of *Mathematics Teacher* by John Grant McLoughlin. Copyright © 2002 by National Council of Teachers of Mathematics. Used by permission of National Council of Teachers of Mathematics. **582** Exercise 35: From the monthly calendar of *Mathematics Teacher* by John Grant McLoughlin. Copyright © 2002 by National Council of Teachers of Mathematics. Used by permission of National Council of Teachers of Mathematics.

CHAPTER 11:   **596** Exercises 65, 66, 75, 76, 77, and 78: From the monthly calendar of *Mathematics Teacher* by John Grant McLoughlin. Copyright © 2002 by National Council of Teachers of Mathematics. Used by permission of National Council of Teachers of Mathematics.   **604** Exercise 47: From the monthly calendar of *Mathematics Teacher* by John Grant McLoughlin. Copyright © 2002 by National Council of Teachers of Mathematics. Used by permission of National Council of Teachers of Mathematics.   **605** Exercises 49 and 50: From the monthly calendar of *Mathematics Teacher* by John Grant McLoughlin. Copyright © 2002 by National Council of Teachers of Mathematics. Used by permission of Teachers of Mathematics.   **615** Exercise 58: From the monthly calendar of *Mathematics Teacher*. Copyright © by National Council of Teachers of Mathematics. Used by permission of National Council of Teachers of Mathematics.   **617** Exercises 93 and 94: From the monthly calendar of *Mathematics Teacher*. Copyright © by National Council of Teachers of Mathematics. Used by permission of National Council of Teachers of Mathematics.   **622** Exercise 43: From the monthly calendar of *Mathematics Teacher*. Copyright © by National Council of Teachers of Mathematics. Used by permission of National Council of Teachers of Mathematics.   **627** Table 15: From *The Mathematics Teacher,* March 1967. Copyright © by National Council of Teachers of Mathematics. Used by permission of National Council of Teachers of Mathematics.   **637** Buffon's Needle Problem: Excerpt from *The History of Mathematics: An Introduction* by David Burton. Published by William C. Brown Publishers, © 1994.

CHAPTER 12:   **667** Exercises 9 and 10: From the monthly calendar of *Mathematics Teacher* by John Grant McLoughlin. Copyright © 2002 by National Council of Teachers of Mathematics. Used by permission of National Council of Teachers of Mathematics; Exercise 16 (table): From "100 U.S. Corporations with Largest Revenues, 2012" by Sarah Janssen from *The World Almanac and Book of Facts.* Published by Simon and Schuster, © 2014.   **668** Exercises 33–34 (table): From "Federal Receipts, Outlays, and Surpluses or Deficits, 1901–2014" by Sarah Janssen from *The World Almanac and Book of Facts.* Published by Simon and Schuster, © 2014; Exercises 35–36 (table): From "World Cell Phone Use by Nation" by Sarah Janssen from *The World Almanac and Book of Facts.* Published by Simon and Schuster, © 2014.

CHAPTER 13:   **710** Financial calculator screenshot: Used by permission of Bishinew Inc.   **725** Financial calculator screenshot: Used by permission of Bishinew Inc.   **736** Financial calculator screenshot: Used by permission of Bishinew Inc.   **750** Stock Quote screenshot: From Google Inc. Used by permission of Google Inc.

CHAPTER 14:   **795** Margin note: Excerpt from "Readings from Scientific American: Mathematics in the Modern World" from *Scientific American.* Published by Graylock Press, © 1968.   **798** Margin note: Tshokwe sand tracing (sona) of leopard skin from *Geometry from Africa—Mathematical and Educational Explorations* by Paul Gerdes. Copyright © 1999 by Mathematical Association of America.

Photo Credits
COVER: Sergey Nivens/Shutterstock

FRONT MATTER: **xix** Sturti/Getty Images **xxii** (top) Courtesy of Vern E. Heeren, (middle) Callie J. Daniels, (bottom) Courtesy of Christopher Heeren

CHAPTER 1:   **1** Courtesy of Terry Krieger **4** RTimages/Fotolia **6** Lakov Kalinin/Shutterstock **7** Altocumulus/Fotolia **13** Miket/Fotolia **15** Pearson Education **16** Fotofermer/Fotolia **20** (top) AP Images, (bottom) Pearson Education **21** Book shot of "We All Use Math Everyday" used by permission of National Council of Teachers of Mathematics **22** Pearson Education **23** Hunta/Fotolia **26** Bikeriderlondon/Shutterstock **28** Andrii Muzyka/Shutterstock **29** (left) Jupiterimages/Photos.com/Thinkstock, (right) Studio306fotolia/Fotolia **31** Stephen Coburn/Fotolia **32** Adrian825/iStock/360/Getty Images **33** (top) Beth Anderson/Pearson Education, (bottom) Everett Collection **34** (top) Zuma Press, Inc./Alamy, (bottom) April Saul/KRT/Newscom **35** Poznyakov/Shutterstock **36** Bertys30/Fotolia **37** Elena Schweitzer/Fotolia **40** (left) R. Mackay Photography, LLC/Shutterstock, (right) Photos.com/Thinkstock

CHAPTER 2:   **47** Wavebreakmedia/Shutterstock **48** Pearson Education **51** Beth Anderson/Pearson Education **59** Beth Anderson/Pearson Education **60** Beth Anderson/Pearson Education **69** OtnaYdur/Shutterstock **73** Viki2win/Shutterstock **75** Everett Collection **76** Pictorial Press Ltd/Alamy **77** Christopher Black/Everett Collection Inc./Alamy **78** MC2 Eric C. Tretter/Defenseimagery.mil

CHAPTER 3:   **83** Milanmarkovic78/Fotolia **84** Pearson Education **85** Pearson Education **86** Erich Lessing/Art Resource **89** Monkey Business Images/Shutterstock **94** (top) Pearson Education, (bottom) Dover Publications **95** Pearson Education **97** Pearson Education **101** Rich Legg/Getty Images **102** (top) Pearson Education, (bottom) Courtesy of John Hornsby **108** Denys Prykhodov/Fotolia **109** (top) urosr/Fotolia, (bottom) Courtesy of Christopher Heeren **110** (top) Olena Zaskochenko/Shutterstock, (bottom) Demarfa/Fotolia **112** Pearson Education **113** Pearson Education **114** Pictorial Press Ltd/Alamy **115** Pearson Education **117** Pearson Education **118** Pearson Education **121** Steve Liss/The LIFE Images Collection/Getty Images **126** Mary Evans/Python Pictures/Ronald Grant/Everett Collection **128** (top) Wonderstock/Alamy, (bottom) Monkey Business/Fotolia **131** (left) Michael Ciranni/Shutterstock, (right) Aliagreen/Fotolia

CHAPTER 4:   **139** Dotshock/Shutterstock **140** DK Images **141** (both) DK Images **142** Kmit/Fotolia **143** Mediagram/Fotolia **146** Gary Ombler/DK Images **153** Canada [Addison Wesley Canada]/Pearson Education **154** The Art Gallery Collection/Alamy **155** Trinity College, Cambridge **156** (top) Maxx-Studio/Shutterstock, (bottom) Payless Images/Shutterstock **157** (top) Pearson Education, (bottom) Photo Researchers/Science Source **162** Photosani/Shutterstock **163** Photos.com/Thinkstock **167** Courtesy of John Hornsby **168** Wavebreakmedia/Shutterstock

CHAPTER 5:   **177** Belinda Images/SuperStock **180** Hugh C. Williams, University of Manitoba **186** (top) Pearson Education, (bottom) Courtesy of Charles D. Miller **189** Michael Sohn/AP Images **194** (top) Pearson Education, (bottom) TriStar Pictures/Courtesy of Everett Collection **195** (top) Pearson Education,

INDEX OF APPLICATIONS

INDEX